Muscle and its Innervation

An atlas of fine structure

Muscle and its Innervation

An atlas of fine structure

Yasuo Uehara

Professor of Anatomy
Ehime University, Japan

Gordon R. Campbell

Ph.D. Zoology Department
Melbourne University, Australia

Geoffrey Burnstock

Professor of Anatomy
Department of Anatomy and Embryology
University College, London
formerly of Melbourne University, Australia

Edward Arnold

First published 1976
by Edward Arnold Publishers Limited
25 Hill Street,
London, W1X 8LL

ISBN: 0 7131 2520 9

Printed in Great Britain by
Butler and Tanner Limited
Frome and London

Preface

The aim of this book is to give a coherent account of the fine structure of muscle and its innervation through visual presentation of a series of electronmicrographs of a wide variety of muscle types from different animals. The account is organized in such a way that it covers every aspect of muscle structure from overall form and cellular inter-relationships to a detailed description of organelles. Various types of muscle innervation are also included. While no attempt is made to present a comprehensive comparative account of all the variations in muscle structure found in every animal group, examples have been chosen to illustrate some of the variations in different species. Various aspects of the development of muscle are considered at the ends of several chapters. The atlas is directed at undergraduate and postgraduate students in medicine and science and also research workers. It includes a description of vertebrate smooth muscle—which has been neglected in most texts on muscle—vertebrate skeletal and cardiac muscle and selected examples of various invertebrate smooth and striated muscles. Wherever possible, a brief account of the functional role of the structures described is included in the introductions to the chapters or in the legends to the figures. An extensive reference list of each section has also been included (up to late 1974). An addendum (pp. 503–512) includes references to key reviews and articles up to April 1976, published since the manuscript was completed.

The aesthetic motivation in the preparation of this book should be mentioned. The authors were acutely aware of this aspect when selecting the micrographs. It was often a rewarding experience to choose from a number of electronmicrographs one that gave visual emphasis to a particular detail, and also had a form and balance which was pleasing to the eye.

In due course it is planned to produce sets of slides based on the photographic illustrations in this volume. Educational establishments and teachers interested in such slides should contact Professor Geoffrey Burnstock, at the Department of Anatomy and Embryology, University College, London.

Shikoku and Melbourne, 1975

Y.U.
G.R.C.
G.B.

Acknowledgements

It is a pleasure to express our appreciation to Dave Davey, Brian Cragg, Don Rogers, Alistair Willis, Bob Cook, Vic Small, Julie Chamley, Mike Fry, Chris Hall-Craggs, Giorgio Gabella, Brian Jewell, Mollie Holman and Betty Twarog for their helpful advice and critical evaluation of the manuscript.

We are also indebted to the following people for their hard work and patience in the preparation of the manuscript: Brian Pump for photographic expertise, Lynne Chapman for technical assistance and illustrations, Jay McKenzie for co-ordination and preparation of the manuscript and John Nailon, Margaret Canney, Grete Fry and Louise Western for technical assistance. We also gratefully acknowledge the patience and understanding of Gail Liddell and Marian Rubio necessary to type the manuscript. The contribution to the typing of Bron Robinson is also acknowledged.

While most of the electron microscopy is the work of the authors, we would like to thank Peter Robinson, John Heath, Matsumo Imaizumi, Bob Cook, Akio Yamauchi, Marg Canney, Vic Small and Neil Merrillees for allowing us to reproduce their material. We are particularly grateful to Michael Hobbs for his skilled help with the proofs and for preparing the Index.

This work was carried out largely in the Department of Zoology, University of Melbourne and was supported by grants from the Australian Research Grants Committee, the National Heart Foundation of Australia and the National Health and Medical Research Council.

Y.U.
G.R.C.
G.B.

Contents

Methods of fixation

Four standard fixation methods (most by immersion at room temperature) were employed throughout this atlas:

1 Osmium tetroxide (OsO_4) fixation.
Tissues were fixed in 2% phosphate-buffered OsO_4 (pH 7·4) for one hour (MILLONIG, 1961).

2 OsO_4–glutaraldehyde–OsO_4 fixation.
Tissues were initially fixed with 1% phosphate buffered OsO_4 (pH 7·4) for one hour, then with 4% phosphate-buffered glutaraldehyde for one hour and finally with unbuffered 1% OsO_4 for one hour (KANASEKI, UEHARA and IMAIZUMI, unpublished data).

3 Glutaraldehyde fixation.
Tissues were fixed in 2–6% phosphate-buffered glutaraldehyde (pH 7·4) for one hour, washed in phosphate buffer for one to three hours and postfixed for one hour in 1% phosphate buffered OsO_4 (SABATINI, BENSCH and BARRNETT, 1963).

4 Paraformaldehyde-glutaraldehyde fixation.
Tissues were fixed with a phosphate-buffered mixture of 4% paraformaldehyde and 4% glutaraldehyde (pH 7·4) for one hour, washed in buffer overnight, then postfixed for one hour in 1% phosphate-buffered OsO_4 (KARNOVSKY, 1965).

The fixed material was usually 'block-stained' in uranyl acetate (TERZAKIS, 1968) before being embedded in Araldite or Epon. Thin sections were stained with 2% aqueous uranyl acetate (HUXLEY and ZUBAY, 1961) and lead citrate (VENABLE and COGGESHALL, 1965).

Further information on techniques of electronmicroscopy can be obtained from books such as those of SIEGEL (1964), KAY (1965), SJÖSTRAND (1967) and HAYAT (1970).

HAYAT, M. A. 1970. *Principles and techniques of electron microscopy: biological applications. Vol. 1.* Van Nostrand Reinhold Company, New York.

HUXLEY, H. E. and G. ZUBAY. 1961. Preferential staining of nucleic acid-containing structures for electron microscopy. *J.biophys.biochem. Cytol.* **11,** 273–296.

KARNOVSKY, M. J. 1965. A formaldehyde–glutaraldehyde fixative of high osmolality for use in electron microscopy. *J. Cell Biol.*, **27,** 137A–138A.

KAY, D. H. 1965. *Techniques for electron microscopy.* Blackwell Scientific Publications, Oxford. 2nd edition.

MILLONIG, G. 1961. Advantages of a phosphate buffer for OsO_4 solutions in fixation. *J.appl.Phys.* **32,** 1637.

SABATINI, D. D., K. BENSCH and R. J. BARRNETT. 1963. Cytochemistry and electron microscopy. The preservation of cellular ultrastructure and enzymatic activity by aldehyde fixation. *J.Cell Biol.*, **17,** 19–31.

SIEGEL, B. M. 1964. ed. *Modern developments in electron microscopy.* Academic Press, New York.

SJÖSTRAND, F.S. 1967. *Electron microscopy of cells and tissues.* Vol. 1. 'Instrumentation and techniques'. Academic Press, New York.

TERZAKIS, J. A. 1968. Uranyl acetate, a stain and a fixative. *J.Ultrastruct.Res.* **22,** 168–184.

UEHARA, Y. and K. HAMA. 1965. Some observations on the fine structure of the frog muscle spindle. (1) On the sensory terminals and motor endings of the muscle spindle. *J.electron Microsc.*, **14,** 14–34.

VENABLE, J. H. and R. COGGESHALL. 1965. A simplified lead citrate stain for use in electron microscopy. *J.Cell Biol.*, **25,** 407–408.

Summary of abbreviations used in plates

A A-band
Ac accompanying axon
Ax axon
B blood space
Bf bag fibre
Bm basement membrane or basal lamina
Bs blood sinus
C collagen
Ca cardiac muscle
Cb collagen bundle
Ce centriole
Cf chain fibre
Ch chloragogen cell
Ci inner spindle capsule
Co outer spindle capsule
Cu 'cuticle'
D desmosome
Db dark body
e electron dense material
El elastin
En endothelial cell
Ep epithelial cell
Et elaborate network of tubules
Ex extrafusal fibre
ER rough endoplasmic reticulum
f fenestration
F fibroblast
Fa *fascia adhaerens*
fb foliated basement membrane
G gap junction
Gr granules
H H-zone
I I-band
Ic inner circular coat
If intrafusal muscle fibre
Im inner mesaxon
In invagination
l lumen of capillary
L lipid droplet
Le leptomere fibrils
M M-line
Me motor ending
Mf myofibril
Mi mitochondria
Mn myoendothelial cell
Mp myoepithelial cell
Mu muscle cell or fibre
Mv multivesicular body
My myofilaments
N nerve bundles
Nc nucleus
Nl nucleolonema
Nm motor nerve fibre
Ns sensory nerve fibre
Nt nerve terminal
Nu nucleolus
Ol outer longitudinal coat
Om outer mesaxon
P plasmalemmal vesicle
Pe peritoneum
R free ribosomes
S satellite cell
Sc spindle capsule
Se sensory ending
Sf subneural fold
Sm smooth muscle cell
Sp septal cell
SR sarcoplasmic reticulum
sarcotubular system in smooth muscle
Sv synaptic vesicle
Sw Schwann cell
t terminal cisternae of sarcoplasmic reticulum
T T-tubule
Tr triad
Z Z-disc

1 Muscle as a Tissue

The object of this opening chapter is to give a general survey of the classifications, organization and basic variations in form of the muscle types found in the animal kingdom. Various aspects touched upon briefly are dealt with in more detail in later chapters.

A specific feature of muscle is its ability to transform chemical energy into mechanical force. Muscle is concerned with the generation and control of both fast and slow movements of the whole animal and/or parts of the animal.

Vertebrate muscle consists of two components: connective tissue elements and uni- or multinucleate muscle cells (also referred to as muscle fibres). Collagen, elastic and reticular fibres and various cell types such as fibroblasts compose the connective tissue elements. Connective tissue sheaths not only provide tracts for the passage of blood vessels and nerves, but envelop individual muscle cells and transmit the force exerted by them. The contractile proteins (actin, myosin and others) form a large part of muscle cells. They may be organized in a precise pattern, detectable with the light microscope as a series of discrete and regular transverse bands along the length of the muscle fibre ('striations') or they may be organized in a manner resulting in a smooth ('non-striated') appearance. Thus on this morphological basis muscle has been subdivided into two major categories, called *striated* and *smooth* muscle respectively. Further classifications have been made on an anatomical as well as histological basis, for example by dividing striated muscle into *skeletal* (Plate 1) and *cardiac* (Plate 2) muscle. Skeletal muscle is so called because it is usually attached to one or more points upon firm supporting tissues, which may be either endoskeletal (vertebrates) or exoskeletal (many invertebrates); some striated muscle fibres may however occur without relation to skeletal parts, in the upper oesophagus (man) or even more generally throughout the alimentary canal (tench). Cardiac muscle is found in the wall of the heart and extends into the proximal portions of the pulmonary veins.

In vertebrates, smooth muscle forms the contractile walls of blood vessels (Plate 7) and visceral organs (Plate 3) including the alimentary canal, urinary and genital tracts, extra-embryonic membranes, respiratory system and large lymphatic trunks. The muscle cells are usually arranged in a circular fashion, thereby controlling the flow down the hollow tube. Another layer of muscle cells, arranged longitudinally, is usually present in the walls of the viscera. Smooth muscle is also found in the dermis, the scrotum, the penis, the nipple, the iris, the ciliary body and in the capsule of some organs.

Another group of contractile cells is found in mammary, salivary and sweat glands. These cells contain features characteristic of both epithelial cells and smooth muscle and are consequently called *myoepithelial* cells (Plate 8). Myoepithelial cells have also been described in some invertebrates. The terms *myofibroblasts* and *myoendothelial* cells have been used to describe cells containing features of both smooth muscle and fibroblasts or endothelial cells respectively (Plates 9 and 10). The two latter terms should be adopted cautiously as there are a large number of cells which are distinct from muscle, in that they do not demonstrate an organized contractile pattern, but nevertheless contain contractile elements. Blood platelets, fibroblasts, neurons, epithelial cells, glial cells and the *Amoeba*, to name just a few, all contain actomyosin-like proteins. These proteins appear to take part in contractile activities, but may be involved largely in the process of cytoplasmic streaming.

In many invertebrates, it is often convenient to classify the muscular system in a similar manner to that of vertebrates. Thus they are often classified as skeletal (Plate 4), cardiac and visceral. However, this analogy with vertebrate muscle is not always applicable, since invertebrate visceral muscle fibres are often striated, and invertebrate smooth muscle has a number of different forms. For example, there are *obliquely striated* muscles (originally called 'helical smooth muscle') which have an irregular oblique banding pattern such as in earthworm body wall and intestine (Plate 6), or a regular oblique pattern such as in the octopus mantle. Invertebrate smooth muscle, in which no striations are seen with the light microscope, include powerful muscles such as the anterior byssal retractor muscle (ABRM) of the lamellibranchs (Plate 5). Since they contain thick filaments of extremely large diameter, formed largely of the contractile protein, paramyosin, they are often called *paramyosin smooth muscles*. There is some evidence to suggest these may have a common evolutionary origin with obliquely striated muscle. Another type of invertebrate smooth muscle (sometimes called *classical smooth muscle*), in which the cells contain mixed thick and thin myofilaments, occurs in animals such as coelenterates. It must be admitted that these present classifications of muscle are inadequate. However, there is still insufficient data to allow us to propose a serious alternative.

In the chapters that follow, the basic pattern of organization is to consider each topic in the following sequence: vertebrate skeletal muscle; vertebrate cardiac muscle; vertebrate smooth muscle; invertebrate muscle; development.

Plate 1

Vertebrate skeletal muscle cells or fibres (a transverse section of which is shown in Plate 1) are usually 10–100 μm in diameter and extend for distances of up to 34 cm. They are multinucleate, that is they contain numerous nuclei (Nc) throughout their length. Each muscle fibre is enclosed by a plasmamembrane, the *sarcolemma*, and an associated protein–polysaccharide coating, the *basal lamina* (or basement membrane; see Chapter 4). The bulk of the volume of the muscle fibre is occupied by contractile proteins called *myofilaments* (My) (see Chapter 2C), arranged in myofibrils (see Chapter 2B). The sarcoplasm, which corresponds to the cytoplasm of other cell types, contains mitochondria (see Chapter 2G), Golgi complex (see Chapter 2H) and several other organelles. The muscle cells are separated from each other by delicate connective tissue composed of collagen (C), elastin (not represented in this Plate; see Plate 93), and fibroblasts (F). For descriptive purposes, the connective tissue elements of skeletal muscle are divided into three categories (see Fig. 1). The *endomysium* penetrates between the fibres and contains capillaries and nerves. It is continuous with the *perimysium* which surrounds a number of fibres forming a bundle. A muscle is composed of many such bundles surrounded by another connective tissue sheath, the *epimysium*. *Satellite cells* (S) are often present in close association with muscle fibres (see Chapter 9).

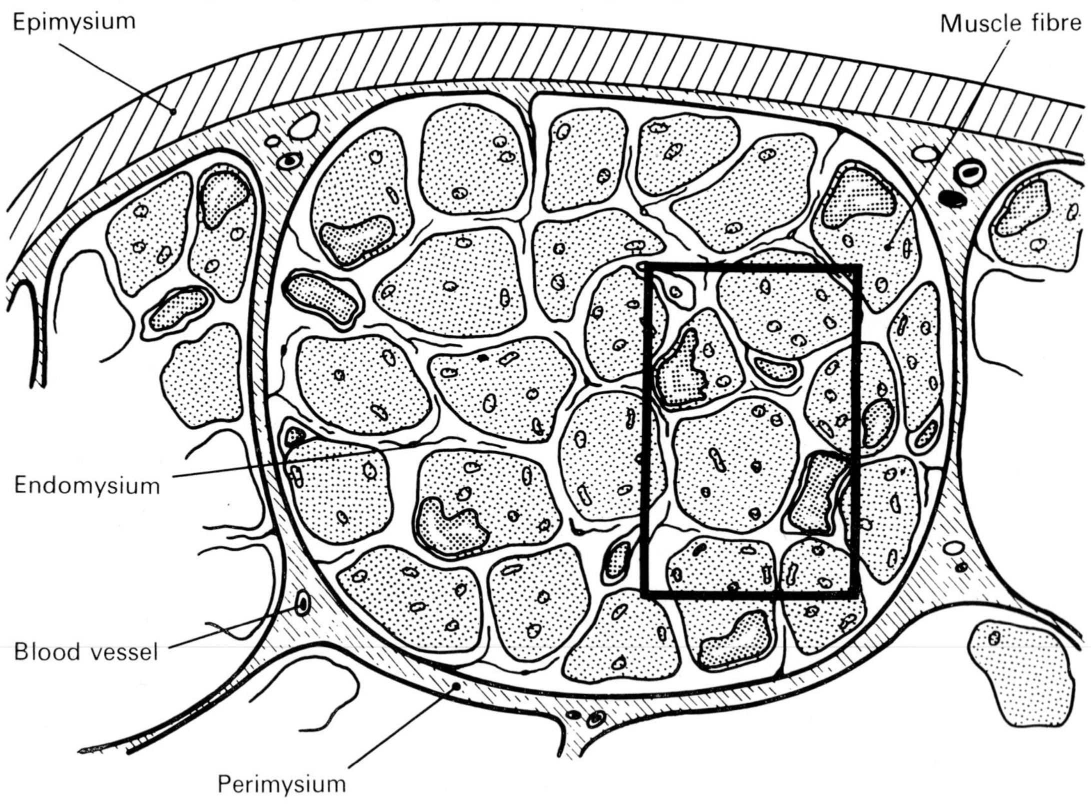

Fig. 1 Diagrammatic representation of connective tissue elements in skeletal muscle

Vertebrate skeletal muscle: newborn rat sternothyroid. Transverse section. Glutaraldehyde fixation. ×9800.

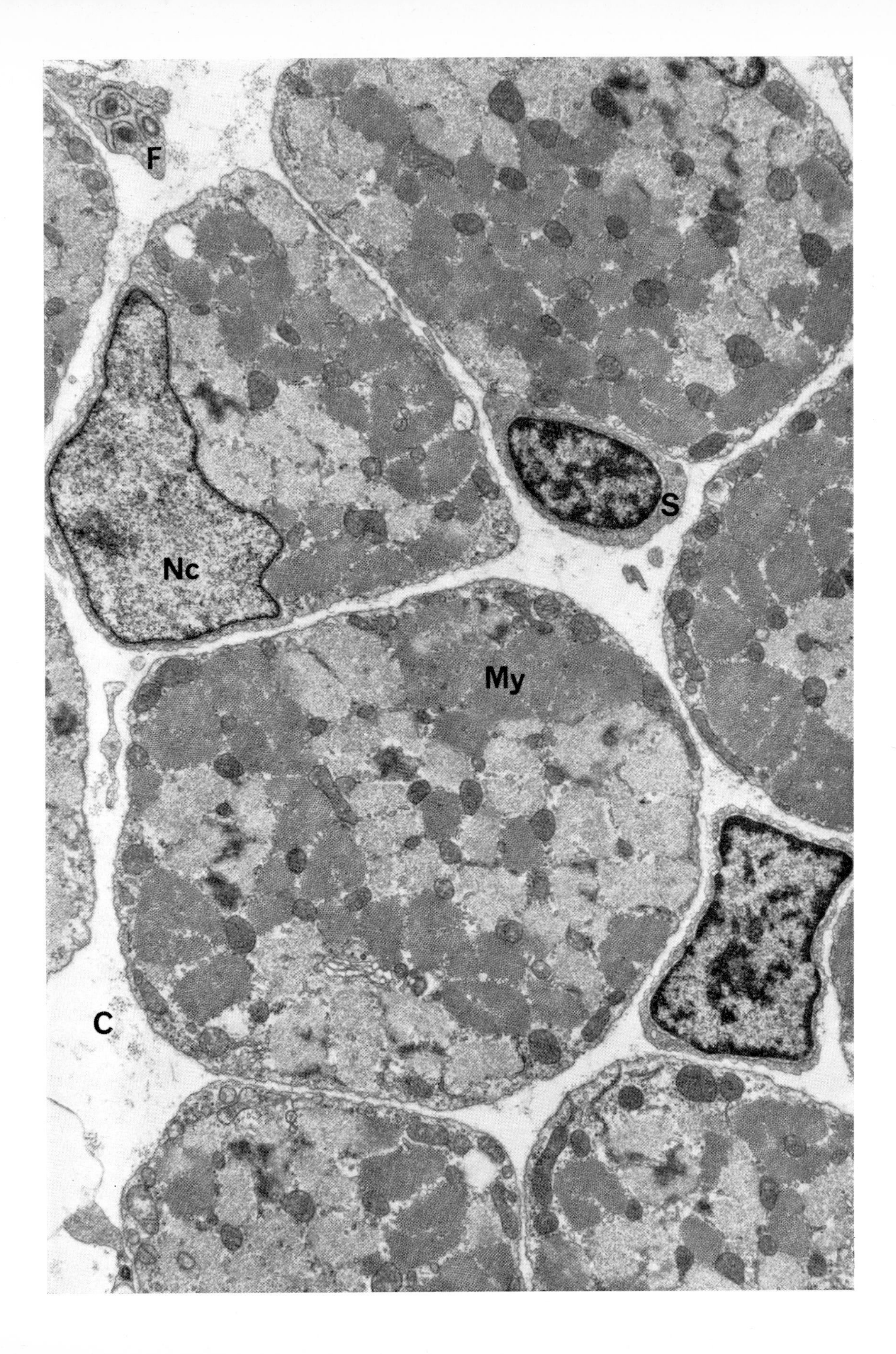
F
S
Nc
My
C

Plate 2

In vertebrates, both skeletal and cardiac muscle are classified as *striated* muscle. This refers to their alternate light and dark banding pattern as seen with the light microscope, which is due to the ordered arrangement of thick myosin-containing and thin actin-containing myofilaments (see Chapter 2C). When examined with polarized light, the dark portions are clearly birefringent and are therefore called anisotropic bands, or *A-bands* (A). The light portions are only very weakly birefringent and are consequently called isotropic bands, or *I-bands* (I). A transverse line, the *Z-disc* (Z), can be detected bisecting each I-band. These regions are illustrated on the accompanying electron-micrograph.

Vertebrate cardiac muscle (a longitudinal section of 3 cells is shown in Plate 2) differs from skeletal muscle in that the cells are not multinucleate but have a single nucleus usually in the centre of the cells; the fibres are not cylindrical units but often bifurcate and connect with adjacent fibres (see Chapter 6A) thereby forming a complex three-dimensional structure. The endomysium contains lymphatic capillaries as well as blood capillaries and nerve fibres.

Vertebrate cardiac muscle: rat ventricle. Longitudinal section. Glutaraldehyde fixation. ×7700.

A
Z
I

Plate 3

Vertebrate smooth muscle lacks any banding pattern but both thick and thin myofilaments are present (containing myosin and actin respectively); these myofilaments are plentiful, but have a less regular organization than in striated muscle (see Chapter 2C). Electron-dense *dark bodies* are associated with these myofilaments. *Dense areas* and *plasmalemmal vesicles* (sometimes called micropinocytotic vesicles or caveolae intracellulares) are present along the sarcolemma or plasmamembrane. The muscle cells are usually spindle-shaped, 2–5μm in diameter, with tapered ends and have a single nucleus, placed approximately midway along their length, which is usually 100 to 300μm, but can be up to 600μm in some tissues (e.g. pregnant uterus, axolotl viscera). Connective tissue elements are present in the narrow extracellular space.

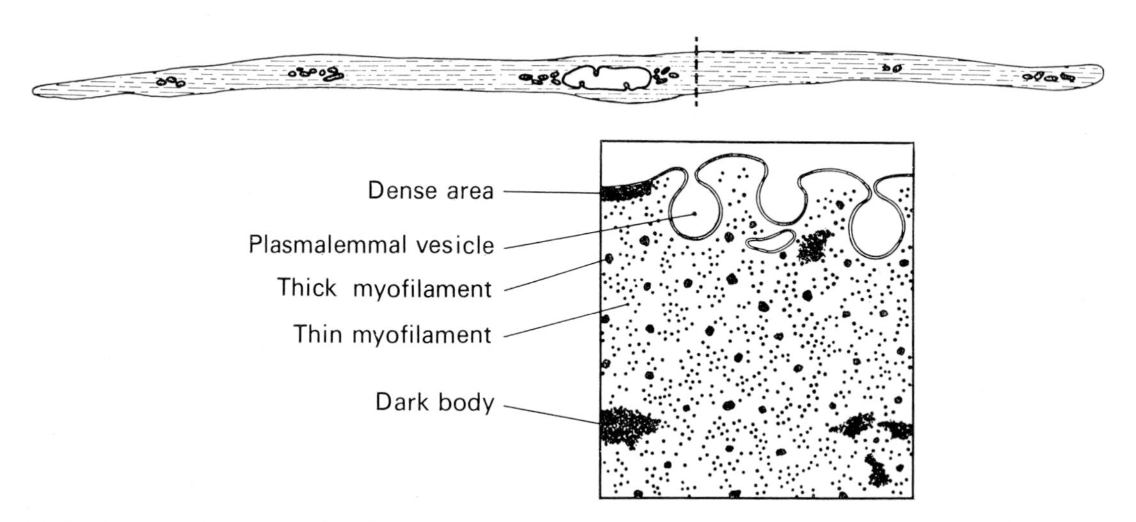

Fig. 2 Diagrammatic representation of a whole vertebrate smooth muscle cell in longitudinal section. Rectangle represents a transverse section of the muscle cell at higher magnification.

Vertebrate visceral smooth muscle: love-bird gizzard. Longitudinal section. OsO_4—glutaraldehyde—OsO_4 fixation. ×6500. (Courtesy of M. Imaizumi, Department of Internal Medicine, University of Osaka).

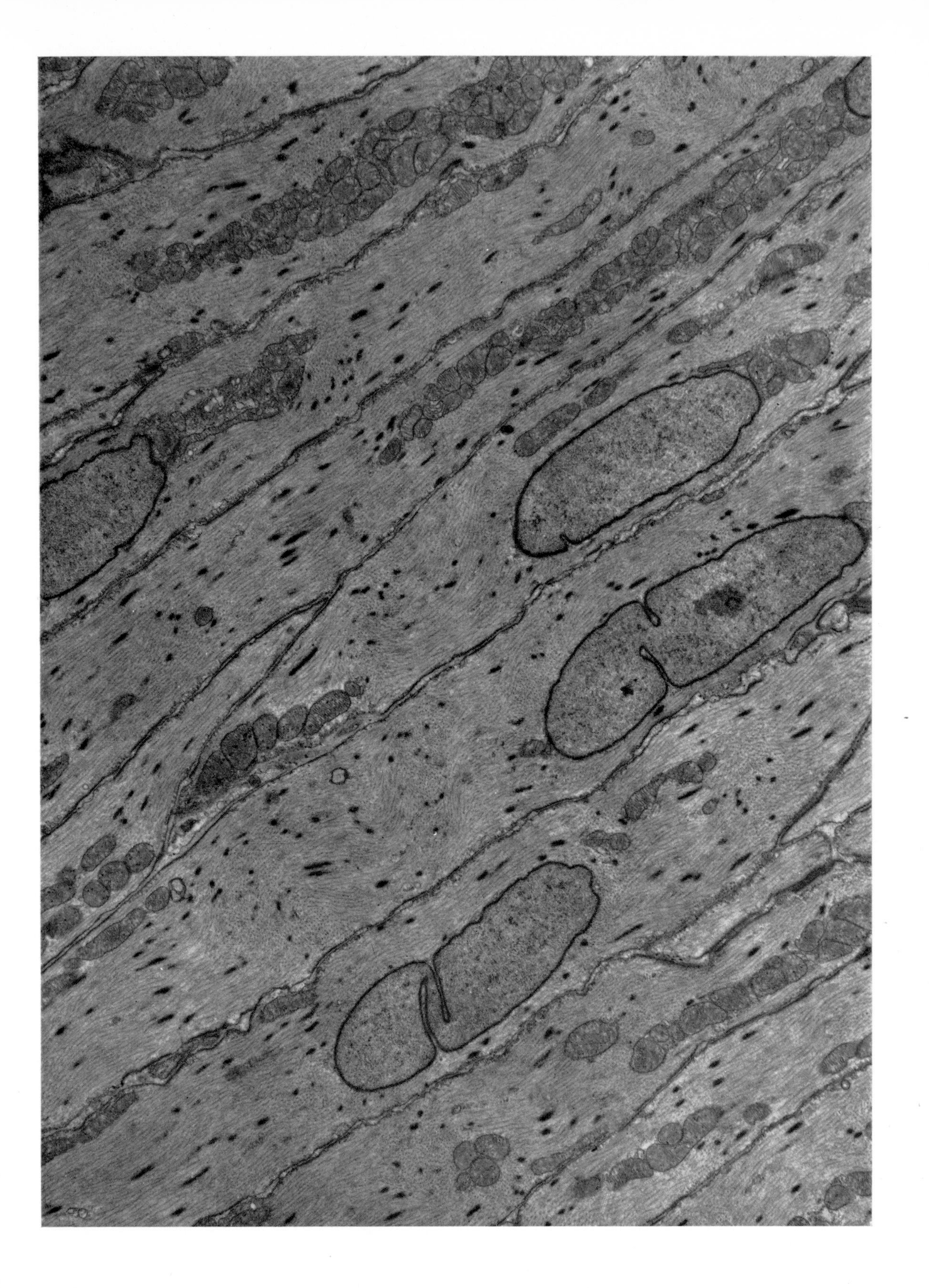

Plate 4

There is considerable variety in the skeletal muscle fibres of the invertebrates. In arachnids, insects and crustaceans, skeletal muscle fibres originate and insert upon the cuticular exoskeleton and are involved in the movement of body segments, legs, wings or tentacles. In contrast, in other invertebrates such as platyhelminthes and annelids, there is no exoskeleton, and muscle cells are located in the body wall, where they are usually termed somatic muscles (see Plate 24). The muscle fibres in the spider leg are tubular in form with a central core of sarcoplasm and nuclei. The contractile elements surround the central core, and are arranged in a radial lamellar pattern.

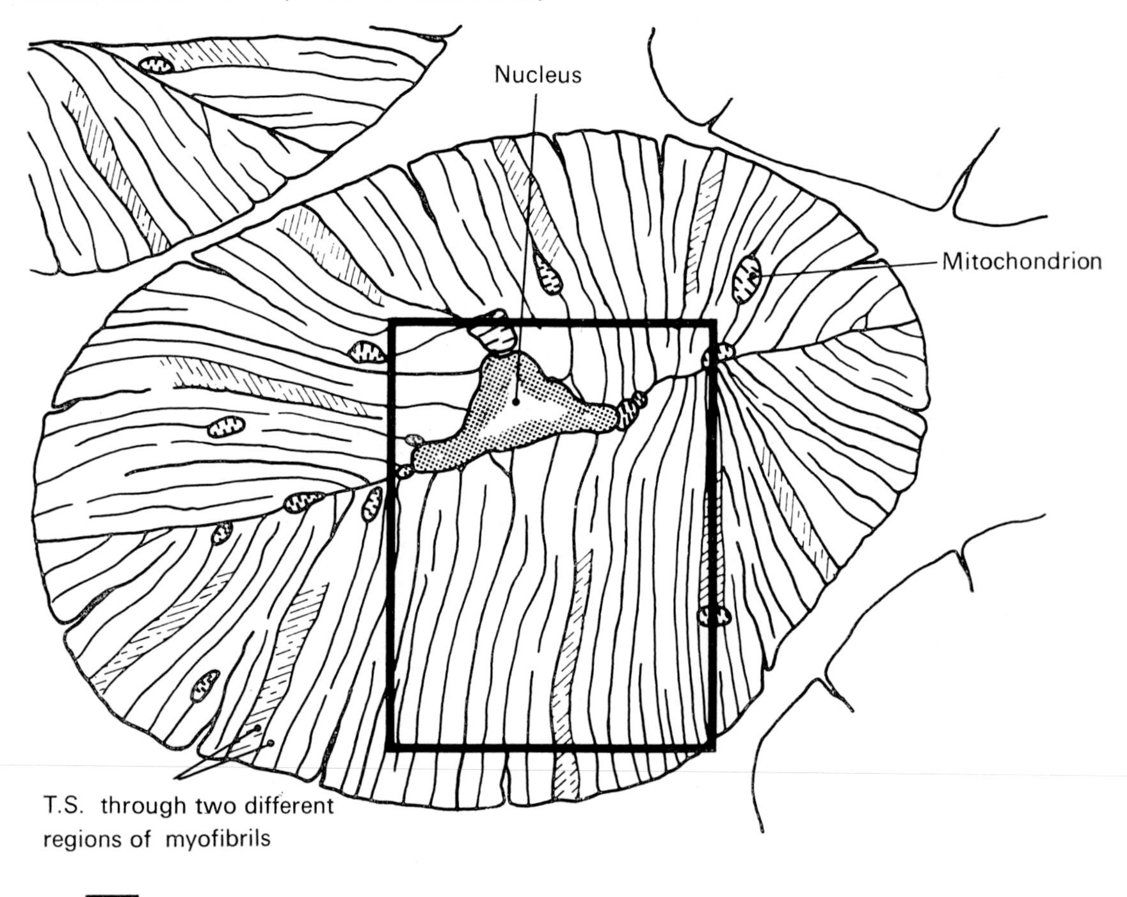

Fig. 3 Diagram showing the organization of a muscle fibre in a spider leg.

Invertebrate skeletal muscle: spider leg muscle. Transverse section. Glutaraldehyde fixation. ×15 000.

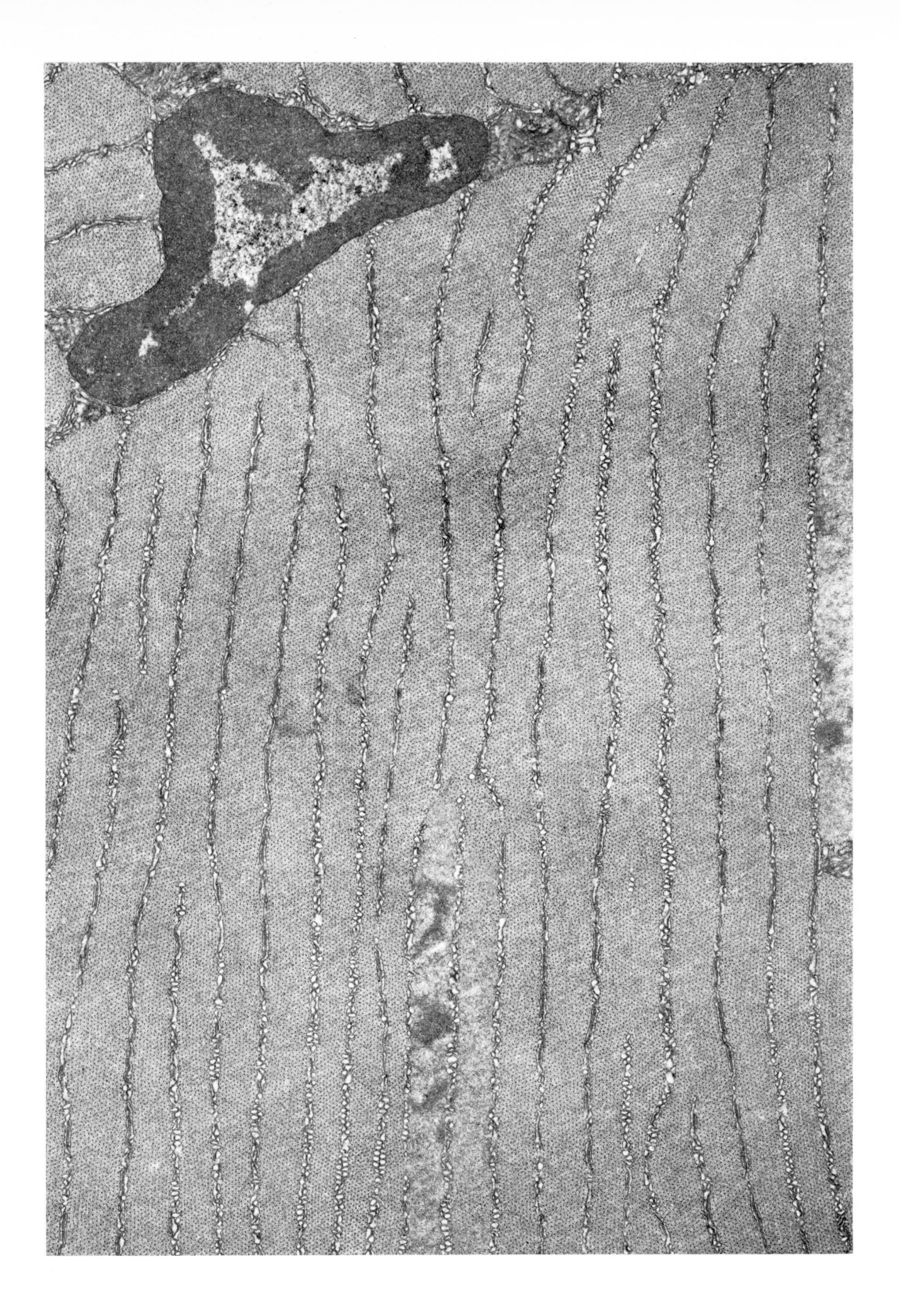

Plate 5

Invertebrate paramyosin smooth muscle cells of the anterior byssus retractor, like vertebrate smooth muscles, are uninucleate. However, they are much longer, often being 1·2–1·8 mm in length. Very thick paramyosin-containing and thin actin-containing myofilaments are present (see Chapter 2C). Dark bodies among the myofilaments and dense areas along the plasma membrane are both present, as in vertebrate smooth muscle. This muscle is capable of a brief phasic contraction as well as a sustained maintenance of tension, as if locked in the contracted state, and is consequently called a *catch* muscle. Its contractile mechanism is powerful, generating 15 kg cm^{-2} tension in contrast to the frog sartorius muscle which generates 3–5 kg cm^{-2} tension.

The cell on the left has been sectioned transversely, whereas the cell on the right has been sectioned longitudinally.

Invertebrate paramyosin smooth muscle: mussel anterior byssus retractor muscle (ABRM). Glutaraldehyde fixation. $\times$ 50 500.

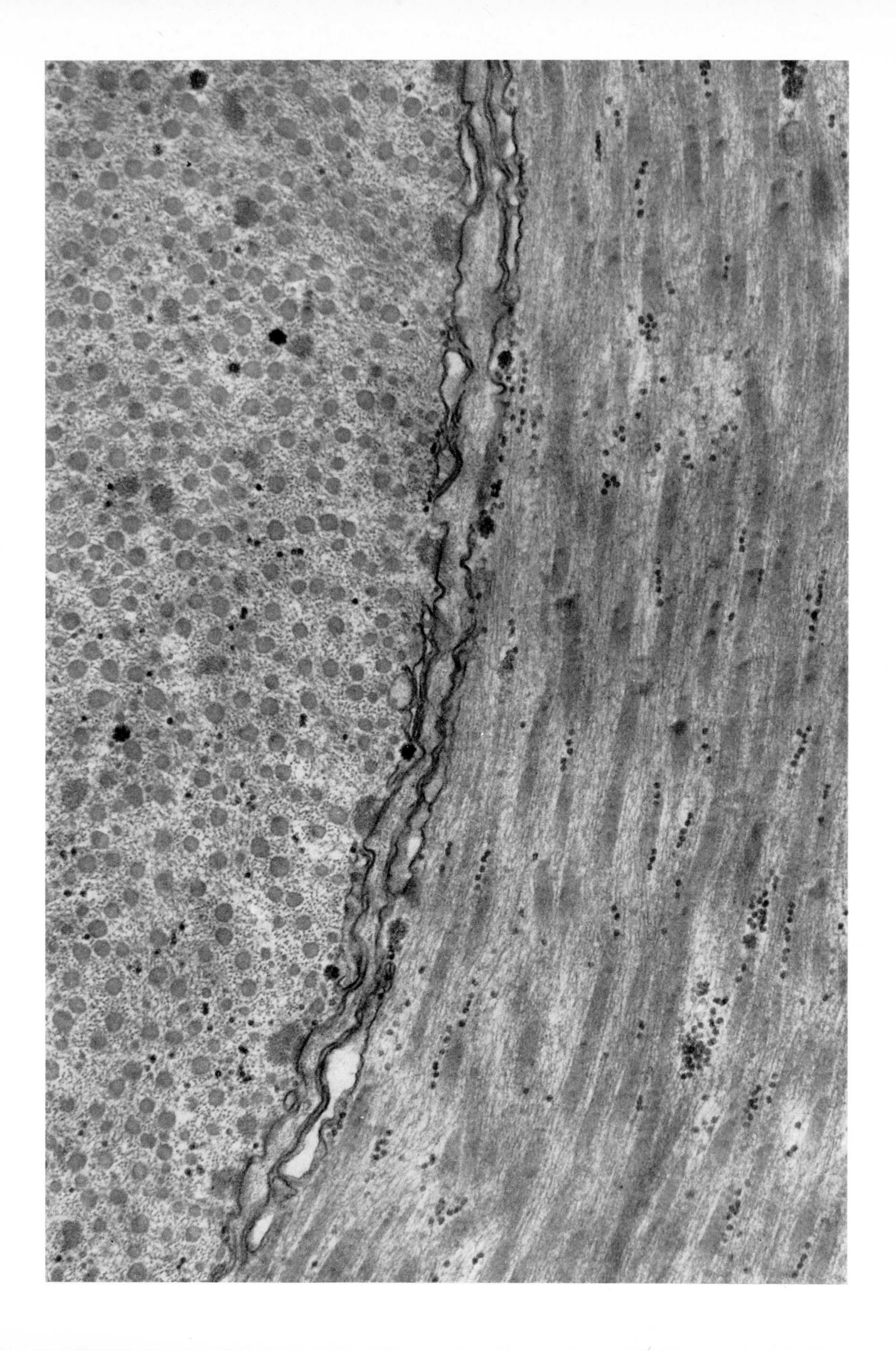

Plate 6

The basic muscle layer arrangement in the digestive system of all vertebrates and many invertebrates consists of an inner circular layer usually at right angles to the axis of the tube and an outer longitudinal layer parallel to it. In some organs of the urogenital system, this arrangement is reversed with inner longitudinal and outer circular muscle coats. Contraction of the circular coat in the digestive system leads to constriction of the lumen while contraction of the longitudinal coat leads to shortening of the tube.

The earthworm intestine consists of an epithelium (Ep), an inner circular (Ic) and an outer longitudinal (Ol) muscle layer and the peritoneum. The peritoneum in this species contains chloragogen cells (Ch), whose physiological role may be analogous to that of the liver of vertebrates. Immediately between the epithelial layer and the inner muscular layer is the alimentary plexus. This consists of blood sinuses (Bs) in direct contact with the overlying cells, any true endothelial lining being either entirely lacking or sparse. (N) represents a nerve bundle in the epithelial layer.

Invertebrate obliquely striated muscle: earthworm intestinal muscle. Transverse section. Glutaraldehyde fixation. × 14 000.

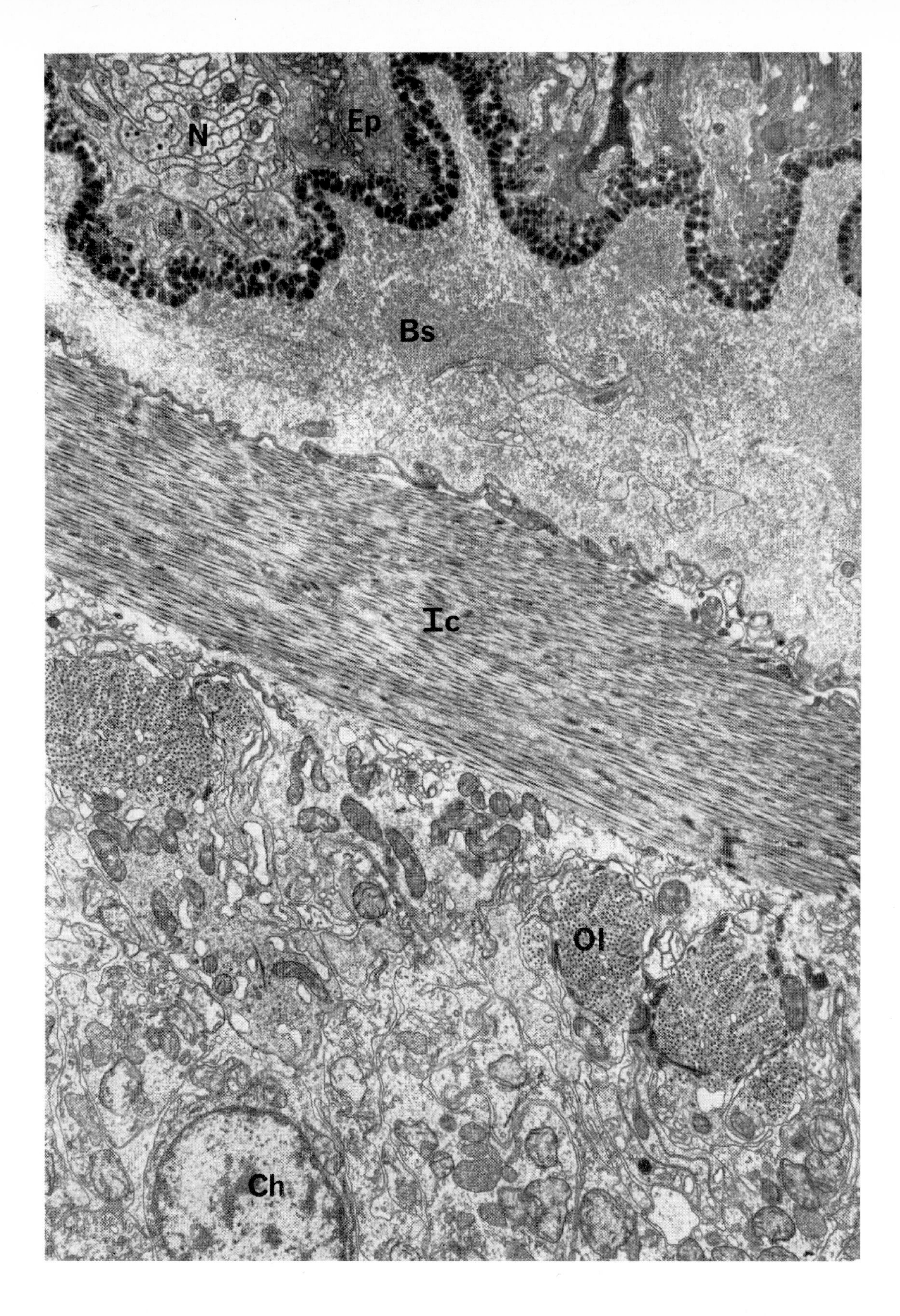
N
Ep
Bs
Ic
Ol
Ch

Plate 7

The walls of vertebrate blood vessels are usually composed of an inner *tunica intima* consisting of endothelial cells (En) and connective tissue, a *tunica media* containing smooth muscle cells (Sm) and elastin, and an outer *tunica adventitia* containing connective tissue and nerves. The cellular composition of these layers varies considerably in different sized vessels. In large arteries there are many smooth muscle cell layers in the tunica media but in arterioles this may be restricted to as little as one, as illustrated here in the guinea-pig heart (Ca, cardiac muscle). Unlike the digestive and urogenital tracts, most blood vessels do not have a longitudinal muscle coat. Instead there is a coat of cells orientated at an angle of from 10° to 30° to the longitudinal axis which tends to pass spirally along the length of the artery. Constriction of long segments of the vessel can be produced by contraction of these smooth muscle cells.

Vertebrate vascular smooth muscle cells contain all the features of the visceral smooth muscles except that their shape is often irregular, their dimensions are smaller (15–20 μm in length and about 2 μm diameter), and they often have extensive dense areas.

Vertebrate vascular smooth muscle: arteriole in guinea-pig heart. Longitudinal section. Glutaraldehyde fixation. ×32 600. (Courtesy of T. Yohro and G. Burnstock. Reproduced by permission, *Z. Zellforsch. mikrosk. Anat.*, **138,** 85–95, 1973.)

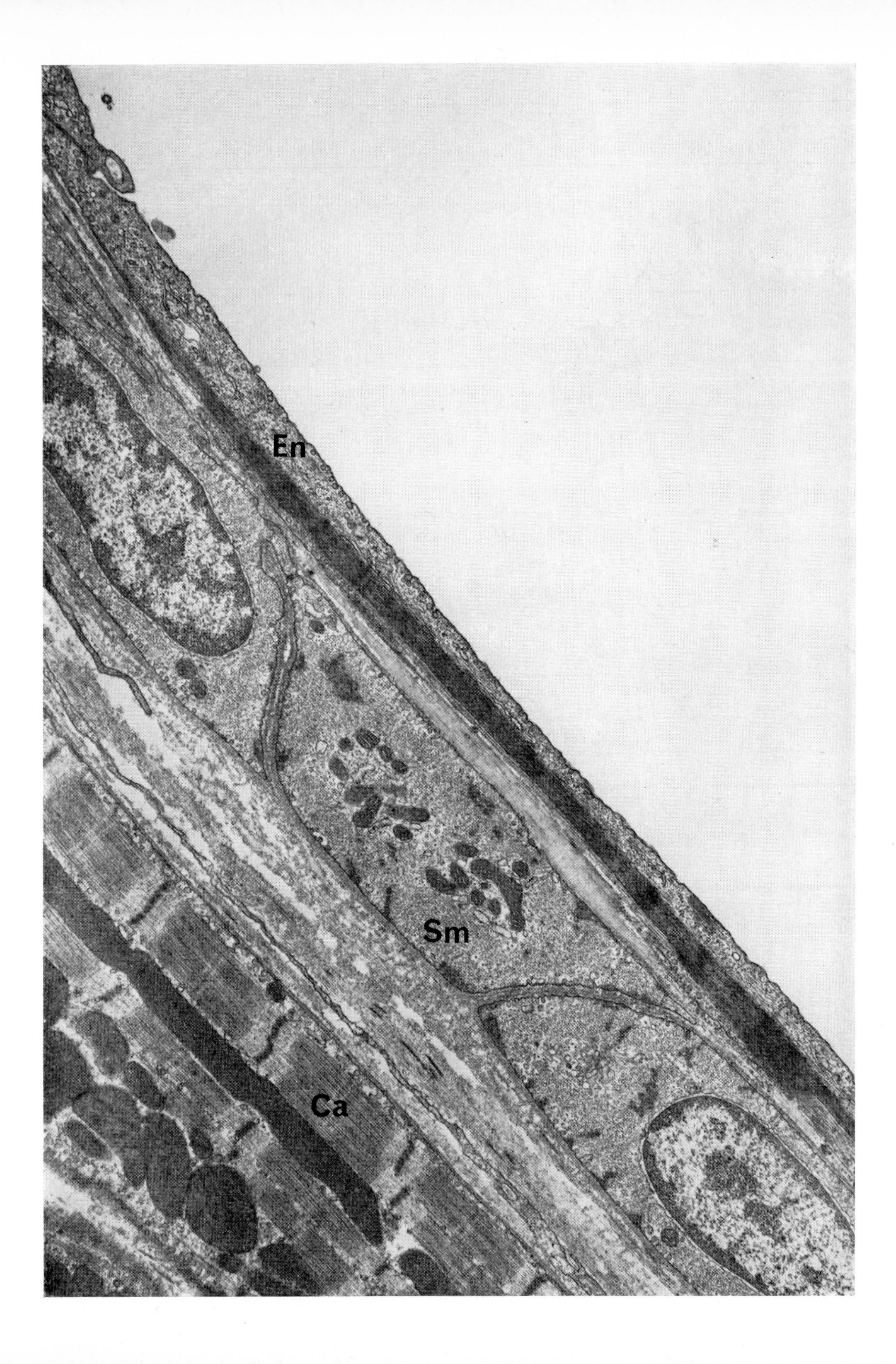
En
Sm
Ca

Plate 8

In mammary, sweat, lacrimal and submaxillary glands, contractile cells with branched processes are associated with the terminal portions and/or the ducts.

These cells contain myofilaments, dark bodies and dense areas, features identical to those seen in smooth muscle. However, unlike the majority of smooth muscle cells, they are believed to be ectodermal rather than mesenchymal in origin and are called *myoepithelial cells* (Mp). Myoepithelial cells are irregular in shape, often stellate and usually lie between the glandular cells and the basal lamina. Contraction aids secretion and movement of secretory materials.

Vertebrate myoepithelial cells: guinea-pig submaxillary gland. Glutaraldehyde fixation. ×10 800.

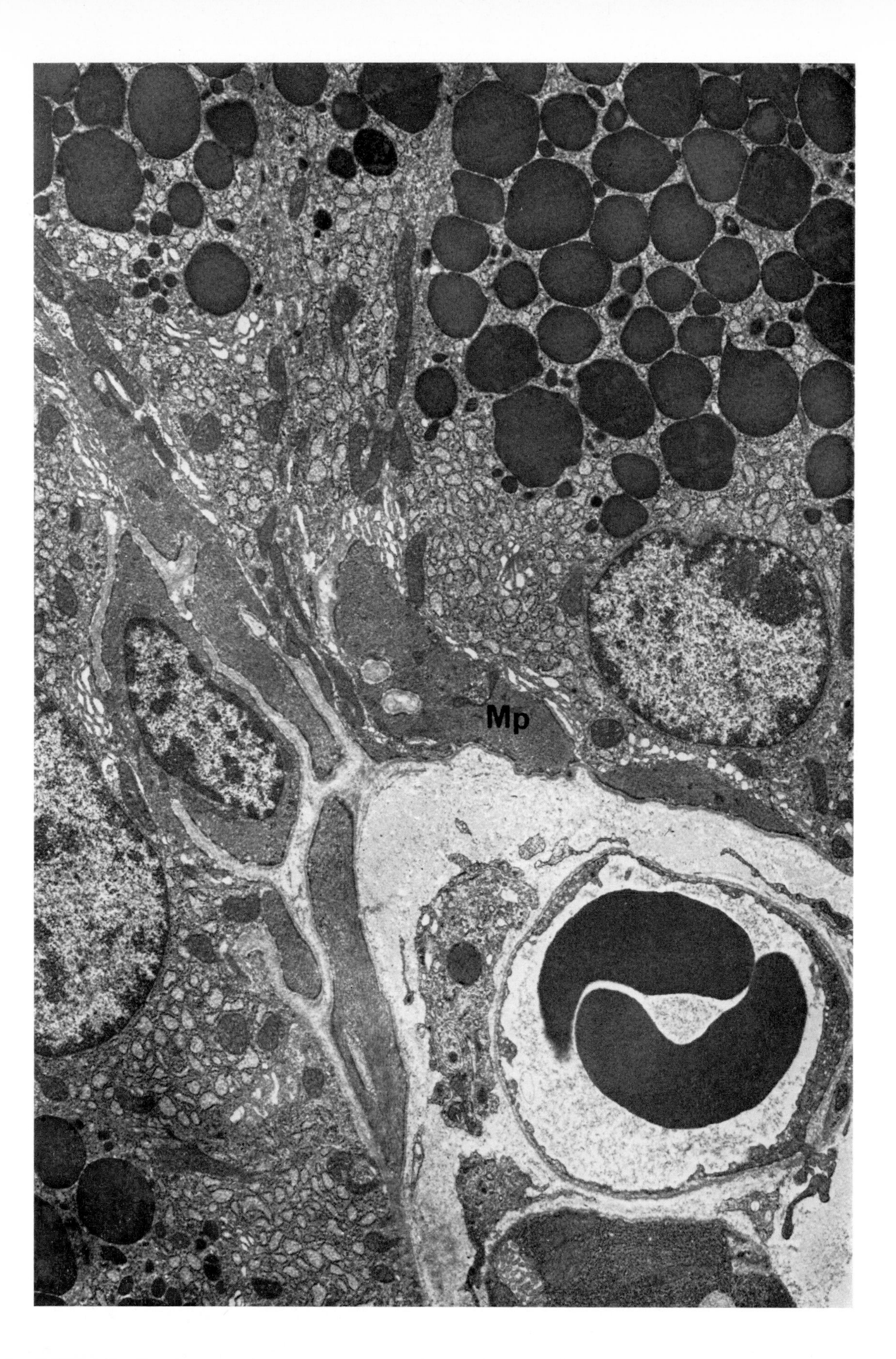
Mp

Plate 9

Most invertebrates have an open circulatory system, but some, for example the earthworm, have a closed circulatory system lined internally by an extracellular 'cuticle' (Cu) consisting of collagen and basal lamina. The blood pigment is the iron compound *erythrocruorin*, which is in solution in the plasma of the blood sinus (Bs). The vessels are lined by cells which have features of both endothelial cells and obliquely striated muscle similar to that present in the body wall and are consequently called myoendothelial cells (Mn). In some areas of the dorsal vessel the cellular processes are fenestrated and the walls are often infolded. The myoendothelial cells illustrated here are orientated parallel to the long axis of the vessel.

Invertebrate vascular myoendothelial cells: earthworm dorsal artery. Transverse section. Glutaraldehyde fixation. × 25 500.

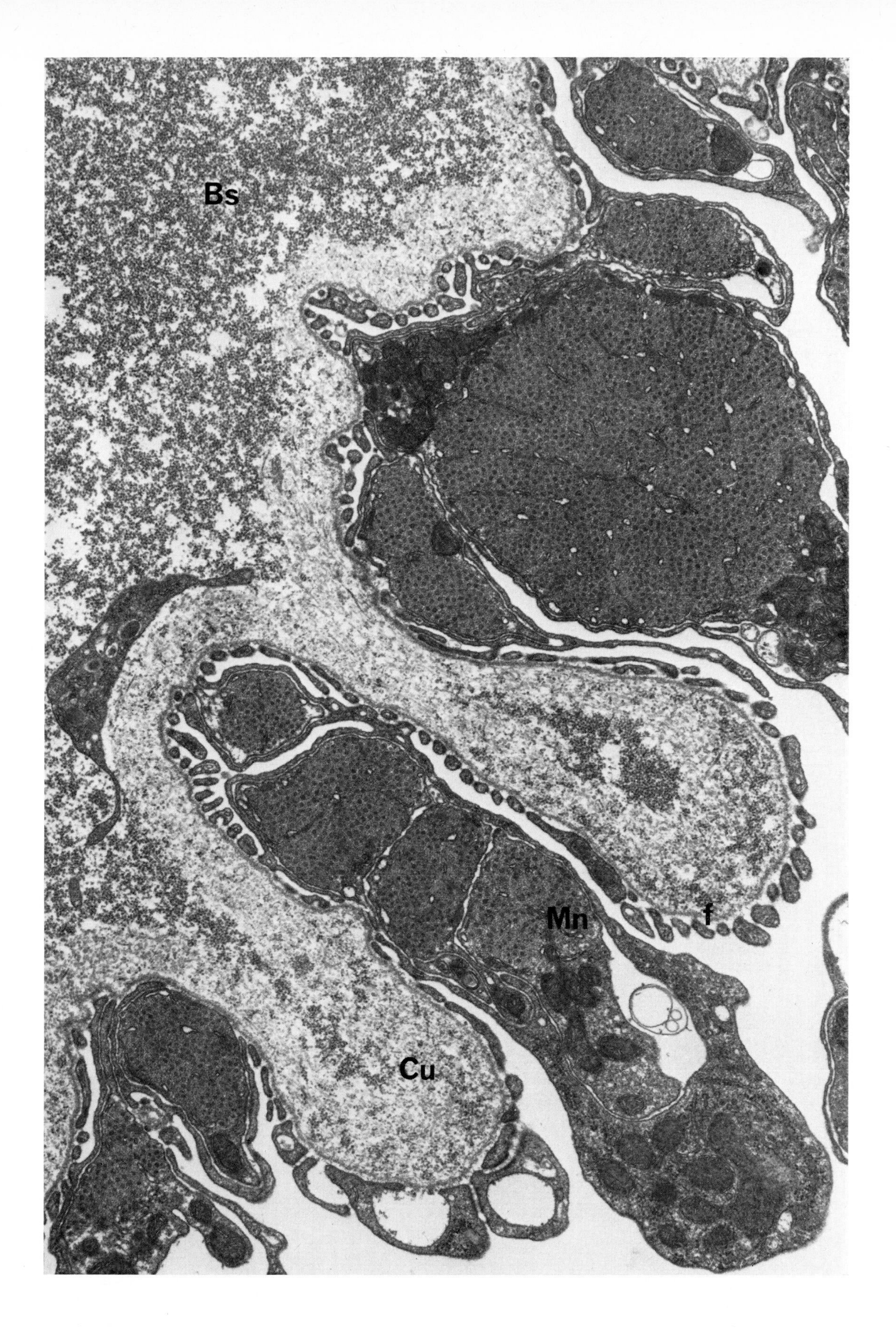

Bs
Mn
f
Cu

Plate 10

The heart of the earthworm also contains myoendothelial cells. Irregular projections or infoldings of the circularly orientated myoendothelial cells extend into the lumen and are enveloped by the 'cuticle' (Cu). The myofilaments in the projections run nearly parallel to the long axis of the heart, and those in the cell bodies are disposed nearly circularly around the heart.

Invertebrate cardiac myoendothelial cells: earthworm lateral heart. Transverse section. Glutaraldehyde fixation. × 37 500.

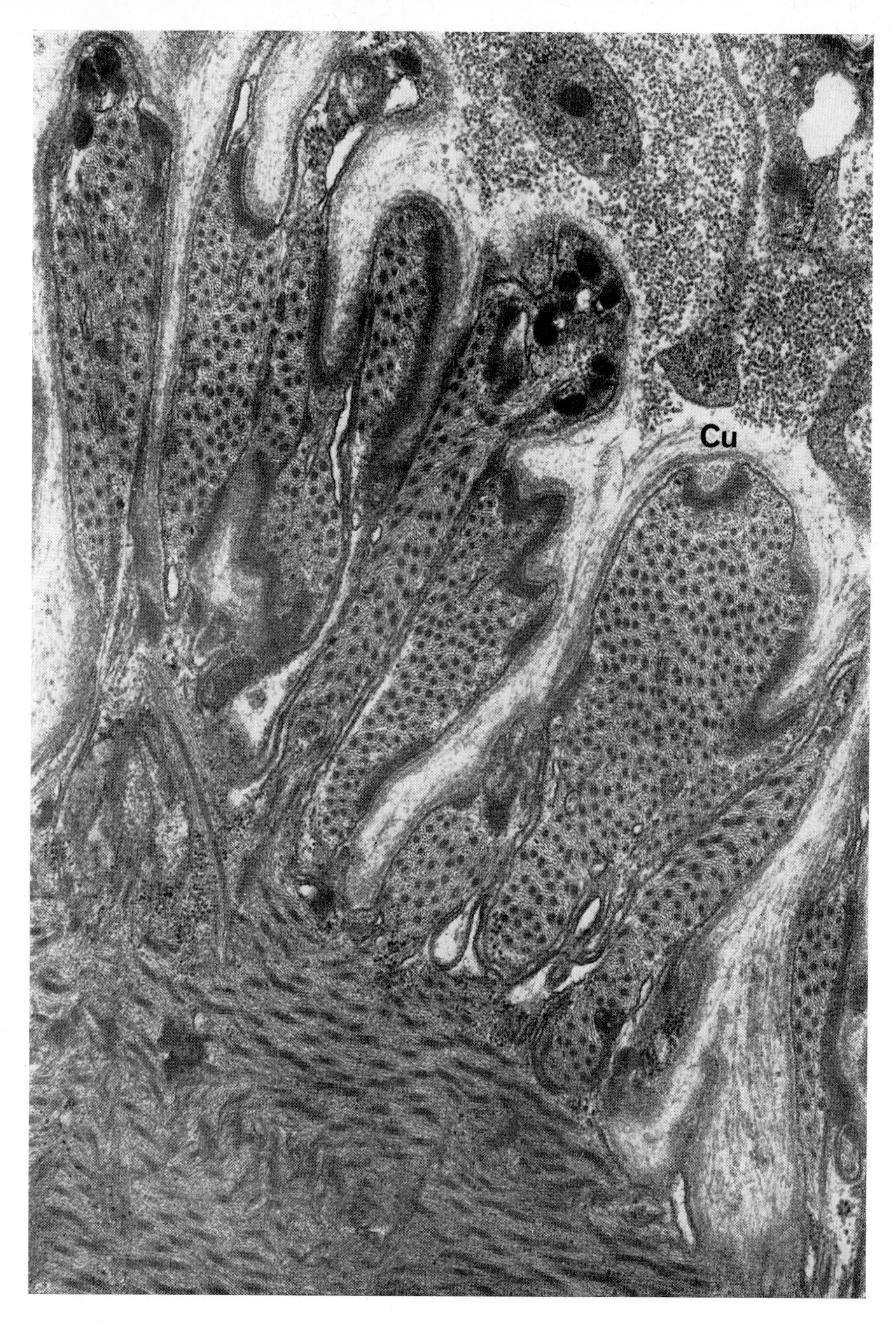
Cu

Selected reviews

Locomotion of Tissue Cells. 1973. *Ciba Foundation Symposium*, **14,** (new series). Associated Scientific Publishers, Amsterdam.

The Mechanisms of Muscle Contraction. 1973. *Cold Spring Harb. Symp. quant. Biol.*, **37,** 1–704.

BENDALL, J. R. 1969. *Muscles, Molecules and Movement*. Heinemann Educational Books, London.

BLOOM, W. and D. W. FAWCETT. 1968. *A Textbook of Histology*. 9th edition. W. B. Saunders, Philadelphia, Pennsylvania.

BOURNE, G. H. (ed.) 1973. *The Structure and Function of Muscle*. Vols. 1, 2, 3, 4. 2nd edition. Academic Press, New York.

BÜLBRING, E. and D. M. NEEDHAM (eds.). 1973. A discussion on recent developments in vertebrate smooth muscle physiology. *Phil. Trans. R. Soc. Ser. B.*, **265,** 1–231.

BURNSTOCK, G. 1970. Structure of smooth muscle and its innervation. In *Smooth Muscle*, E. Bülbring, A. Brading, A. Jones and T. Tomita (eds.). Edward Arnold, London. 1–69.

CASSENS, R. G. (ed.). 1972. *Muscle Biology: a Series of Advances*. Vol. 1. Marcel Dekker, New York.

CLOSE, R. I. 1972. Dynamic properties of mammalian skeletal muscles. *Physiol. Rev.*, **52,** 129–197.

DE HAAN, R. L. (ed.). 1970. Symposium on development and ultrastructure of the embryonic heart. *Am. J. Cardiol.*, **25,** 139–310.

DREIZEN, P. and L. C. GERSHMAN. 1970. Molecular basis of muscle contraction. Myosin. *Trans. N.Y. Acad. Sci.*, **32,** 170–203.

DRUMMOND, G. I. 1967. Muscle metabolism. *Fortschr. Zool.*, **18,** 359–429.

GERGELY, J. (ed.). 1964. *Biochemistry of Muscle Contraction*. Little, Brown and Co., Boston.

GERGELY, J. 1966. Contractile proteins. *A. Rev. Biochem.*, **35,** 691–722.

GIBBONS, I. R. 1968. The biochemistry of motility. *A. Rev. Biochem.*, **37,** 521–546.

HANSON, J. and J. LOWY. 1964. The structure of molluscan tonic muscles. In *Biochemistry of Muscle Contraction*. J. Gergely (ed.). Little, Brown & Co., Boston. 400–411.

HILL, A. V. 1965. *Trails and Trials in Physiology*. Edward Arnold, London.

HILL, A. V. 1970. *First and Last Experiments in Muscle Mechanics*. Cambridge University Press, London.

HOLTZER, H. and J. W. SANGER. 1972. Myogenesis: Old views rethought. In *Research in Muscle Development and in the Muscle Spindle*. B. Q. Banker, R. J. Przybylski, J. P. Van Der Meulen and M. Victor (eds.). ICS 240, *Excerpta Medica*, Amsterdam. 122–133.

HOYLE G. 1967*a*. Diversity of striated muscle. *Am. Zool.*, **7,** 435–449.

HOYLE, G. 1967*b*. Specificity of muscle. In *Invertebrate Nervous Systems*. C. A. G. Wiersma (ed.). University of Chicago Press, Chicago. 151–167.

HUXLEY, A. F. 1964. Muscle. *A. Rev. Physiol.*, **26,** 131–152.

HUXLEY, A. F. 1974. Muscular contraction. *J. Physiol.* **243,** 1–43.

HUXLEY, H. E. 1971. The structural basis of muscle contraction. *Proc. R. Soc. Ser. B.*, **178,** 131–149.

HUXLEY, H. E. 1973. Muscular contractions and cell motility. *Nature, Lond.*, **243,** 445–449.

JASMIN, G. and E. BAJUSY (eds.). 1962. International Symposium on Progress in Muscle Research. Structure and function of normal muscle. *Revue can. Biol.*, **21,** 191–334.

KATZ, A. M. 1970. Contractile proteins of the heart. *Physiol. Rev.*, **50,** 63–158.

KETELSEN, U.-P. 1974. Möglichkeiten und Grenzen ultrastruktureller Untersuchungen bei Erkranküngen der Skelettmuskulatur. *Beitr. Path. Bd.*, **151,** 1–29.

LAKI, K. (ed.). 1971. *Contractile Proteins and Muscle*. Marcel Dekker, New York.

LANGER, G. A. and A. J. BRADY. 1974. *The Mammalian Myocardium*. J. Wiley, New York.

MAIR, W. G. P. and F. M. S. TOMÉ. 1972. *Atlas of the Ultrastructure of Diseased Human Muscle*. Churchill Livingstone, Edinburgh.

MOMMAERTS, W. F. H. M. 1969. The energetics of muscle contraction. *Physiol. Rev.*, **49,** 427–508.

NEEDHAM, D. M. 1971. *Machina Carnis. The Biochemistry of Muscular Contraction in its Historical Development*. Cambridge University Press, London.

PAUL, W. M., E. E. DANIEL, C. M. KAY and G. MONCKTON. (eds.). 1965. *Muscle*. Pergamon Press, London.

PEACHEY, L. D. 1968. Muscle. *A. Rev. Physiol.*, **30,** 401–440.

PELLEGRINO C. and C. FRANZINI-ARMSTRONG. 1969. Recent contributions of electron microscopy to the study of normal and pathological muscle. *Int. Rev. exp. Path.*, **7,** 139–226.

PEPE, F. 1971. Structural components of the striated muscle fibril. In *Biological Macromolecules.* Vol. 5. S. N. Timasheff and G. D. Fasman (eds.). Marcel Dekker, New York. 323–353.

PODOLSKY, R. J. 1971. *Contractility of Muscle Cells and Related Processes.* Prentice Hall, New Jersey.

PRINGLE, J. W. 1967. The contractile mechanism of insect fibrillar muscle. *Prog. Biophys.*, **17**, 1–60.

RHODIN, J. A. G. 1963. *An Atlas of Ultrastructure.* W. B. Saunders, Philadelphia.

ROBBINS, S. L. 1974. Cardiac pathology–a look at the last five years. *Human pathol.* **5,** 9–24.

RÜEGG, J. C. 1971. Smooth muscle tone. *Physiol. Rev.*, **51,** 201–248.

SANDOW, A. 1970. Skeletal muscle. *A. Rev. Physiol.*, **32,** 87–138.

SANO, T., V. MIZUHIRA and K. MATSUDA. (eds.). 1967. *Electrophysiology and Ultrastructure of the Heart.* Bundoko, Tokyo, Japan.

SMITH, D. S. 1972. *Muscle.* Academic Press, New York.

SOMLYO, A. P. and A. V. SOMLYO. 1968. Vascular smooth muscle. I. Normal structure, pathology, biochemistry and biophysics. *Pharmac. Rev.*, **20,** 197–272.

SZENT-GYÖRGYI, A. G. 1968. The role of actin-myosin interaction in contraction. *Symp. Soc. exp. Biol.*, **22**, 17–42.

TAYLOR, E. W. 1972. Chemistry of muscle contraction. *A. Rev. Biochem.* **41,** 577–616.

TONOMURA, Y. and F. OOSAWA. 1972. Molecular mechanism of contraction. *A. Rev. Biophys. & Bioeng.*, **1,** 159–190.

WALKER, S. M. 1967. Contraction of skeletal muscle. *Am. J. phys. Med.*, **46,** 151–172.

WEBER, A. and J. M. MURRAY. 1973. Molecular and control mechanisms in muscle contraction. *Physiol. Rev.*, **53,** 612–673.

WILKIE, D. R. 1966. Muscle. *A. Rev. Physiol.*, **28,** 17–38.

WILKIE, D. R. 1968. *Muscle.* Studies in Biology no. 11. Edward Arnold, London.

YOUNG, M. 1969. The molecular basis of muscle contractions. *A. Rev. Biochem.*, **38,** 913–950.

Selected articles

Vertebrate Skeletal Muscle

ATERMAN, K. and S. PATEL. 1970. Striated muscle in the lung. *Am. J. Anat.*, **128,** 341–358.

BENNETT, H. S. and K. R. PORTER. 1953. An electron microscope study of sectioned breast muscle of the domestic fowl. *Am. J. Anat.*, **93,** 61–105.

CHENG, K. and G. M. BREININ. 1966. A comparison of the fine structure of extraocular and interosseus muscles in the monkey. *Invest. Opthal.*, **5,** 535–549.

CHENG, K., J. DAVIDOWITZ, A. LIEBOWITZ and G. M. BREININ. 1968. Fine structure of extraocular muscle in rabbit. *J. Cell Biol.*, **39**, 193–196.

EISENBERG, B. R., A. M. KUDA and J. B. PETER. 1974. Stereological analysis of mammalian skeletal muscle. I. Soleus muscle of the adult guinea pig. *J. Cell Biol.*, **60,** 732–754.

ENGEL, A. G. and R. D. MACDONALD. 1970. Ultrastructural reactions in muscle disease and their light-microscope correlates. In *International Congress on Muscle Diseases,* Milan (May 1969). J. N. Walton, N. Canal and G. Scarlato, (eds.). *Excerpta Medica Foundat.*, Amsterdam. 71–89.

GRINYER, I. and J. C. GEORGE. 1969. Some observations on the ultrastructure of the hummingbird pectoral muscles. *Can. J. Zool.*, **47,** 771–774.

HUXLEY, H. E. and J. HANSON. 1954. Changes in cross-striations of muscle during contraction and stretch and their structural interpretation. *Nature, Lond.*, **173,** 973–976.

KILARSKI, W. 1967. The fine structure of striated muscles in teleosts. *Z. Zellforsch. mikrosk. Anat.*, **79,** 562–580.

LARSON, P. F., M. JENKINSON and P. HUDGSON. 1970. The morphological development of chick embryo skeletal muscle grown in tissue culture as studied by electron microscopy. *J. neurol. Sci.*, **10,** 385–405.

PAGE, S. G. 1968. Fine structure of tortoise skeletal muscle. *J. Physiol., Lond.*, **197,** 709–715.

PAGE, S. G. and H. E. HUXLEY. 1963. Filament lengths in striated muscle. *J. Cell Biol.*, **19,** 369–390.

PEACHEY, L. D. 1961. Structure of the longitudinal body muscles of amphioxus. *J. biophys. biochem. Cytol.*, **10,** Suppl., 159–176.

PELLEGRINO, C. and C. FRANZINI-ARMSTRONG. 1969. Recent contributions of electron microscopy to the study of normal and pathological muscle. *Int. Rev. exp. Pathol.*, **7,** 139–226.

PILAR, G. and P. C. VAUGHAN. 1971. Ultrastructure and contractures of the pigeon iris striated muscle. *J. Physiol., Lond.*, **219,** 253–266.

RAVIOLA, E. and G. RAVIOLA. 1967. Striated muscle cells in the thymus of reptiles and birds: an electron microscopic study. *Am. J. Anat.*, **121,** 623–645.

REGER, J. F. 1966. The fine structure of iridial constrictor pupillae muscle of *Alligator mississippiensis*. *Anat. Rec.*, **155,** 197–216.

ROWE, R. W. D. and G. GOLDSPINK. 1969*a*. Muscle fibre growth in five different muscles in both sexes of mice. I. Normal mice. *J. Anat.*, **104,** 519–530.

ROWE, R. W. D. and G. GOLDSPINK. 1969*b*. Muscle fibre growth in five different muscles in both sexes of mice. II. Dystrophic mice. *J. Anat.*, **104,** 531–538.

SCHAFFINO, S., V. HANZLÍKOVÁ and S. PIEROBON. 1970. Relations between structure and function in rat skeletal muscle fibers. *J. Cell Biol.*, **47,** 107–119.

SHIMADA, Y., D. A. FISCHMAN and A. A. MOSCONA. 1967. The fine structure of embryonic chick skeletal muscle cells differentiated *in vitro*. *J. Cell Biol.*, **35,** 445–453.

TÖRO, I., I. OLÁH, P. RÖHLICH and SZ. VIRÁGH. 1969. Electron microscopic observations on myoid cells of the frog's thymus. *Anat. Rec.*, 165, 329–342.

VERATTI, E. 1902. Richerche sulle fine struttura della fibra muscolare striata. *Men. Ist. lomb. Sci. Lett. Classe Sc. Mat. Nat.* **19,** 87–133. (English transl.): *J. biophys. biochem. Cytol.*, **10,** 3–59.

Vertebrate cardiac muscle

BALDWIN, K. M. 1970. The fine structure and electrophysiology of heart muscle cell injury. *J. Cell. Biol.*, **46,** 455–476.

BATTIG, C. G. and F. N. LOW. 1961. The ultrastructure of human cardiac muscle and its associated tissue space. *Am. J. Anat.*, **108,** 199–229.

BISHOP, S. P. and C. R. COLE. 1969. Ultrastructural changes in the canine myocardium with right ventricular hypertrophy and congestive heart failure. *Lab. Invest.*, **20,** 219–229.

DENOIT, F. and E. CORABOEUF. 1965. Étude comparative de l'ultrastructure du myocarde chez le rat et le cobaye. *Compt. Rend. Soc. Biol.*, **159,** 2118–2121.

DIDIO, L. J. A. 1967. Myocardial ultrastructure and electrocardiograms of the hummingbird under normal and experimental conditions. *Anat. Rec.*, **159,** 335–352.

EDWARDS, G. A. and C. E. CHALLICE. 1958. The fine structure of cardiac muscle cells of newborn and suckling mice. *Expl. Cell Res.*, **15,** 247–250.

FAWCETT, D. W. and MCNUTT, N. S. 1969. The ultrastructure of the cat myocardium. I. Ventricular papillary muscle. *J. Cell Biol.*, **42,** 1–45.

FAWCETT, D. W. and C. C. SELBY. 1958. Observations on the fine structure of the turtle atrium. *J. biophys. biochem. Cytol.*, **4,** 63–72.

FENOGLIO, J. J. JR., T. D. PHAM, A. L. WIT, A. L. BASSETT and M. WAGNER. 1972. Canine mitral complex ultrastructure and electromechanical properties. *Circulation Res.*, **31,** 417–430.

FERRANS, V. J., R. G. HIBBS and L. M. BUJA. 1969. Nucleoside phosphatase activity in atrial and ventricular myocardium of the rat: a light and electron microscopic study. *Am. J. Anat.*, **125,** 47–86.

FORBES, M. S. and N. SPERELAKIS. 1971. Ultrastructure of lizard ventricular muscle. *J. Ultrastruct. Res.*, **34,** 439–451.

FORBES, M. S. and N. SPERELAKIS. 1972. Ultrastructure of cardiac muscle from dystrophic mice. *Am. J. Anat.* **134,** 271–290.

GROS, D. and J. SCHRÉVEL. 1970. Ultrastructure comparée du muscle cardiaque ventriculaire de l'Ambystome et de sa larve, l'axolotl. *J. Microsc. (Fr.)*, **9,** 765–784.

HIBBS, R. G. and V. J. FERRANS. 1969. An ultrastructural and histochemical study of rat atrial myocardium. *Am. J. Anat.*, **124,** 251–280.

HIRAKOW, R. 1970. Ultrastructural characteristics of the mammalian and sauropsidian heart. *Am. J. Cardiol.*, **25,** 195–203.

HIRAKOW, R. 1971. The fine structure of the *Necturus* (amphibia) heart. *Am. J. Anat.*, **132,** 401–422.

HOWSE, H. D., V. J. FERRANS and R. G. HIBBS. 1969. Observations on the fine structure of the ventricular myocardium of a salamander, *Ambystoma maculatum* Shaw. *Herpetologica*, **25,** 75–85.

HUANG, C. Y. 1967. Electron microscopic study of the development of heart muscle of the frog, *Rana pipiens. J. Ultrastruct. Res.*, **20,** 211–226.

JAMES, T. N. and L. SHERF. 1968. Ultrastructure of myocardial cells. *Am. J. Cardiol.*, **22,** 389–416.

JOHNSON, E. A. and J. R. SOMMER. 1967. A strand of cardiac muscle. Its ultrastructure and the electrophysiological implications of its geometry. *J. Cell Biol.*, **33,** 103–129.

KISCH, B. 1962. Electron microscopy of the frog's heart. *Expl Med. Surg.*, **19,** 104–142.

KISCH, B. and D. E. PHILPOTT. 1963*a*. Electron microscopy of the heart of fish. I. The goldfish heart. *Expl Med. Surg.*, **21,** 28–53.

KISCH, B. and D. E. PHILPOTT. 1963*b*. Electron microscopy of the heart of fish. II. The heart of selachians (dogfish and torpedo). *Expl Med. Surg.*, **21,** 54–74.

LEAK, L. V. 1967. The ultrastructure of myofibers in a reptilian heart: the boa constrictor. *Am. J. Anat.*, **120,** 553–582.

LEAK, L. V. 1969. Electron microscopy of cardiac tissue in a primitive vertebrate *Myxine glutinosa. J. Morph.*, **128,** 131–157.

LEAK, L. V. and J. F. BURKE. 1964. The ultrastructure of human embryonic myocardium. *Anat. Rec.*, **149,** 623–650.

LEGATO, M. 1969. The correlation of ultrastructure and function in the mammalian myocardial cell. *Prog. cardiovasc. Dis.*, **11,** 391–409.

LEGATO, M. J., D. SPIRO and G. A. LANGER. 1968. Ultrastructural alterations produced in mammalian myocardium by variation in perfusate ionic compositions. *J. Cell Biol.*, **37,** 1–12.

McCALLISTER, L. P. 1974. Ultrastructural study of normal and ischemic rat myocardium. *Anat. Rec.*, **178,** 406

McNUTT, N. S. and D. W. FAWCETT. 1969. The ultrastructure of the cat myocardium. II. Atrial muscle. *J. Cell Biol.*, **42,** 46–67.

MAZZA, V. L., P. ANVERSA, L. MORGUTTI and A. TOSO. 1969. Changes of the myocardial ultrastructure during open heart surgery with extracorporeal circulation. *J. Cardiovasc. Surg.*, **10,** 212–228.

MELLO, W. C. DE, G. E. MOTTA and M. CHAPEAU. 1969. A study on the healing-over of myocardial cells of toads. *Circulation Res.*, **24,** 475–487.

MILLHOUSE, E. W., JR., J. J. CHIAKULAS and L. E., SCHEVING. 1971. Long-term organ culture of the salamander heart. *J. Cell Biol.*, **48,** 1–14.

MITOMO, Y., K. NAKAO and A. ANGRIST. 1969. The fine structure of the heart valves in the chicken. I. Mitral valve. *Am. J. Anat.*, **125,** 147–168.

MOORE, D. H. and H. RUSKA. 1957. Electron microscope study of mammalian cardiac muscle cells. *J. biophys. biochem., Cytol.*, **3,** 261–268.

MUIR, A. R. 1967. The effects of divalent cations on the ultrastructure of the perfused rat heart. *J. Anat.* **101,** 239–261.

MUSCATELLO U., I. PASQUALI-RONCHETTI and A. BARASA. 1968. An electron microscope study of myoblasts from chick embryo heart cultured *in vitro. J. Ultrastruct. Res.*, **23,** 44–59.

NAYLOR, W. G. and N. C. R. MERRILLEES. 1964. Some observations on the fine structure and metabolic activity of normal and glycerinated ventricular muscle of toad. *J. Cell Biol.*, **22,** 533–550.

OKITA, S. 1972. The fine structure of the atrial muscle cells of the soft-shelled turtle heart (*Amyda*). *J. Electron Microsc.*, **21,** 214.

PAGE, E. and L. P. McCALLISTER. 1973. Quantitative electron microscopic description of heart muscle cells: application to normal, hypertrophied and thyroxine – stimulated heart. *Am. J. Cardiol.*, **31,** 172–181.

PAGE, S. G. and R. NIEDERGERKE. 1972. Structures of physiological interest in the frog heart ventricle. *J. Cell Sci.*, **11,** 179–204.

POCHE, R. 1969. Ultrastructure of heart muscle under pathological conditions. *Ann. N.Y. Acad. Sci.*, **156,** 34–47.

RUSKA, H. 1965. Electron microscopy of the heart. In *Electrophysiology of the Heart.* B. Taccardi and G. Marchetti (eds.). Pergamon Press, Oxford. 1–19.

SANTER, R. M. and J. L. S. COBB. 1972. The fine structure of the heart of the teleost, *Pleuronectes platessa* L. *Z. Zellforsch. mikrosk. Anat.*, **131,** 1–14.

SCHIEBLER, T. H. and H. H. WOLFF. 1966. Elektronenmikroskopische Untersuchungen am Herzmuskel der Ratte während der Entwicklung. *Z. Zellforsch. mikrosk. Anat.*, **69,** 22–40.

SCHIPPEL, K. and D. REISSIG. 1966. Über die Feinstruktur der Befestigung der Chorda tendinea an der Herzmuskulatur. *Z. mikrosk. -anat. Forsch.*, **75,** 210–223.

SHOCK, N. W., R. ANDRES, M. LANDOWNE, A. H. NORRIS, E. SIMONSEN and F. C. SWARTZ. 1965. Aging of the cardiovascular system. In *The Heart and Circulation. Second National Conference on Cardiovascular Diseases*, Vol. 1. E. C. Andrus and C. H. Maxwell (eds.). *Fed. Am. Soc. Exp. Biol.*, Washington, D. C. 558–583.

SOMMER, J. R. and E. A. JOHNSON. 1969. Cardiac muscle. A comparative ultrastructural study with special reference to frog and chicken hearts. *Z. Zellforsch. mikrosk. Anat.*, **98,** 437–468.

STALEY, N. A. and E. S. BENSON. 1968. The ultrastructure of frog ventricular cardiac muscle and its relationship to mechanisms of excitation–contraction coupling. *J. Cell Biol.* **38,** 99–115.

STENGER, R. J. and D. SPIRO. 1961. The ultrastructure of mammalian cardiac muscle. *J. biophys. biochem. Cytol.*, **9,** 325–351.

TOMANEK, R. J. and U. L. KARLSSON. 1973. Myocardial ultrastructure of young and senescent rats. *J. Ultrastruct., Res.*, **42,** 201–220.

TRAVIS, D. F. and A. TRAVIS. 1972. Ultrastructural changes in the left ventricular rat myocardial cells with age. *J. Ultrastruct. Res.*, **39,** 124–148.

YAMAMOTO, T. J. 1965. Fine structure of the atrial muscle in snake heart. *J. Electron Microsc.*, **14,** 134.

YAMAUCHI, A. and G. BURNSTOCK. 1968. An electronmicroscopic study on the innervation of the trout heart. *J. comp. Neurol.*, **32,** 567–588.

Vertebrate smooth muscle

ALBERT, E. N. and D. C. PEASE. 1968. An electron microscopic study of uterine arteries during pregnancy. *Am. J. Anat.*, **123,** 165–194.

BACKWINKEL, K.-P., H. THEMANN, G. SCHMITT and W. H. HAUSS. 1973. Elektronenmikroskopische Untersuchungen über das Verhalten glatter Muskelzellen in der Arterienwand unter verschiedenen experimentellen Bedingungen. *Virchows Arch. Abt. A Path. Anat.*, **359,** 171–184.

BENNETT, T. and J. L. S. COBB. 1969. Studies on the avian gizzard: Morphology and innervation of the smooth muscle. *Z. Zellforsch. mikrosk. Anat.* **96,** 173–185.

BERGMAN, R. A. 1968. Uterine smooth muscle fibers in castrate and estrogen-treated rats. *J. Cell Biol.*, **36**: 639–647.

BERMAN, M. J., W. McNARY, D. AUSPRUNK, E. LEE, S. WEAVER and R. SAPAWI. 1972. Innervation and fine structure of the precapillary sphincter in the frog retrolingual membrane. *Microvasc. Res.*, **4,** 51–61.

BO, W. J., D. L. ODOR and M. L. ROTHROCK. 1969. Ultrastructure of uterine smooth muscle following progesterone or progesterone–estrogen treatment. *Anat. Rec.*, **163,** 121–131.

BURDEN, H. W. 1972. Ultrastructural observations on ovarian perifollicular smooth muscle in the cat, guinea pig, and rabbit. *Am. J. Anat.*, **133,** 125–141.

BÜSSOW, H. and U. WULFHEKEL. 1972. Die Feinstruktur der glatten Muskelzellen in den grossen muskulären Arterien der Vögel. *Z. Zellforsch. mikrosk. Anat.*, **125,** 339–352.

CAESAR, R., G. A. EDWARDS and H. RUSKA. 1957. Architecture and nerve supply of mammalian smooth muscle tissue. *J. biophys. biochem. Cytol.*, **3,** 867–878.

CAMPBELL, G. R., Y. UEHARA, G. MARK and G. BURNSTOCK. 1971. Fine structure of smooth muscle cells grown in tissue culture. *J.Cell Biol.*, **49,** 21–34.

CHOI, J. K. 1963. The fine structure of the urinary bladder of the toad, *Bufo marinus*. *J.Cell Biol.*, **16,** 53–72.

CHOPRA, H. C. 1965. Investigations on the fine structure of smooth muscle fibres of prostate gland. *Cellule*, **65,** 213–217.

CLIFF, W. J. 1967. The aortic tunica media in growing rats studied with the electron microscope. *Lab. Invest.*, **17,** 599–615.

CLIFF, W. J. 1970. The aortic tunica media in aging rats. *Exp. mol. Pathol.*, **13,** 172–189.

FAWCETT, D. W. 1959. The fine structure of capillaries, arterioles and small arteries. In *The Microcirculation. Symposium on Factors Influencing Exchange of Substances Across Capillary Wall.* S. R. M. Reynolds and B. W. Zweifach, (eds.). University of Illinois Press, Urbana, 1–27.

FRIEDERICI, H. H. and R. J. DE CLOUX. 1968. The early response of immature rat myometrium to estrogenic stimulation. *J. Ultrastruct. Res.*, **22,** 402–412.

GABELLA, G. 1974. Special muscle cells and their innervation in the mammalian small intestine. *Cell Tissue Res.*, **153,** 63–77.

GANSLER, H. 1961. Struktur und Funktion der glatten Muskulatur. II. Licht- und elektronenmikroskopische Befunde an Hohlorganen von Ratte, Meerschweinchen und Mensch. *Z. Zellforsch. mikrosk. Anat.*, **55,** 724–762.

GOODMAN, T. F. 1972. Fine structure of the cells of the Suquet-Hoyer canal. *J. invest. Derm.*, **59,** 363–369.

GOSLING, J. A. and J. S. DIXON. 1970. Further observations on upper urinary tract smooth muscle. A light and electron microscope study. *Z. Zellforsch. mikrosk. Anat.*, **108,** 127–134.

GUNN, M. 1972. Structural features in the smooth muscle of the gut and their physiological significance. *Acta Anat.*, **82,** 473–496.

ISHIKAWA, H. and E. YAMADA. 1972. Electron microscopic observations on smooth muscles of cat nictitating membrane. *J. Electron Microsc.*, **21,** 214.

ISHIKAWA, T. 1962. Fine structure of the human ciliary muscle. *Invest. Ophthal.*, **1,** 587–608.

JAEGER, J. 1963. Zer Ultrastruktur der menschlichen Uterus-Muskelzelle unter der Geburt. *Arch. Gynaek*, **199,** 173–181.

JELLINGER, K. 1974. Intimal cushions in ciliary arteries of the dog. *Experientia*, **30,** 188–189.

KARRER, H. E. 1961. An electron microscope study of the aorta in young and aging mice. *J. Ultrastruct. Res.*, **5,** 1–27.

KEECH, M. K. 1960. Electron microscope study of the normal rat aorta. *J. biophys. biochem. Cytol.*, **7,** 533–538.

KÖNIG, B., JR. 1971. Das Verhalten zwischen glatten Muskelzellen und Bindegewebe menschlicher, Uteri. *Anat. Anz.*, **129,** 541–550.

LAGUENS, R. and J. LAGRUTTA. 1964. Fine structure of human uterine muscle in pregnancy. *Am. J. Obstet. Cynec.*, **89,** 1040–1048.

LANE, B. P. and J. A. G. RHODIN. 1964. Fine structure of the lamina muscularis mucosae. *J. Ultrastruct. Res.*, **10,** 484–497.

LEESON, C. R. and T. S. LEESON. 1965. The fine structure of the rat umbilical cord at various times of gestation. *Anat. Rec.*, **151,** 183–198.

LEESON, T. S. 1974. Muscle in the mammalian testicular capsule. *J. Anat.*, **118,** 363.

LIBERTINO, J. A. and R. M. WEISS. 1972. Ultrastructure of human ureter. *J. Urol.*, **108,** 71–76.

LUFT, J. H. 1963. The fine structure of the vascular wall. In *Evolution of the Atherosclerotic Plaque*. R. J. Jones, (ed.). University of Chicago Press, Chicago, London, 3–14.

MOFFAT, D. M. and M. CREASEY. 1971. The fine structure of the intra-arterial cushions at the origins of the juxtamedullary afferent arterioles in the rat kidney. *J. Anat.*, **110,** 409–419.

MOVAT, H. Z. and N. V. P. FERNANDO. 1963. The fine structure of the terminal vascular bed. I. Small arteries with an internal elastic lamina. *Exp. & mol. Pathol.*, **2,** 549–563.

MULLINS, G. L. and W. G. GUNTHEROTH. 1965. A collagen net hypothesis for force transference of smooth muscle. *Nature, Lond.*, **206,** 592–594.

NEMETSCHEK-GANSLER, H. 1967. Ultrastructure of the myometrium. In *Cellular Biology of the Uterus*. R. M. Wynn (ed.). North Holland, Amsterdam. 353–385.

NOTLEY, R. G. 1970. The musculature of the human ureter. *Br. J. Urol.*, **42,** 724–727.
OSVALDO-DECIMA, L. 1970. Smooth muscle in the ovary of the rat and monkey. *J. Ultrastruct. Res.*, **30,** 218–237.
PARKER, F. 1958. An electron microscope study of coronary arteries. *Am. J. Anat.*, **103,** 247–273.
PAULE, W. J. 1963. Electron microscopy of newborn rat aorta. *J. Ultrastruct. Res.*, **8,** 219–235.
PEASE, D. C. and S. MOLINARI. 1960. Electron microscopy of muscular arteries; pial vessels of the cat and monkey. *J. Ultrastruct. Res.*, **3,** 447–468.
PEASE, D. C. and W. J. PAULE. 1960. Electron microscopy of elastic arteries; the thoracic aorta of the rat. *J. Ultrastruct. Res.*, **3,** 469–483.
PHELPS, P. C. and J. H. LUFT. 1969. Electron microscopical study of relaxation and constriction in frog arterioles. *Am. J. Anat.*, **125,** 399–428.
POPOVIC, N. A., D. G. McLEOD and A. A. BORSKI. 1973. Ultrastructure of the human vas deferens. *Invest. Urol.*, **10,** 266–277.
REES, P. M. 1968. Electron microscopical observations on the architecture of the carotid arterial wall, with special reference to the sinus portion. *J. Anat.*, **103,** 35–48.
RHODIN, J. A. G. 1967. The ultrastructure of mammalian arterioles and precapillary sphincters. *J. Ultrastruct. Res.*, **18,** 181–223.
RHODIN, J. A. G. 1968. Ultrastructure of mammalian venous capillaries, venules and small collecting veins. *J. Ultrastruct. Res.*, **25,** 452–500.
ROSS, R. 1971. The smooth muscle cell. II. Growth of smooth muscle in culture and formation of elastic fibers. *J. Cell Biol.*, **50,** 172–186.
ROSS, R. and S. J. KLEBANOFF. 1967. Fine structural changes in uterine smooth muscle and fibroblasts in response to estrogen. *J. Cell Biol.*, **32,** 155–168.
ROSS, R. and S. J. KLEBANOFF. 1971. The smooth muscle cell. I. *In vivo* synthesis of connective tissue proteins. *J. Cell Biol.*, **50,** 159–171.
SETHI, N. and M. BROOKS. 1971. Ultrastructure of the blood vessels in the chick allantois and chorioallantois. *J. Anat.*, **110,** 1–16.
SHEPPARD, B. L. and A. J. BISHOP. 1973. Electron microscopical observations on sheep umbilical vessels. *Quart. Jl exp. Physiol.*, **58,** 39–45.
SHIVELY, J. N. and G. P. EPLING. 1969. Fine structure of the canine eye: Iris. *Am. J. vet. Res.*, **30,** 13–25.
SCHOENBERG, C. F. 1958. An electron microscope study of smooth muscle in pregnant uterus of the rabbit. *J. biophys. biochem. Cytol.*, **4,** 609–614.
STEHBENS, W. E. and R. M. LUDATSCHER. 1973. Ultrastructure of the renal arterial bifurcation of rabbits. *Exp. & mol. Pathol.* **18,** 50–67.
SUZUKI, K. and G. OONEDA. 1972. Cerebral arterial lesions in experimental hypertensive rats: Electron microscopic study of middle cerebral arteries. *Exp. & mol. Pathol.*, **16,** 341–352.
TAKAYANAGI, T., M. L. RENNELS and E. NELSON. 1972. An electron microscopic study of intimal cushions in intracranial arteries of the cat. *Am. J. Anat.*, **133,** 415–430.
TOUSIMIS, A. J. and B. S. FINE. 1959. Ultrastructure of the iris: an electron microscopic study. *Am. J. Ophthal. Proc.*, **48,** 397–417.
VEGGE, T. and A. RINGVOLD. 1969. Ultrastructure of the wall of human iris vessels. *Z. Zellforsch. mikrosk. Anat.*, **94,** 19–31.
WEISS, P. 1968. Submikroskopische Charakteristika und Reaktionsformen der glatten Muskelzelle unter besonderer Berücksichtigung der Gefässwandmuskelzelle. *Z. mikrosk. -anat. Forsch.*, **78,** 305–331.
YAMAMOTO, I. 1962. An electron microscope study of the rabbit arterial wall. Smooth muscle and the intercellular components with special reference to the elastic fiber. *J. Electron Microsc.*, **11,** 212–225.
YOHRO, T. and G. BURNSTOCK. 1973. Fine structure of 'intimal cushions' at branching sites in coronary arteries of vertebrates. A scanning and transmission electron-microscope study. *Z. Anat. EntwGesch.*, **140,** 187–202.

Myoepithelial, myoendothelial and myofibroblastic cells

ARCHER, F. L., J. S. BECK and J. M. O. MELVIN. 1971. Localization of smooth muscle protein in myoepithelium by immunofluorescence. *Am. J. Path.*, **63,** 109–118.

ASAGAMI, C. 1969. Electron microscopic study of differentiation of the mesenchymal cells of human skin. 3. Differentiation of the arrector pilorum forming smooth muscle. *Acta Derm., Kyoto.*, **64,** 189–207.

BERTOLINI, R., D. REISSIG and K. SCHIPPEL. 1969. Elektronenmikroskopische Befunde an den Zellen in der Chorionplatte der reifen menschlichen Plazenta. *Z. mikrosk. -anat. Forsch.*, **80,** 358–368.

BÖCK, P., G. BREITENECKER and G. LUNGLMAYR. 1972. Kontraktile Fibroblasten (Myofibroblasten) in der Lamina propria der Hodenkanälchen vom Menschen. *Z. Zellforsch. mikrosk. Anat.*, **133,** 519–527.

BÖCK, P. and N. LERTPRAPAI. 1972. A sarcoplasmic reticulum in myoepithelial cells of the venomenous glands in the skin of the orange-speckled toad (*Bombina variegata variegata* L.) *Cytobiologie*, **6,** 476–480.

ELLIS, R. A. 1965. Fine structure of the myoepithelium of the eccrine sweat glands of man. *J. Cell Biol.*, **27,** 551–563.

GABBIANI, G., B. J. HIRSCHEL, G. B. RYAN, P. R. STATKOV and G. MAJNO. 1972. Granulation tissue as a contractile organ. A study of structure and function. *J. exp. Med.*, **135,** 719–734.

HAMA, K. 1960. The fine structure of some blood vessels of the earthworm *Eisenia foetida*. *J. biophys. biochem. Cytol.*, **7,** 717–723.

LEESON, T. S. and C. R. LEESON. 1971. Myoepithelial cells in the exorbital lacrimal and parotic glands of the rat in frozen-etched replicas. *Am. J. Anat.*, **132,** 133–146.

McREYNOLDS, H. D. and C. M. SIRAKI. 1973. Smooth muscle-like cells in ovaries of the hamster and gerbil. *Anat. Rec.*, **175,** 380.

MATRICON, I. 1973. Quelques données ultrastructurales sur un myoépithélium: le pharynx d'un Bryozaire. *Z. Zellforsch. mikrosk. Anat.*, **136,** 569–578.

O'SHEA, J. D. 1970. An ultrastructural study of smooth muscle-like cells in the theca externa of ovarian follicles in the rat. *Anat. Rec.*, **167,** 127–140.

RADNOR, C. J. P. 1972*a*. Myoepithelial cell differentiation in rat mammary glands. *J. Anat.*, **111,** 381–398.

RADNOR, C. J. P. 1972*b*. Myoepithelium in involuting mammary glands of the rat. *J. Anat.*, **112,** 355–365.

RYAN, G. B., W. J. CLIFF, G. GABBIANI, C. IRLE, D. MONTANDON, P. R. STATKOV and G. MAJNO. 1974. Myofibroblasts in human granulation tissue. *Human Pathol.*, **5,** 55–67.

TAMARIN, A. 1966. Myoepithelium of the rat submaxillary gland. *J. Ultrastruct. Res.*, **16,** 320–338.

TANDLER, B., C. R. DENNING, I. D. MANDEL and A. H. KUTSCHER. 1970. Ultrastructure of human labial salivary glands. III. Myoepithelium and ducts. *J. Morph.*, **130,** 227–245.

WEINKER, H.-G. 1967. Elektronenmikroskopische Untersuchungen über Feinbau und Nervenversorgung des M. arrector pili der Hauskatz. *Z. mikrosk. -anat. Forsch.*, **77,** 197–265.

WEINKER, H.-G. 1969. Elektronenmikroskopische Untersuchungen über den M. arrector pili des Menschen. *Z. mikrosk. -anat. Forsch.*, **80,** 230–240.

YAMAUCHI, A. and G. BURNSTOCK. 1967. Nerve-myoepithelium and nerve-glandular epithelium contacts in the lacrimal gland of the sheep. *J. Cell Biol.*, **34,** 917–919.

Contractile proteins in other cell types

ABERCROMBIE, M., J. E. M. HEAYSMAN and S. M. PEGRUM. 1971. The locomotion of fibroblasts in culture. IV. Electron microscopy of the leading lamella. *Expl Cell Res.*, **67,** 359–367.

ABRAMOWITZ, J., M. N. MALIK, A. STRACHER and T. C. DETWILER. 1973. Studies on the contractile proteins from blood platelets. In *The Mechanism of Muscle Contraction. Cold Spring Harb. Symp. quant. Biol.*, **37,** 595–598.

ACHTERRATH, M. 1969. Die Reaktion von glycerin-extrahierten Protoplasmatropfen von *Physarum polycephalum* auf Zugabe von ATP. *Cytobiologies*, **1,** 169–183.

ADELSTEIN, R. S. and M. A. CONTI. 1973. The characterization of contractile proteins from platelets and fibroblasts. In *The Mechanism of Muscle Contraction. Cold Spring Harb. Symp. quant. Biol.*, **37,** 599–606.

BECK, R., H. HINSSEN, H. KOMNICK, W. STOCKEM and K. E. WOHLFARTH-BOTTERMANN. 1970. Weitreichende, fibrilläre Protoplasmadifferenzierungen und ihre Bedeutung für die Protoplasmaströmung. V. Kontraktion, ATPase-Aktivität und Feinstruktur isolierter Actomyosin-Fäden von *Physarum polycephalum*. *Cytobiologie*, **2,** 259–274.

BECKER, C. G. 1972. Demonstration of actomyosin in mesangial cells of the renal glomerulus. *Am. J. Path.*, **66,** 97–110.

BECKER, C. G. and G. E. MURPHY. 1969. Demonstration of contractile protein in endothelium and cells of the heart valves endocardium, intima arteriosclerotic plaques and Aschoff bodies of rheumatic heart disease. *Am. J. Path.*, **55,** 1–37.

BECKER, C. G. and R. L. NACHMAN. 1973. Contractile proteins of endothelial cells platelets and smooth muscle. *Am. J. Path.*, **71,** 1–22.

BEHNKE, O., B. I. KRISTENSEN and L. E. NEILSEN. 1971. Electron microscopical observations on actinoid and myosinoid filaments in blood platelets. *J. Ultrastruct. Res.*, **37,** 351–369.

BERL, S., S. PUSZKIN and W. J. NICKLAS. 1973. Actomyosin-like protein in brain. *Science, N.Y.*, **179,** 441–446.

DE BRUYN, P. P. N. and Y. CHO. 1974. Contractile structures in endothelial cells of splenic sinusoids. *J. Ultrastruct. Res.*, **49,** 24–33.

DE MARTINO, C., L. ACCINNI and G. PROCICCHIANI. 1973. Ultrastructural study on contractile structures in mammalian nephron. Their development in the metanephros of human embryo. *Z. Zellforsch. mikrosk. Anat.*, **140,** 101–124.

DURHAM, A. C. 1974. Unified theory of control of actin and myosin in nonmuscle movements. *Cell*, **2,** 123.

GOLDMAN, R. D. and D. M. KNIPE. 1973. Functions of cytoplasmic fibers in nonmuscle cell motility. In *The Mechanism of Muscle Contraction. Cold Spring Harb. Symp. quant. Biol.*, **37,** 523–534.

GRÖSCHEL-STEWART, U., B. M. JONES and R. B. KEMP. 1970. Detection of actyomyosin-type protein at the surface of dissociated embryonic chick cells. *Nature, Lond.*, **227,** 280.

HUANG, B. and D. R. PITELKA. 1973. The contractile process in the ciliate, *Stentor coeruleus*. I. The role of microtubules and filaments. *J. Cell Biol.*, **57,** 704–728.

ISHIKAWA, H., R. BISCHOFF and H. HOLTZER. 1969. Formation of arrowhead complexes with heavy meromyosin in a variety of cell types. *J. Cell Biol.*, **43,** 312–328.

KEYSERLINGK, D. GRAF. 1970. Über die Bedeutung des intracellulären, kontraktilen Systems für die Lokomotion der Fibroblasten. *Cytobiologie*, **1,** 259–272.

KOMNICK, H., W. STOCKEM and K. E. WOHLFARTH-BOTTERMANN. 1973. Cell motility: mechanisms in protoplasmic streaming and ameboid movement. *Int. Rev. Cytol.*, **34,** 169–249.

McNUTT, N. S., L. A. CULP and P. H. BLACK. 1973. Contact-inhibited revertant cell lines isolated from SV 40-transformed cells. IV. Microfilament distribution and cell shape in untransformed, transformed and revertant Balb/c 3T3. *J. Cell Biol.*, **56,** 412–428.

NACHMIAS, V. T. 1964. Fibrillar structures in the cytoplasm of *Chaos chaos*. *J. Cell Biol.*, **23,** 183–188.

NEWSTEAD, J. D. 1971. Filaments in renal parenchymal and interstitial cells. *J. Ultrastruct. Res.*, **34,** 316–328.

ORKIN, R. W., T. D. POLLARD and E. D. HAY. 1973. SDS gel analysis of muscle proteins in embryonic cells. *Devl Biol.*, **35,** 388–394.

PEASE, D. C. 1968. Myoid features of renal corpuscles and tubules. *J. Ultrastruct. Res.*, **23,** 304–320.

POLLARD, T. D. and E. D. KORN. 1971. Filaments of *Amoeba proteus*. II. Binding of heavy meromyosin by thin filaments in motile cytoplasmic extracts. *J. Cell Biol.*, **48,** 216–218.

RINALDI, R. A. and W. R. BAKER. 1969. A sliding filament model of amoeboid motion. *J. theor. Biol.*, **23,** 463–474.

ROSENBLUTH, J. 1971. Myosin-like tactoids in trypsin-treated blood platelets. *J. Cell Biol.*, **50,** 900–904.

ROSS, M. H. and REITH, E. J. 1970. Myoid elements in the mammalian nephron and their relationship to other specializations in the basal part of kidney tubule cells. *Am. J. Anat.*, **129,** 399–416.

ROSTGAARD, J., B. J. KRISTENSEN and L. E. NIELSEN. 1972. Myofilaments in nonmuscular cells. In *Histochemistry and Cytochemistry. Proc. 4th Int. Cong. Histochem. Cytochem. Kyoto*, 377.

SCHÄFER-DANNEEL, S. 1967. Strukturelle und funktionelle Voraussetzungen für die Bewegung von *Amoeba proteus. Z. Zellforsch. mikrosk. Anat.*, **78,** 441–462.

SCHÄFER-DANNEEL, S. and N. WEISSENFELS. 1969. Licht- und elektronenmikroskopische Untersuchungen über die ATP-abhängige Kontraktion kultivierter Fibroblasten nach Glycerin-Extraktion. *Cytobiologie*, **1,** 85–98.

SPOONER, B. S., J. F. ASH, J. T. WRENN, R. B. FRATER and N. K. WESSELLS. 1973. Heavy meromyosin binding to microfilaments involved in cell and morphogenetic movements. *Tissue & Cell*, **5,** 37–46.

WANG, E. and R. D. GOLDMAN. 1974. Functions of cytoplasmic fibers in intracellular movements. *J. Cell Biol.*, **63,** 363a.

WEBBER, W. A. 1973. Contractility of the parietal layer of Bowman's capsule. *Anat. Rec.*, **175,** 465.

WEBBER, W. A. and W. T. WONG. 1973. The function of the basal filaments in the parietal layer of Bowman's capsule. *Can. J. Physiol. Pharmacol.*, **51,** 53–60.

YANG, Y. ZU and J. PERDUE. 1974. Tropomyosin from cultured chick embryo fibroblasts and the evidence for the presence of troponin-T and troponin-I. *J. Cell Biol.*, **63,** 382a.

YOHRO, T. and G. BURNSTOCK. 1973. Filament bundles and contractility of endothelial cells in coronary arteries. *Z. Zellforsch. mikrosk. Anat.*, **138,** 85–95.

Invertebrate skeletal muscle

ARMITAGE, P., A. MILLER, C. D. RODGER and R. T. TREGEAR. 1973. The structure and function of insect muscle. In *The Mechanism of Muscle Contraction., Cold Spring Harb. Symp. quant. Biol.*, **37,** 379–388.

ASHHURST, D. E. 1967. The fibrillar flight muscles of giant waterbugs: an electron-microscope study. *J. Cell Sci.* **2,** 435–444.

BRANDT, P. W., J. P. REUBEN, L. GIRARDIER and H. GRUNDFEST. 1965. Correlated morphological and physiological studies on isolated single muscle fibers. I. Fine structure of the crayfish muscle fiber. *J. Cell Biol.*, **25,** Suppl. 3, 233–260.

DEWEY, M. M., R. J. C. LEVINE and D. E. COLFLESH. 1973. Structure of *Limulus* striated muscle: the contractile apparatus at various sarcomere lengths. *J. Cell Biol.*, **58,** 574–593.

GOLDSTEIN, M. A. and W. J. BURDETTE. 1971. Striated visceral muscle of *Drosophila melanogaster. J. Morph.*, **134,** 315–334.

HAGOPIAN, M. 1966. The myofilament arrangement in the femoral muscle of the cockroach, *Leucophaea maderae* Fabricius. *J. Cell Biol.*, **28,** 545–562.

HODGE, A. J. 1956. The fine structure of striated muscle. A comparison of insect flight muscle with vertebrate and invertebrate skeletal muscle. *J. biophys. biochem. Cytol.*, **2,** Suppl., 131–142.

HOYLE, G., P. A. McNEIL and A. I. SELVERSTON. 1973. Ultrastructure of barnacle giant muscle fibers. *J. Cell Biol.*, **56,** 74–91.

HUDDART, H. and K. OATES. 1970. Ultrastructure of stick insect and locust skeletal muscle in relation to excitation-contraction coupling. *J. Insect Physiol.*, **16,** 1467–1483.

JAHROMI, S. S. and H. L. ATWOOD. 1971. Structural and contractile properties of lobster leg-muscle fibers. *J. exp. Zool.*, **176,** 475–486.

McNEILL, P., M. BURROWS and G. HOYLE. 1972. Fine structure of muscles controlling the strike of the mantis shrimp, *Hemisquilla. J. exp. Zool.*, **179,** 395–416.

PRINGLE, J. W. S. 1965. Locomotion: flight. In *The Physiology of Insecta*, Vol. 2. M. Rockstein (ed.). Academic Press, New York. 283–329.

REGER, J. F. 1967. A comparative study on striated muscle fibers of the first antenna and the claw muscle of the crab, *Pinnixia* sp. *J. Ultrastruct. Res.*, **20,** 72–82.

REGER, J. F. and D. P. COOPER. 1967. A comparative study on the fine structure of the basalar muscle of the wing and the tibial extensor muscle of the leg of the lepidopteran *Achalarus lyciades. J. Cell Biol.*, **33,** 531–542.

RICHARDOT, M. and J. WAUTIER. 1971. Une structure intermédiare entre muscle lisse et muscle strié. La fibre musculaire du bulbe buccal de *Ferrissia wautieri* (Moll. Basomm. Ancylidae). *Z. Zellforsch. mikrosk. Anat.*, **115,** 100–109.

SACKTOR, B. 1970. Regulation of intermediary metabolism, with special reference to the control mechanisms in insect flight muscle. *Adv. Insect Physiol.*, **7,** 267–347.

SANDBORN, E. B., S. DUCLOS, P.-E. MESSIER and J. J. ROBERGE. 1967. Atypical intestinal striated muscle in *Drosophila melanogaster*. *J. Ultrastruct. Res.*, **18,** 695–702.

SCHAEFER, C. W., J. P. VANDERBERG and J. RHODIN. 1967. The fine structure of mosquito midgut muscle. *J. Cell Biol.*, **34,** 905–910.

SHAFIQ, S. A. 1963. Electron microscopic studies on the indirect flight muscles of *Drosophila melanogaster*. I. Structure of the myofibrils. *J. Cell Biol.*, **17,** 351–362.

SMITH, D. S. 1961. The organization of the flight muscle in a dragonfly *Aeshna* sp. (Odonata). *J. Cell Biol.*, **11,** 119–146.

SMITH, D. S. 1963. The structure of flight muscle sarcomeres in the blowfly, *Calliphora erythrocephala* (Diptera). *J. Cell Biol.*, **19,** 115–138.

SMITH, D. S. 1965. The organization of flight muscle in an aphid, *Megoura viciae* (Homoptera). With a discussion on the structure of synchronous and asynchronous striated muscle fibers. *J. Cell Biol.*, **27,** 379–393.

SMITH, D. S. 1966. The organization of flight muscle fibers in the Odonata. *J. Cell Biol.*, **28,** 109–126.

SMITH, D. S. 1968. *Insect Cells, Their Structure and Function*. Oliver & Boyd, Edinburgh.

SMITH, D. S., J. DEL CASTILLO and M. ANDERSON. 1973. Fine structure and innervation of an annelid muscle with the longest recorded sarcomere. *Tissue & Cell*. **5,** 281–302.

TOSELLI, P. A. and F. A. PEPE. 1968. The fine structure of the ventral intersegmental abdominal muscles of the insect *Rhodnius prolixus* during the molting cycle. I. Muscle structure at molting. *J. Cell Biol.*, **37,** 445–461.

Invertebrate obliquely striated muscle

ANDERSON, W. A. and R. A. ELLIS. 1967. A comparative electron microscope study of visceral muscle fibres in *Cambarus, Drosophila* and *Lumbricus*. *Z. Zellforsch. mikrosk. Anat.*, **79,** 581–591.

BEAMS, H. W. and S. S. SEKHON. 1967. Fine structure of the body wall and cells in the pseudocoelom of the nematode *Rhabditis pellio*. *J. Ultrastruct. Res.*, **18,** 580–594.

CHAPRON, C. and P. VALEMBOIS. 1967. Infrastructure de la fibre musculaire pariétale des Lombriciens. *J. Microsc.* **6,** 617–626.

HAMA, K. 1960. The fine structure of some blood vessels of the earthworm *Eisenia foetida*. *J. biophys. biochem. Cytol.*, **7,** 717–723.

HAMMERSEN, F. and H.-W. STAUDTE. 1969. Beiträge zum Feinbau der Blutgefässe von Invertebraten. I. Die Ultrastruktur des Sinus lateralis von *Hirudo medicinalis* L. *Z. Zellforsch., mikrosk. Anat.*, **100,** 215–250.

HEUMANN, H.-G. and E. ZEBE. 1967. Über Feinbau und Funktionsweise der Fasern aus dem Hautmuskelschlauch des Regenwurms, *Lumbricus terrestris* L. *Z. Zellforsch. mikrosk. Anat.*, **78,** 131–150.

HIRUMI, H., D. J. RASKI and N. O. JONES. 1971. Primitive muscle cells of nematodes: Morphological aspects of platymyarian and shallow coelomyarian muscles in two plant parasitic nematodes, *Trichodorus christiei* and *Longidorus elongatus*. *J. Ultrastruct. Res.*, **34,** 517–543.

IKEMOTO, N. 1963. Further studies in electron microscopic structure of the oblique striate muscle of the earthworm *Eisenia foetida*. *Biol. J. Okayama Univ.*, **9,** 81–126.

JAMUAR, M. P. 1966. Electron microscope studies on the body wall of the nematode *Nippostrongylus brasiliensis*. *J. Parasit.*, **52,** 209–232.

KAWAGUTI, S. and N. IKEMOTO. 1959. Electron microscope patterns of earthworm muscle in relation and contraction induced by glycerol and adenosinetriphosphate. *Biol. J. Okayama Univ.*, **5,** 57–72.

KNAPP, M. F. and P. J. MILL. 1971. The contractile mechanism in obliquely striated body wall muscle of the earthworm, *Lumbricus terrestris*. *J. Cell Sci.*, **8,** 413–426.

LEE, C.-C. and J. H. MILLER. 1967. Fine structure of *Dirofilaria immitis* body-wall musculature. *Expl Parasit.*, **20,** 334–344.

MacRAE, E. K. 1963. Observations on the fine structure of pharyngeal muscle in the planarian *Dugesia tigrina*. *J. Cell Biol.*, **18,** 651–662.

MacRAE, E. K. 1965. The fine structure of muscle

in a marine turbellarian. *Z. Zellforsch. mikrosk. Anat.*, **68,** 348–362.
MILL, P. J. and M. F. KNAPP, 1970. The fine structure of obliquely striated body wall muscles in the earthworm, *Lumbricus terrestris* Linn. *J. Cell Sci.*, **7,** 233–262.
MORITA, M. 1965. Electron microscopic studies on planaria. I. Fine structure of muscle fiber in the head of the planarian *Dugesia dorotocephala*. *J. Ultrastruct. Res.*, **13,** 383–395.
PUCCI, I. and B. A. AFZELIUS. 1962. An electron microscope study of sarcotubules and related structures in the leech muscle. *J. Ultrastruct. Res.*, **7,** 210–224.
REGER, J. F. 1969. Studies on the fine structure of muscle fibres and contained crystalloids in basal socket muscle of the entoproct, *Barentsia gracilis*. *J. Cell Sci.*, **4,** 305–325.
ROSENBLUTH, J. 1965*a*. Ultrastructural organization of obliquely striated muscle fibres in *Ascaris lumbricoides*. *J. Cell Biol.*, **25,** 495–516.
ROSENBLUTH, J. 1965*b*. Ultrastructure of somatic muscle cells in *Ascaris lumbricoides*. II. Intermuscular junctions, neuromuscular junctions, and glycogen stores. *J. Cell Biol.*, **26,** 579–592.
ROSENBLUTH, J. 1967. Obliquely striated muscle. III. Contraction mechanism of *Ascaris* body muscle. *J. Cell Biol.*, **34,** 15–33.
ROSENBLUTH, J. 1968. Obliquely striated muscle. IV. Sarcoplasmic reticulum, contractile apparatus and endomysium of the body muscle of a polychaete, *Glycera*, in relation to its species *J. Cell Biol.*, **36,** 245–259.
STAUBESAND, J. and K.-H. KERSTING. 1964. Feinbau und Organisation der Muskelzellen des Regenwurms. *Z. Zellforsch. mikrosk. Anat.*, **62,** 416–442.

Invertebrate paramyosin smooth muscle

CHAPMAN, D. M., C. F. A. PANTIN and E. A. ROBSON. 1962. Muscle in coelenterates. *Revue can. Biol.*, **21,** 267–278.
COHEN, C., A. G. SZENT-GYÖRGYI and J. KENDRICK-JONES. 1971. Paramyosin and the filaments of molluscan 'catch' muscles. I. Paramyosin: structure and assembly. *J. molec. Biol.*, **56,** 223–237.
HEUMANN, H.-G. and E. ZEBE. 1968. Über die Funktionsweise glatter Muskelfasern. Elektronenmikroskopische Untersuchungen am Byssusretraktor (ABRM) von *Mytilus edulis*. *Z. Zellforsch. mikrosk. Anat.*, **85,** 534–551.
HUNT, S. 1972. The fine structure of the smooth muscle in the hypobranchial gland of the gastropod *Buccinum undatum* L. *Tissue & Cell.*, **4,** 479–492.
LOWY, J. and B. M. MILLMAN. 1963. The contractile mechanism of the anterior byssus retractor muscle of *Mytilus edulis*. *Phil. Trans. R. Soc. Ser. B.*, **246,** 105–148.
MILL, P. J. and M. F. KNAPP. 1970. The fine structure of obliquely striated body muscles in the earthworm, *Lumbricus terrestrio* Linn. *J. Cell Sci.*, **7,** 233–261.
ROGERS, D. C. 1969. Fine structure of smooth muscle and neuromuscular junctions in the foot of *Helix aspersa*. *Z. Zellforsch. mikrosk. Anat.*, **99,** 315–335.
SILK, M. H. and I. M. SPENCE. 1969. Ultrastructural studies of the blood fluke—*Schistosoma mansoni*. II. The musculature. *S. Afr. J. Med. Sci.*, **34,** 11–20.
SOBIESZEK, A. 1973. The fine structure of the contractile apparatus of the anterior byssus retractor muscle of *Mytilus edulis*. *J. Ultrastruct. Res.*, **43,** 313.

Invertebrate classical smooth muscle

BAGBY, R. M. 1966. The fine structure of myocytes in the sponges *Microciona prolifera* (Ellis & Solander) and *Tedania ignis* (Duchassaing & Michelotti). *J. Morph.* **118,** 167–181.
SLAUTTERBACK, D. B. 1967. The cnidoblast-musculoepithelial cell complex in the tentacles of hydra. *Z. Zellforsch. mikrosk. Anat.*, **79,** 296–318.

Invertebrate cardiac muscle

BACCETTI, B. and E. BIGLIARDI. 1969*a*. Studies on the fine structure of the dorsal vessel of arthropods. I. The 'heart' of an arthropteran. *Z. Zellforsch. mikrosk. Anat.*, **99,** 13–24.
BACCETTI, B. and E. BIGLIARDI. 1969*b*. Studies on the fine structure of the dorsal vessel of arthropods. II. The 'heart' of a crustacean. *Z. Zellforsch. mikrosk. Anat.*, **99,** 25–36.
BLOOM, G. D. 1962. The fine structure of cyclostome cardiac muscle cells. *Z. Zellforsch. mikrosk. Anat.*, **57,** 213–239.

BURCH, G. E., R. SOHAL and L. D. FAIRBANKS. 1970. Ultrastructural changes in *Drosophila* heart with age. *Archs Path.*, **89,** 128–136.

COUTEAUX, R. and P. LAURENT. 1957. Étude au microscope électronique du cœur de l'Anguille: observations sur la structure du tissu musculaire de l'oreillette et son innervation. *C.r. hebd. Séanc. Acad. Sci. Paris.*, **245,** 2097–2100.

FORBES, M. S., R. RUBIO and N. SPERELAKIS. 1972. Tubular systems of *Limulus* myocardial cells investigated by use of electron-opaque tracers and hypertonicity. *J. Ultrastruct. Res.*, **39,** 580–597.

IRASAWA, A. and K. HAMA. 1965. Some observations on the fine structure of the mantis shrimp heart. *Z. Zellforsch. mikrosk. Anat.*, **68,** 674–688.

KOMURO, T. 1969. The fine structure of the crayfish cardiac muscle. *J. Electron Microsc.*, **18,** 291–297.

LEYTON, R. A. and E. H. SONNENBLICK. 1971. Cardiac muscle of the horseshoe crab, *Limulus polyphemus.* I. Ultrastructure. *J. Cell Biol.*, **48,** 101–119.

NORTH, R. J. 1963. The fine structure of the myofibers in the heart of the snail *Helix aspersa. J. Ultrastruct. Res.*, **8,** 206–218.

SCHIPP, R. and A. SCHÄFER. 1969. Vergleichende electronenmikroskopische Untersuchungen an den zentralen Herzorganen von cephalopoden (*Sepia officianlis*). Die Feinstruktur des Herzens. *Z. Zellforsch. mikrosk. Anat.*, **98,** 576–598.

SHERMAN, R. G. 1973. Ultrastructural features of cardiac muscle cells in a Tarantula spider. *J. Morph.*, **140,** 215–241.

SMITH, D. S. and M. E. ANDERSON. 1972. The disposition of membrane systems in cardiac muscle of a lobster, *Homarus americanus. Tissue & Cell*, **4,** 629–645.

SMITH, J. R. 1963. Observations on the ultrastructure of the myocardium of the common lobster. (*Homarus americanus*) especially of the myofibrils. *Anat. Rec.*, **145,** 391–400.

SOHAL, R. S. and V. F. ALLISON. 1971. Senescent changes in the cardiac myofiber of the house fly, *Musca domestica.* An electron microscopic study. *J. Geront.*, **26,** 490–496.

SPERELAKIS, N. 1971. Ultrastructure of the neurogenic heart of *Limulus polyphemus. Z. Zellforsch. mikrosk. Anat.*, **116,** 443–463.

STEIN, R. J., W. R. RICHTER, R. A. ZUSSMAN and G. BRYNJOLFSSON. 1966. Ultrastructural characterization of *Daphnia* heart muscle. *J. Cell Biol.*, **29,** 168–170.

Muscle development and regeneration

ALLBROOK, D. 1962. An electron microscopic study of regenerating skeletal muscle. *J. Anat.*, **96,** 137–152.

ALLEN, E. R. and F. A. PEPE. 1965. Ultrastructure of developing muscle cells in the chick embryo. *Am. J. Anat.*, **116,** 115–148.

BEINBRECH, G. 1968. Elektronenmikroskopische Untersuchungen über die Differenzierung von Insektenmuskeln während der Metamorphose. *Z. Zellforsch. mikrosk. Anat.*, **90,** 463–494.

BENNETT, T. and J. L. S. COBB. 1969. Studies on the avian gizzard: the development of the gizzard and its innervation. *Z. Zellforsch. mikrosk. Anat.*, **98,** 599–621.

BHAKTHAN, N. M. G., J. H. BORDEN and K. K. NAIR. 1970. Fine structure of degenerating and regenerating flight muscles in a bark beetle, *Ips confuses.* I. Degeneration. *J. Cell Sci.*, **6,** 807–819.

BHAKTHAN, N., K. K. NAIR and J. H. BORDEN. 1971. Fine structure of degenerating and regenerating flight muscles in a bark beetle, *Ips confusus.* II. Regeneration. *Can. J. Zool.*, **49,** 85–89.

CARAVITA, S. and G. GIBERTINI. 1966. Osservazioni sull'ultrastruttura del cuore di embrione di pollo durante la miogenesi. *Archo ital. Anat. Embriol.*, **71,** 49–74.

CHACKO, K. 1972. Ultrastructural observations on mitosis in myocardial cells of the rat embryo. *Am. J. Anat.*, **135,** 305–310.

CHALLICE, C. E. and S. VIRÁGH. 1974. The architectural development of the early mammalian heart. *Tissue & Cell*, **6,** 447–462.

CHLEBOWSKI, J. S., R. J. PRZYBYLSKI and P. G. COX. 1973. Ultrastructural studies of lizard (*Anolis carolinensis*) myogenesis *in vitro. Devl Biol.*, **33,** 80–99.

CLIFF, W. J. 1967. The aortic tunica media in growing rats studied with the electron microscope. *Lab. Invest.*, **17,** 599–615.

DESSOUKY, D. A. and R. G. HIBBS. 1965. An electron microscope study of the development of the somatic muscle of the chick embryo. *Am. J. Anat.*, **116,** 523–566.

FIRKET, H. 1967. Ultrastructural aspects of myofibrils formation in cultured skeletal muscle. *Z. Zellforsch. mikrosk. Anat.*, **78,** 313–327.

FISCHMAN, D. A. 1967. An electron microscope study of myofibril formation in embryonic chick skeletal muscle. *J. Cell Biol.*, **32,** 557–575.

FISCHMAN, D. A. 1970. The synthesis and assembly of myofibrils in embryonic muscle. In *Current Topics in Developmental Biology.* Vol. 5. A. A. Moscona and A. Monroy (eds.). Academic Press, New York. 235–280.

FISCHMAN, D. A. 1972. The fine structure of muscle differentiation in monolayer culture. In *Research in Muscle Development and the Muscle Spindle.* B. Q. Baker, R. J. Przybylski, J. P. Van der Maulen and M. Victor (eds.). *Excerpta Medica,* International Congress Series No. 240, Amsterdam. 88–104.

FORSSMANN, W. G., G. SIEGERIST and L. GIRARDIER. 1966. Ultrastrukturelle Befunde an embryonalen Rattenherzen. *Verh. anat. Ges., Jena,* **120,** 71–80.

GOLDSPINK, G. 1970. The proliferation of myofibrils during muscle fibre growth. *J. Cell Sci.*, **6,** 593–603.

GOLDSPINK, G. and R. W. D. ROWE. 1968. The growth and development of muscle fibres in normal and dystrophic mice. In *Research in Muscular Dystrophy. Proceedings of the 4th Symposium.* Pitman Medical Publishing, London. 116–131.

GREGORY, D. W., R. W. LENNIE and L. M. BIRT. 1968. An electronmicroscope study of flight muscle development in the blowfly *Lucilia cuprina. Jl R. microsc. Soc.*, **88,** 151–175.

HAY, E. D. 1959. Electron microscopic observations of muscle dedifferentiation in regenerating *Amblystoma* limbs. *Devl Biol.*, **1,** 555–585.

HAY, E. D. 1962. Cytological studies of dedifferentiation and differentiation in regenerating amphibian limbs. In *Regeneration.* D. Rudnick, (ed.). Ronald Press, New York. 117–210.

HAY, E. D. 1963. The fine structure of differentiating muscle in the salamander tail. *Z. Zellforsch. mikrosk. Anat.*, **59,** 6–34.

HEROLD, R. C. 1965. Development and ultrastructural changes of sarcosomes during honey bee flight muscle development. *Devl Biol.*, **12,** 269–286.

HEUSON-STIENNON, J.-A. 1965. Morphogenèse de la cellule musculaire striée, étudiée au microscope électronique. I. Formation des structures fibrillaires. *J. Microsc. (Fr.)*, **4,** 657–678.

HIBBS, R. C. 1956. Electron microscopy of developing cardiac muscle in chick embryos. *Am. J. Anat.*, **99,** 17–52.

HILFER, S. R., R. L. SEARLS and V. G. FONTE. 1973. An ultrastructural study of early myogenesis in the chick wing bud. *Devl Biol.*, **30,** 374–391.

HITCHCOCK, S. E. 1970. The appearance of a functional contractile apparatus in developing muscle. *Devl Biol.*, **23,** 399–423.

HITCHCOCK, S. E. 1971. Detection of actin filaments in homogenates of developing muscle using heavy meromyosin. *Devl Biol.*, **25**, 492–501.

HOLTZER, H. 1970. Myogenesis. In *Cell Differentiation.* O. Schjeide and J. De Vellis (eds.). Van Nostrand Reinhold, New York. 476–503.

HOLTZER, H., J. W. SANGER, H. ISHIKAWA and K. STRAHS. 1973. Selected topics in skeletal myogenesis. In *The Mechanism of Muscle Contraction. Cold Spring Harb. Symp. quant. Biol.*, **37,** 549–566.

HUANG, C. Y. 1967. Electron microscopic study of the development of heart muscle of the frog *Rana pipiens. J. Ultrastruct. Res.* **20,** 211–226.

IMAIZUMI, M. and T. KUWABURA. 1971. Development of the rat iris. *Invest. Opthal.*, **10,** 733–744.

JIRMANOVÁ, I. and S. THESLEFF. 1972. Ultrastructural study of experimental muscle degeneration and regeneration in the adult rat. *Z. Zellforsch. mikrosk. Anat.*, **131,** 77–97.

KARRER, H. E. 1960. Electron microscope study of developing chick embryo aorta. *J. Ultrastruct. Res.*, **4,** 420–454.

KAWAGUTI, S. and N. IKEMOTO. 1957. Electron microscopy of myogenesis in the earthworm, *Eisenia foetida. Biol. J. Okayama Univ.*, **3,** 239–247.

KAWAGUTI, S. and T. KOBAYASHI. 1960. Electron microscopic study of the cardiac myogenesis in a mammalian embryo. *Biol. J. Okayama Univ.*, **6,** 53–60.

KELLY, A. M. and S. I. ZACKS. 1969. The histogenesis of rat intercostal muscle. *J. Cell Biol.*, **42,** 135–153.

LAI, Y.-L. 1972*a*. The development of the sphincter muscle in the iris of the albino rat. *Exp. Eye Res.*, **14,** 196–202.

LAI, Y.-L. 1972*b*. The development of the dilator muscle in the iris of the albino rat. *Exp. Eye Res.*, **14,** 203–207.

LEAK, L. V. and J. F. BURKE. 1964. The ultrastructure of human embryonic myocardium. *Anat. Rec.*, **149,** 623–650.

LEESON, C. R. and T. S. LEESON. 1965. The fine structure of the rat umbilical cord at various times of gestation. *Anat. Rec.*, **151,** 183–198.

LEESON, T. S. and C. R. LEESON. 1965. The rat ureter. Fine structural changes during its development. *Acta anat.*, **62,** 60–79.

LEGATO, M. J. 1972. Ultrastructural characteristics of the rat ventricular cell grown in tissue culture, with special reference to sarcomeragenesis. *J. mol. & cell. Cardiol.*, **4,** 299–317.

LEMANSKI, L. F. 1973. Morphology of developing heart in cardiac lethal mutant Mexican axolotls, (*Ambystoma mexicanum*). *Devl Biol.*, **33,** 312–333.

LENTZ, T. L. 1969. Cytological studies of muscle dedifferentiation and differentiation during limb regeneration of the newt *Triturus. Am. J. Anat.*, **124,** 447–479.

LINDNER, E. 1960. Myofibrils in the early development of chick embryo hearts as observed with the electron microscope. *Anat. Rec.*, **136,** 234–235.

MAIER, A. and E. ELDRED. 1974. Postnatal growth of the extra- and intrafusal fibers in the soleus and medial gastrocnemius of the cat. *Am. J. Anat.*, **141,** 161–178.

MANASEK, F. J. 1968. Embryonic development of the heart. I. Light and electron microscopic study of myocardial development in the early chick embryo. *J. Morph.*, **125,** 329–365.

MANASEK, F. J. 1970. Histogenesis of the embryonic myocardium. *Am. J. Cardiol.*, **25,** 149–168.

MEDOFF, J. and E. ZWILLING. 1972. Appearance of myosin in the chick limb bud. *Devl Biol.*, **28,** 138–141.

MUSCATELLO, U., I. PASQUALI-RONCHETTI and A. BARASA. 1968. An electron microscope study of myoblasts from chick embryo heart cultured *in vitro*. *J. Ultrastruct. Res.*, **23,** 44–59.

NASS, N. M. K. 1962. Developmental changes in frog actomyosin characteristics. *Devl Biol.*, **4,** 289–320.

OBINATA, T., M. YAMAMOTO and K. MARUYAMA. 1966. The identification of randomly formed thin filaments in differentiating muscle cells of the chick embryo. *Devl Biol.*, **14,** 192–213.

OBINATA, T., M. YAMAMOTO and K. MARUYAMA. 1967. Morphological and biochemical studies on myofibrillar formation in developing chick embryo. *J. Fac. Sci. Univ. Tokyo, Sec. IV*, **11,** 95–120.

OGAWA, Y. 1962. Synthesis of skeletal muscle proteins in early embryos and regenerating tissue of chick and Triturus. *Expl Cell Res.* **26,** 269–274.

OHSHIMA, Y., K. MARUYAMA and H. NODA. 1965. Developmental changes in chick muscle contractile proteins. In *Molecular Biology of Muscular Contraction*. S. Ebashi, F. Oosawa, R. Sekine and Y. Tonomura (eds.). Igaku Shoin, Tokyo and Elsevier, Amsterdam. 132–144.

OKAZAKI, K. and H. HOLTZER. 1966. Myogenesis: fusion, myosin synthesis and the mitotic cycle. *Proc. natn. Acad. Sci. U.S.A.*, **56,** 1484–1490.

OLIVO, O. M., R. LASCHI and M. L. LUCCHI. 1964. Genesi delle miofibrille del cuore embrionale di pollo osservate al microscopico elettronico e inizio dell'attività contrattile. *Sperimentale*, **114,** 69–78.

PRZYBYLSKI, R. J. and J. M. BLUMBERG. 1966. Ultrastructural aspects of myogenesis in the chick. *Lab. Invest.*, **15,** 836–863.

SCHATTENBERG, P.-J. 1973. Licht- und elektronenmikroskopische Untersuchungen über die Entstehung der Skelettmuskulatur von Fischen. *Z. Zellforsch. mikrosk. Anat.*, **143,** 569–586.

SCHULZE, W. 1961. Elektronenmikroskopische und histometrische Untersuchungen des Herzmuskelgewebes von Hund während des postnatalen Wachstums. *Acta biol. med. germ.*, **7,** 24–31.

SCHULZE, W. 1962. Elektronenmikroskopische Untersuchung des embryonalen Hundeherzmuskels. *Z. mikrosk. -anat. Forsch.*, **68,** 271–284.

SHAFIQ, S. A. and M. A. GORYCKI. 1965. Regeneration in skeletal muscle of mouse: some electron-microscope observations. *J. Path. Bact.*, **90,** 123–127.

SHIMADA, Y., D. A. FISCHMAN and A. A. MOSCONA. 1967. The fine structure of embryonic chick skeletal muscle cells differentiated *in vitro*. *J. Cell Biol.*, **35,** 445–453.

SPIRO, H. and M. HAGOPIAN. 1967. On the assemblage of myofibrils. In *Formation and Fate of Cell Organelles*. K. B. Warren (ed.). Academic Press, New York. 71–98.

STRÉTER, F., S. HOLTZER, J. GERGELY and H. HOLTZER. 1972. Some properties of embryonic myosin. *J. Cell Biol.*, **55,** 586–594.

TOSELLI, P. A. and F. A. PEPE. 1968*a*. The fine structure of the ventral intersegmental abdominal muscles of the insect *Rhodnius prolixus* during the molting cycle. I. Muscle structure at molting. *J. Cell Biol.*, **37,** 445–461.

TOSELLI, P. A. and F. A. PEPE. 1968*b*. The fine structure of the ventral intersegmental abdominal muscles of the insect *Rhodnius prolixus* during the molting cycle. II. Muscle changes in preparation for molting. *J. Cell Biol.*, **37,** 462–482.

VIRAGH, S. and C. E. CHALLICE. 1973. Origin and differentiation of cardiac muscle cells in the mouse. *J. Ultrastruct. Res.*, **42,** 1–24.

WAINRACH, S. and J. R. SOTELO. 1961. Electron microscope study of the developing chick embryo heart. *Z. Zellforsch. mikrosk. Anat.*, **55,** 622–634.

WARREN, R. H. 1974. Microtubular organization in elongating myogenic cells. *J. Cell Biol.*, **63,** 550–556.

WARREN, R. H. and K. R. PORTER. 1969. An electron microscope study of differentiation of the molting muscles of *Rhodnius prolixus*. *Am. J. Anat.*, **124,** 1–30.

WEINRACH, S. and J. R. SOTELO. 1961. Electron microscope study of the developing chick embryo heart. *Z. Zellforsch. mikrosk. Anat.*, **55,** 622–634.

WISSOCQ, J. C. 1967. Étude ultrastructurale de l'évolution des muscles longitudinaux lors de la stolonisation expérimentale de *Syllis amica* (Quatrefages) (Annélide Polychète). *Z. Zellforsch. mikrosk. Anat.*, **83,** 449–467.

YAFFE, D. 1971. Development changes preceding cell fusion during muscle differentiation *in vitro*. *Expl Cell Res.*, **66,** 33–48.

YAMAMOTO, I. 1961. An electron microscope study on development of uterine smooth muscle. *J. Electron Microsc.*, **10,** 145–160.

YAMAUCHI, A. and G. BURNSTOCK, 1969. Post-natal development of smooth muscle cells in the mouse vas deferens. A fine structural study. *J. Anat.*, **104,** 1–15.

ZAK, R. 1974. Development and proliferative capacity of cardiac muscle cells. *Circulation Res.*, **35,** Suppl. II, 17–26.

2 Cell Organelles

A Nucleus

The genetic material, deoxyribonucleic acid (DNA) is found within the nucleus. In common with all cells, the nucleus of muscle cells is concerned with the control of metabolic activity and of ribonucleic acid (RNA) production and ultimately protein synthesis. The contribution of the nucleus to the total cell mass may be as low as 5% in some smooth muscle cells or up to 30% in skeletal muscle (compared with 50% or more of the total cell mass of cells of the thymus gland).

Skeletal muscle fibres are multinucleate and may have many hundred nuclei per muscle cell, whereas both cardiac and smooth muscle cells normally have only one approximately central nucleus. In the majority of mammalian skeletal muscles the nuclei are peripherally located, immediately beneath the sarcolemma. However, in the slow muscles of many lower vertebrates, the nuclei are either centrally or eccentrically located within the fibre. Invertebrate striated muscle fibres are usually multinucleate and as far as is known invertebrate smooth muscles are always mononucleate.

Ultrastructurally, little variation can be seen among nuclei of muscle cells and those of most other cell types. They vary considerably in size from 5–18 μm by 4–7 μm in skeletal muscles, 11–25 μm by 1–4 μm in vertebrate smooth muscles and 2–5 μm by 1–2 μm in vertebrate cardiac muscles and are generally elongated along the long axis of the fibre.

Muscle nuclei are frequently convoluted, a feature considered by many to be due to the state of contraction; in some muscles the myofilaments may be attached directly to the nuclear envelope. However, observations on isolated skeletal muscle nuclei and denervated muscle suggest invaginations may be related to other factors, such as changes in the ionic environment especially of bivalent cations.

Plate 11

Nuclei are bounded by a *nuclear envelope* (arrows) or perinuclear sac, within which are one or more *nucleoli* (Nu) and a heterogeneous collection of granules or particles (although they are not clearly distinguished on the micrograph), of which two types have been recognized: (1) the perichromatinic granules, which are usually 30–35 nm in diameter and are surrounded by a clear halo: (2) the interchromatinic granules which are 15–50 nm in diameter and usually occur in clumps. Some of the chromatin of the chromosomes remains condensed and appears as irregular clumps called *heterochromatin*. Regions of the chromosomes that are dispersed comprise the *euchromatin*.

Interphase nucleus: lizard ilio-tibialis muscle. Glutaraldehyde fixation. × 27 000.

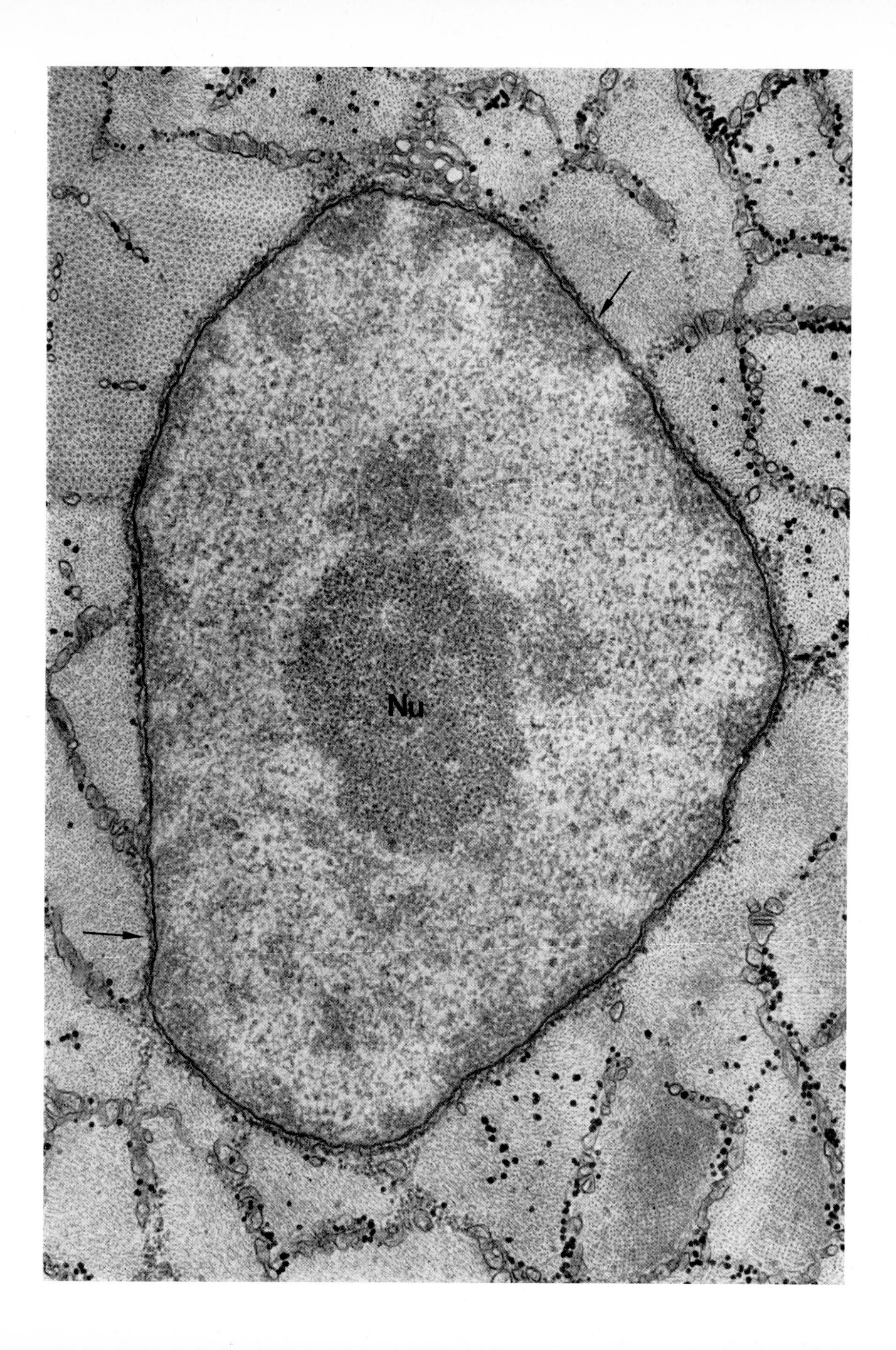
Nu

Plate 12

The nuclear envelope is interrupted at intervals by *nuclear pore complexes* of constant size (arrows). These pores are the apertures through which nucleocytoplasmic interactions take place. Apart from these regions, the sarcoplasm is normally separated from the nuclear contents by two unit membranes divided by a perinuclear space. At the pore complex, barriers to the passage of some molecules still occurs due to the presence of a diaphragm.

Nuclear pores: finch ureter. Transverse section. Glutaraldehyde fixation (note that the perinuclear envelope (see Plate 11) has expanded, a common fixation artefact). ×65 000.

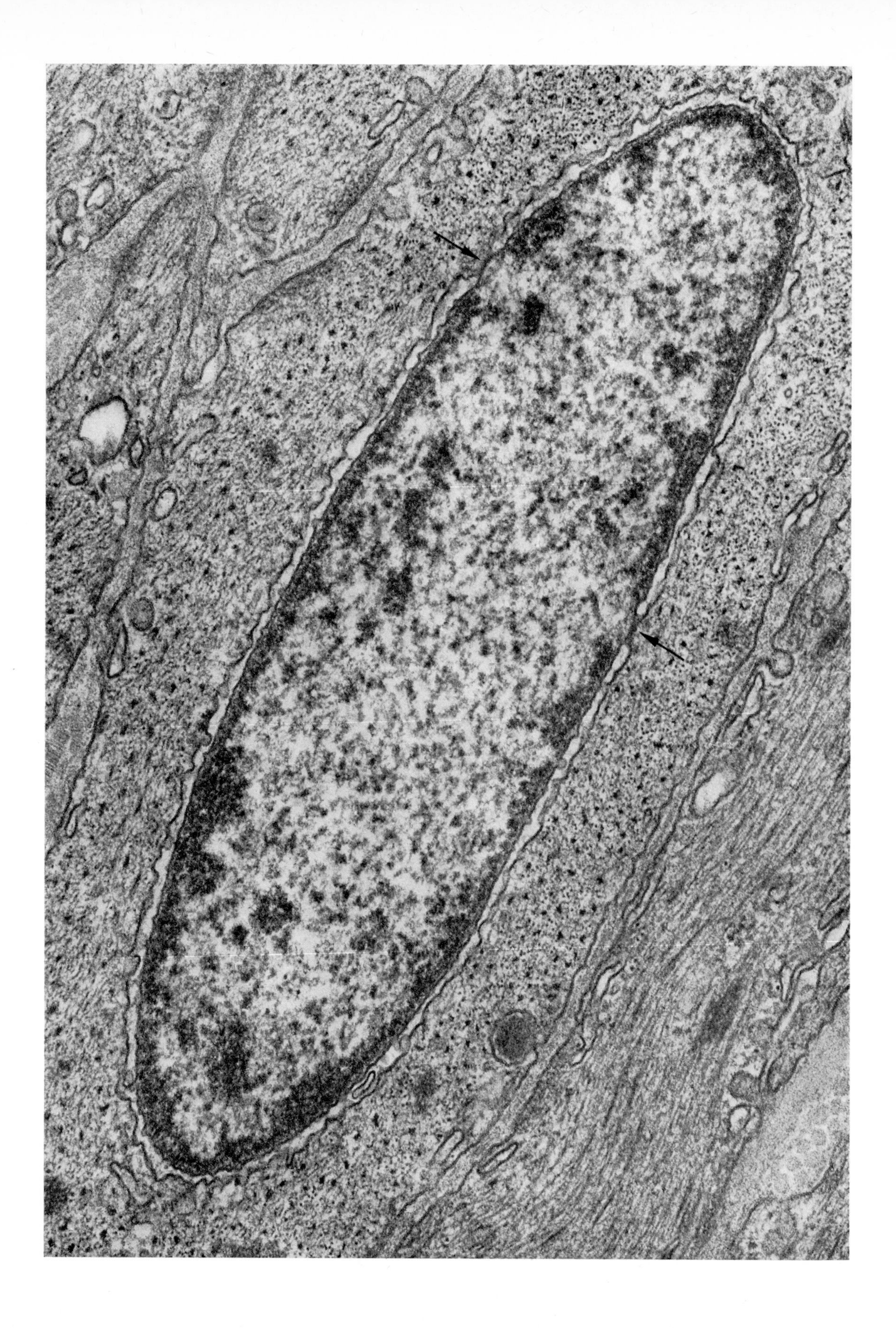

Plate 13

The nuclear pore complexes are circular (arrows), approximately 50 nm in diameter and consist of a complex of units. The margin or annulus of the pore is made up of eight regularly spaced subunits or granules. Another granule is generally located in the centre and is attached to the annulus by a number of fibrils. Amorphous material also projects from the annulus and takes part in the formation of the diaphragm.

Nuclear pores: cultured chicken gizzard smooth muscle. Glancing section. Glutaraldehyde fixation. ×30 500.

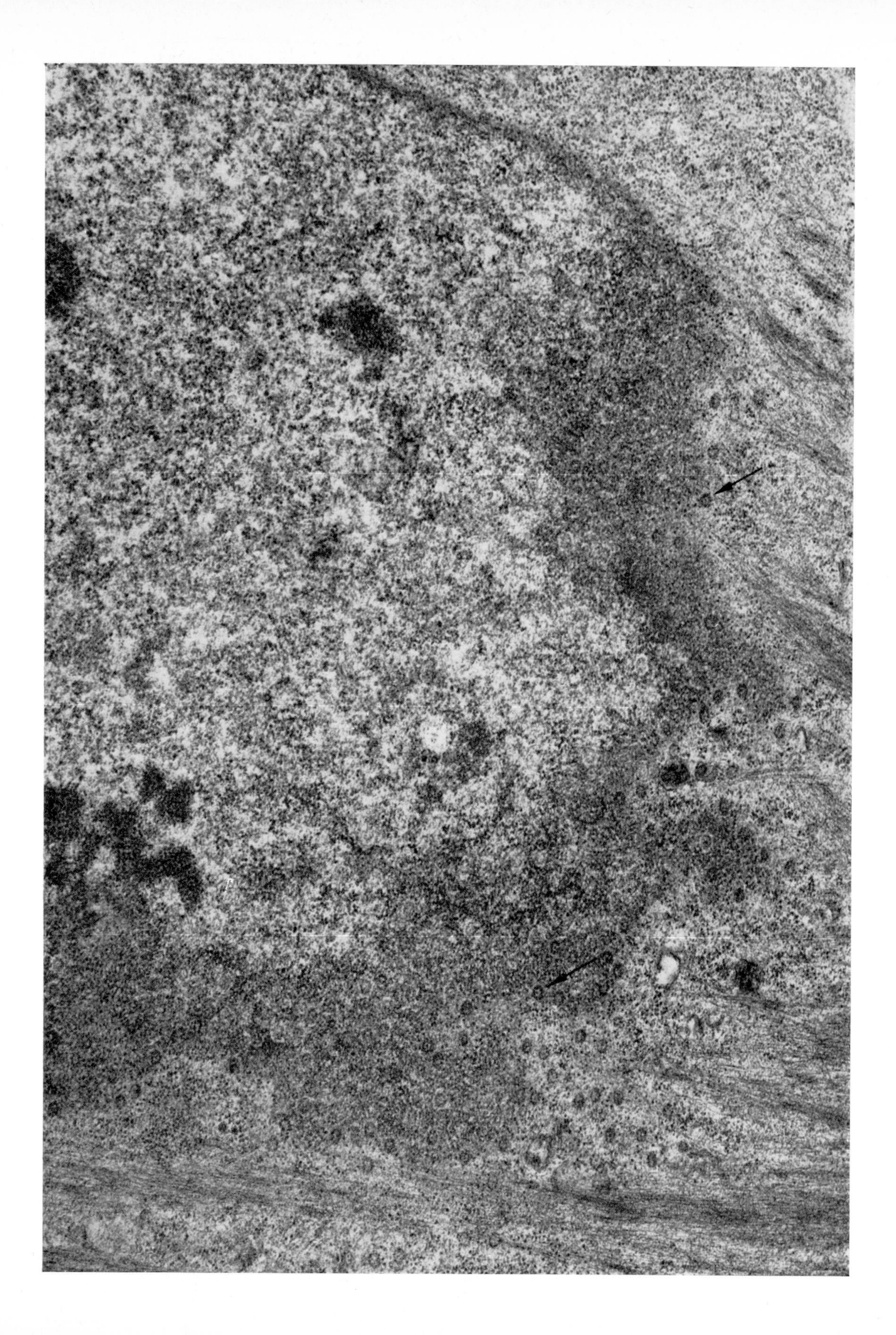

Plate 14

While condensed chromatin in the nucleus of vertebrate striated and smooth muscle is diffuse and mainly concentrated peripherally, in some invertebrates, such as the earthworm, the nucleus often shows additional central patches of condensed chromatin. The nuclei of the muscle cells of the outer longitudinal coat (Ol) of the earthworm intestine are also peculiar in that they are located in a specialized compartment together with various other cellular organelles, while myofilaments are contained in a separate compartment. Note the centriole (Ce) (see Chapter 2, I). These cells are enclosed by the peritoneum (Pe) and the inner circular coat of muscle (Ic). Note also the nerve fibre (N) in contact with the muscle.

Interphase nucleus: earthworm intestine. Transverse section. Glutaraldehyde fixation. ×33 000.

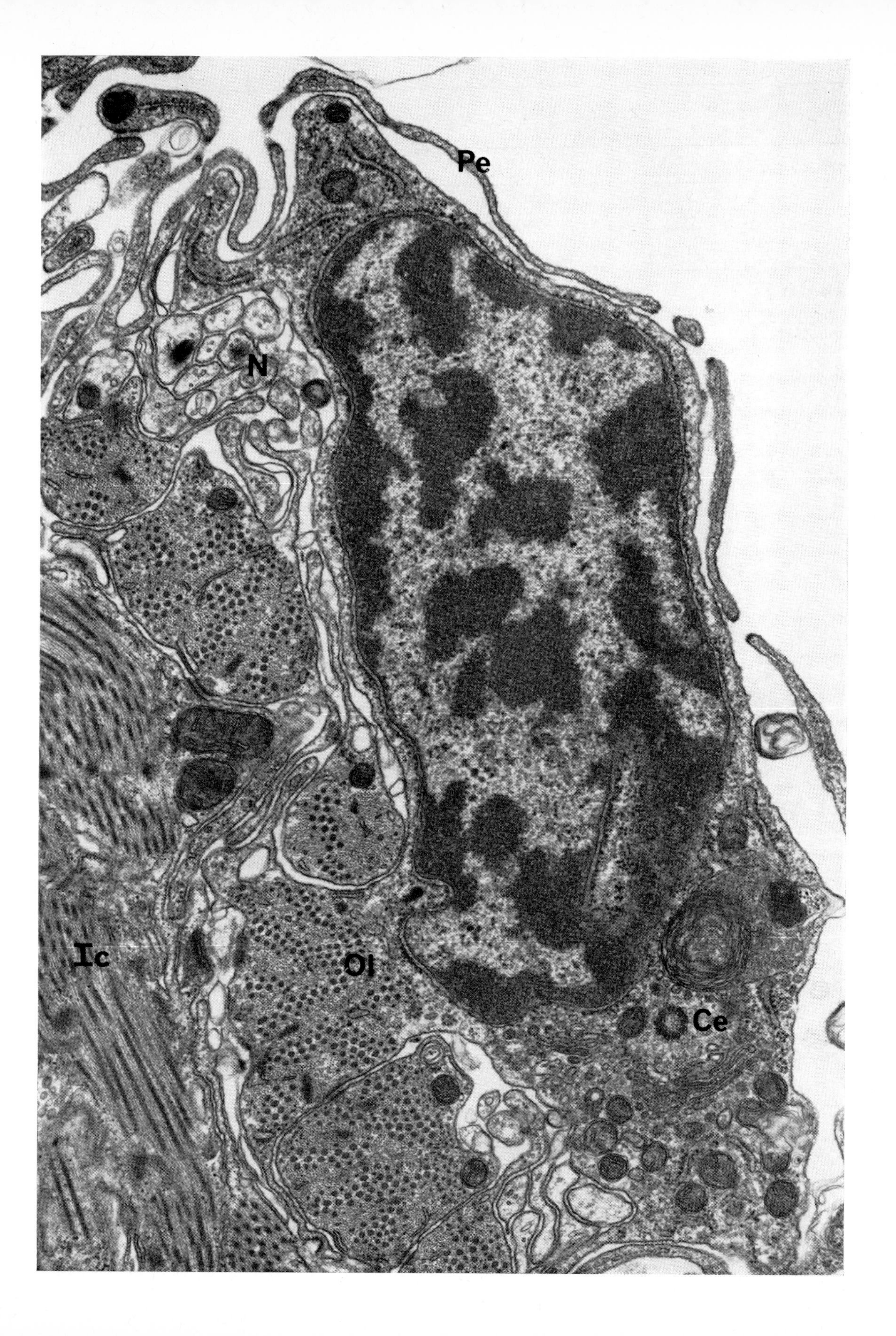

Pe
N
Ic
Ol
Ce

Plate 15

When observed with the light microscope the nucleolus is seen as an eccentrically placed body which is stained intensely by basic and many acid dyes. Using the electron microscope it is shown to comprise two parts, the *pars amorpha* or *pars fibrosa* and the *nucleolonema* or *pars granulosa*. The pars amorpha consists of a mass of filaments, 5 nm thick and has the appearance of a dense amorphous fibrous substance. The nucleolonema is usually in the form of branching and anastomosing strands, 60–80 nm in diameter. It also consists of 5 nm thick filaments, but usually contains granules 15 nm in diameter similar in appearance to ribosomes, giving it an overall granular texture. However the nucleolonema is not of uniform density and some areas appear to be devoid of granules. It is therefore often difficult to distinguish the pars amorpha from the nucleolonema (Nl) at the ultrastructural level.

Nucleolus: rat rectus femoris muscle. Glutaraldehyde fixation. ×74 800.

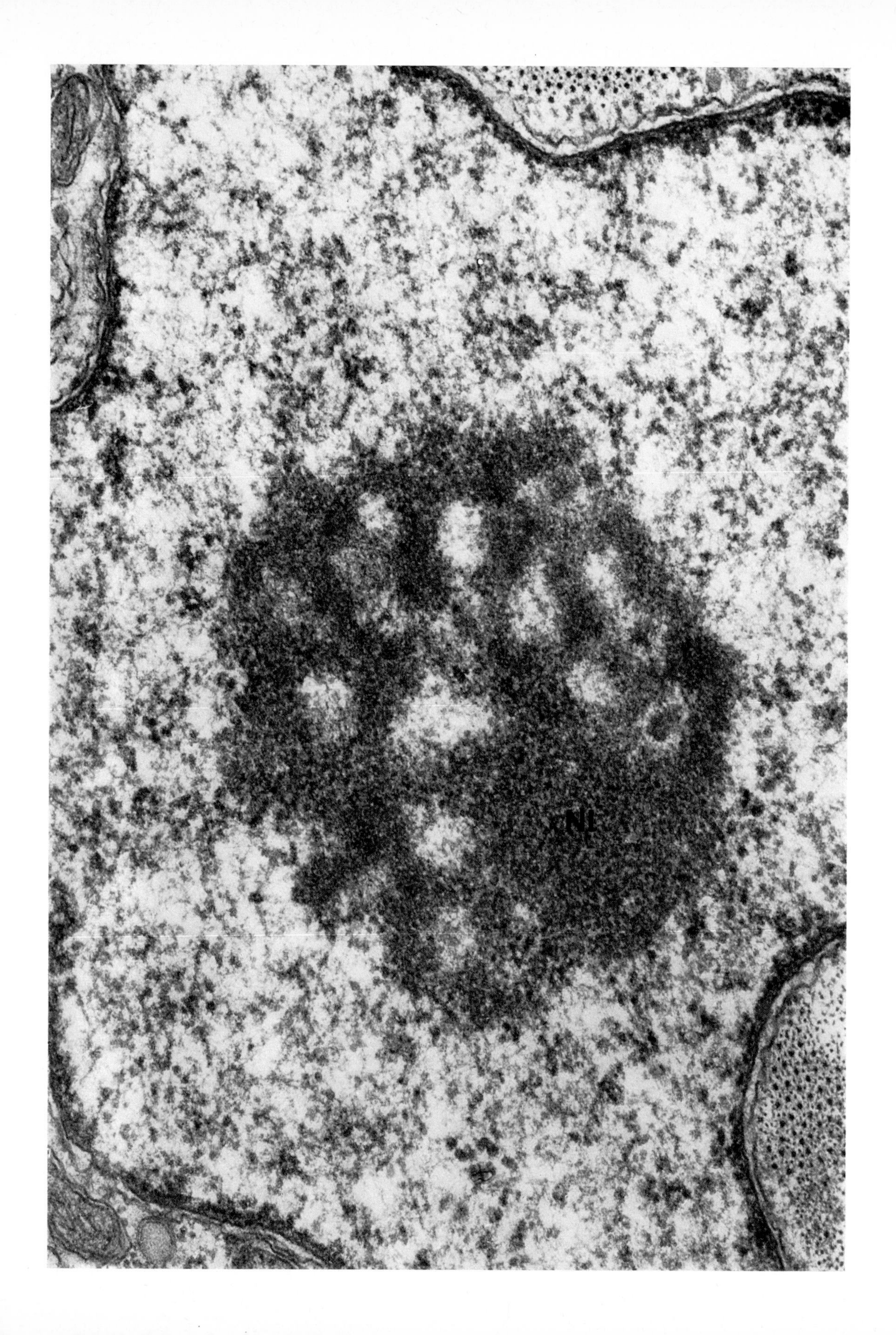
Nl

Plate 16

Nuclear inclusions are usually of two types, nuclear bodies and intranuclear fibrillar bundles. *Nuclear bodies* have a characteristic spherical appearance and vary in size from 50–150 nm in diameter. They do not usually have a limiting membrane. *Intranculear fibrillar bundles* usually appear as rod-shaped bundles of closely packed fibrils. These two types of inclusions do not have any apparent relationship to each other. Although they have more frequently been observed in pathological conditions, they are also present under normal circumstances. Variations of these inclusions have also been described. In the nucleus demonstrated here, the nuclear inclusions consist of fine filaments 6–8 nm in diameter (double headed arrow). Note also the nuclear pores (arrows).

Nuclear inclusion: smooth muscle from finch gizzard. Longitudinal section. Glutaraldehyde fixation. ×62 100.

Selected articles

ABELSON, H. T. and G. H. SMITH. 1970. Nuclear pores: The pore–annulus relationship in thin section. *J. Ultrastruct. Res.*, **30,** 558–588.

BISCHOFF, R. and H. HOLTZER. 1969. Mitosis and the processes of differentiation of myogenic cells *in vitro*. *J. Cell Biol.*, **41,** 188–200.

BLOOM, S. 1970. Structural changes in nuclear envelopes during elongation of heart muscle cells. *J. Cell Biol.*, **44,** 218–222.

BLOOM, S. and P. A. CANCILLA. 1969. Conformational changes in myocardial nuclei of rats. *Circulation Res.*, **24,** 189–196.

BOUTEILLE, M., S. R. KALIFAT and J. DELARUE. 1967. Ultrastructural variations of nuclear bodies in human diseases. *J. Ultrastruct. Res.*, **19,** 474–486.

CHAMLEY, J. H. and G. R. CAMPBELL. 1974. Mitosis of contractile smooth muscle cells in tissue culture. *Expl Cell Res.*, **84,** 105–110.

COBB, J. L. S. and T. BENNETT. 1970. An ultrastructural study of mitotic division in differentiated gastric smooth muscle cells. *Z. Zellforsch. mikrosk. Anat.*, **108,** 177–189.

COLONNIER, M. 1965. On the nature of intranuclear rods. *J. Cell Biol.*, **25,** 646–653.

DAHL, E. 1970. The fine structure of nuclear inclusions. *J. Anat.*, **106,** 255–262.

ECKERT, W. A., W. W. FRANKE and U. SCHEER. 1972. Actinomycin D and the central granules in the nuclear pore complex: Thin sectioning versus negative staining. *Z. Zellforsch. mikrosk. Anat.*, **127,** 230–239.

EDELMAN, J. C., P. M. EDELMAN, K. M. KNIGGE and I. L. SCHWARTZ. 1965. Isolation of skeletal muscle nuclei. *J. Cell Biol.*, **27,** 365–378.

FABERGÉ, A. C. 1973. Direct démonstration of eight-fold symmetry in nuclear pores. *Z. Zellforsch. mikrosk. Anat.*, **136,** 183–190.

FAWCETT, D. W. 1966*a*. On the occurrence of a fibrous lamina on the inner aspect of the nuclear envelope in certain cells of vertebrates. *Am. J. Anat.*, **119,** 129–146.

FAWCETT, D. W. 1966*b*. *An Atlas of Fine Structure. The Cell, Its Organelles and Inclusions.* W. B. Saunders, Philadelphia.

FRANKE, W. W. 1966. Isolated nuclear membranes. *J. Cell Biol.*, **31,** 619–623.

FRANKE, W. W. 1970*a*. On the universality of nuclear pore complex structure. *Z. Zellforsch. mikrosk. Anat.*, **105,** 405–429.

FRANKE, W. W. 1970*b*. Attachment of muscle filaments to the outer membrane of the nuclear envelope. *Z. Zellforsch. mikrosk. Anat.*, **111,** 143–148.

FRANKE, W. W. 1971. Relationship of nuclear membranes with filaments and microtubules. *Protoplasma*, **73,** 263–292.

FRANKE, W. W. and W. SCHINKO. 1969. Nuclear shape in muscle cells. *J. Cell Biol.*, **42,** 326–331.

GALL, J. G. 1967. Octagonal nuclear pores. *J. Cell Biol.*, **32,** 391–400.

KASTEN, F. H. 1972. Rat myocardial cells *in vitro*: Mitosis and differentiated properties. *In Vitro*. **8,** 128–149.

KAYE, G. I., L. F. SIEGAL and R. R. PASCAL. 1971. Cell replication of mesenchymal elements in adult tissues. II. Replication of smooth muscle cells in the colonic musclularis externa of adult rabbits. *Am. J. Anat.*, **132,** 93–102.

KESSEL, R. G. 1973. Structure and function of the nuclear envelope and related cytomembranes. *Prog. Surf. Membrane Sci.*, **6,** 243–329.

KILARSKI, W. and A. JASINSKI. 1970. The formation of multivesicular bodies from the nuclear envelope. *J. Cell Biol.*, **45,** 205–211.

KÖNIG, P. 1968. Verschiedene Kerngrößen bei einfach und multipel innervierten Hühnermuskeln. *Acta anat.*, **71,** 79–81.

LANE, B. P. 1965. Alterations in the cytological detail of intestinal smooth muscle cells in various stages of contraction. *J. Cell Biol.*, **27,** 199–214.

MANASEK, F. J. 1968. Mitosis in developing cardiac muscle. *J. Cell Biol.*, **37,** 191–196.

MAUL, G. G. 1971. On the octagonality of the nuclear pore complex. *J. Cell Biol.*, **51,** 558–562.

MENTRÉ, P. 1969. Présence d'acide ribo nucléique dans l'anneau osmiophile et le granule central des pores nucléaires. *J. Microsc. (Fr.)*, **8,** 51–68.

MOSS, F. P. 1968. The relationship between the dimensions of the fibres and the number of nuclei during normal growth of skeletal muscle in the domestic fowl. *Am. J. Anat.*, **122,** 555–563.

MOSS, F. P. and C. P. LEBLOND. 1970. Nature of dividing nuclei in skeletal muscle of growing rats. *J. Cell Biol.*, **44,** 459–461.

OBERPRILLER, J. and J. C. OBERPRILLER. 1971. Mitosis in adult newt ventricle. *J. Cell Biol.*, **49,** 560–563.

RUMYANTSEV, P. P. 1967. Electron microscopical analysis of cell elements differentiation and proliferation processes in developing myocardium. (In Russian.) *Archs Anat. Histol. Embryol.*, **52,** 67–77.

RUMYANTSEV, P. P. 1972. Electron microscope study of the myofibril partial disintegration and recovery in the mitotically dividing cardiac muscle cells. *Z. Zellforsch. mikrosk. Anat.*, **129,** 471–499.

RUMYANTSEV, P. P. and E. S. SNIGIREVSKAYA. 1968. The ultrastructure of differentiating cells of the heart muscle in the state of mitotic division. *Acta morph. hung.* **16,** 271–283.

SCHEER, U. 1972. The ultrastructure of the nuclear envelope of amphibian oocytes: IV. On the chemical nature of the nuclear pore complex material. *Z. Zellforsch. mikrosk. Anat.*, **127,** 127–148.

SCHNEIDER, R. and P. PFITZER. 1973. Die Zahl der Kerne in isolierten Zellen des menschlichen Myokards. *Virchows Arch. Abt. B. Zellpath.*, **12,** 238–258.

SHAFIQ, S. A., M. A. GORYCKI and A. MAURO. 1968. Mitosis during postnatal growth in skeletal and cardiac muscle of the rat. *J. Anat.*, **103,** 135–141.

SMETANA, K., F. GYORKEY, P. GYORKEY and H. BUSCH. 1970. Studies on the ultrastructure of nucleoli in human smooth muscle cells. *Expl Cell Res.*, **60,** 175–184.

WALKER, B. E. and E. K. ADRIAN, JR. 1966. DNA synthesis in the myocardium of growing, mature, senescent and dystrophic mice. *Cardiologia*, **49,** 319–328.

WATSON, M. L. 1955. The nuclear envelope. Its structure and relation to cytoplasmic membranes. *J. biophys. biochem. Cytol.*, **1,** 257–270.

WEINSTEIN, R. B. and E. D. HAY. 1970. Deoxyribonucleic acid synthesis and mitosis in differentiated cardiac muscle cells of chick embryos. *J. Cell Biol.*, **47,** 310–316.

WEISSENFELS, N. 1970. Die Wirkung von RNase und DNase auf die Kernfeinstruktur kultivierter Hühnerherzmyoblasten. *Cytobiologie*, **2,** 123–138.

WHALEY, W. G., H. H. MOLLENHAUER and J. H. LEECH. 1960. Some observations on the nuclear envelope. *J. biophys. biochem. Cytol.*, **8,** 233–246.

WIENER, J., D. SPIRO and W. R. LOEWENSTEIN. 1965. Ultrastructure and permeability of nuclear membranes. *J. Cell Biol.*, **27,** 107–118.

B Myofibrils

Muscle fibres consist of many myofibrils in a sarcoplasmic matrix, each running from one end to the other of the muscle fibre and consisting of a sequence of sarcomeres. The sarcomeres are the contractile units of the muscle and are composed of myofilaments (see Chapter 2C). It is the alignment of sarcomeres in parallel myofibrils which results in the characteristic cross striations of skeletal muscle seen in the light microscope. Each myofibril is delineated by regularly organized networks of sarcoplasmic reticulum together with mitochondria and glycogen granules. There is considerable variation in the number and arrangement of these elements in different muscle types.

There is also variation in size and form of the myofibrils. For example, the myofibrils in some vertebrate skeletal muscles are 1–2 μm in diameter and cylindrical. In others, the myofibrils are fused together to form a diffuse irregular pattern. Correlation of these different myofibril patterns with different physiological properties has been the subject of controversy. However, correlation of a variety of physiological properties such as resistance to fatigue, with histochemical characteristics such as oxidative enzyme activity, has shown that many mammalian skeletal muscles can be classified into three groups. The three basic histochemical 'fibre types' exactly match three physiologically defined groups. Thus *α white muscle* fibres (αw), determined by histochemical methods, are equivalent to fast-contracting, *fast-fatigue muscle* fibres (FF) (can probably be equated with the term *fast-twitch fibres*); α *red muscle* fibres (αR) are equivalent to fast-contracting, *fatigue-resistant* (FR) (can probably be equated with the term *intermediate fibres*); and β *red muscle* fibres (βR) are equivalent to *slow-contracting muscle* fibres (S) (can probably be equated with the term *slow-twitch fibres*). These three categories of twitch muscle characterize the skeletal muscle fibres of mammals. There are exceptions, however, such as mammalian extraocular muscles which contain a fourth class of slow-tonic as well as fast-twitch fibres. Slow-tonic fibres identified in amphibian muscle appear to be absent from the limbs of mammals. It should also be remembered that most mammalian muscles are not just of one fibre type alone, but consist of different proportions of red and white muscle fibres.

Two functionally different types of muscle fibre have been recognized in insects. The *asynchronous type* is characterized by a very high frequency of contraction and the absence of a positive process of relaxation, for example certain flight muscles. The *synchronous type*, such as those in the leg and in other flight muscles are characterized by a complete cycle of contraction and relaxation. Asynchronous muscles have cylindrical myofibrils separated by numerous mitochondria and a poorly developed sarcoplasmic reticulum and T-system. Synchronous muscles have closely packed myofibrils and possess a highly developed sarco-tubular system and few mitochondria.

Smooth muscles in vertebrates and invertebrates have morphologically indistinct myofibrils; the sarcoplasmic reticulum is unevenly distributed and never divides the contractile elements into discrete units.

Plate 17

The myofibrils (Mf) are composed of myofilaments, and are well defined since they are almost completely surrounded by sarcoplasmic reticulum (SR), mitochondria and glycogen, which delineate them as separate units within the muscle fibre. The shape of the myofibrils in transverse section is variable, ranging from almost circular to a flattened plate. The diameter of myofibrils varies from 0.1 μm to 3 μm. These discrete cylindrical type myofibrils are also found in fast twitch muscle fibres in amphibia and in fish white muscles and are often called 'Fibrillenstruktur' or fibrillar-type of muscle fibre. Each fibril consists of a number of hexagonally arranged myofilaments of two kinds.

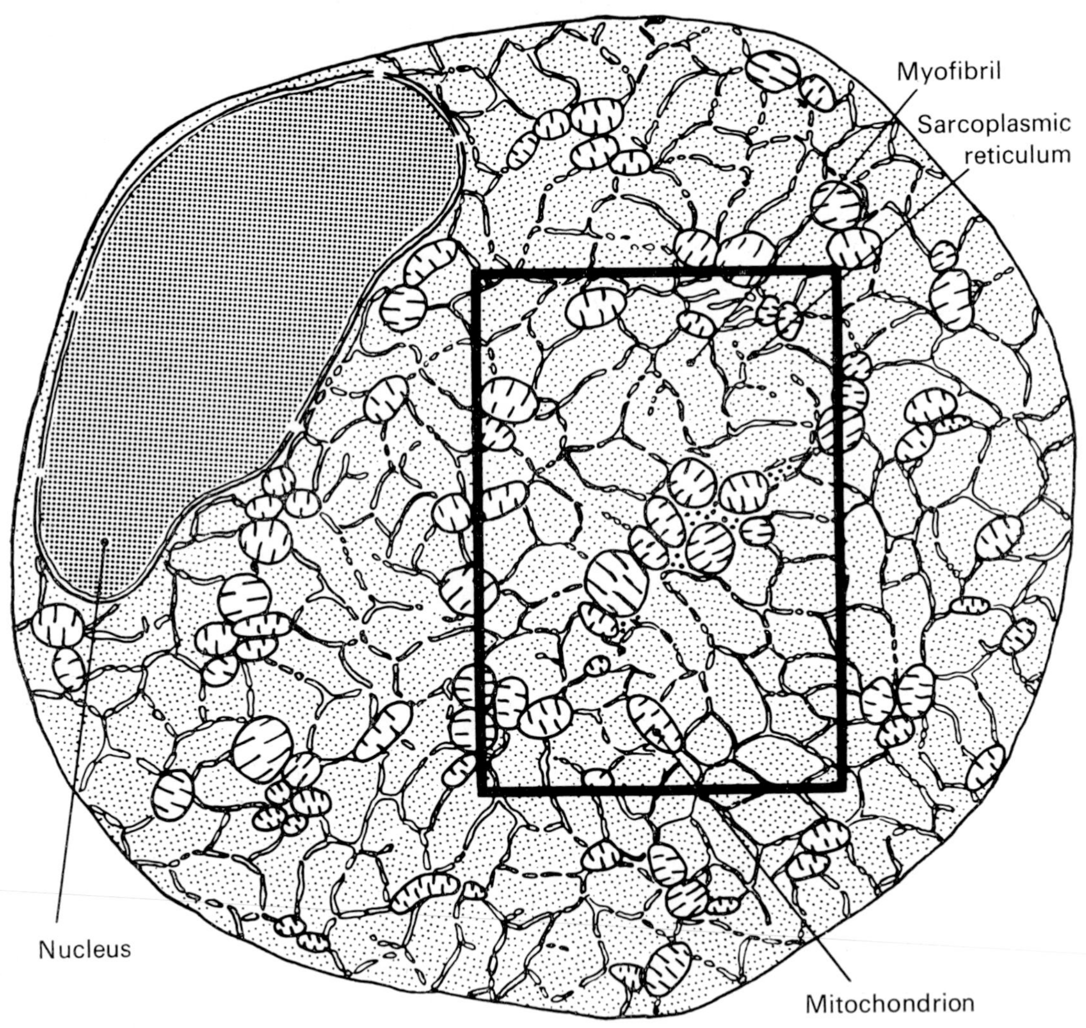

Indicates area of muscle fibre represented by Plate 17

Fig. 4 Diagram of vertebrate skeletal muscle fibre showing arrangement of myofibrils.

Myofibrils in fibrillar type muscle fibres: guinea-pig rectus oculi superior muscle. Transverse section. Glutaraldehyde fixation. ×15 000.

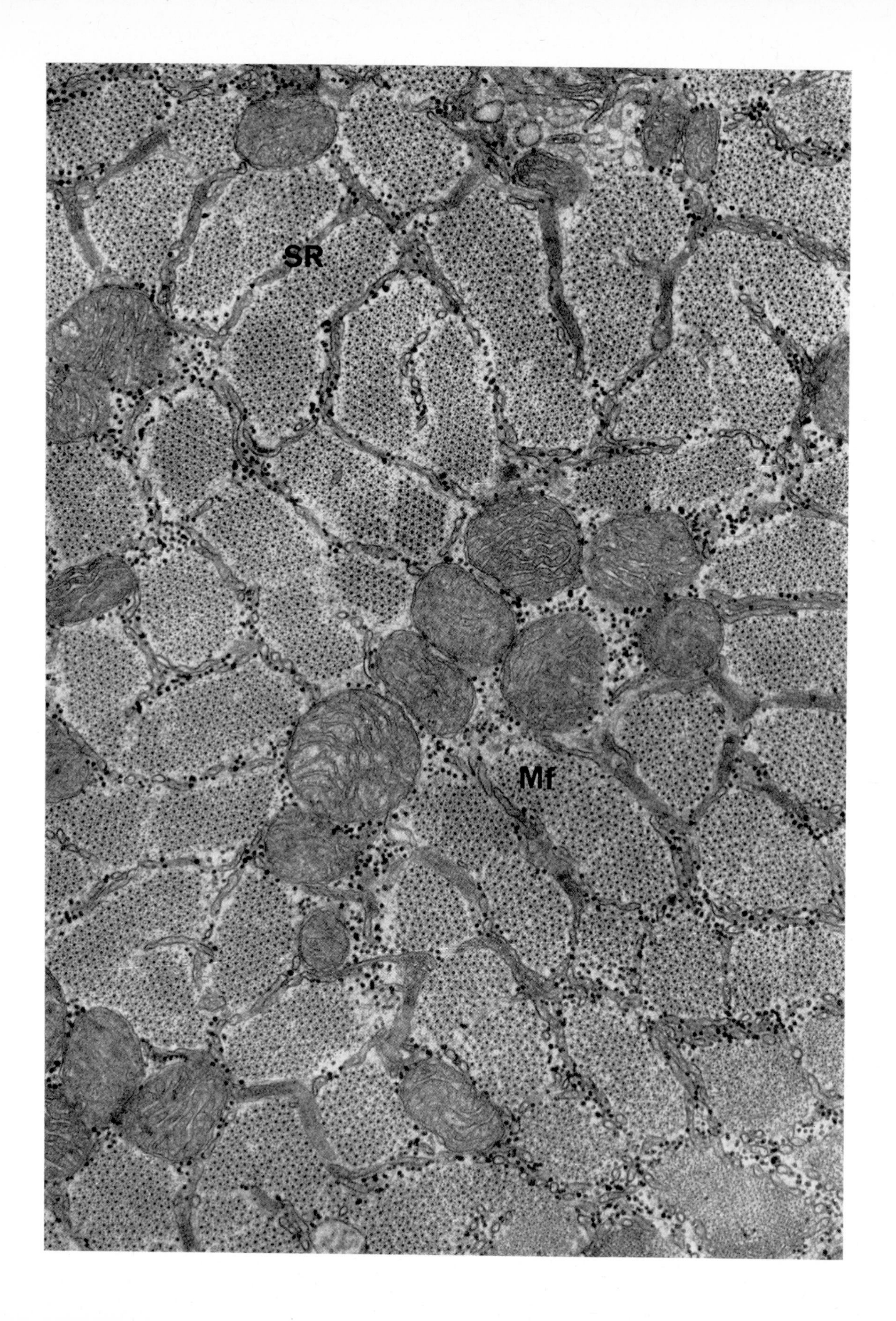
SR
Mf

Plate 18

Fish have two types of muscle, red and white, and physiological studies have shown that in many ways they resemble the slow tonic and fast twitch fibres respectively of the frog.

The myofibrils (Mf) in this white muscle are separated from each other by elements of the sarcoplasmic reticulum and T-system (see Chapter 2E). Each myofibril consists of a number of repeating units, the sarcomeres, delineated by narrow electron dense lines, the Z-discs (Z).

The components of each sarcomere are aligned parallel to those in adjacent myofibrils and it is this arrangement that gives striated muscle its characteristic appearance under the light microscope.

Myofibrils in white muscle fibre: goldfish flexor pinnae pectoralis. Longitudinal section. Glutaraldehyde fixation. ×28 000.

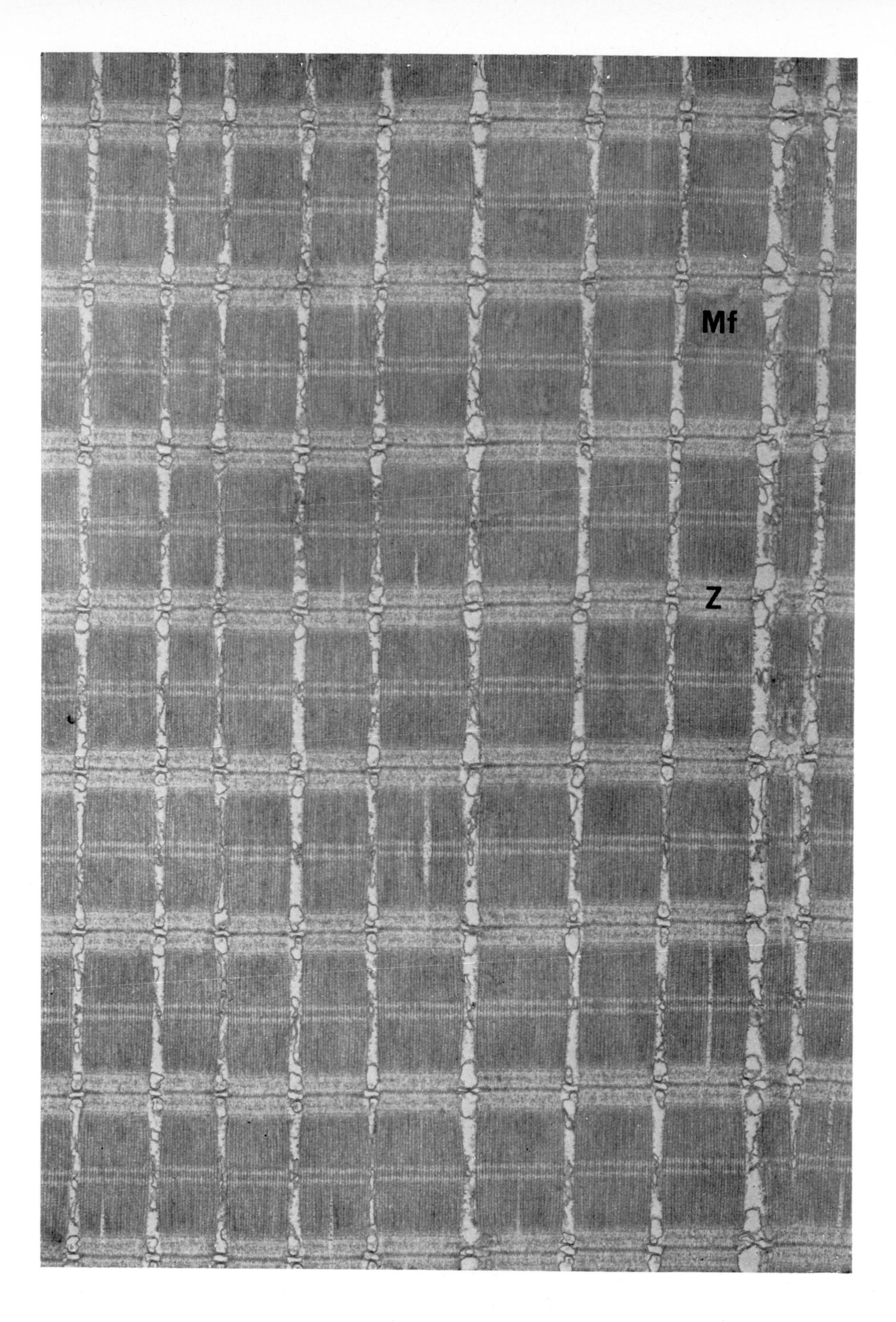
Mf
Z

Plate 19

In this example of a red muscle, most of the myofibrils have a polygonal or Y-shaped cross section. They are completely surrounded by sarcoplasmic reticulum and glycogen granules. An extensive accumulation of mitochondria is seen beneath the sarcolemma.

Within the sarcoplasm of most striated muscles is found the protein *myoglobin*. Red fibres contain more myoglobin than white fibres. The myoglobins combine with molecular oxygen to form complexes, *oxymyoglobins*, which serve to facilitate diffusion of O_2.

Myofibrils in vertebrate red muscle fibres: lizard tongue muscle. Transverse section. Glutaraldehyde fixation. ×12 200. (Courtesy of M. Canney, Department of Zoology, University of Melbourne.)

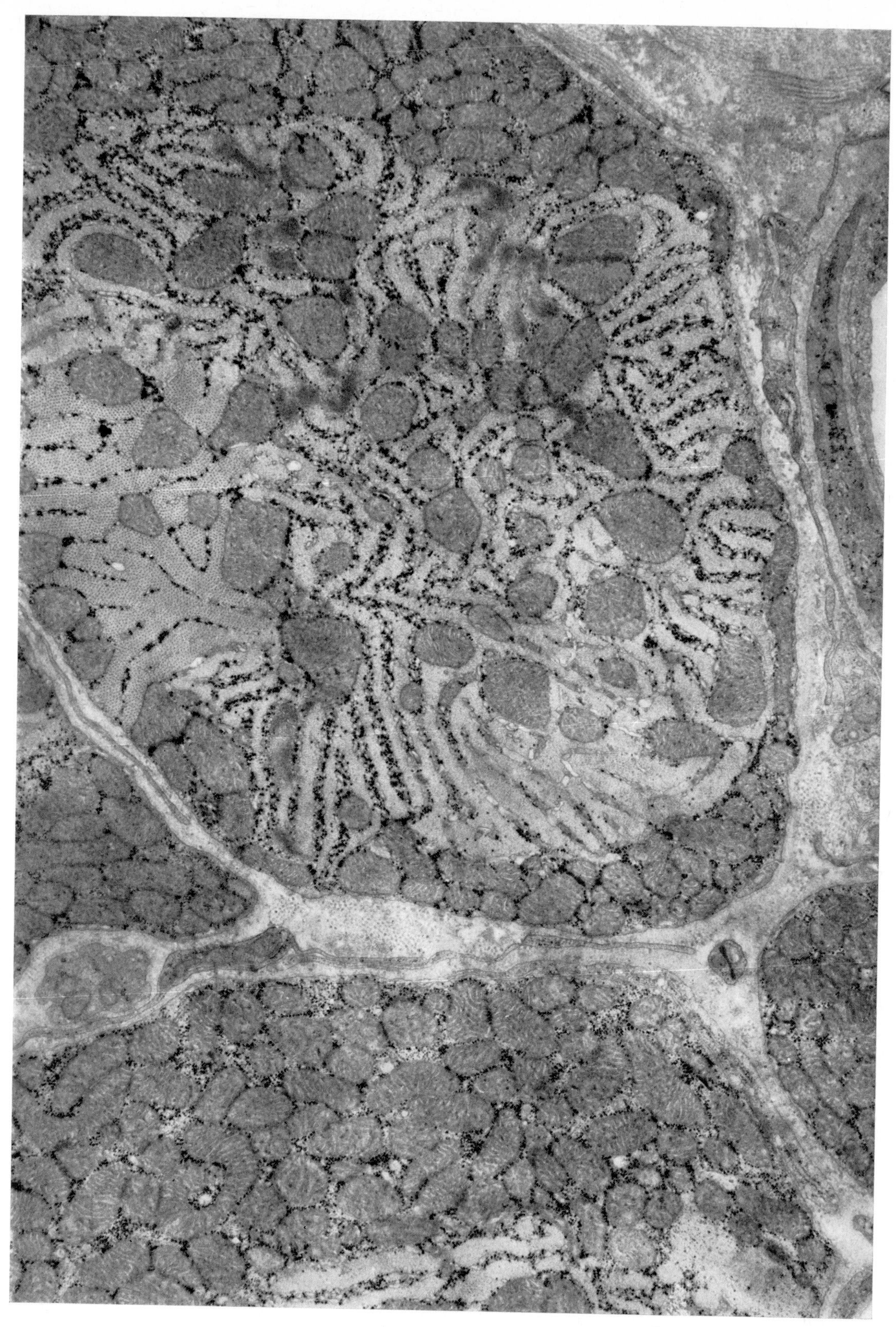

Plate 20

The anterior latissimus dorsi of the chicken is an example of a slow tonic muscle, often called 'Felderstruktur' muscle or area-type muscle, since they have a diffuse myofibril structure. This is because sarcoplasmic reticulum and mitochondria are sparse and do not completely surround the myofibrils, and triads are rarely found (see Chapter 2E). These muscles lack the well defined myofibrils found in most mammalian fast twitch muscles and in the white muscles of lower vertebrates which have been called 'Fibrillenstruktur' or fibrillar-type muscle.

The Z-disc of slow tonic fibres appears less complete than that of fast twitch fibres. Also, the filaments of the I-band are irregularly packed to the level of their insertion into the Z-disc and there are no bridges between the myosin filaments in the centre of the sarcomere as are seen in twitch muscles at the M-line level (see Chapter 2C).

Myofibrils in vertebrate slow tonic muscle fibres: anterior latissimus dorsi of chicken. Transverse section. Glutaraldehyde fixation. ×46 000.

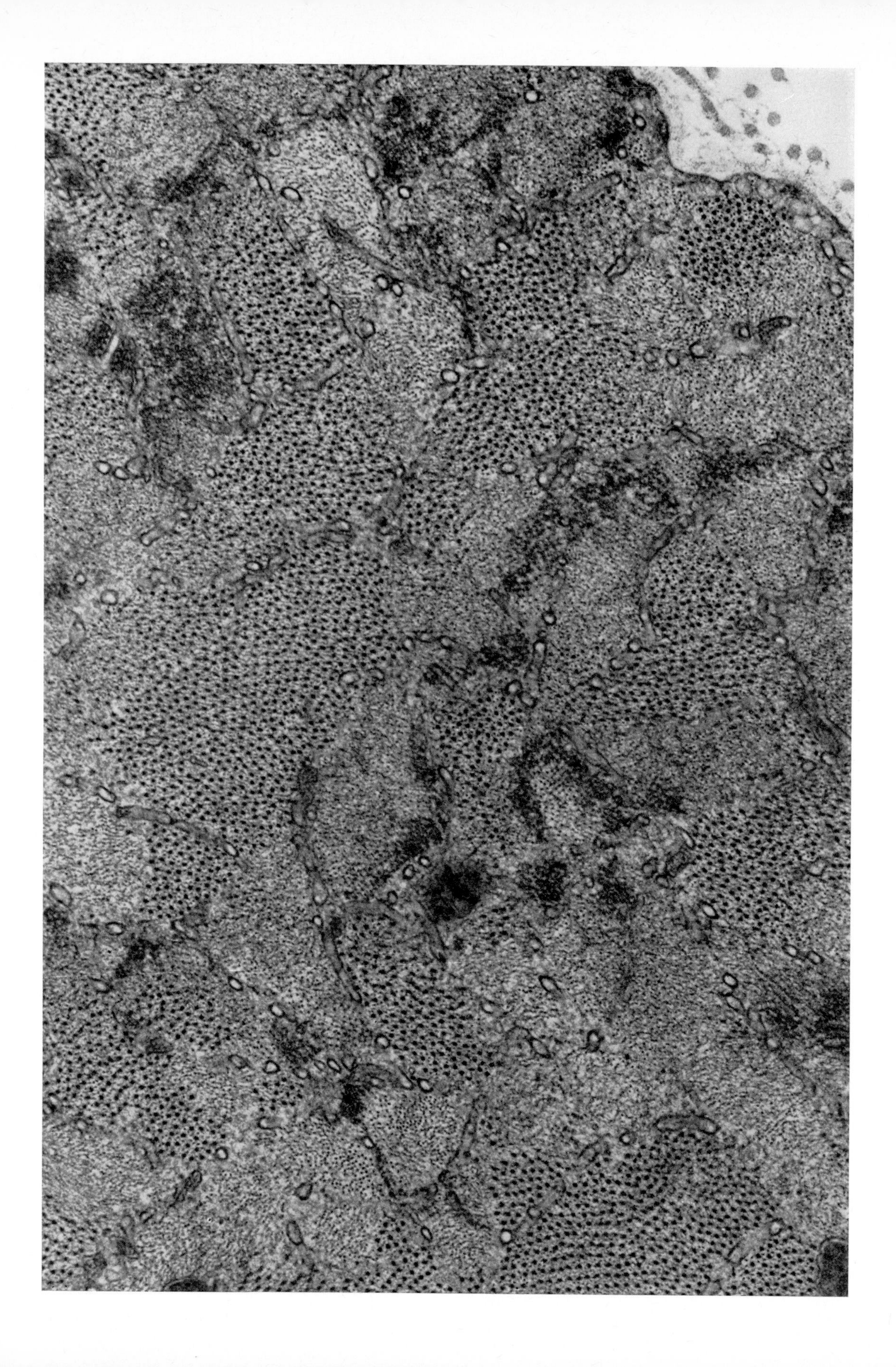

Plate 21

Intrafusal muscle fibres form the basis of muscle spindles (see Chapter 7G). This example has the appearance of a 'Felderstruktur' muscle. The myofibrils are not clearly delineated and there is only a small amount of sarcoplasmic reticulum.

Myofibrils in an intrafusal fibre of a muscle spindle: rat sternothyroid muscle. Transverse section. OsO_4–glutaraldehyde–OsO_4 fixation. ×49 500.

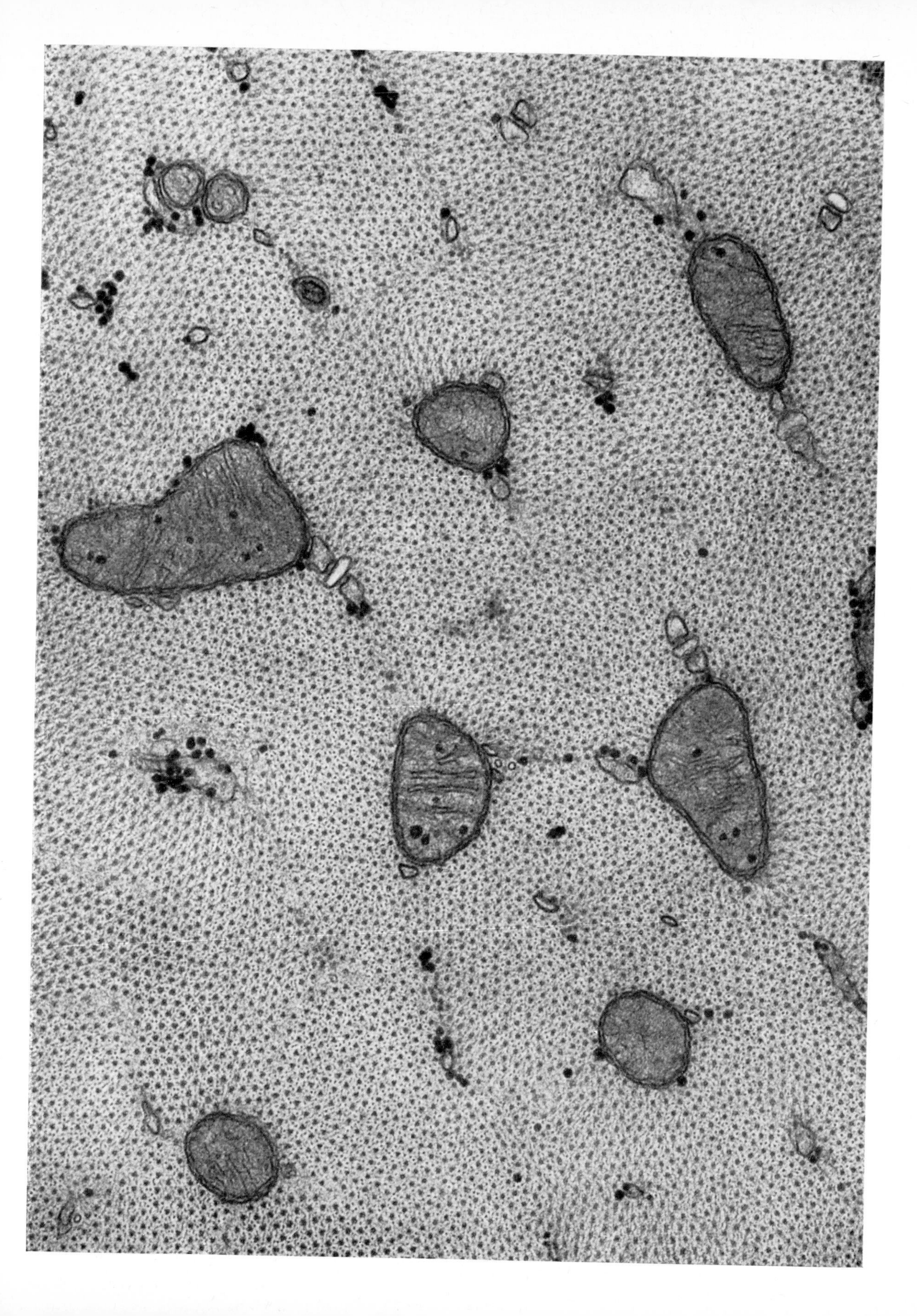

Plate 22

In insect flight muscle, the myofibrils have a regular circular profile with a diameter usually larger than those of vertebrate fast twitch muscles. Some sarcotubular system is present between each of these myofibrils, but the most striking characteristic is the presence of many large mitochondria (Mi) which lie between the fibrils and conform to their shape. The muscle fibres with these myofibrils are characterized by a very high frequency of contraction and the absence of a real process of relaxation and are called asynchronous muscles.

Asynchronous invertebrate muscle: blowfly flight muscle. Transverse section. Glutaraldehyde fixation. ×45 000.

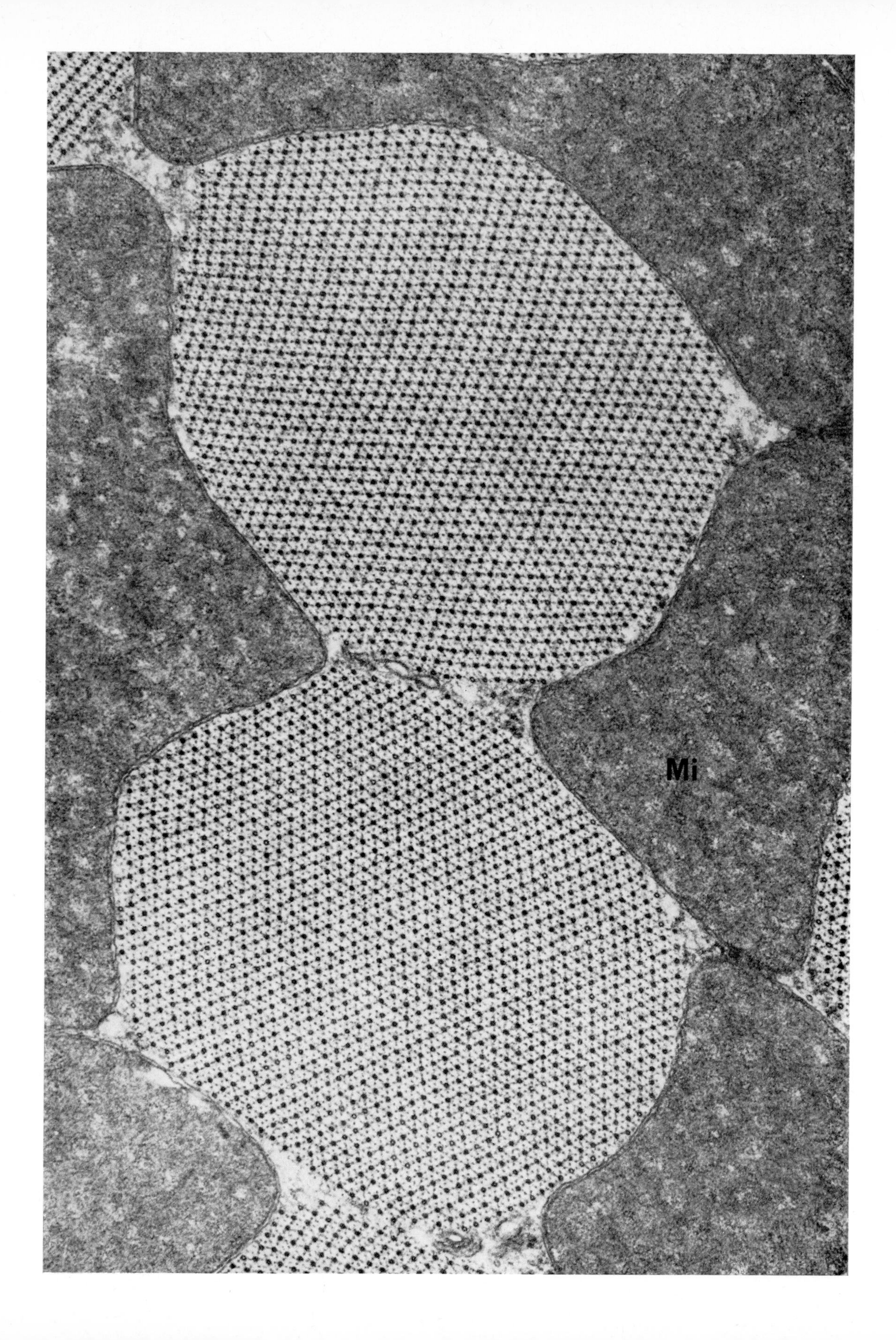
Mi

Plate 23

The myofilaments in spider leg muscle are arranged in parallel lamellar or ribbon-like myofibrils less than 1 μm thick, separated from each other by an extensive sarcotubular system. In contrast to insect flight muscles, few mitochondria are present between the myofibrils, and they have a complete cycle of contraction and relaxation.

Synchronous invertebrate muscle: spider leg muscle. Transverse section. Glutaraldehyde fixation. ×15 000.

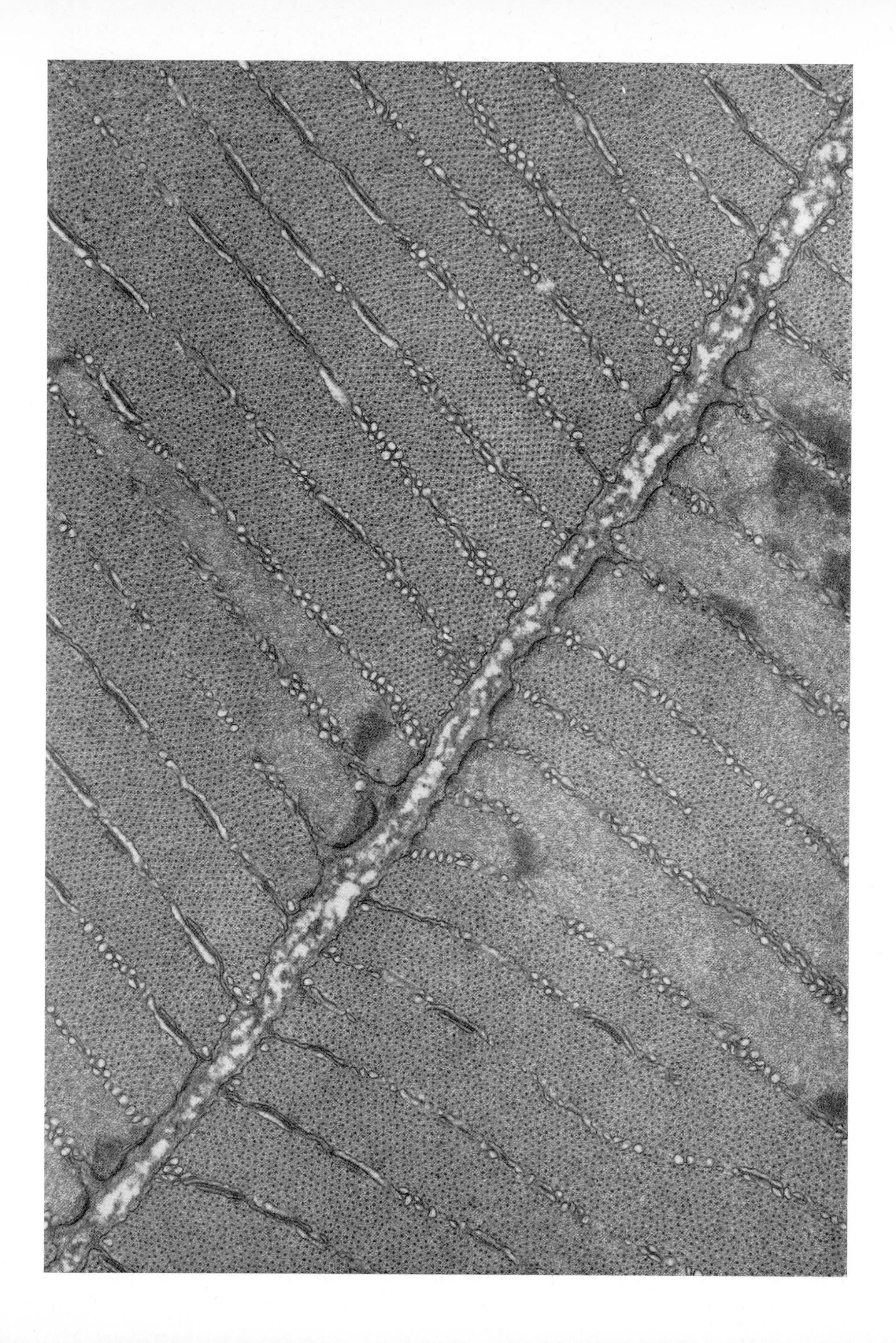

Plate 24

The earthworm somatic muscle is another example where the myofibrils are in a lamellar or ribbon-shaped form, although the sarco-tubular system in this muscle is not as extensive as that of the spider leg muscle (see Plate 23). Tubular elements of the sarcoplasmic reticulum alternate with *dense bodies* (see Fig. 12, p. 88). There is a narrow zone containing glycogen and vesicles of the sarcoplasmic reticulum along the periphery of the muscle fibre.

Myofibrils in obliquely striated muscle: earthworm somatic muscle. Transverse section. Glutaraldehyde fixation. ×61 000.

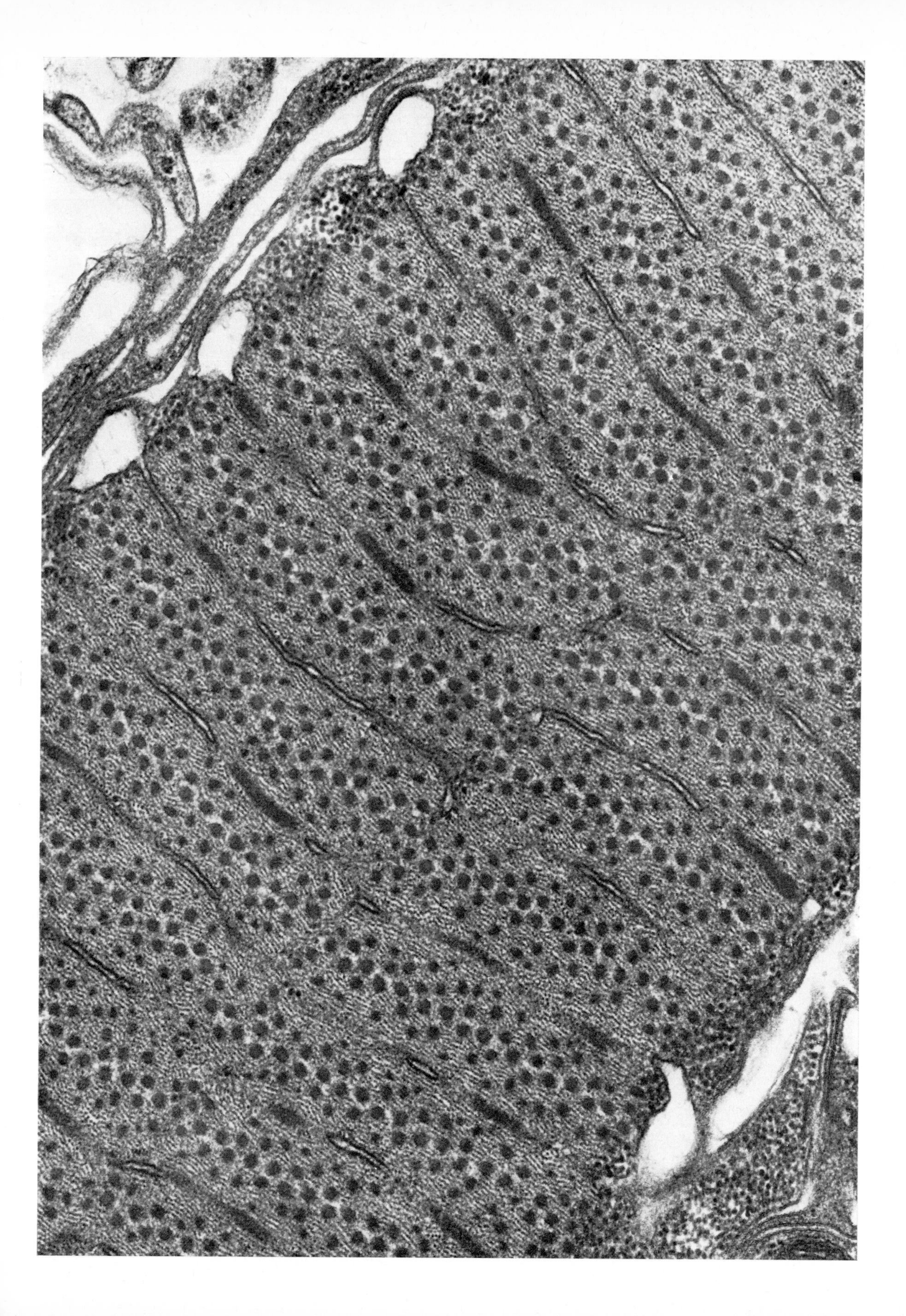

Plate 25

The sarcotubular system of smooth muscle is not well developed and does not have a clear orientation. Therefore myofibrils, as defined in many skeletal muscles, are not recognisable.

The whole smooth muscle cell appears to be the unit of contraction, although there is some suggestion of contractile subunits within cells from phase contrast and polarized light studies of isolated smooth muscle cells. Smooth muscle cells are usually arranged in effector bundles; low resistance pathways or nexuses are present between the individual cells of the effector bundles which facilitate synchronous contractions (see Chapter 6B).

Vertebrate smooth muscle: guinea-pig ureter. Transverse section. OsO_4–glutaraldehyde–OsO_4 fixation. ×50 500.

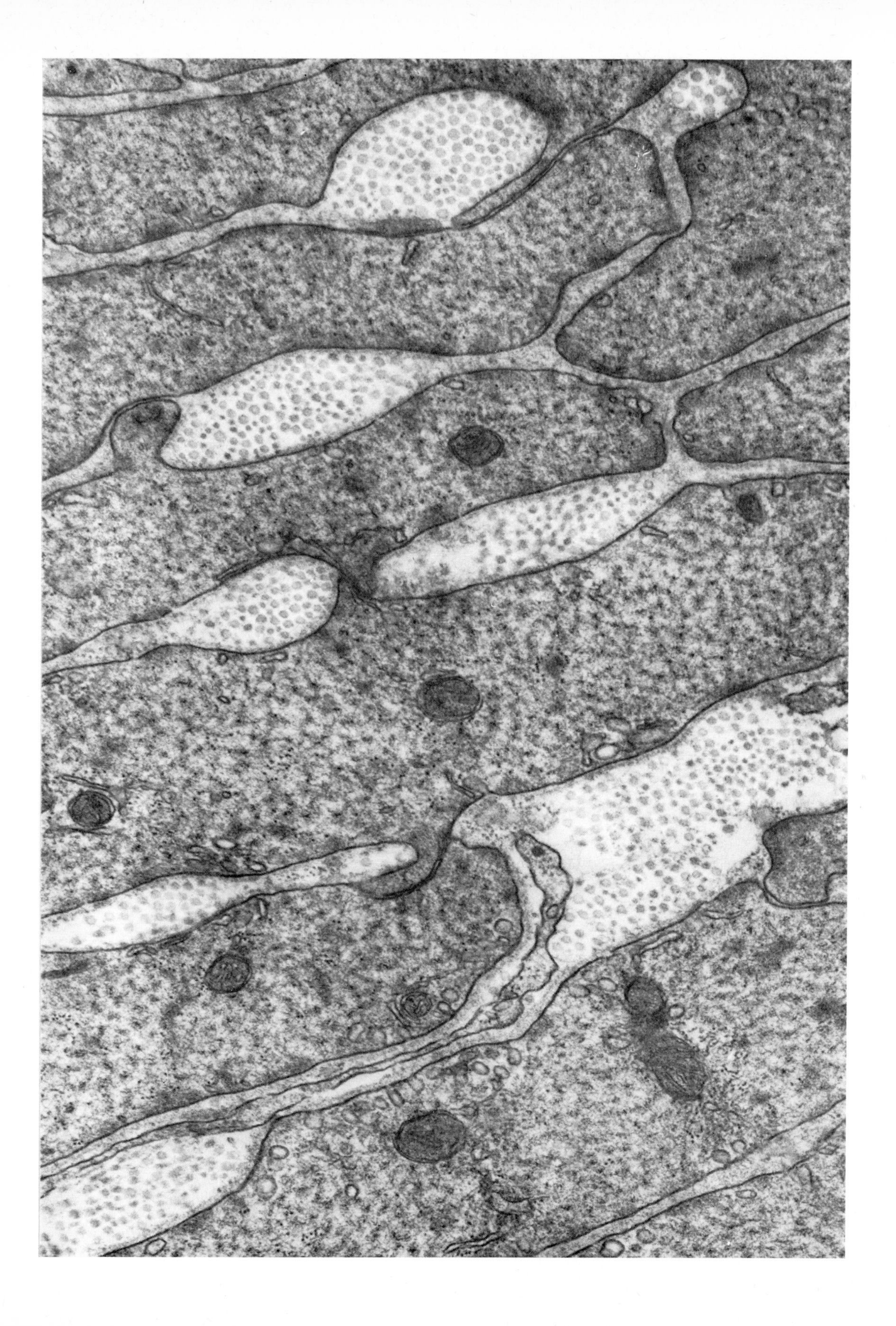

Plate 26

Some vertebrate extraocular muscle and skeletal muscle cells have an unusual peripheral arrangement of myofibrils which encircle and are orientated at right angles to a central longitudinal core of fibrils. Early light microscopists described them as 'Ringbinden' fibres, but the term '*ring fibre*' is more commonly used today. This type of fibre is sometimes seen in normal skeletal and extraocular muscles but is often present in dystrophic muscle which suggests that it may have a pathological nature. These fibres can also be produced experimentally.

'Ring fibre' muscle: guinea-pig rectus superior oculi muscle. Transverse section. Glutaraldehyde fixation. ×62 000.

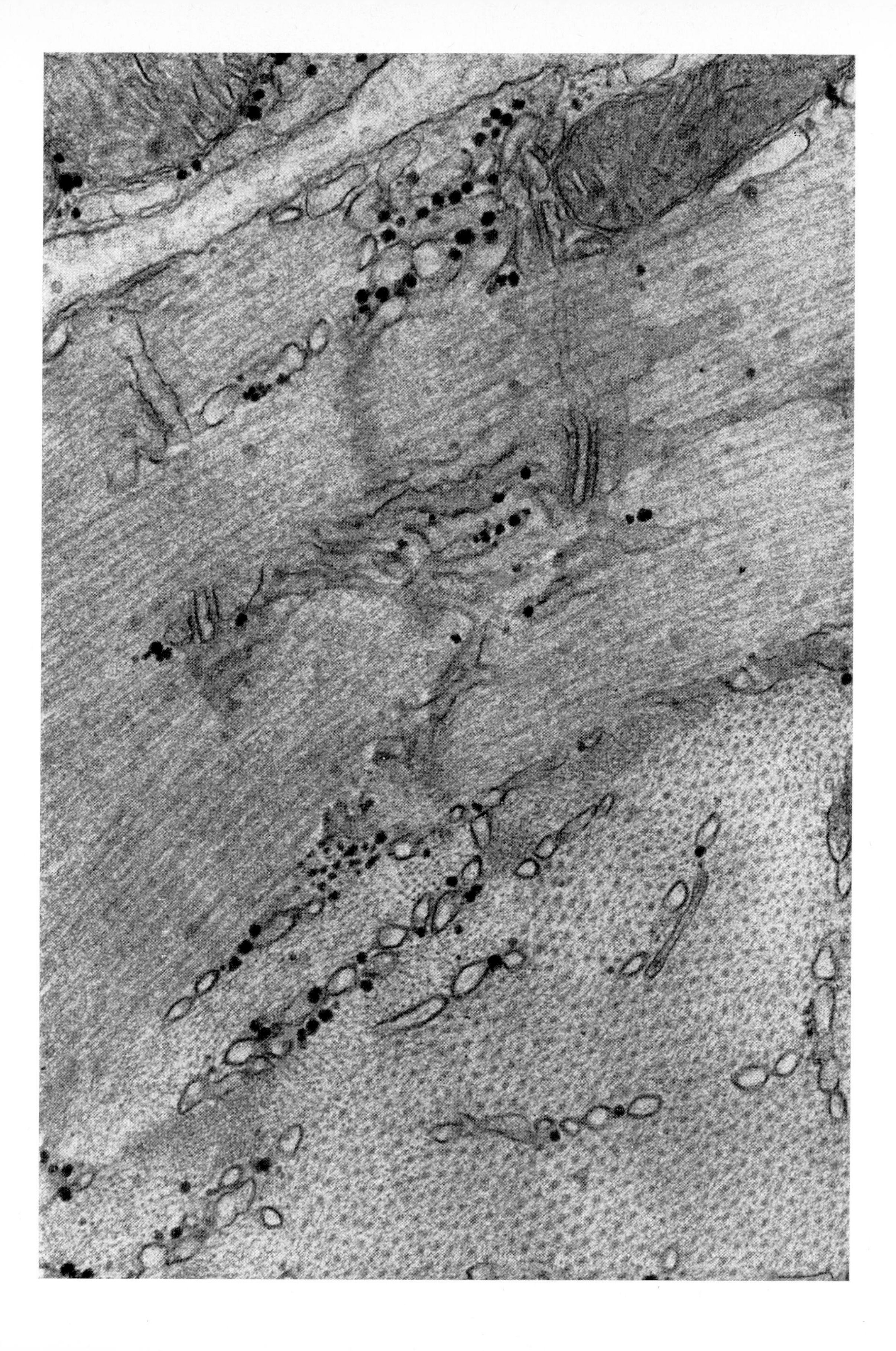

Plate 27

An unusual arrangement of myofibrils is also found in the muscle cells around the earthworm vascular wall where the inner myofibrils are arranged circularly and the outer longitudinally in relation to the long axis of the blood vessel. The effect of contraction of these muscle fibres on blood flow is not clear.

Invertebrate vascular muscle: earthworm blood vessel. Transverse section. Glutaraldehyde fixation. ×64 000.

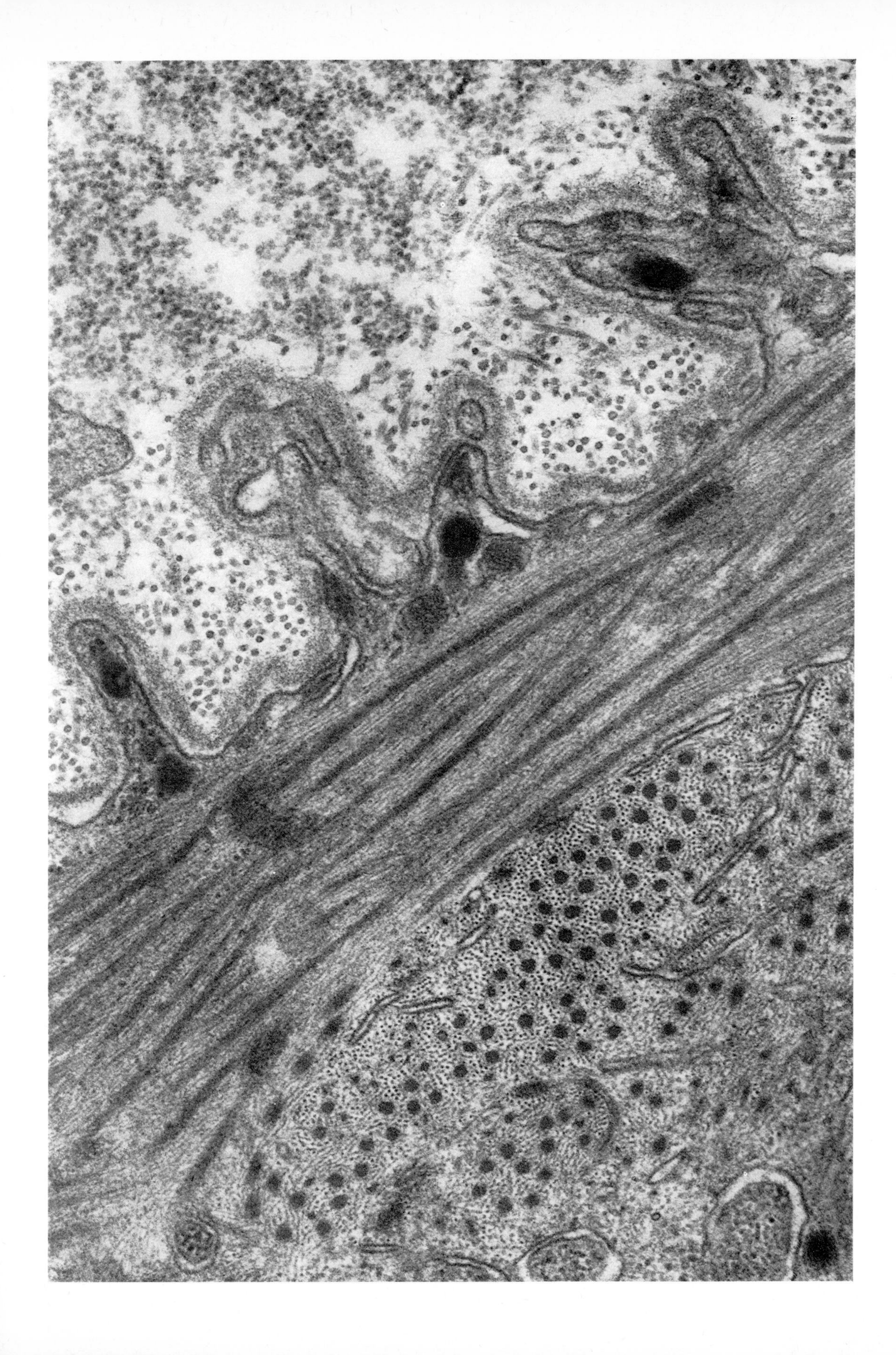

Selected articles

AKESON, A., G. BIÖRCK and R. SIMON. 1968. On the content of myoglobin in human muscles. *Acta med. scand.*, **183,** 307–316.

AL-AMOOD, W. S. and R. POPE. 1972. A comparison of the structural features of muscle fibres from a fast- and a slow-twitch muscle of the pelvic limb of the cat. *J. Anat.*, **113,** 49–60.

ALLEN, E. R. 1973. Sarcomere formation in chick striated muscle. *Z. Zellforsch. mikrosk. Anat.*, **145,** 167–170.

ALVARADO-MALLART, R.-M. 1972. Ultrastructure of muscle fibers of an extraocular muscle of the pigeon. *Tissue & Cell*, **4,** 327–339.

ARONSON, J. 1961. Sarcomere size in developing muscles of a tarsonemid mite. *J. Cell Biol.*, **11,** 147–156.

ARONSON, J. 1962. The elongation of myofibrils from the indirect flight muscle of *Drosophila*. *J. Cell Biol.*, **13,** 33–42.

ARONSON, J. F. 1967. Polarized light observations on striated muscle contraction in a mite. *J. Cell Biol.*, **32,** 169–180.

BERTHRONG, M. and P. GRIFFITH. Ringforms in skeletal muscle *J. Path. Bact.*, **82,** 287–292.

BREEMAN, V. L. VAN. 1952. Myofibril development observed with the electron microscope. *Anat. Rec.*, **113,** 179–186.

BROWN, M. D. 1973. Role of activity in the differentiation of slow and fast muscles. *Nature, Lond.*, **244,** 178–179.

BULLER, A. J. and D. M. LEWIS. 1963. Factors affecting the differentiation of mammalian fast and slow muscle fibers. In *The Effect of Use and Disuse on Neuromuscular Functions*. E. Gutmann and P. Hnik (eds.). Elsevier, Amsterdam. 149–159.

BULLER, A. J., W. F. H. M. MOMMAERTS and K. SERAYDARIAN. 1969. Enzymic properties of myosin in fast and slow twitch muscles of the cat following cross-innervation. *J. Physiol.*, **205,** 581–597.

BURKE, R. E., D. N. LEVINE, P. TSAIRIS and F. E. ZAJAC, III. 1973. Physiological types and histochemical profiles in motor units of the cat gastrocnemius. *J. Physiol., Lond.*, **234,** 732–745.

COHEN, M. J. and A. HESS. 1967. Fine structural differences in 'fast' and 'slow' muscle fibers of the crab. *Am. J. Anat.*, **121,** 285–304.

COOPER, C. C., R. G. CASSENS, L. L. KASTENSCHMIDT and E. J. BRISKEY. 1970. Histochemical characterization of muscle differentiation. *Devl. Biol.*, **2,** 169–184.

COSMOS, E. 1970. Ontogeny of red and white muscles: The enzymic profile and lipid distribution of immature and mature muscles of normal and dystrophic chickens. In *The Physiology and Biochemistry of Muscle as a Food*, Vol. 2. E. J. Briskey, R. G. Cassens and B. B. Marsh (eds.). University of Wisconsin Press, Madison, Wisconsin. 193–209.

EDJTEHADI, G. and D. M. LEWIS. 1974. Structural features of muscle fibres from a fast and a slow twitch muscle in the kitten during postnatal development *J. Anat.* **118,** 253–260.

FAHRENBACH, W. H. 1967. The fine structure of fast and slow crustacean muscles. *J. Cell Biol.*, **35,** 69–79.

FASOLD, M., G. RIEDL and F. JAISLE. 1970. Evidence for an absence of myoglobin from human smooth muscle. *Eur. J. Biochem.*, **15,** 122–126.

FERRANS, V. J. and W. C. ROBERTS. 1973. Intermyofibrillar and nuclear-myofibrillar connections in human and canine myocardium. An ultrastructural study. *J. Mol. & Cell. Cardiol.*, **5,** 247–257.

GARAMVÖLGYI, N. 1972. Slow and fast muscle cells in human striated muscle. *Acta biochim. biophys. Acad. Sci. hung.*, **7,** 165–172.

GAUTHIER, G. F. 1969. On the relationship of ultrastructure and cytochemical features to color in mammalian skeletal muscle. *Z. Zellforsch. mikrosk. Anat.*, **95,** 462–482.

GAUTHIER, G. F. 1970. The ultrastructure of three fiber types in mammalian skeletal muscle. In *The Physiology and Biochemistry of Muscle as a Food*, Vol. 2. E. J. Briskey, R. G. Cassens and B. B. Marsh (eds.). University of Wisconsin Press, Madison, Wisconsin. 103–130.

GAUTHIER, G. F. 1974. Some ultrastructural and cytochemical features of fiber populations in the soleus muscle. *Anat. Rec.*, **180,** 551–565.

GILËV, V. P. 1962. A study of myofibril

sarcomere structure during contraction. *J. Cell Biol.*, **12,** 135–147.

GOLDSPINK, G. 1968. Sarcomere length during post-natal growth of mammalian muscle fibres. *J. Cell Sci.*, **3,** 539–548.

GOLDSPINK, G. 1971. Changes in striated muscle fibres during contraction and growth with particular reference to myofibril splitting. *J. Cell Sci.*, **9,** 123–138.

GOLDSPINK, G. and C. R. SHEAR. 1971. Structural and physiological changes associated with the growth of avian fast and slow muscle. *J. Morph.* **135,** 351–372.

GOLDSPINK, G., J. C. TABARY and G. TARDIEU. 1971. Nature de la rétraction musculaire des I.M.C. Mésure de l'allongement des sarcomères du muscle étiré. *Revue Chir. orthop. repar. Appar. Moteur.*, **57,** 463–470.

GUTH, L., D. H. JEAN, J. B. WELLS and R. W. ALBERS. 1973. Skeletal muscle plasticity. *Anat. Rec.*, **175,** 336.

HAGOPIAN, M. 1970. Contraction bands at short sarcomere length in chick muscle. *J. Cell Biol.*, **47,** 790–795.

HAYWARD, M. and W. G. P. MAIR. 1970. The ultrastructure of ring fibers in dystrophic muscle. *Acta Neuropathol.*, **16,** 161–172.

HEGARTY, P. V. J., K. J. DAHLIN, E. S. BENSON and C. E. ALLEN. 1973. Ultrastructural and light microscope studies on rigor-extended sarcomeres in avian and porcine skeletal muscles. *J. Anat.*, **115,** 203–219.

HEGARTY, P. V. J. and A. C. HOOPER. 1971. Sarcomere length and fibre diameter distributions in four different mouse skeletal muscles. *J. Anat.*, **110,** 249–257.

HESS, A. 1970. Vertebrate slow muscle fibers. *Physiol. Rev.*, **50,** 40–62.

HIKIDA, R. S. 1973. Avian fast and slow muscle: comparison of their ultrastructure, histology, histochemistry and end plates. *Anat. Rec.*, **175,** 344.

HIKIDA, R. S. 1974. Ultrastructure and histochemistry of regenerating fast and slow muscle fibers in pigeons. *Anat. Rec.*, **178,** 375.

HIKIDA, R. S. and W. J. BOCK. 1974. Analysis of fiber types in the pigeon's metapatagialis muscle. I. Histology histochemistry, end plates and ultrastructure. *Tissue & Cell*, **6,** 411–430.

JAHROMI, S. S. and H. L. ATWOOD. 1967. Ultrastructural features of crayfish phasic and tonic muscle fibers. *J. Zool.*, **45,** 601–606.

JAMES, N. T. 1968. Histochemical demonstration of myoglobin in skeletal muscle fibres and muscle spindles. *Nature, Lond.*, **219,** 1174–1175.

JONECKO, A. 1963. Über die quergestreiften Ringbinden der skeletmuskulatur bei Wirbeltieren. *Anat. Anz.*, **113,** 337–356.

KACZMARSKI, F. 1969. The fine structure of extraocular muscles of the lizard *Lacerta agilis* L. *Z. mikrosk.-anat. Forsch.*, **80,** 517–531.

KACZMARSKI, F. 1970*a*. The fine structure of extraocular muscles of the bank vole, *Clethrionomys glareolus* Schr. *Acta Anat.*, **77,** 570–582.

KACZMARSKI, F. 1970*b*. The fine structure of extraocular muscles of the tree sparrow, *Passer montanus* L. *Z. mikrosk.-anat. Forsch.*, **82,** 523–536.

KILARSKI, W. and J. BIGAJ. 1969. Organization and fine structure of extraocular muscles in *Carassius* and *Rana*. *Z. Zellforsch. mikrosk. Anat.*, **94,** 194–204.

LEAK, L. V. 1967. The ultrastructure of myofibers in a reptilian heart: The boa constrictor. *Am. J. Anat.*, **120,** 552–581.

MAIER, A., E. ELDRED and V. R. EDGERTON. 1972. Types of muscles fibers in the extraocular muscles of birds. *Exp. Eye Res.*, **13,** 255–265.

MAYR, R. 1971. Structure and distribution of fibre types in the external eye muscles of the rat. *Tissue & Cell*, **3,** 433–462.

MORITA, S., R. G. CASSENS and E. J. BRISKEY. 1969. Localization of myoglobin in striated muscle of the domestic pig; benzidine and $NADH_2$-TR reactions. *Stain Technol.* **44,** 283–286.

MORITA, S., R. G. CASSENS and E. J. BRISKEY. 1970. Histochemical localization of myoglobin in skeletal muscle of rabbit, pig and ox. *J. Histochem. Cytochem.*, **18,** 364–366.

NAG, A. C. 1972. Ultrastructure and adenosine triphosphatase activity of red and white muscle fibers of the caudal region of a fish, *Salmo gairdneri*. *J. Cell Biol.*, **55,** 42–57.

NAG, A. C. and J. R. NURSALL. 1972.

Histogenesis of white and red muscle fibres of trunk muscles of a fish *Salmo gairdneri*. *Cytobios*, **6,** 227–246.

OGATA, T. 1964. An electron microscopic study on the red, white and intermediate muscle fibers of a mouse. *Acta med., Okayama*, **18,** 271–280.

PAGE, S. G. 1965. A comparison of the fine structure of frog slow and twitch muscle fibres. *J. Cell Biol.*, **26,** 477–497.

PAGE, S. G. 1969. Structure and some contractile properties of fast and slow muscles of the chicken. *J. Physiol., Lond.*, **205,** 131–145.

PATTERSON, S. and G. GOLDSPINK. 1972. The fine structure of red and white myotomal muscle fibres of the coalfish (*Gadus virens*). *Z. Zellforsch. mikrosk. Anat.*, **133,** 463–474.

PEACHEY, L. D. 1966. Fine structure of two fiber types in cat extraocular muscles. *J. Cell Biol.*, **31,** 84A.

PEACHEY, L. D. and A. F. HUXLEY. 1962. Structural identification of twitch and slow striated muscle fibers of the frog. *J. Cell Biol.*, **13,** 177–180.

PEPE, F. A. 1966. Some aspects of the structural organization of the myofibril as revealed by antibody-staining methods. *J. Cell Biol.*, **28,** 505–526.

PILAR, G. and A. HESS. 1966. Differences in internal structure and nerve terminals of the slow and twitch muscle fibers in the cat superior oblique. *Anat. Rec.*, **154,** 243–252.

REGER, J. F. and J. R. HOLBROOK. 1974. The fine structure of tongue muscle of the bat, *Myotis grisescens*, with particular reference to twitch and slow muscle fiber morphology. *Anat. Rec.*, **178,** 445

ROWE, R. W. D. and G. GOLDSPINK. 1969. Muscle fibre growth in five different muscles in both sexes of mice. I. Normal mice. *J. Anat.* **104,** 519–530.

SCHIAFFINO, S., V. HANZLÍKOVÁ and S. PIEROBON. 1970. Relations between structure and function in rat skeletal muscle fibers. *J. Cell Biol.*, **47,** 107–119.

SCHMALBRUCH, H. 1967. Fasertypen in der Unterschenkelmuskulatur der Maus. *Z. Zellforsch. mikrosk. Anat.*, **79,** 64–75.

SCHMALBRUCH, H. 1971. 'Rote' Muskelfasern. *Z. Zellforsch. mikrosk. Anat.*, **119,** 120–146.

SCHOTLAND, D. L., D. SPIRO and P. CARMEL. 1966. Ultrastructural studies of ring fibers in human muscle disease. *J. Neuropath. exp. Neurol.*, **25,** 431–442.

SEIDEN, D. 1971. Slow muscle fibers in the tensor tympani muscle of the guinea pig. *Am. J. Anat.*, **132,** 267–274.

SHAFIQ, S. A. 1963*a*. Electronmicroscopic studies on the indirect flight muscles of *Drosophila melanogaster*. I. Structure of the myofibrils. *J. Cell Biol.*, **17,** 351–362.

SHAFIQ, S. A. 1963*b*. Electronmicroscopic studies on the indirect flight muscles of *Drosophila melanogaster*. II. Differentiation of myofibrils. *J. Cell Biol.*, **17,** 363–374.

SHAFIQ, S. A., M. GORYCKI, L. GOLDSTONE and A. T. MILHORAT. 1966. Fine structure of fiber types in normal human muscle. *Anat. Rec.*, **156,** 283–301.

SHAFIQ, S. A., M. A. GORYCKI and A. T. MILHORAT. 1969. An electron microscope study of fibre types in normal and dystrophic muscles of the mouse. *J. Anat.*, **104,** 281–293.

SHEAR, C. R. 1973. An ultrastructural study of fiber type in tortoise skeletal muscle. *Anat. Rec.*, **175,** 440.

SMITH, D. S. 1963. The structure of flight muscle sarcosomes in the blowfly *Calliphora erythrocephala* (Diptera). *J. Cell Biol.*, **19,** 115–138.

SMITH, J. R. 1964. Observations of the ultrastructure of the myocardium of the common lobster (*Homarus americanus*), especially of the myofibrils. *Anat. Rec.*, **145,** 391–400.

SMITH, R. S. and W. K. OVALLE JR. 1973. Varieties of fast and slow extrafusal fibres in amphibian hind limb muscles. *J. Anat.*, **116,** 1–24.

STEPHENS, R. E. 1965. Analysis of muscle contraction by ultraviolet microbeam disruption of sarcomere structure *J. Cell Biol.*, **25,** 129–140.

SYROVY, I. and E. GUTMANN. 1967. Metabolic differentiation of the anterior and posterior *latissimus dorsi* of the chick during development. *Nature, Lond.*, **213,** 937–939.

TABARY, J. C., C. TABARY, C. TARDIEU, G. TARDIEU and G. GOLDSPINK. 1972. Physiological and structural changes in the cat's soleus muscle due to immobilization at different lengths by plaster casts. *J. Physiol., Lond.*, **224,** 231–244.

TICE, L. W. and R. J. BARRNETT. 1962. Fine structural localization of adenosinetriphosphatase activity in heart muscle myofibrils. *J. Cell Biol.*, **15,** 401–416.

TICE, L. W. and D. S. SMITH. 1965. The localization of myofibrillar ATPase activity in the flight muscles of the blowfly, *Calliphora erythrocephala*. *J. Cell Biol.*, **25,** 121–136.

TOMANEK, R. J., C. R. ASMUNDSON, R. R. COOPER and R. J. BARNARD. 1973. Fine structure of fast-twitch and slow-twitch guinea pig muscle fibers. *J. Morph.*, **139,** 47–66.

TOMANEK, R. J. and R. R. COOPER. 1973. Ultrastructural changes in various twitch muscle fibers after disuse or denervation. *Anat. Rec.*, **175,** 457.

WILLIAMS, P. E. and G. GOLDSPINK. 1971. Longitudinal growth of striated muscle fibres. *J. Cell Sci.*, **9,** 751–768.

WITTENBERG, J. B. 1970. Myoglobin facilitated oxygen diffusion: role of myoglobin in oxygen entry into muscle. *Physiol. Rev.*, **50,** 559–636.

C Myofilaments

Vertebrate striated muscle

The characteristic banding pattern of vertebrate striated muscle is a manifestation of the organized arrangement of *thick filaments containing myosin* (*called from now on myosin filaments*) and *thin filaments containing actin* (*called from now on actin filaments*) (Fig. 5). In transverse section, myosin filaments are arranged in a regular

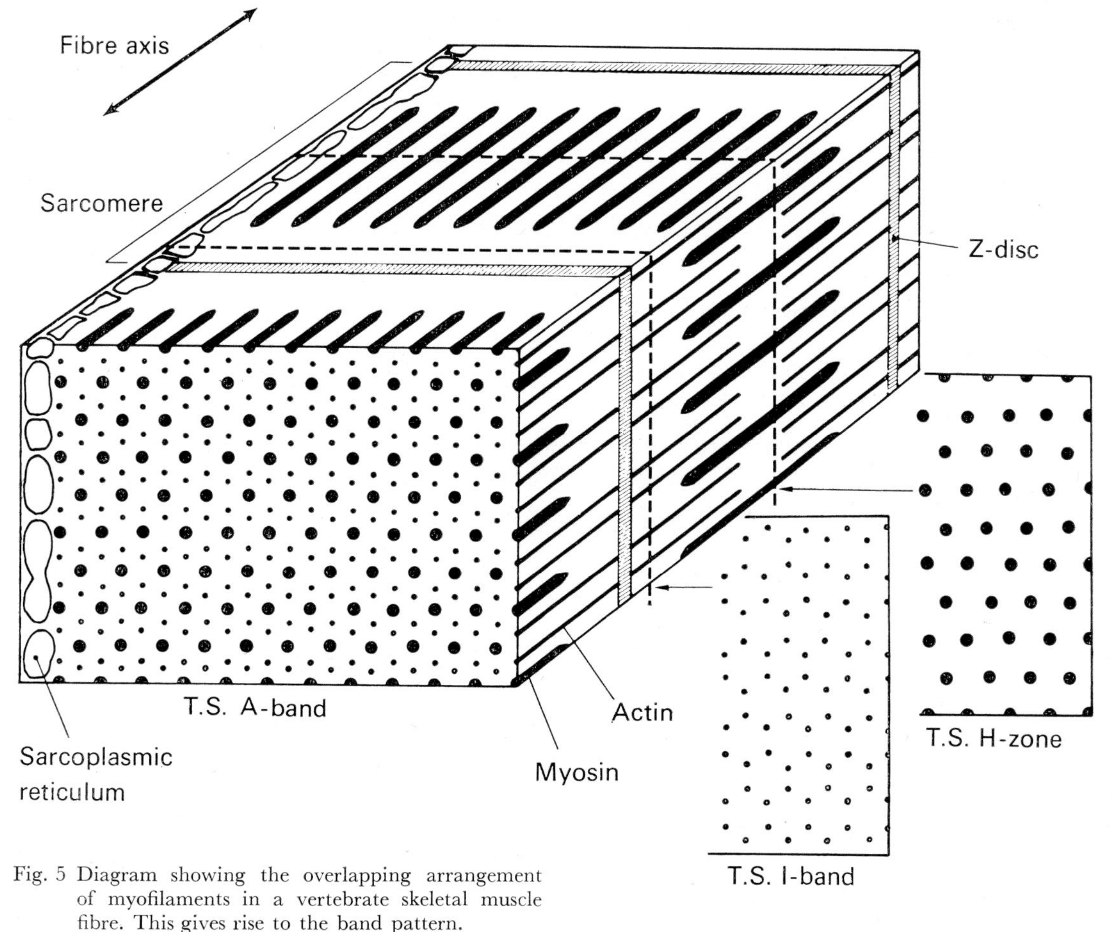

Fig. 5 Diagram showing the overlapping arrangement of myofilaments in a vertebrate skeletal muscle fibre. This gives rise to the band pattern.

hexagonal pattern, each filament being surrounded by six thin actin filaments. The actin filaments attach to the *Z-disc* (also called *Z-line* or *Z-band*) and pass longitudinally towards other actin filaments across the sarcomere. The myosin filaments lie in the centre of the sarcomeres forming the *A-bands* and are not associated with the Z-discs. The *I-band* contains only actin filaments, the *H-zone* only myosin filaments, and the A-band to either side of the H-zone a mixture of both.

Myosin filaments are 12–15 nm in diameter and about 1.6 μm in length, although the length varies slightly in different muscles. Their diameter is greatest in the central region (the region of the M-band where cross-connections between these filaments are present in some

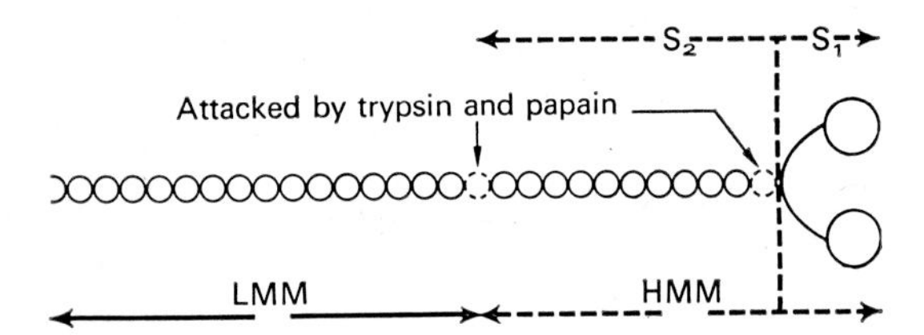

Fig. 6 Model of myosin molecule. (After Lowey, S., H. S. Slater, A. G. Weeds and H. Baker, 1969, *J. molec. Biol.*, **42,** 8.)

striated muscles) and they taper towards their ends. Projections or *cross-bridges of myosin* 5 nm in diameter pass from the thick filaments to the actin filaments at regular intervals of about 43 nm along their length. X-ray diffraction studies have suggested that projections (or cross-bridges) occur on opposite sides of the filaments forming pairs at 14.3 nm intervals, and that each pair is rotated 120° with respect to its neighbour along the filament. In this way a row of cross-bridges along the myosin filaments is directed towards each of the surrounding six actin filaments. The cross-bridges are composed of the enzymatically active part of the myosin molecule and it is the interaction of these cross-bridges with actin that leads to contraction. Myosin molecules of vertebrate striated muscle are rod-shaped, 2 nm in diameter by 150 nm in length and have two globular 'heads' about 10 nm long. Each molecule consists of two linked identical polypeptide chains formed of *light meromyosin* (LMM) and *heavy meromyosin* (HMM). The HMM comprises the *heads* (called HMM-S-1) and part of the *rod* (called HMM-S-2), and the LMM the long helical tail (Fig.6). The thick myosin filaments in vertebrate striated muscle are composed of a backbone of LMM with the HMM-S-1 particles projecting outwards (Fig. 7). However, the number of myosin molecules per cross-bridge has not been resolved and reports vary from 1–6.

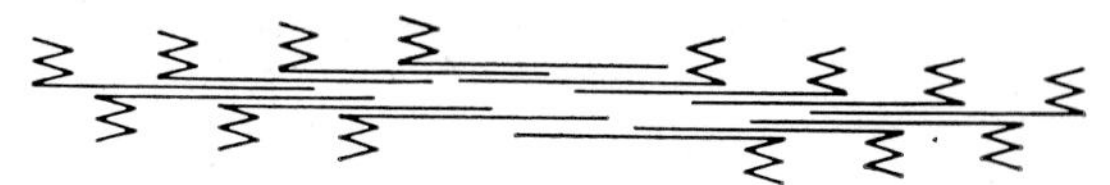

Fig. 7 Diagrammatic representation of arrangement of myosin molecules in thick filaments. (Courtesy of H. E. Huxley, 1972. In *The Structure and Function of Muscle*, Vol. 1, G. H. Bourne (ed.), 351.)

Actin filaments are 5–7 nm in diameter and about 1 μm long. These filaments consist of two chains of globular units wound around each other in a double helix. Each chain has a subunit repeat of 5.46 nm and a helical repeat of 70–75 nm and consists of three components, *G actin*, *tropomyosin* and *troponin-complex*. The latter two components are involved in the regulation by Ca^{2+} of the interaction between actin and myosin during contraction. The model which has been proposed for the structure of the thin filament is as follows: the main component is G actin (5 nm diameter approximately), which is in the form of a chain, *F actin;* two of these F-actin chains are wound around each other to form a two-stranded helix; this leaves two pronounced grooves in which are found the rod-shaped tropomyosin molecules (40 × 2 nm); one molecule of the troponin-complex binds to one molecule of tropomyosin with a periodicity of 40 nm to complete the filament (Fig. 8).

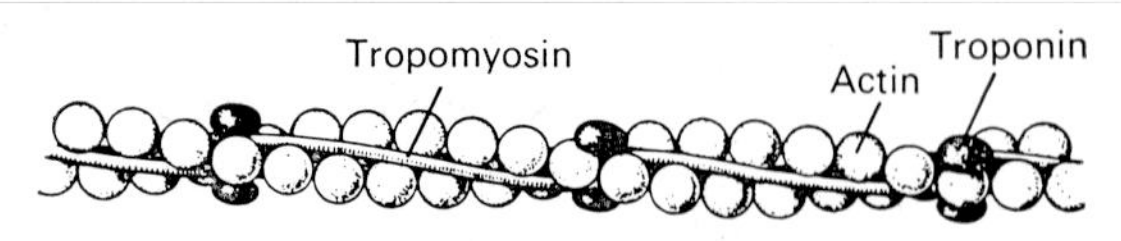

Fig. 8 Model of thin filament. (Courtesy Ebashi, S., M. Endo and I. Ohtsuki, 1969, *Quart. Rev. Biophysics*, **2,** 351.)

A number of other structural proteins have also been isolated from vertebrate striated muscle; these are *α-actinin*, *β-actinin*, *M-protein* and *C-protein*. α-actinin has been found in the

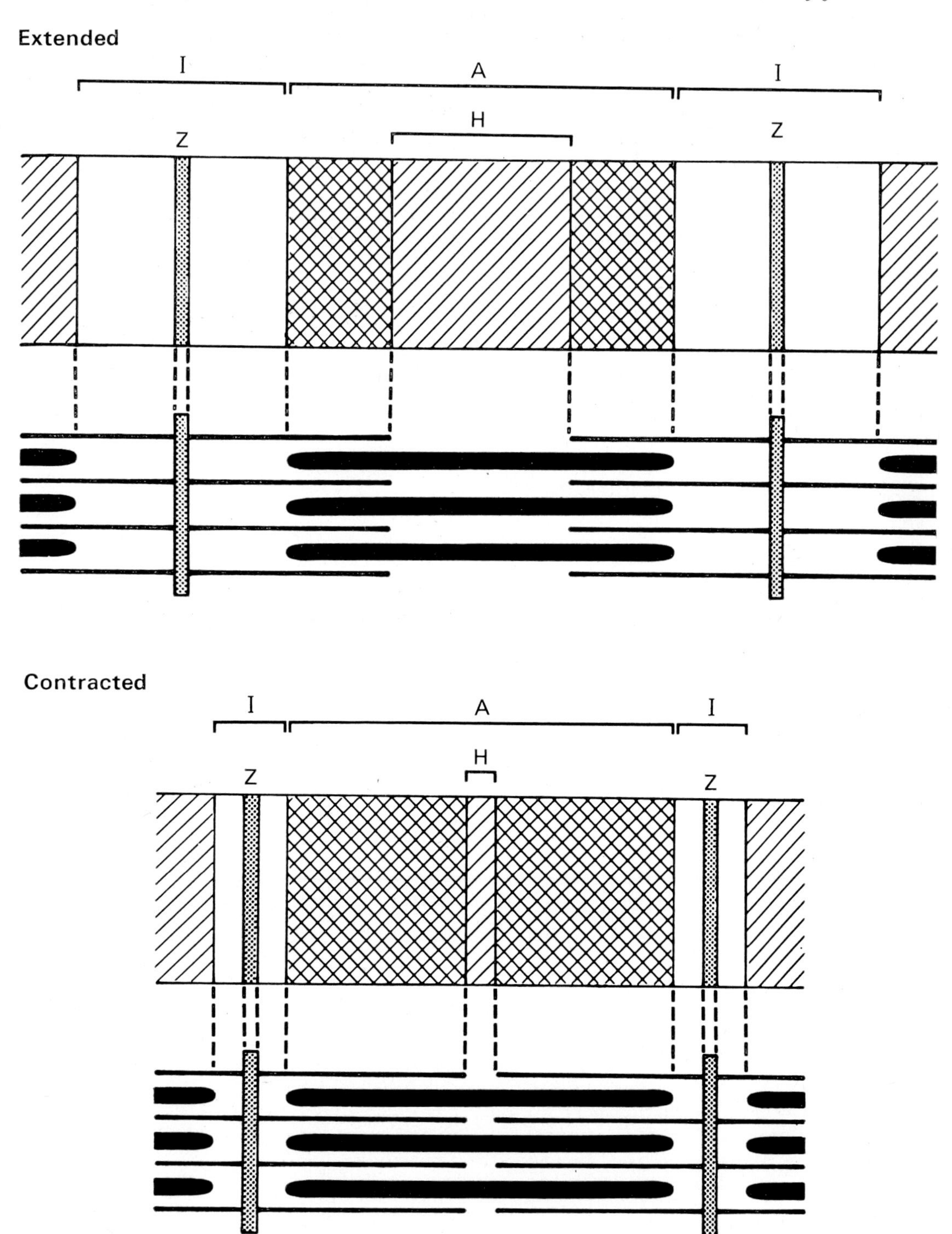

Fig. 9 Diagram representing the 'sliding-filament hypothesis'. This explains the change in appearance of cross striations in a striated muscle fibre at different phases of contraction.

Z-disc, β-actinin at the M-line and C-protein on the thick filaments.

Although there are a number of theories about the mechanism of contraction of vertebrate striated muscle, the most widely accepted is the 'sliding-filament hypothesis'. Under a range of different contraction conditions the A-band remains a constant length, while the length of the I-band changes (Fig. 9). The conclusion from this is that when the muscle contracts or relaxes the myosin and actin filaments slide past each other. Complex interactions of the myosin cross-bridges and actin filaments are involved in this process. The energy for these is provided by the dephosphorylation of adenosine triphosphate (ATP) to adenosine diphosphate (ADP).

Tropomyosin and the troponin-complex (so called because it has three known components) are called the *regulatory proteins* of striated muscle. The contraction-relaxation cycle of striated muscle is controlled by changes in the concentration of Ca^{2+}. At the resting intracellular Ca^{2+} concentration, troponin, through tropomyosin, exerts an effect which prevents the actin subunits from interacting with myosin. On excitation, Ca^{2+} enters the myofibril (see Chapter 2E) and binds to one of the troponin components. This results in a structural change of the actin-tropomyosin complex which releases the inhibition of the acto-myosin interaction and hence sliding and muscle shortening can occur.

Invertebrate striated muscle

Invertebrate striated muscle fibres show a similar banding pattern to vertebrate muscle. This pattern is produced by an essentially similar organization of two kinds of myofilaments: thin myofilaments containing actin, and thick myofilaments containing myosin. However, a number of variations of these basic elements exist both between vertebrate and invertebrate muscle and between different invertebrate groups. One of the most striking variations is the number and arrangement of thick and thin filaments in the A-band. In vertebrate striated muscle, as mentioned above, each thick filament is surrounded by six thin filaments. However, in invertebrate muscles, although the arrangement of thick filaments still remains the same, they are surrounded by different numbers of thin filaments, depending on the muscle. In insect flight muscles for example, there are 6 thin filaments surrounding each thick filament (see Plate 33) while some muscles of spiders and millipedes have as many as 12 thin filaments about each thick filament (see Plate 35 and Fig. 10).

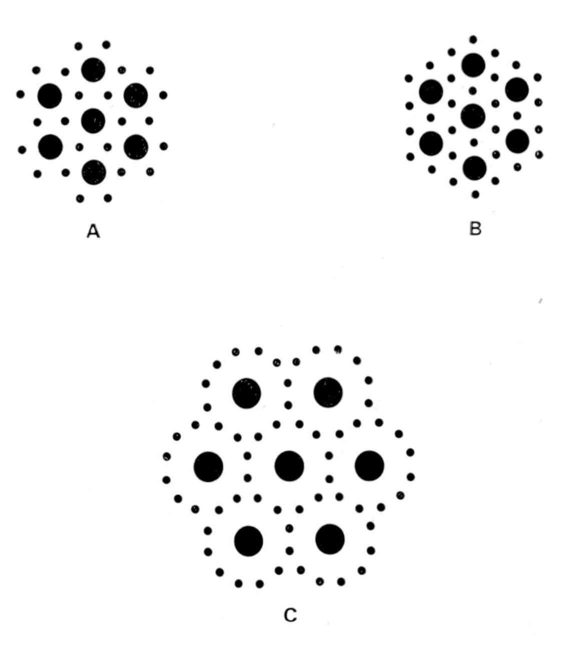

Fig. 10 Diagrammatic representation of the arrangement of thick and thin myofilaments in the lateral A-band region. **A,** Vertebrate skeletal muscle. **B,** Insect flight muscle. **C,** Spider leg muscle. (Adapted from Toselli, P. A. and F. A. Pepe, 1968, *J. Cell., Biol.*, **37,** 445.)

Many other variations exist between invertebrate striated muscles, including: (*a*) a variation in A-band and both thick and thin filament lengths. For example in arthropod muscles, there is up to 25% length difference in the A-bands belonging to the same fibre; (*b*) individual thick filaments of barnacle giant muscle fibres have thin (11 nm) hollow regions alternating with thick (34 nm) solid regions throughout their length and cross-connections occur between these thick filaments apparently randomly and are not concentrated at the M-band; (*c*) asynchronous flight muscles are found in bees, wasps, flies, mosquitoes, beetles, and some bugs, and are so called because the contraction frequency of the fibre exceeds that of the motor nerve impulses reaching the muscle. In these muscle fibres, unlike vertebrate muscle, the thick myosin filaments are tubular and in blowfly flight muscle they have tapered ends which extend into the Z-disc (see Fig. 11).

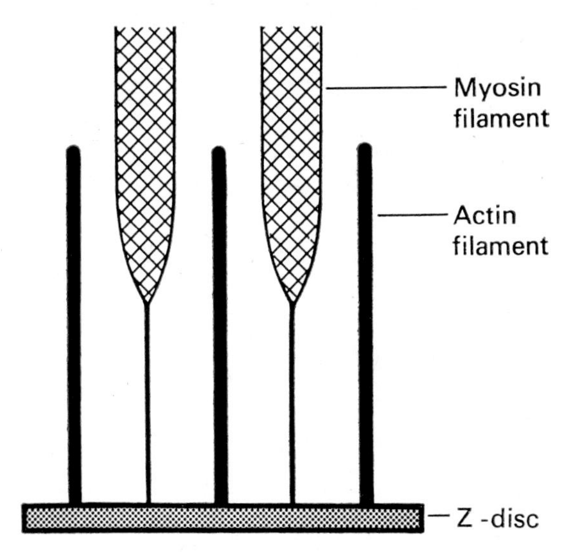

Fig. 11 Connection between myosin filaments and Z-disc in blowfly flight muscle. (Modified from Auber, J. and R. Couteaux, 1963, *J. Microsc.* (*Fr.*), **2,** 316.)

The synchronous flight muscles of insects however, are very similar to vertebrate striated muscles with the thick filaments ending at the edge of the I-band; (*d*) another interesting phenomenon in some invertebrate muscles is the process of *supercontraction.* This is the contraction of striated muscle below half of the rest-length, in some cases reversibly down to one sixth. These muscles are apparently able to achieve this enormous degree of contraction by alterations in their Z-disc structure, which allow the thick filaments to pass from one sarcomere to another.

Obliquely striated muscle resembles vertebrate striated muscle fibres in several respects: both contain two interdigitating myofilament types arranged in an ordered fashion and both exhibit sliding of thin filaments towards the centre of the sarcomere on muscle contraction. That is to say the 'sliding-filament theory' still applies to this situation. However, a number of differences between the two exist. Obliquely striated muscle cells usually resemble vertebrate smooth muscle in both size and shape, and, unlike vertebrate striated muscle whose striations run perpendicular to the axis of the muscle fibre, those of obliquely striated muscle run obliquely to the axis of the fibre (see Fig. 12.) The thin filaments are similar to the actin filaments of vertebrate striated muscle. However, the thick filaments are usually much thicker, consist of paramyosin as well as myosin and in all cases taper towards the tips. Cross-bridges can be often seen between the thick and the thin filaments in longitudinal section.

Invertebrate smooth muscle

Of all invertebrate smooth muscle, the anterior byssus retractor muscle of the mussel has been the most widely studied. This muscle is composed of spindle shaped cells with single nuclei, approximately 4–4.5 μm in diameter and 1.6 mm in length. No banding pattern has been observed with the light or electron microscope. Two types of myofilaments, thick and thin, are again present in these muscle cells with a ratio of about 1:17 respectively. The thick myofilaments vary in diameter from 10–75 nm, (by virtue of the fact that they are tapered at their ends like most paramyosin-containing filaments), their diameter in the centre being 65–75 nm. Their length is usually about 25 μm but can be up to 30 μm. These thick filaments are thought to be composed of a paramyosin core with myosin located on the outside. Cross-bridges between thick and thin filaments have been observed by some workers. The thin myofilaments are 5 nm in diameter by an average length of 11 μm and are packed in a regular 'actin lattice'. They are often attached to amorphous electron-dense structures 0.3–1 μm long and 0.1–0.3 μm wide. These structures, often called 'dense bodies', are uniformly distributed throughout the muscle. Molluscan thin filaments contain only actin and tropomyosin; troponin being absent. This is an interesting situation, because it is the troponin of vertebrate actin filaments which binds Ca^{2+}, thereby initiating contraction. One might expect Ca^{2+}, therefore, to have little effect upon this molluscan muscle. However, the reverse is the case, since it has been shown that Ca^{2+} is essential to the regulatory mechanism. These

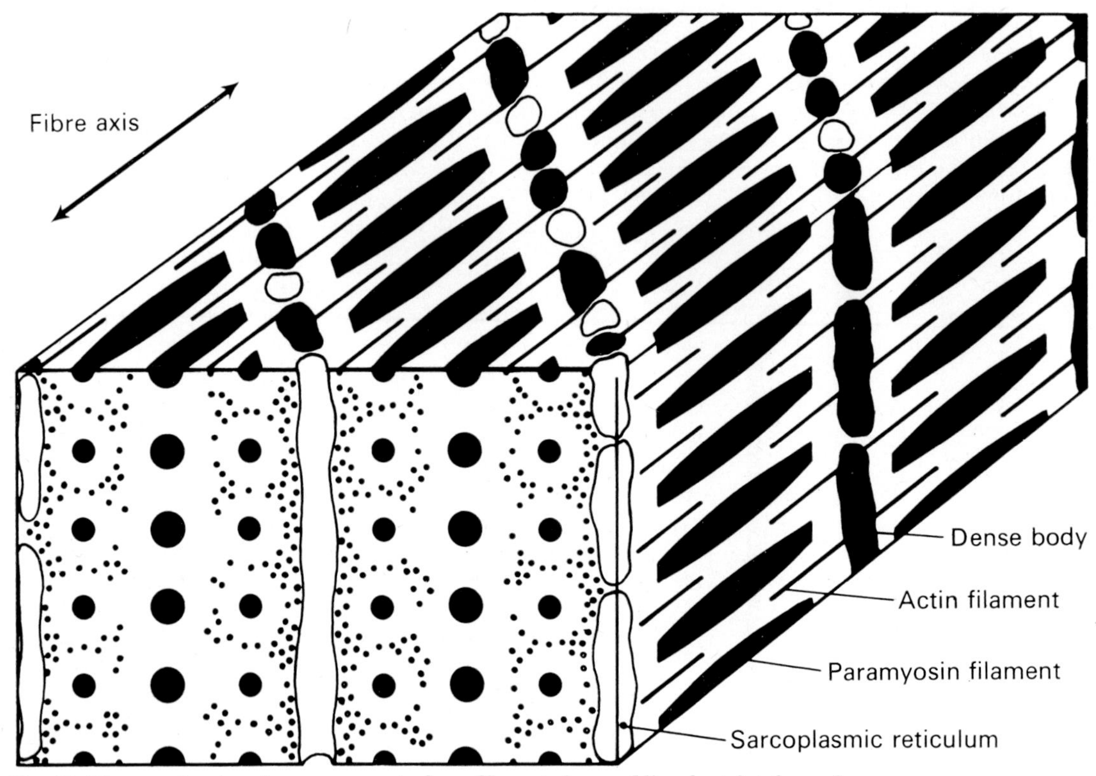

Fig. 12 Diagram showing the arrangement of myofilaments in an obliquely striated muscle.

muscles appear to have a myosin-like regulatory system. Thus, in molluscan muscles such as anterior byssus retractor muscle (ABRM), Ca^{2+} triggers contraction by interacting with myosin of the thick myofilaments, whereas in vertebrates and arthropod striated muscle, Ca^{2+} reacts with components of the thin actin filaments. It has been suggested that this myosin-linked regulatory system is also involved in the 'catch' mechanism of the ABRM. The ABRM is an example of a type of muscle which can perform two distinct types of contraction. One is a phasic contraction that relaxes after cessation of stimulation and the second is known as *catch* in which the contraction continues long after stimulation has ended. A high level of intracellular Ca^{2+} is present during 'catch', a reduction of which causes relaxation.

Vertebrate smooth muscle

Vertebrate smooth muscle contains similar contractile proteins to striated muscle, namely: myosin, actin, tropomyosin and troponin. However, apart from actin which appears to be similar in all vertebrate muscle types, variations exist in these proteins between the two muscle types. For example, tropomyosin not only has a different amino acid composition, but is found in larger amounts in smooth than in striated muscle. Troponin has only recently been isolated and it also varies slightly from that of striated muscle. Myosin, although its overall substructure does not differ from that of skeletal and cardiac myosin, has differing properties. For example, smooth muscle myosin has a different salting-out range from skeletal muscle myosin (i.e. the myosin precipitates in the presence of different concentrations of salts from that of skeletal muscle) and the globular head of smooth muscle myosin has a different ATPase activity from that of skeletal muscle.

Although both thick and thin myofilaments have been demonstrated ultrastructurally, these thick filaments are extremely labile. So labile in fact, that some workers still maintain they do not exist *in vivo*. Their argument is based on two facts. (1) Thick filaments can be made to appear prominently in vertebrate smooth muscle under a number of unphysiological conditions, such as soaking in Ringer solution for 24 hours (see Plate 43), by the action of trypsin (see Plate 45) or when treated with urea. (2) Small changes in equilibrium or fixation procedures, such as the alteration of temperature or ion concentrations can affect the electron microscopic appearance of thick filaments.

However, X-ray diffraction studies of living guinea-pig taenia coli muscle have shown a reflection on the meridian with a spacing of 14.3 nm; this is identical to that displayed by myosin in vertebrate striated muscle. These X-ray studies suggest that smooth muscle myosin is in the form of filaments orientated approximately parallel to the fibre axis. In preparations of filaments from purified smooth muscle myosin, cross-bridges have been identified, but, unlike those of myosin filaments in skeletal muscle, they are present along the entire length and there is no central bare zone.

Thick filaments have been reported in vertebrate smooth muscle cells for a number of years, but vary in size, shape and total number and these are not always reproducible. Recently however, thick filaments in smooth muscle cells have been consistently produced by fixing while bathed in an oxygenated Krebs-Ringer solution or after incubation in a hypertonic medium and/or rather high degrees of stretch for prolonged periods. However, two types of filament, *round* (12–16 nm in diameter) and *ribbon* shaped (8–10 nm by 20–110 nm in cross section) respectively, can be produced depending upon the methods of preparation. These differences arise because of the difficulty in preserving the contractile apparatus in vertebrate smooth muscle and the form of thick filaments *in vivo* is still not clear.

Thin filaments, 6–8 nm in diameter and resembling the actin-containing filaments of striated muscle are also found in vertebrate smooth muscle. Under certain conditions, these filaments appear in organized arrays with thick filaments suggesting that the sliding-filament mechanism of contraction may also apply in this muscle. The thick filaments form a fairly regular lattice with a spacing of 40–70 nm and the interstices contain arrays of thin filaments. The ratio of thick to thin filaments is about 1:11–15.

Various approaches are being used to gain more information about smooth muscle contractile proteins, including: investigations of the assembly properties of structural proteins of smooth muscle such as myosin, actin, tropomyosin and troponin; freeze-etch studies of unfixed material; and studies of isolated smooth muscle cells. Of these, the latter may prove to be the most fruitful since an organized myofibrillar pattern in isolated smooth muscle cells has been demonstrated under the light microscope.

Plate 28

The sarcomere is divided into a number of regions. The denser, more birefringent region is known as the *A (anisotropic)-band* (A) spanned by the thick myosin filaments (10–12 nm in diameter). This is separated from the *Z-disc* (Z) by a region of lower density and birefringence, the *I (isotropic)-bands* (I) composed of thin filaments (5–7 nm in diameter). The central region of the A-band contains a slightly less dense region, the *H-zone* (H) where there is no overlap between thick and thin filaments. The narrow dense line in the centre of this zone is called the *M-line* (M), and is usually flanked on either side by a slightly less dense band than the rest of the H-zone.

Myofilament arrangement in vertebrate skeletal muscle sarcomere: goldfish flexor pinnae pectoralis. Longitudinal section. Glutaraldehyde fixation. ×76 000.

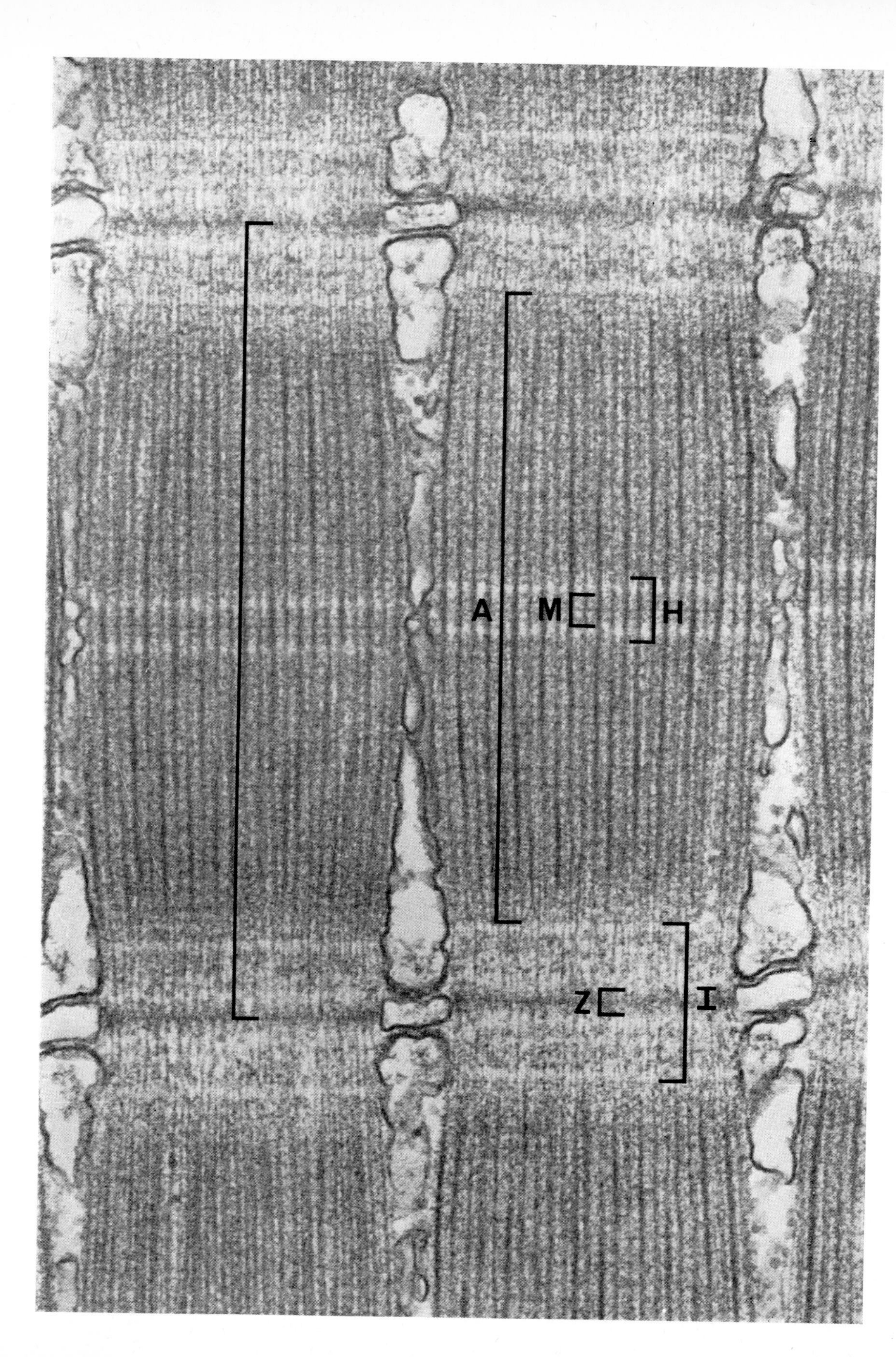
A
M
H
Z
I

Plate 29

The appearance and arrangement of myofilaments varies in transverse sections through different regions of the sarcomere.

Thick myosin filaments are the only myofilaments present in the M-line. These filaments are in a hexagonal array and bridges can be clearly seen in the space between them, i.e. each thick filament is surrounded by six others, symmetrically arranged as if at the corners of a hexagon. In the region of the A-band two types of myofilaments can be seen, thick filaments and thin actin filaments. These are arranged in a double hexagonal array, with each thick filament surrounded by six thin filaments (see Fig. 10, p. 86).

The framework of the M-line consists of a number of arrays of transverse M-bridges 20 nm apart, connecting each A filament with its six neighbours. M filaments, parallel to the A filaments, pass through the M-line and link each set of M-bridges together. It has been suggested that the function of the M-line is similar to that of the Z-disc in maintaining the spacial relationship of myofilaments.

Myofilaments in vertebrate skeletal muscle: goldfish flexor pinnae pectoralis muscle. Transverse section through the A-band and M-line. Glutaraldehyde fixation. × 238 000.

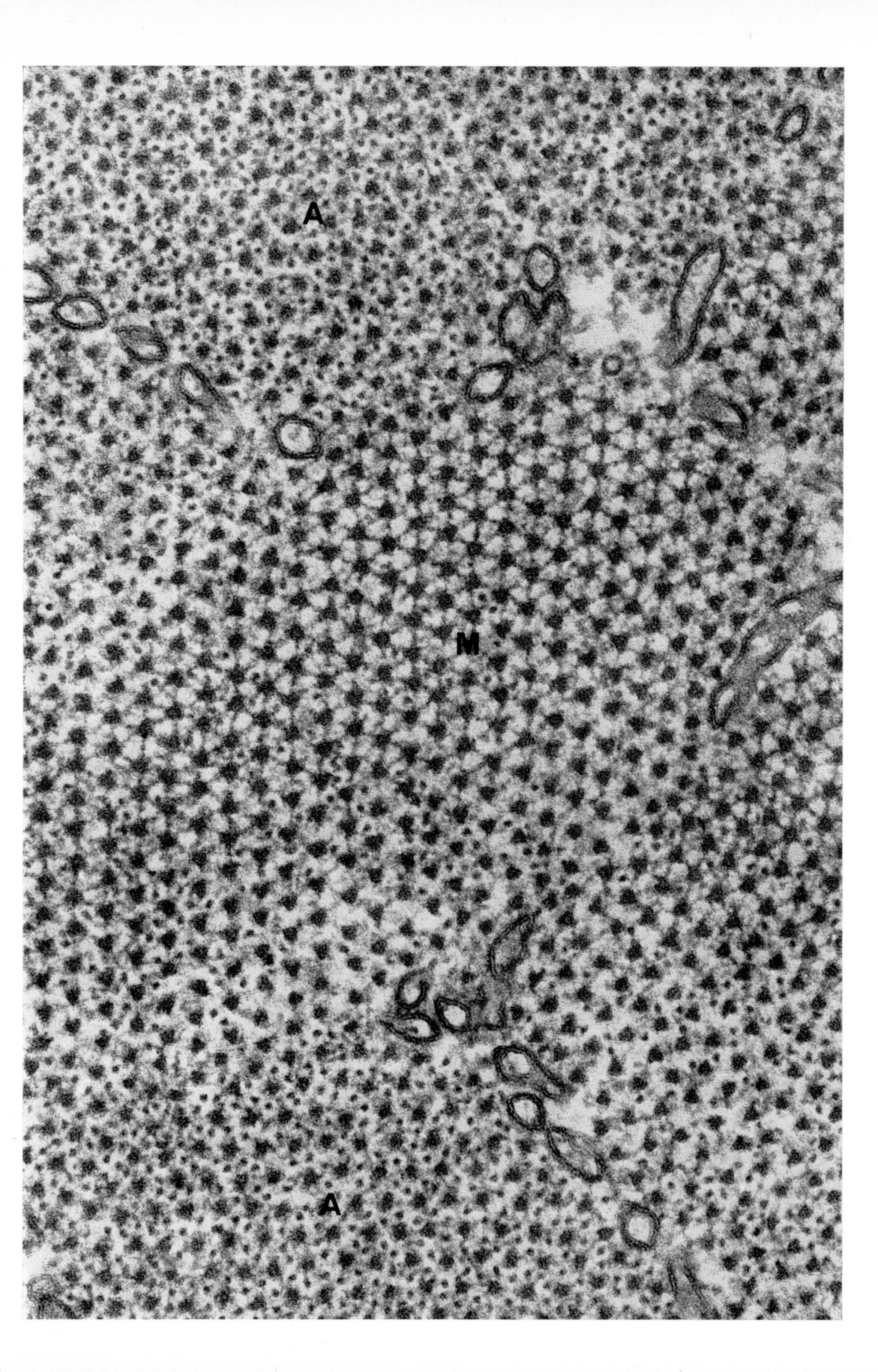
A
M
A

Plate 30

When observed in longitudinal section, the Z-disc of fish skeletal muscle appears as a zig-zag filamentous structure 40–50 nm in width.

Two models have been developed concerning the form of the Z-disc. The first involves individual I filaments from the sarcomere obliquely linked to two or more I filaments of the adjacent sarcomere by slender 'Z filaments'. This can be most easily visualized in the simple Z-disc of the fish.

Z-discs of most mammalian skeletal muscle are more complex. White fibres have the thinnest Z-discs, red fibres the thickest with intermediate fibres between (see Chapter 2B for definition of muscle fibre types). Their structure can be most easily visualized by the second model which proposes that the Z-disc is composed of filamentous loops which arise from each thin filament and join these thin filaments to adjacent filaments from the same sarcomere. This model proposes that in white skeletal muscle fibres all the loops on one side of the Z-disc are in the same plane, whereas in red and intermediate fibres the loops are in three and two planes respectively. (See Fig. 13, p. 96).

Z-disc in vertebrate skeletal muscle: goldfish flexor pinnae pectoralis muscle. Longitudinal section. Glutaraldehyde fixation. ×127 000.

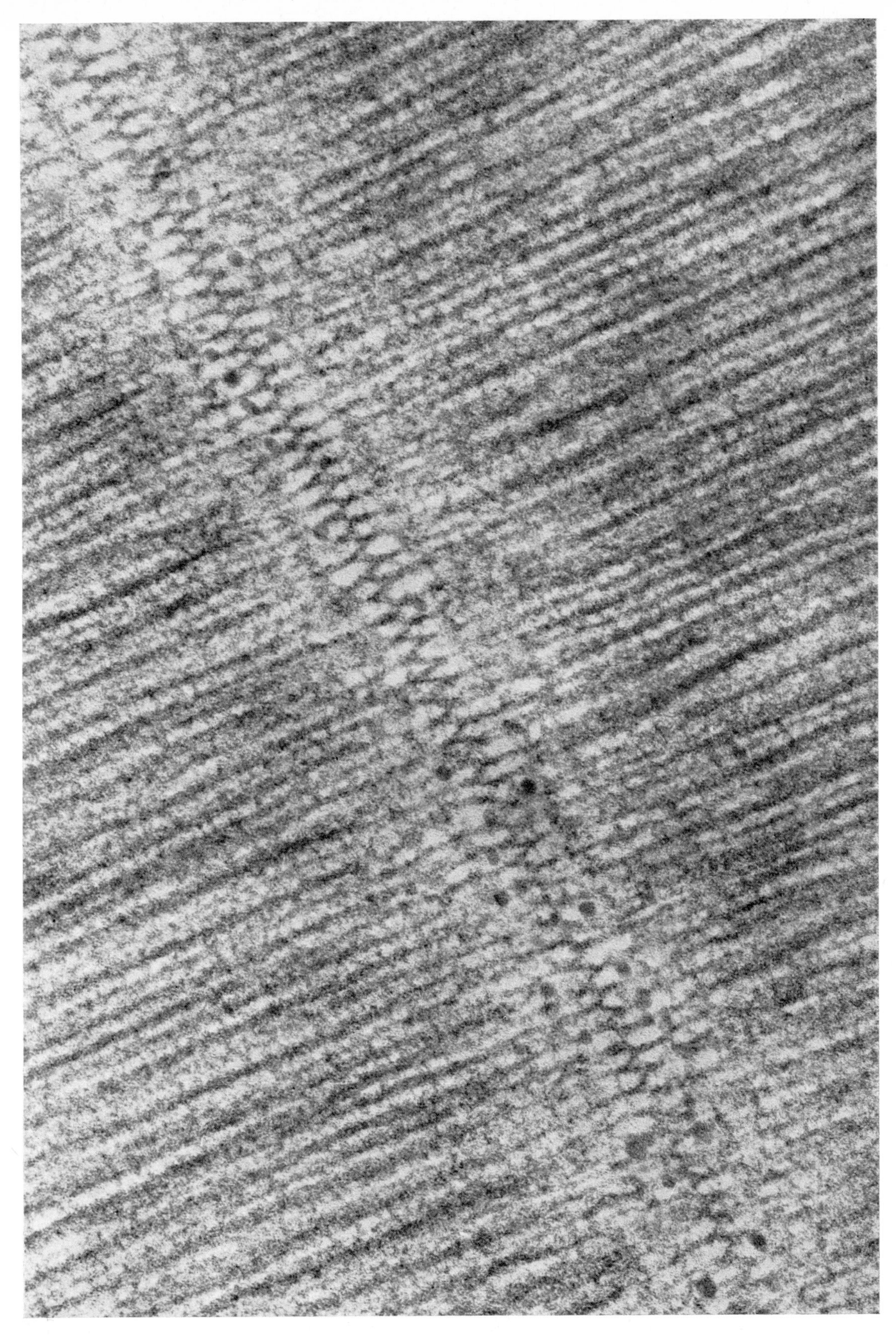

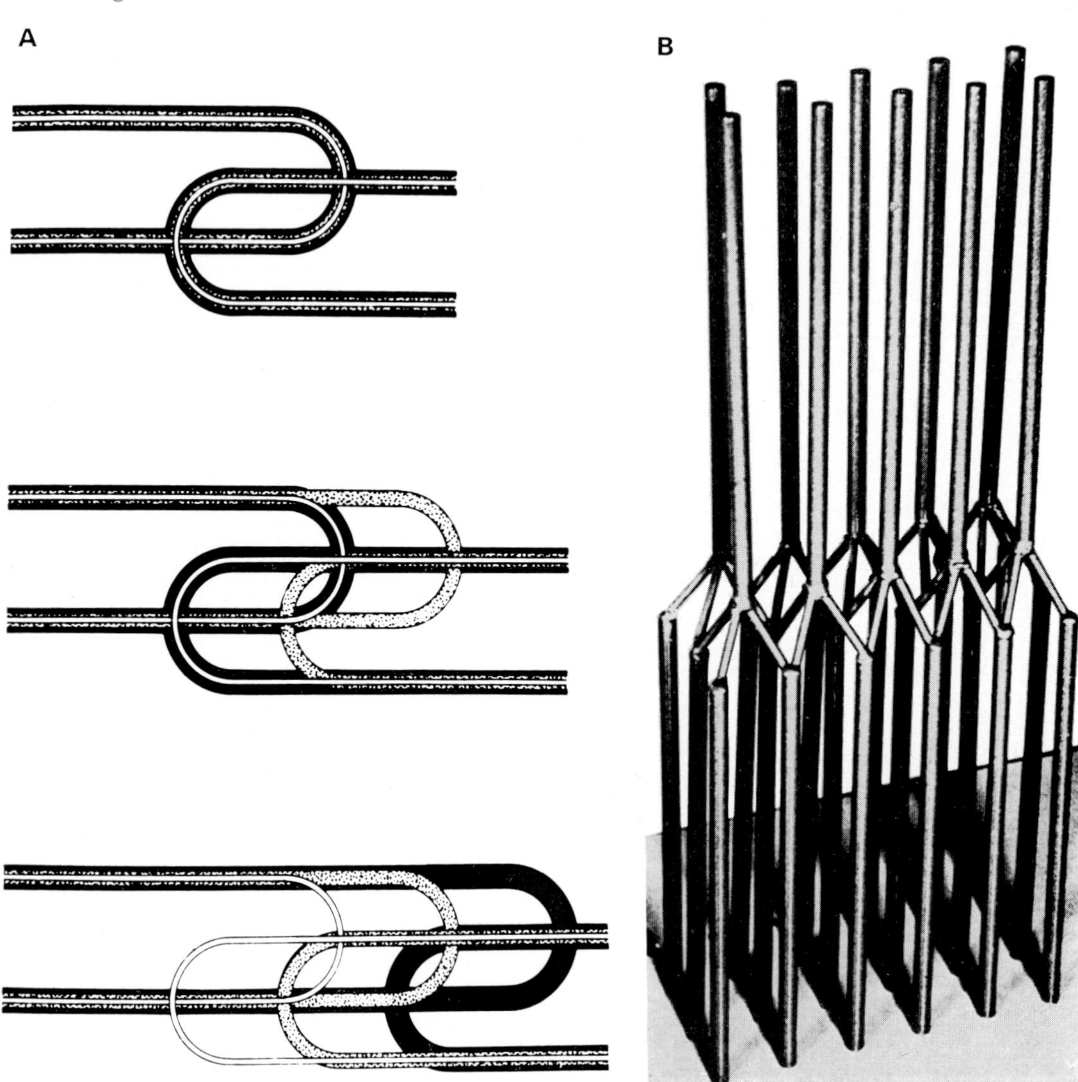

Fig. 13

A Diagrammatic representation of a model of the Z-disc, demonstrating its appearance in longitudinal section. Shading indicates different filament loops. White fibre Z-discs have all the loops on the same plane (upper diagram); loops of intermediate fibre Z-discs exist on one of two planes (middle diagram); loops of red fibre Z-discs exist on one of three planes (lower diagram). (Courtesy Rowe, R. W. D., 1973, *J. Cell Biol.*, **57,** 261.)

B A 3-dimensional representation of another model of the Z-disc of skeletal muscle. This model was gained by tilting the Z-disc in an electron microscope fitted with a goniometer stage. (Courtesy of Katchburian, E., A. M. C. Burgess and F. R. Johnson, 1973, *Experienta*, **29,** 1020.)

Plate 31

When seen in transverse section, the Z-disc (Z) appears as a square lattice with a spacing of about 22 nm, or as a square lattice with an 11 nm spacing, or as a rectangular woven lattice with a 15.5 nm spacing with its axes offset 45° from the axes of lateral alignment of the thin actin filament files in the adjacent I-band, prior to their entry into the disc. The I-band (I) appears as a group of filaments 5–7 nm in diameter, sometimes in a regular square array and sometimes irregularly placed. Two lines called the *N lines* cross the I-band (although these are not shown in the accompanying micrograph). The N1 line is closer to the Z-disc and the filaments in this area are in a square array. At the N2 line, the filaments are in closely spaced clusters and are often separated by glycogen granules.

Z-disc in vertebrate skeletal muscle: rat rectus femoris muscle. Transverse section. Glutaraldehyde fixation. ×100 000.

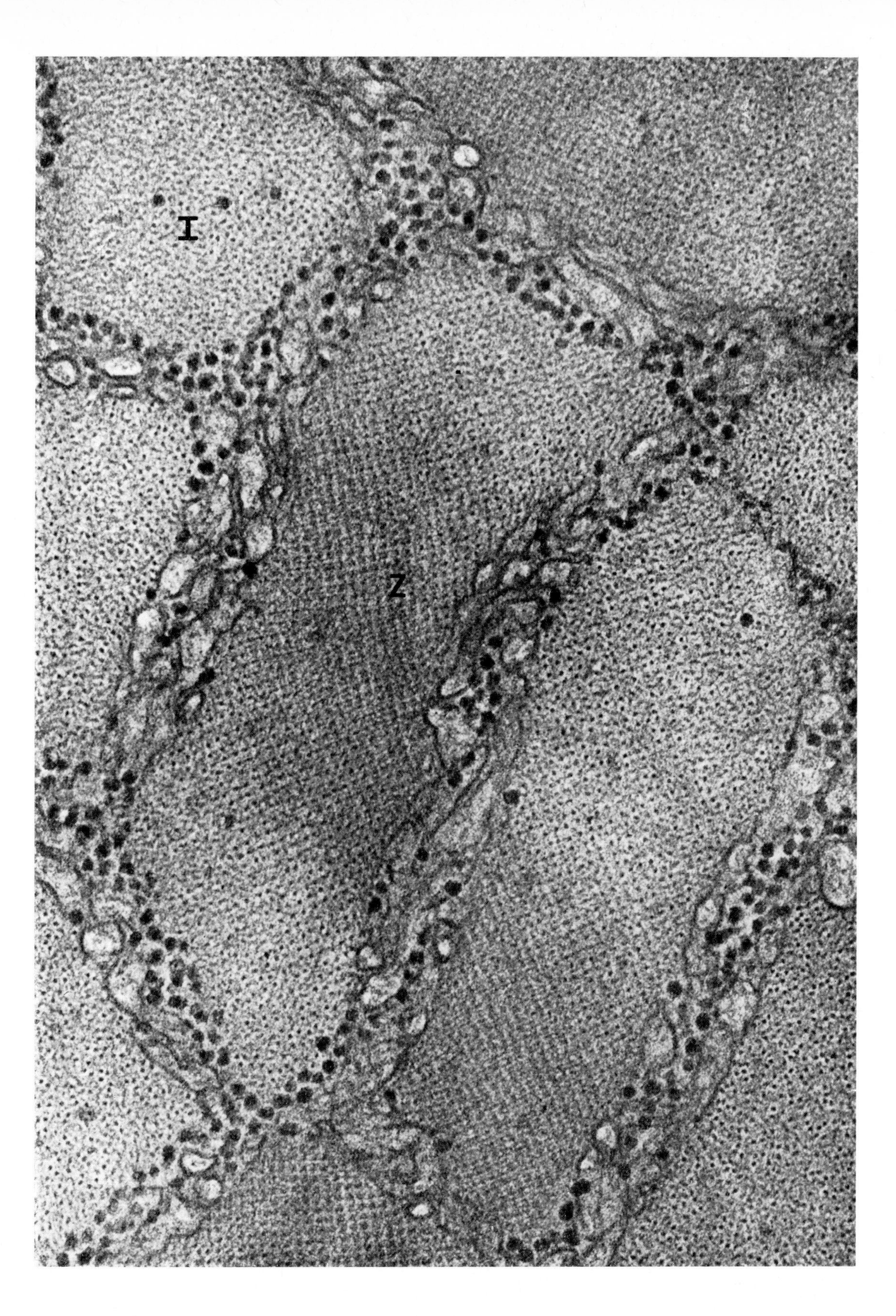
I
Z

Plate 32

Invertebrate striated muscle fibres are very similar to those of vertebrates. They show the same banding patterns, although in this micrograph the fibre is contracted so that the I-band is virtually absent. There are two filament types present, thick filaments, diameter 15 nm and thin filaments, diameter 5 nm.

Myofilament arrangement in an invertebrate striated muscle sarcomere: blowfly flight muscle. Longitudinal section. Glutaraldehyde fixation. ×65 000.

Plate 33

The thick filaments in blowfly flight muscle are in the form of a regular hexagonal pattern, each surrounded by six thin filaments, and one thin filament between every two thick filaments (see Fig. 10, p. 86). In contrast to vertebrate thick filaments, the filaments here appear as tubular structures with a dense cortex and a lighter inner core.

Myofilaments in an invertebrate striated muscle: blowfly flight muscle. Transverse section through the A-band. Glutaraldehyde fixation. ×360 000.

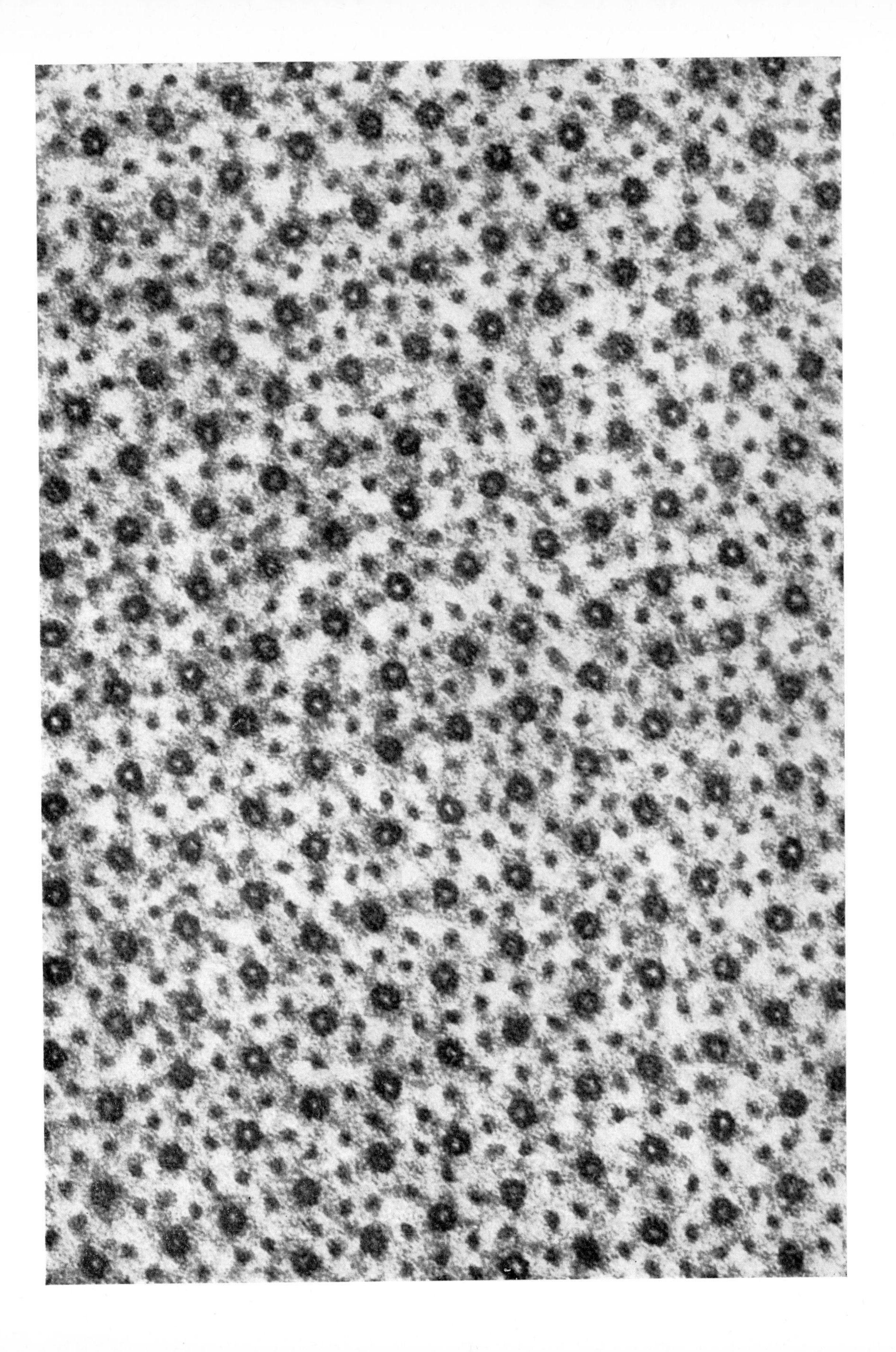

Plate 34

The hexagonal spacing of thin filaments in the I-band in blowfly flight muscle is preserved in the Z-disc and, as there is no evidence of thin filament splitting or of Z filament formation, it has been suggested that the thin filaments are held in position by the amorphous Z-disc material. The Z-disc material is so distributed that each hexagon is composed of alternate filaments from the two sarcomeres surrounded by a less dense 'hole', so that the disc appears to be composed of a regular hexagonal lattice. This structure of the Z-disc contrasts with that seen in vertebrate skeletal muscle (see Plate 31).

Z-disc and I-band in an invertebrate striated muscle: blowfly flight muscle. Transverse section. Glutaraldehyde fixation. ×330 000.

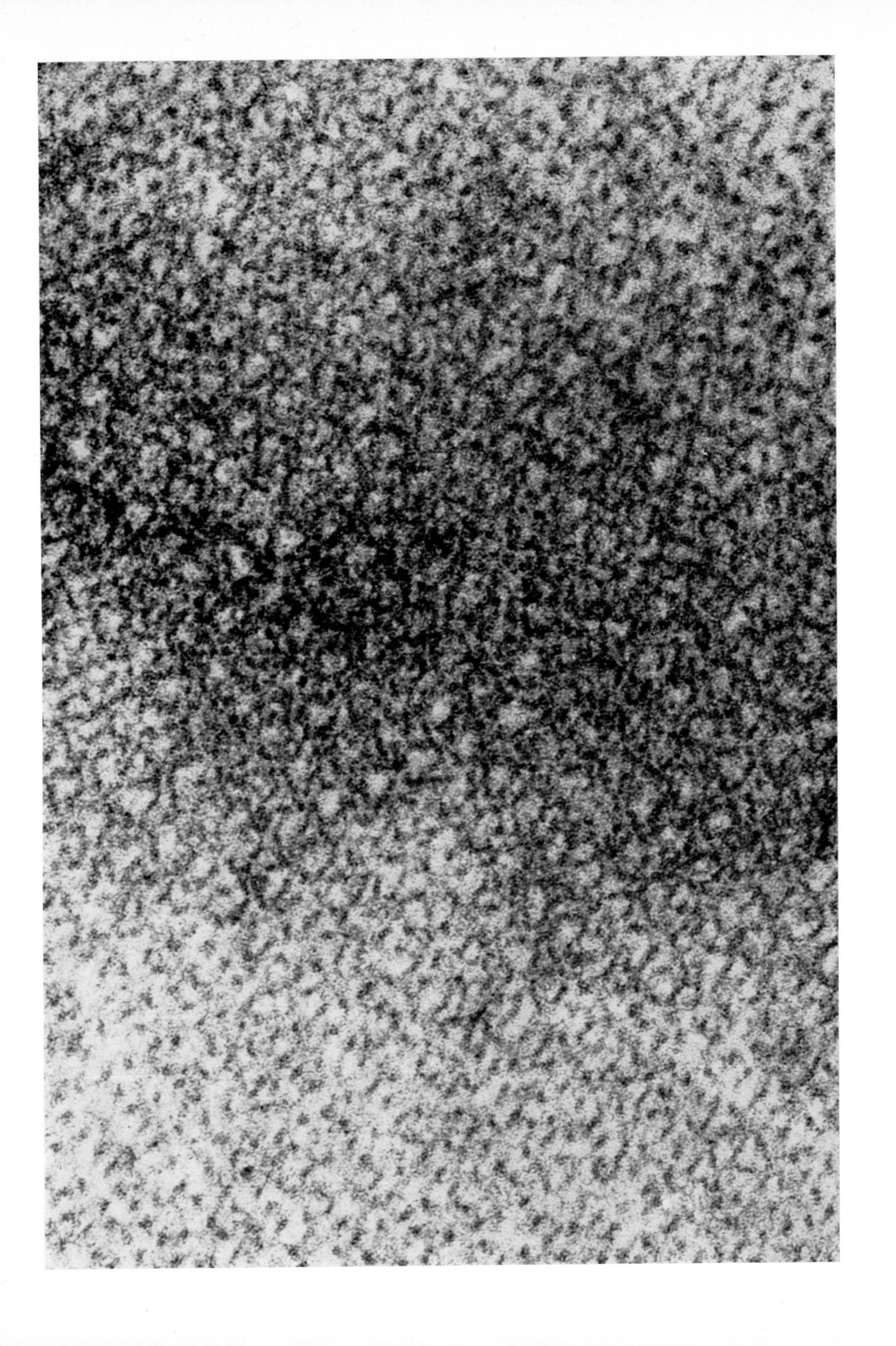

Plate 35

Both thick (16–18 nm) and thin (4–6 nm) myofilaments are present in millipede gut muscle. Each thick filament is arranged in a similar manner to that seen in vertebrate skeletal muscle, which has one filament surrounded by six others in a hexagonal pattern. However, in the millipede, these filaments, instead of being surrounded by six thin filaments are surrounded by a ring of twelve, giving an overall ratio of thin to thick filaments of 6:1 (see Fig. 10, p. 86). The thick filaments in this species do not appear as a hollow cylinder at any level through the A-band.

Myofilament arrangement in invertebrate visceral striated muscle: millipede gut. Transverse section. Glutaraldehyde fixation. × 320 000.

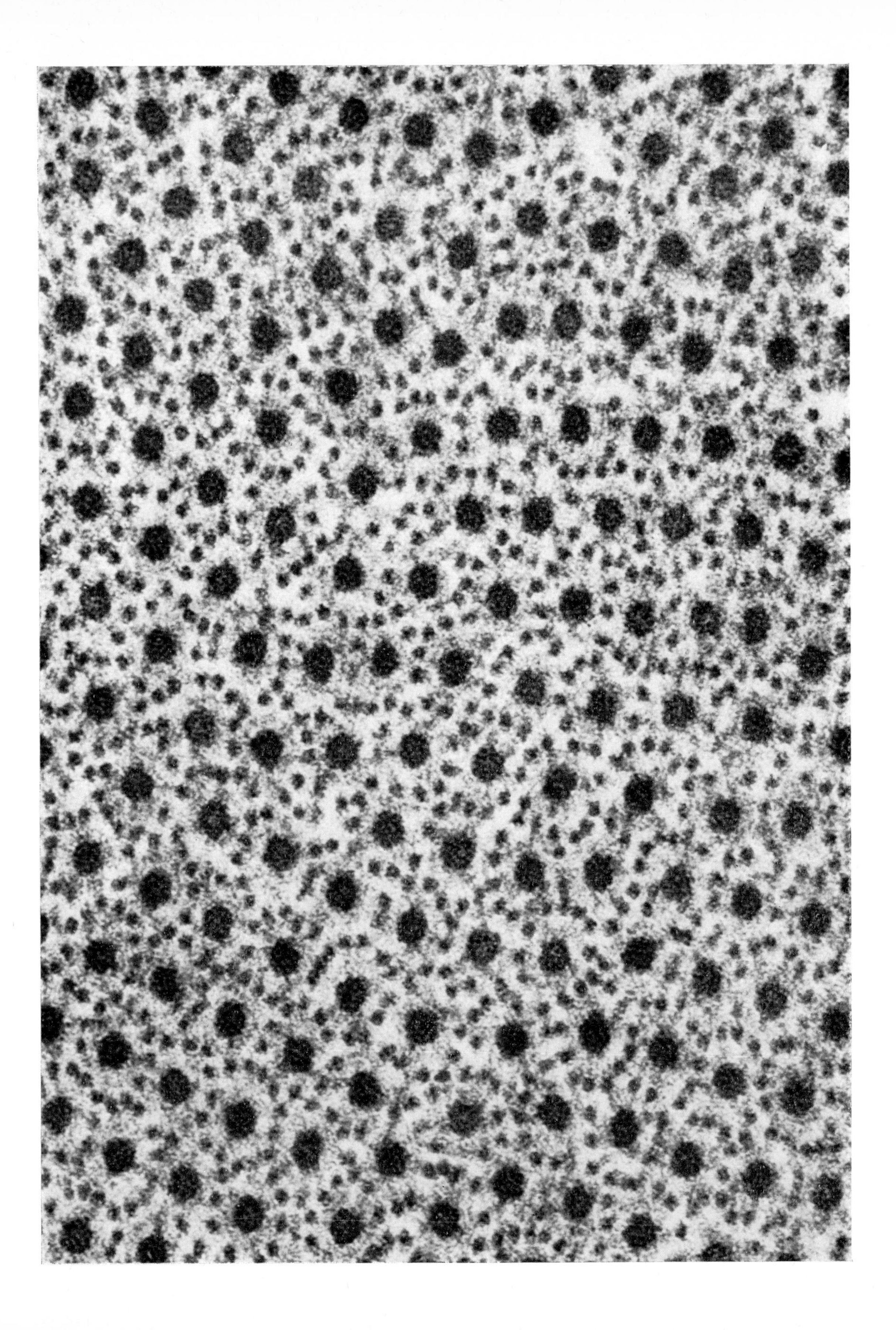

Plate 36

Although annelid muscle contains two types of myofilaments, they differ in diameter and arrangement from those found in vertebrates and arthropods. Thick, paramyosin-containing myofilaments are present in the myofibrils, which are sometimes not completely separated by sarcoplasmic reticulum. The thick filaments are usually 20–30 nm in diameter although sometimes they exceed 70 nm. The thin myofilaments are 4–6 nm in diameter. Thick filaments are surrounded by twelve thin filaments. However, in some areas both types of filament are found segregated from each other. A diagram (Fig. 12) illustrating the arrangement of thick and thin filaments in obliquely striated muscle is shown on p. 88.

Myofilament arrangement in an obliquely striated muscle: earthworm somatic muscle. Transverse section. Glutaraldehyde fixation. ×186 000.

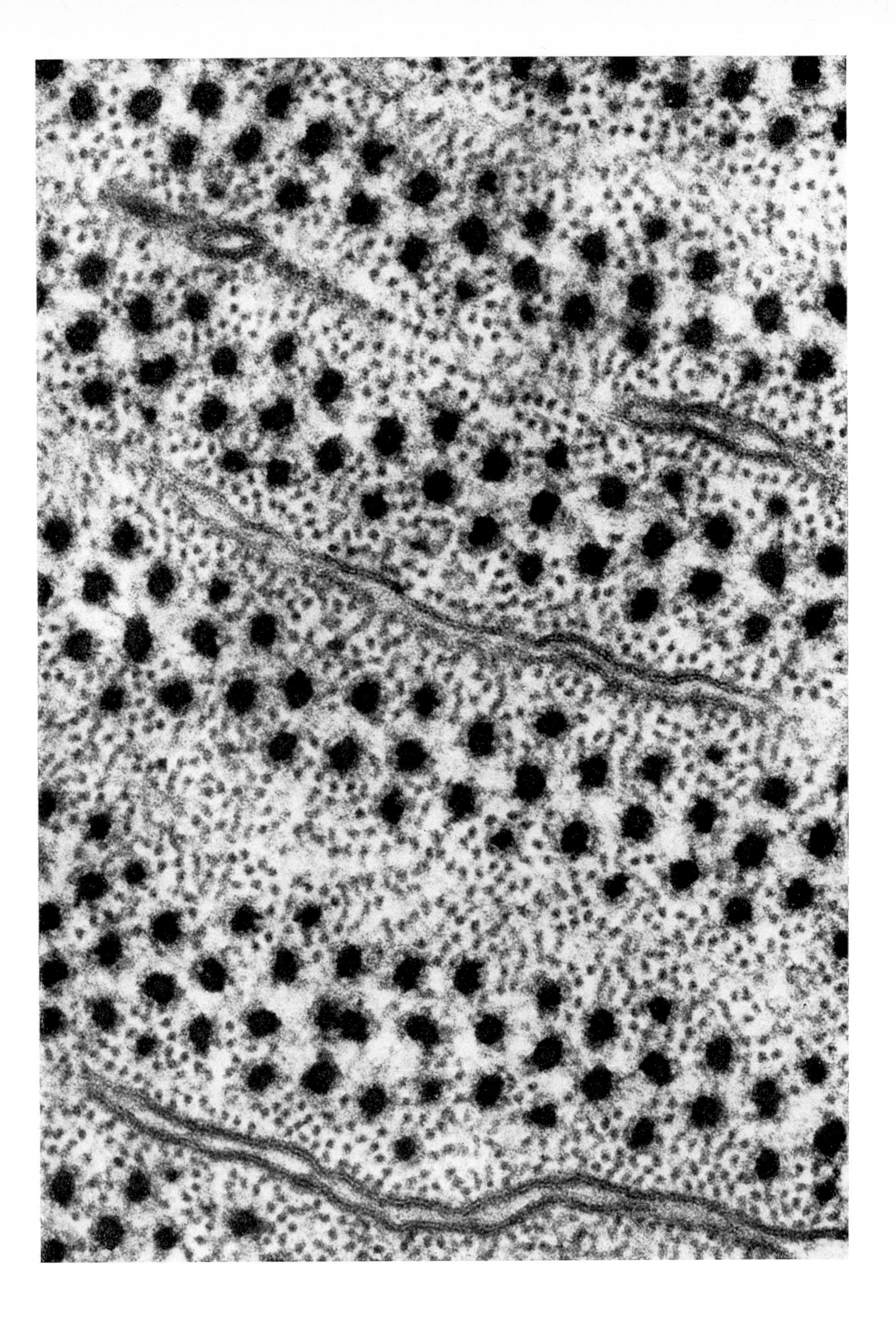

Plate 37

Myofilaments in obliquely striated muscle cells of earthworm vessels sometimes show an unusual orientation. This may be due to fixation conditions, to the plane of section, to the state of contraction or a combination of these possibilities.

Myofilament arrangement in an obliquely striated muscle: earthworm vascular muscle. Transverse section. Glutaraldehyde fixation. ×26 000.

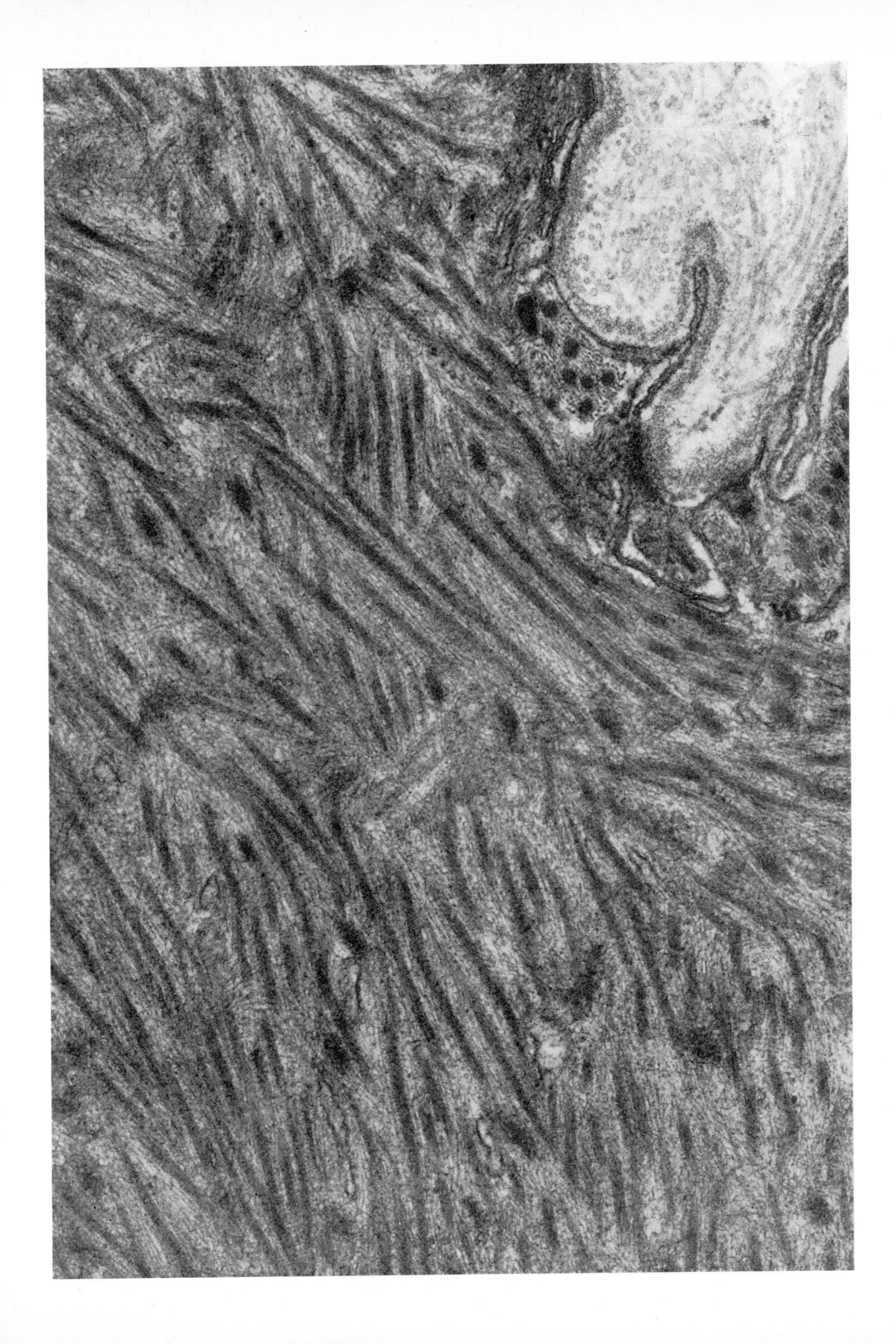

Plate 38

The thick filaments in the ABRM are tapered and are about 70 nm in diameter in their central regions. In longitudinal section, paramyosin-containing filaments show a periodicity (banding pattern) of 14.5 nm. These filaments contain both paramyosin and myosin. The thick filaments show a minimum separation of about 70 nm and appear to be arranged in a hexagonal fashion. The thin filaments are 5–7 nm in diameter but their precise organization relative to the thick filaments is only just beginning to be understood. The ratio of thin to thick filament is about 17:1.

Arrangement of myofilaments in a paramyosin smooth muscle: mussel anterior byssal retractor muscle (ABRM). Osmium fixation. × 77 300.

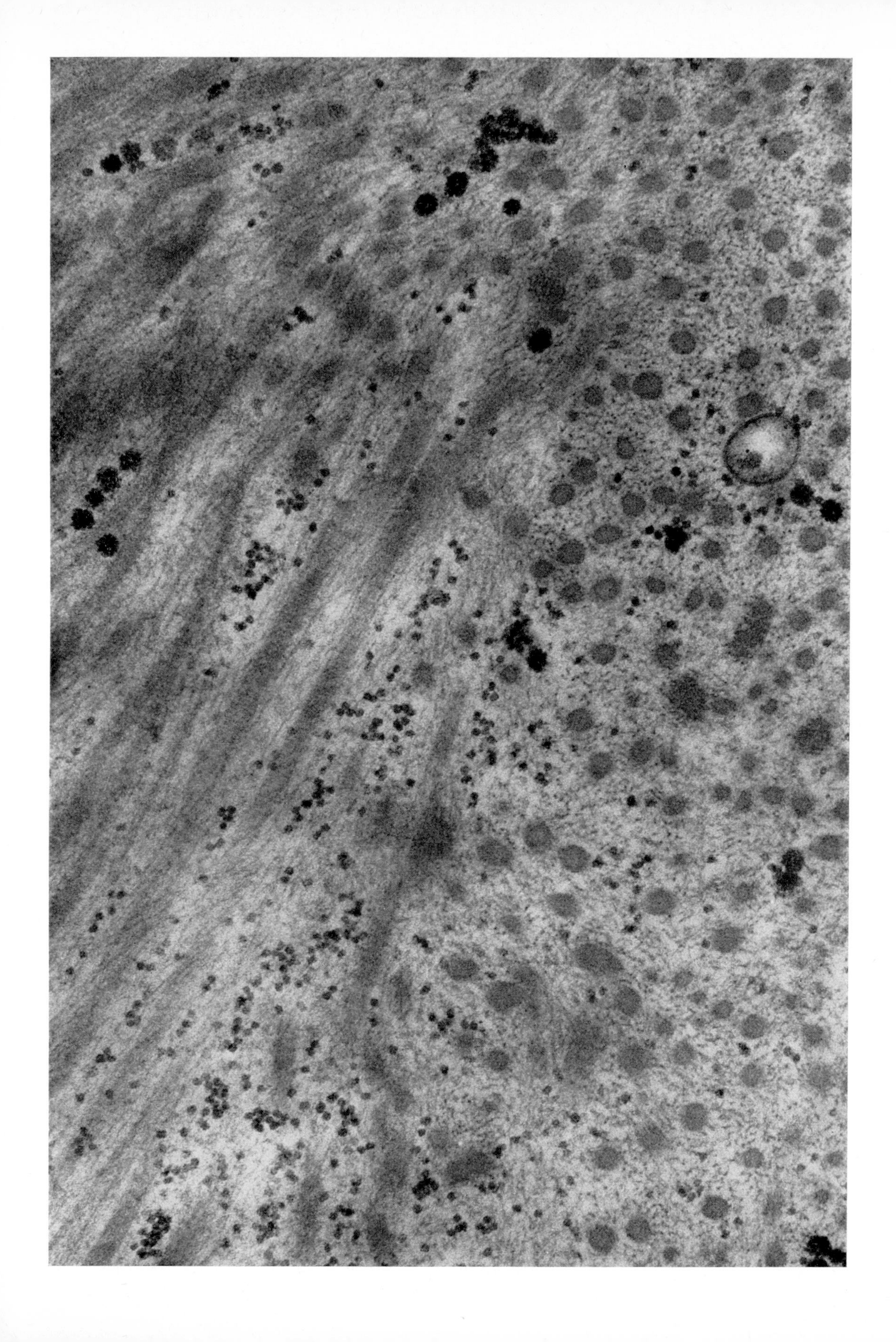

Plate 39

In vertebrate smooth muscle, both thick (12–16 nm) and thin (6–8 nm) myofilaments are present. The precise manner in which these filaments interrelate during contraction is as yet unresolved (see Introduction, p. 88, and Fig. 2, p. 8). Electron dense bodies are present among the myofilaments (‘*dark bodies*’) and along the plasma membrane (‘*dense areas*’). It has been suggested that the ‘dark bodies’ are equivalent to the Z-discs of skeletal muscle, but as yet there is no clear evidence of this.

Myofilaments in vertebrate smooth muscle: mouse vas deferens. Transverse section. Glutaraldehyde fixation. ×63 000.

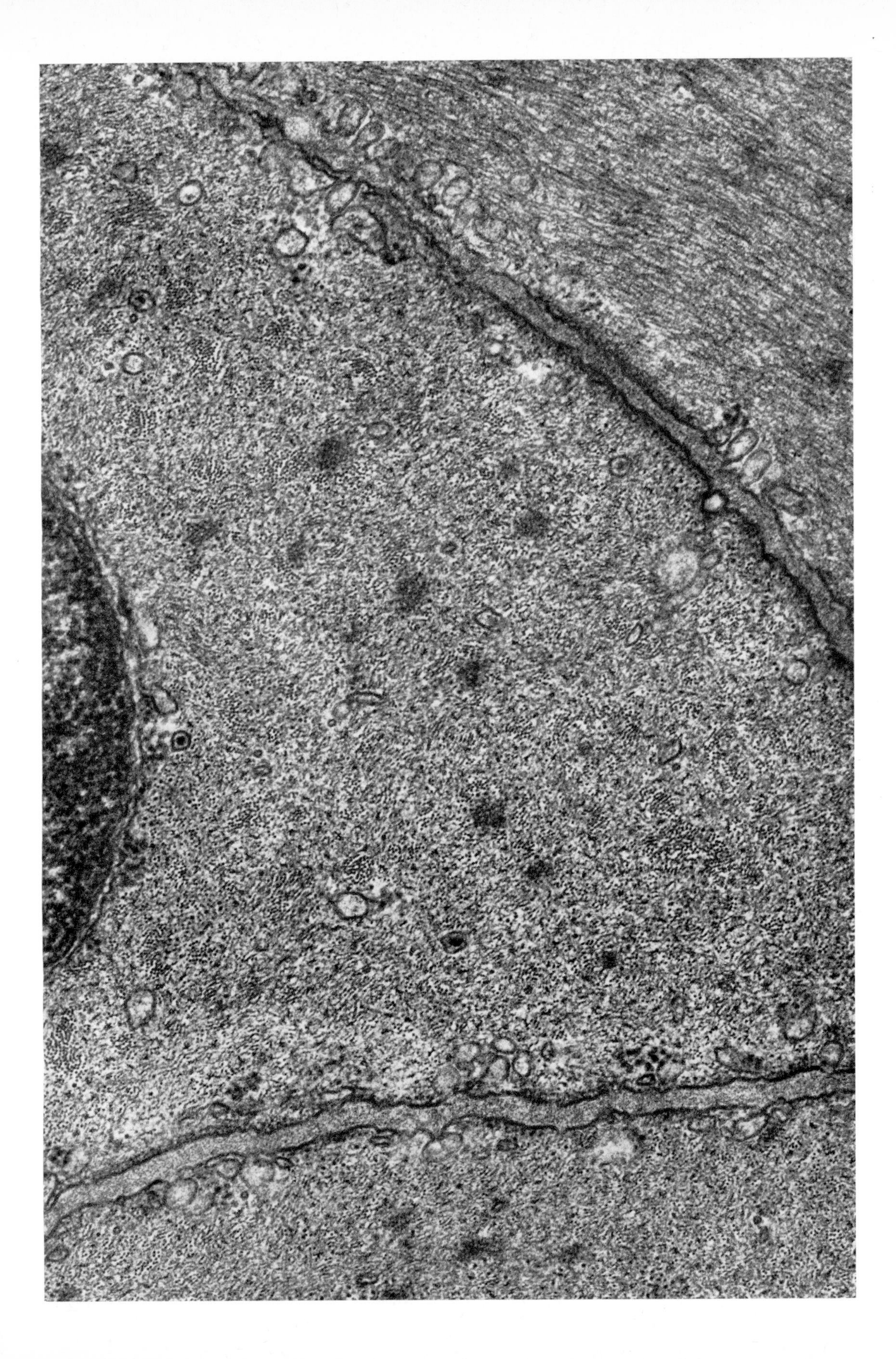

Plate 40

The arrangement of thick and thin myofilaments with respect to each other and to dark bodies in vertebrate smooth muscle is illustrated here in longitudinal section. There is some evidence to suggest that thin filaments penetrate and/or attach to dark bodies (Db).

Myofilaments in vertebrate smooth muscle: mouse vas deferens. Longitudinal section. Glutaraldehyde fixation. ×73 000.

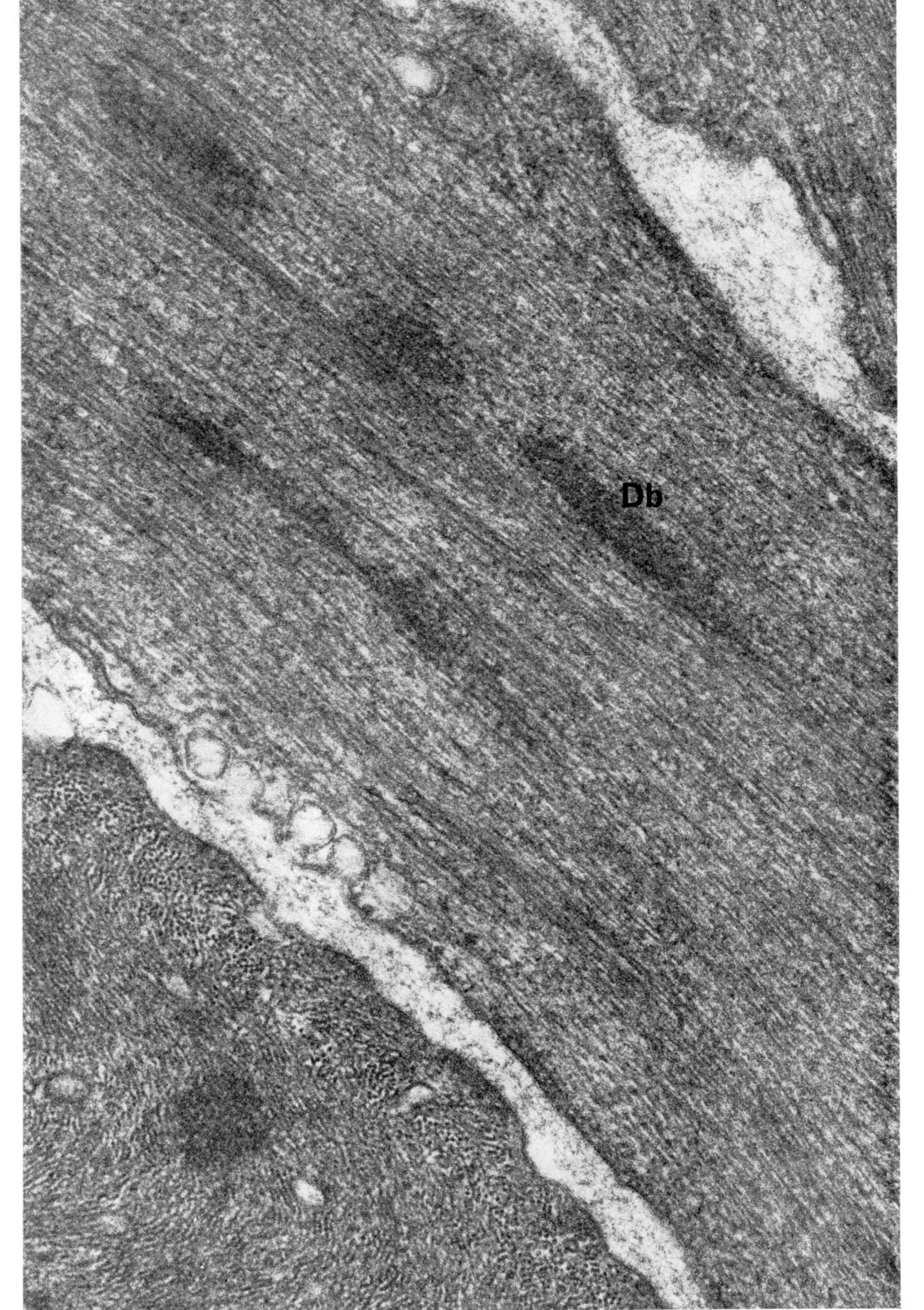
Db

Plate 41

Three types of filament are illustrated in this smooth muscle cell. Thin actin filaments are clustered together in groups or arrays throughout the cell; thick myosin filaments form a lattice with minimum separation of 40–70 nm. The ratio of thick to thin filaments is about 1:11–15. In addition to these two types of myofilament, filaments with a diameter of about 10 nm (termed 'intermediate' or 100 Å filaments) can be seen in association with the dark bodies (see Chapter 2D).

Myofilaments in vertebrate smooth muscle: mouse vas deferens. Transverse section. Glutaraldehyde fixation. ×200 000.

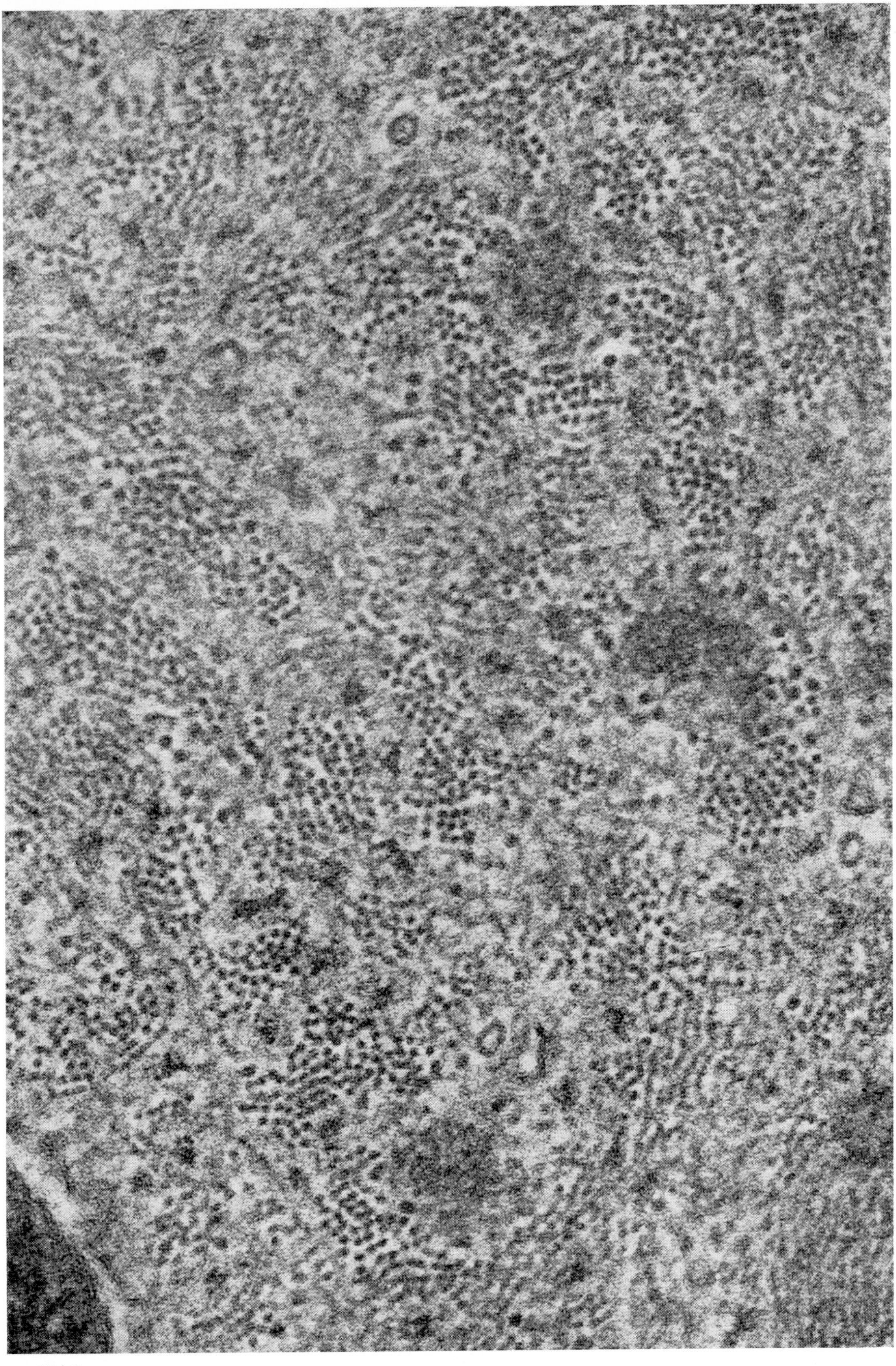

Plate 42

Several workers have shown that a ribbon form of thick filament can be produced when pieces of smooth muscle under tension are suspended in oxygenated Ringer solution. These ribbons vary between 8–10 nm by 20–110 nm in cross section and are surrounded by a clear halo. In longitudinal section (bottom figures) the ribbons are up to 5 μm long and can be clearly recognized by their halo. They are separated by regular parallel arrays of thin actin filaments. It is not yet clear whether these ribbons represent an *in vivo* form of the myosin component of vertebrate smooth muscle or an artefactual form induced under some preparation conditions.

'Myosin ribbons' in vertebrate smooth muscle: guinea-pig taenia coli. Glutaraldehyde fixation. Upper micrograph: transverse section. ×110 000. Bottom three micrographs: longitudinal sections. Upper, thin filaments ×108 000; middle, thin filaments and myosin ribbons ×80 000; lower, thin filaments and myosin ribbons ×51 000. (Courtesy of J. V. Small and J. M. Squire. 1972. *J. molec. Biol.*, **67**, 117.)

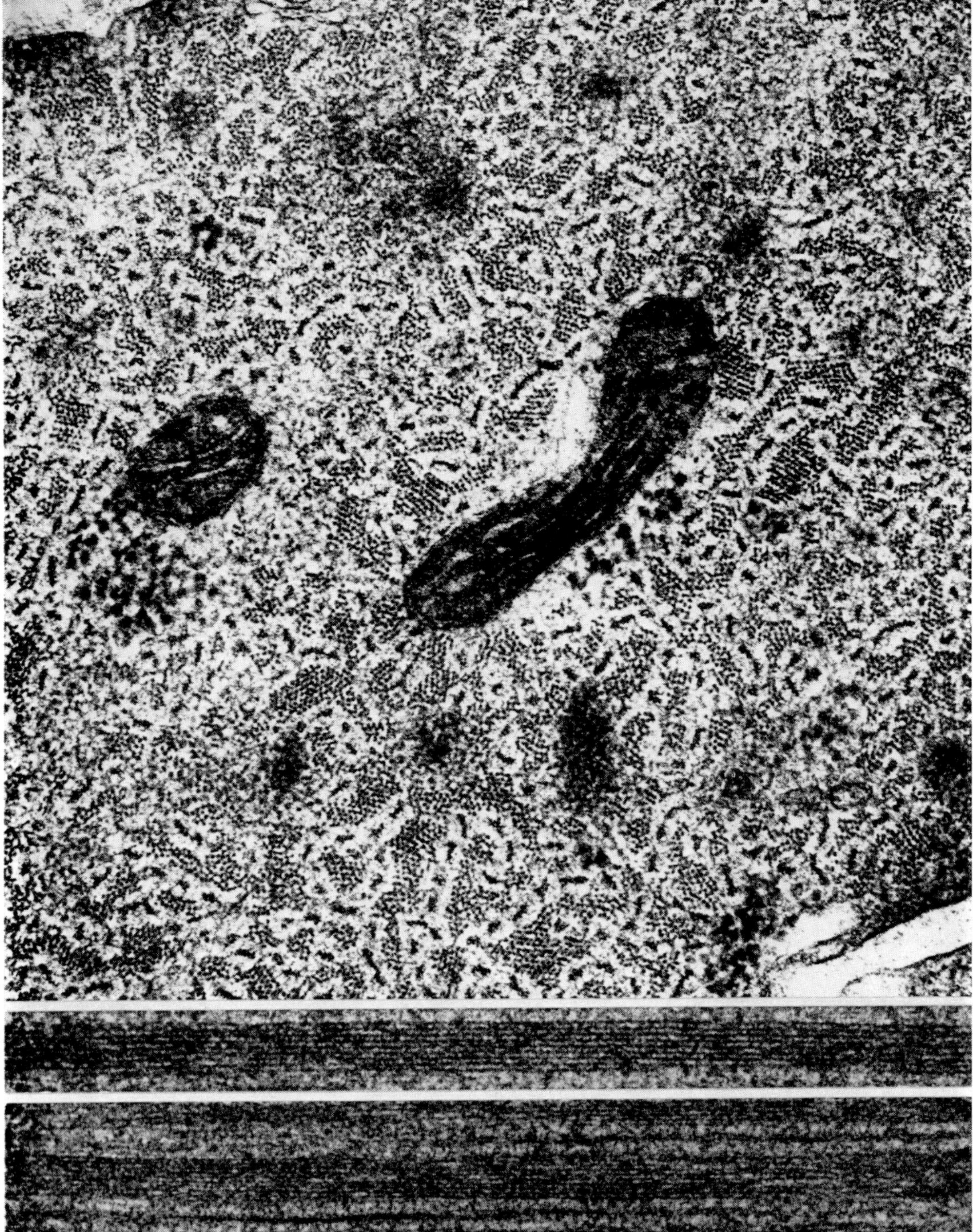

Plate 43

The labile nature of filament preservation in vertebrate smooth muscle under different conditions is illustrated in Plates 43, 44 and 45. In this plate, the tissue was relaxed in oxygenated Ringer at 38°C for 24 hours before fixation. Only aggregations of filaments with an irregular outline (20–40 nm) are present. Just prior to fixation the organ was stimulated in an organ bath and found to contract with a comparable amplitude to muscle removed directly from the animal. No dark bodies are visible in these cells.

Aggregation of filaments in vertebrate smooth muscle: mouse vas deferens. Transverse section. Glutaraldehyde fixation. ×138 000.

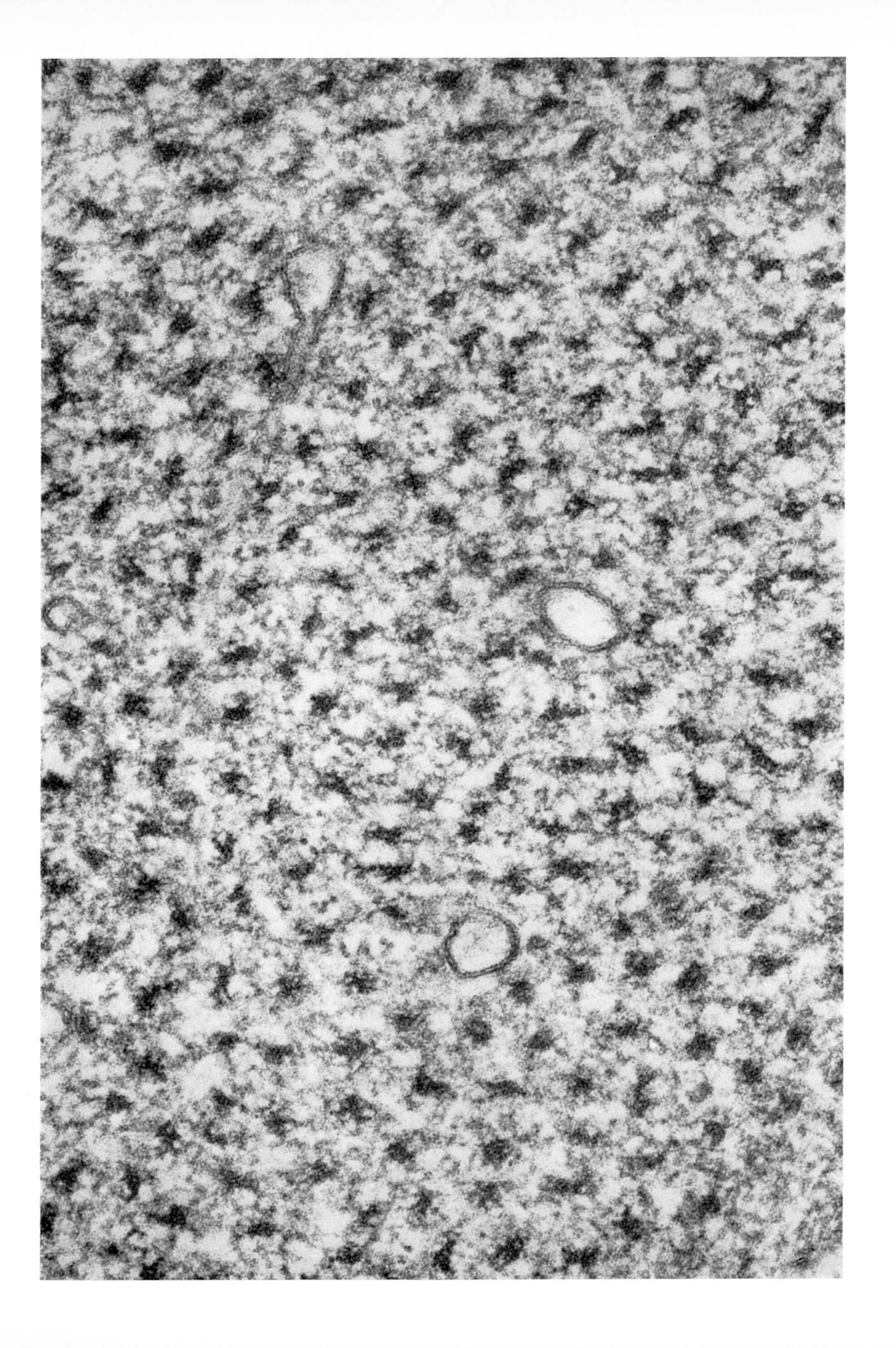

Plate 44

Prior to fixation, this preparation was mechanically damaged such that the plasmamembranes of cells were ruptured. Two types of filaments are observed under these conditions, namely thin filaments 6–8 nm in diameter and thick aggregations of filaments with a diameter of 25–50 nm and a length of about 0.1 μm. No dark bodies are visible in these cells.

Aggregation of filaments in vertebrate smooth muscle: mouse vas deferens. Glutaraldehyde fixation. $\times$113 000.

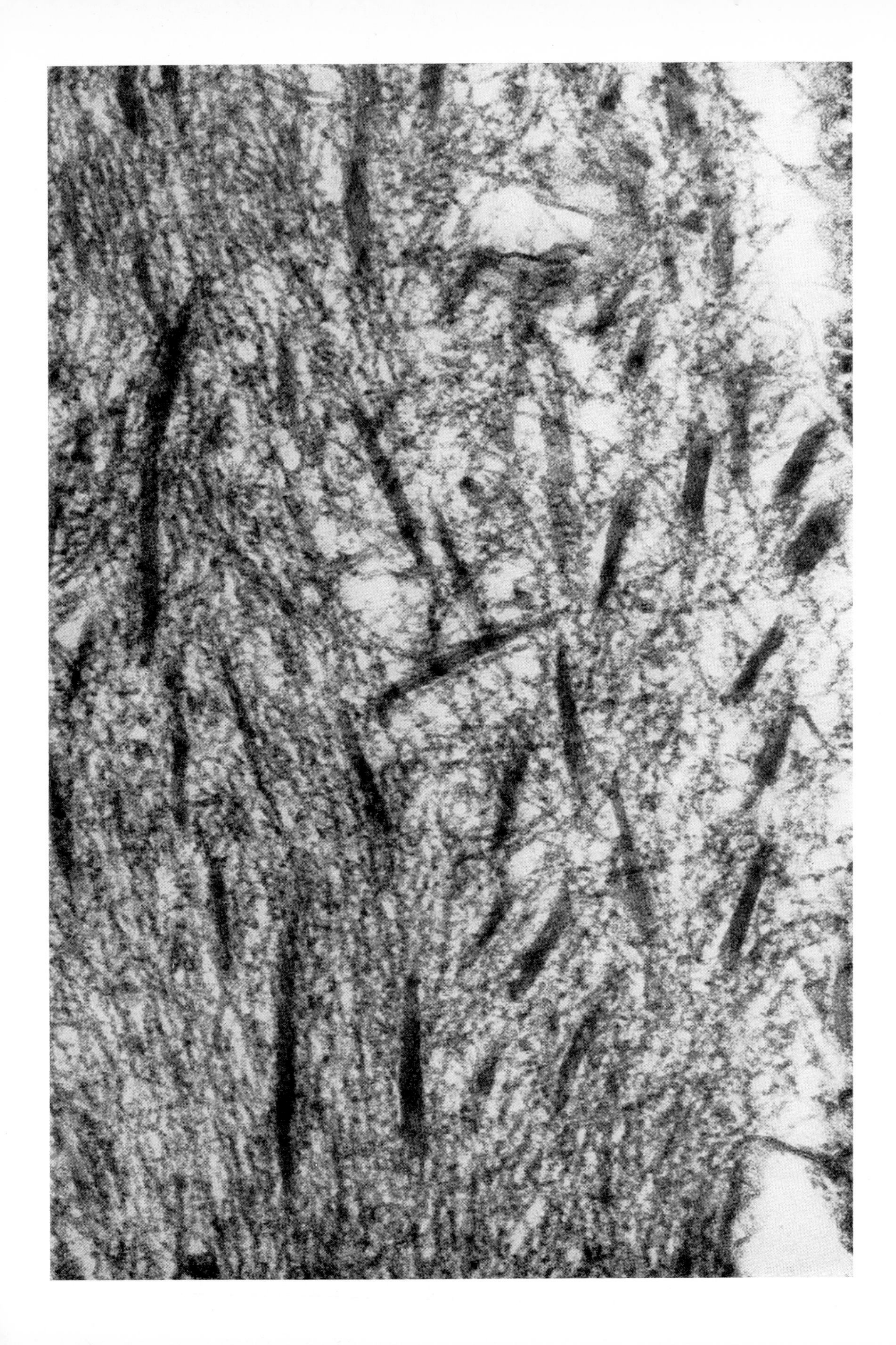

Plate 45

This preparation was fixed after immersion in Ringer solution containing 2.0 mg cm^{-3} trypsin for one hour. A large accumulation of thin filaments is evident close to the plasma membrane. The central region of the cell contains aggregations of filaments, 25–30 nm in diameter. Some of these aggregations display an axial periodicity of 14.4 nm, which corresponds to that of myosin in vertebrate skeletal muscle. No dark bodies are visible in these cells. It has been suggested by some workers that vertebrate smooth muscle myosin exists among the actin filaments in a relatively disaggregated state and that trypsin can induce aggregation by altering the conformation of the myosin molecule.

Aggregation of filaments in vertebrate smooth muscle: mouse vas deferens. Transverse section. Glutaraldehyde fixation. $\times$75 000.

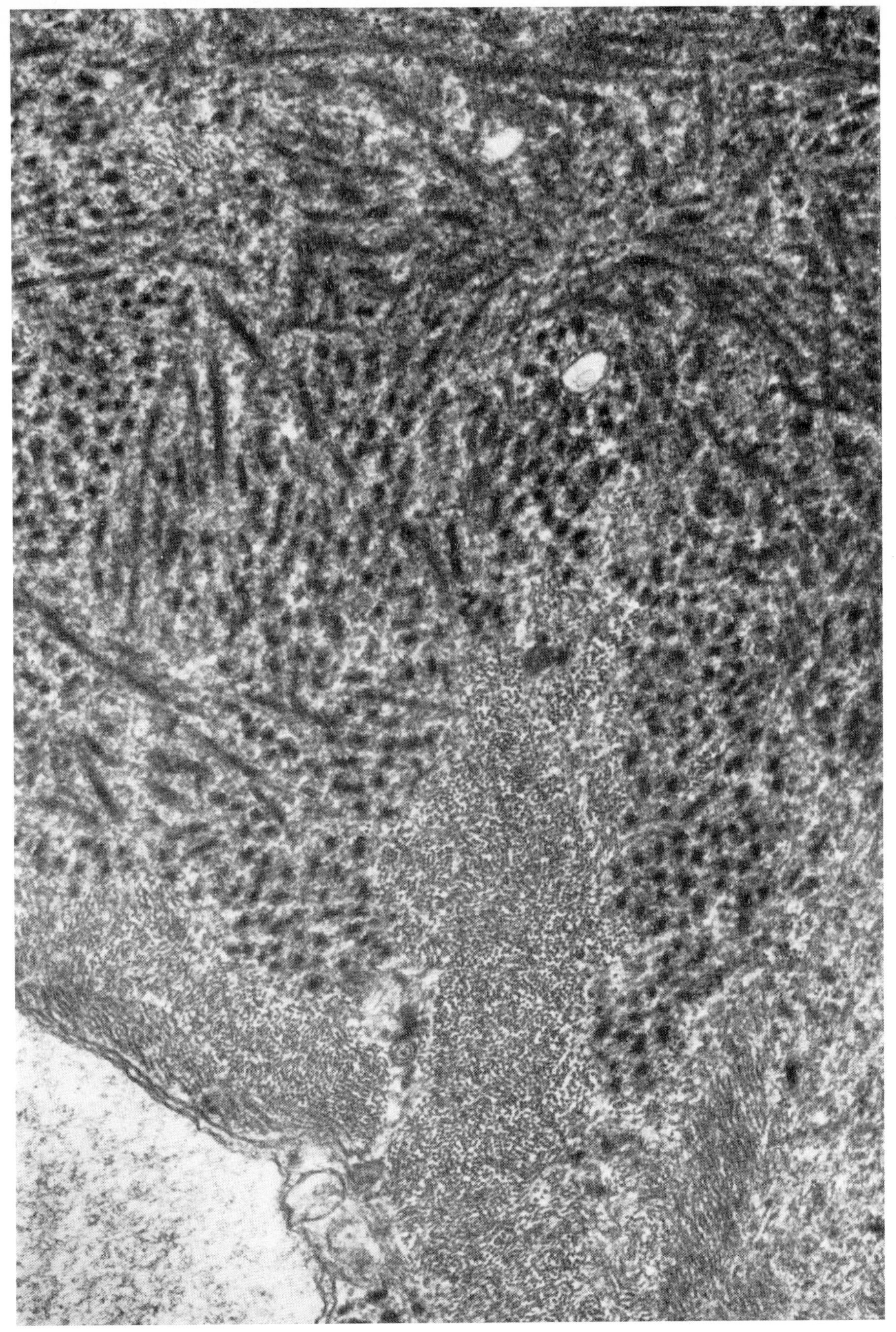

Plate 46

Although clusters of both thick and thin filaments in developing vertebrate skeletal muscle can be observed at the periphery of the muscle cells at an early stage of development, the spatial relationship of these filaments is irregular. The development of the myofibril in striated muscle is not well understood in spite of a number of studies and there is disagreement as to the sequence of events that occur. In smooth muscle development, thin filaments appear first, followed by the formation of the thick filaments.

Myofilaments in developing vertebrate skeletal muscle: extrafusal fibre from the 18-day-old foetal rat sternothyroid. Longitudinal section. Glutaraldehyde fixation. ×72 000.

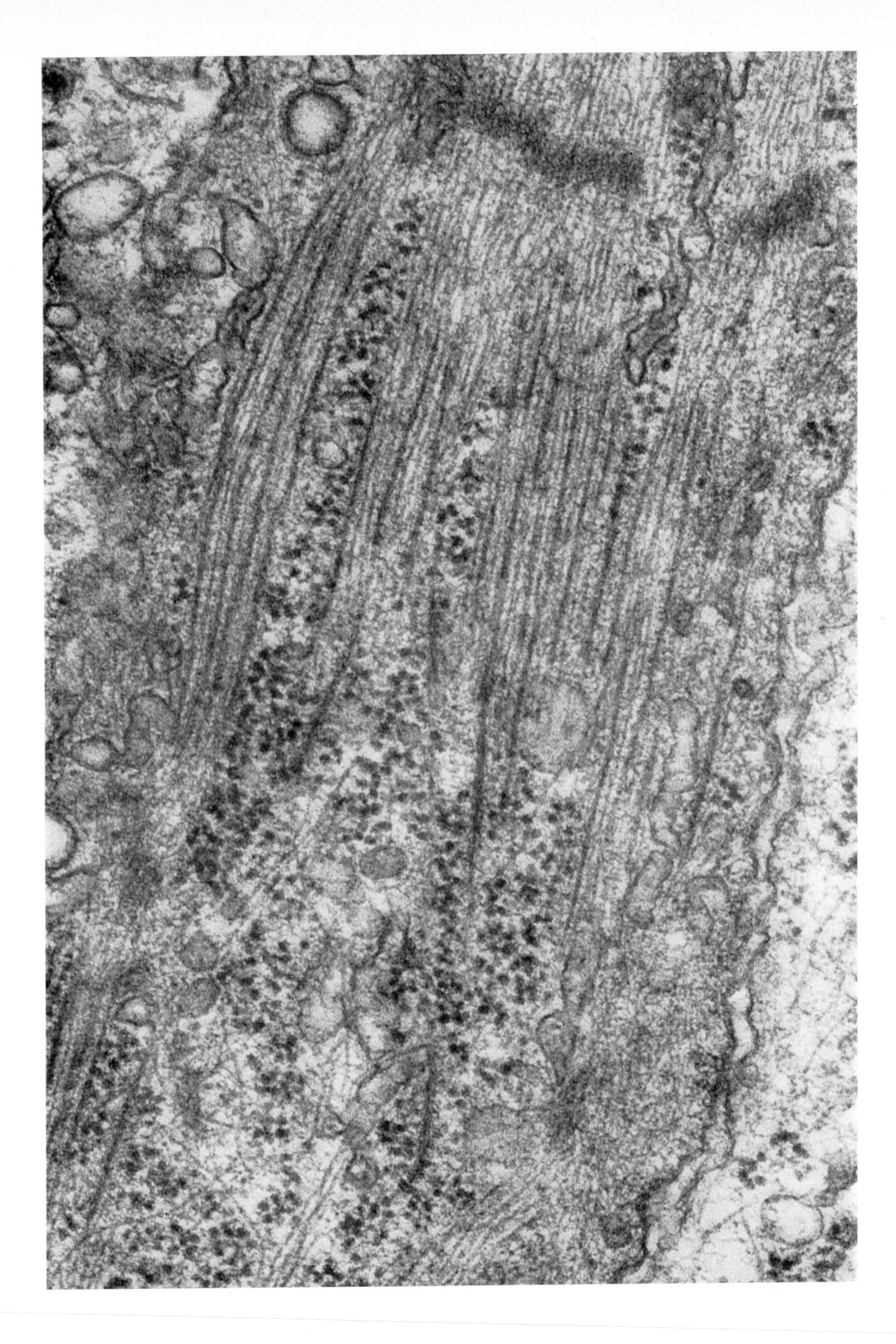

Selected articles

Vertebrate skeletal muscle

ALLEN, E. R. and C. F. TERRENCE. 1968. Immunochemical and ultrastructural studies of myosin synthesis. *Proc. natn. Acad. Sci. U.S.A.*, **60,** 1209–1215.

APRIL, E. W., P. W. BRANDT and G. F. ELLIOTT. 1971. The myofilament lattice: studies on isolated fibers. I. The constancy of the unit-cell volume with variation in sarcomere length in a lattice in which the thin-to-thick myofilament ratio is 6:1. *J. Cell Biol.*, **51,** 72–82.

APRIL, E. W., P. W. BRANDT and G. F. ELLIOTT. 1972. The myofilament lattice, studies on isolated fibers. II. The effects of osmotic strength, ionic concentration and pH upon the unit-cell volume. *J. Cell Biol.*, **53,** 53–65.

ASTBURY, W. T., S. V. PERRY, R. REED and L. C. SPARK. 1947. An electron microscope and X-ray study of actin. *Biochim. biophys. Acta*, **1,** 379–392.

ASTBURY, W. T., R. REED and L. C. SPARK. 1948. An X-ray and electron microscope study of tropomyosin. *Biochem. J.*, **43,** 282–287.

BACCETTI, B. 1965. Nouvelles observations sur l'ultrastructure du myofilament. *J. Ultrastruct. Res.*, **13,** 245–256.

BÁRÁNY, M. and K. BÁRÁNY. 1973. A proposal for the mechanism of contraction in intact frog muscle. In *The Mechanism of Muscle Contraction. Cold Spring Harb. Symp. quant. Biol.*, **37,** 157–168.

BERTAUD, W. S., D. G. RAYNS and F. O. SIMPSON. 1970. Freeze-etch studies on fish skeletal muscle. *J. Cell Sci.*, **6,** 537–557.

BIRÓ, N. A., L. SZILAGYI and M. BÁLINT. 1973. Studies on the helical segment of the myosin molecule. In *The Mechanism of Muscle Contraction. Cold Spring Harb. Symp. quant. Biol.*, **37,** 55–64.

BOTTS, J., R. COOKE, C. dos REMEDIOS, J. DUKE, R. MENDELSON, M. F. MORALES, T. TOKIWA, G. VINIEGRA and R. YOUNT. 1973. Does a myosin cross-bridge progress arm-over-arm on the actin filament? In *The Mechanism of Muscle Contraction. Cold Spring Harb. Symp. quant. Biol.*, **37,** 195–200.

BOWEN, W. J. 1964. Glycerol-treated muscle as working model of contraction and diffusion of the ATP through it. In *Biochemistry of Muscle Contraction*. J. Gergely (ed.). Little Brown & Co., Boston. 441–447.

BRANDT, P., E. LOPEZ, J. REUBEN and H. GRUNDFEST. 1967. The relationship between myofilament packing density and sarcomere length in frog striated muscle. *J. Cell Biol.*, **33,** 255–263.

BRAY, D. 1973. Cytoplasmic actin: a comparative study. In *The Mechanism of Muscle Contraction. Cold Spring Harb. Symp. quant. Biol.*, **37,** 567–572.

BULLIVANT, S., D. G. RAYNS, W. S. BERTAUD, J. P. CHALCROFT and G. F. GRAYSON. 1972. Freeze-fractured myosin filaments. *J. Cell Biol.*, **55,** 520–523.

CARLSEN, F., F. FUCHS and G. G. KNAPPEIS. 1965*a*. Contractility and ultrastructure in glycerol-extracted muscle fibers. I. The relationship of contractility to sarcomere length. *J. Cell Biol.*, **27,** 25–34.

CARLSEN, F., F. FUCHS and G. G. KNAPPEIS. 1965*b*. Contractility and ultrastructure in glycerol-extracted muscle fibers. II. Ultrastructure in resting and shortened fibers. *J. Cell Biol.*, **27,** 35–46.

CARLSEN, F., G. G. KNAPPEIS and F. BUCHTHAL. 1961. Ultrastructure of the resting and contracted striated muscle fiber at different degrees of stretch. *J. Cell Biol.*, **11,** 95–117.

CASPAR, D. L. D., C. COHEN and W. LONGLEY. 1969. Tropomyosin: crystal structure, polymorphism and molecular interactions. *J. molec. Biol.*, **41,** 87–107.

CHAUDONNERET, J. 1962. Nouvelle hypothèse sur les mécanismes intimes de la contraction de la fibre striée. *C.r. hebd. Séanc. Acad. Sci., Paris.*, **254,** 168–170.

COHEN, C., D. L. D. CASPAR, J. P. JOHNSON, K. NAUSS, S. S. MARGOSSIAN and D. A. D. PARRY. 1973. Tropomyosin-troponin assembly. In *The Mechanism of Muscle Contraction. Cold Spring Harb. Symp. quant. Biol.*, **37,** 287–298.

COHEN, C., S. LOWEY, R. G. HARRISON, J. KENDRICK-JONES and A. G. SZENT-GYÖRGYI. 1970. Segments from myosin rods. *J. molec. Biol.*, **47,** 605–609.

COLBY, R. H. 1971. Intrinsic birefringence of glycerinated myofibrils. *J. Cell Biol.*, **51,** 763–771.

COOKE, R. and M. F. MORALES. 1971.

Interaction of globular actin with myosin subfragments. *J. molec. Biol.*, **60,** 249–261.

CORSI, A., U. MUSCATELLO and I. RONCHETTI. 1967. Electron microscope observations of the location of actin and tropomyosin in the rabbit myofibril. *J. Ultrastruct. Res.*, **19,** 260–272.

DAVIES, R. E. 1963. A molecular theory of muscle contractions: Calcium-dependent contractions with hydrogen bond formation plus ATP-dependent extensions of part of the myosin-actin cross-bridges. *Nature, Lond.*, **199,** 1068–1074.

DAVIES, R. E. 1965. The role of ATP in muscle contraction. In *Muscle.* W. M. Paul, E. E. Daniel, C. M. Kay and G. Monckton (eds.). Pergamon, Oxford. 46–69.

D'HAESE, J. and H. KOMNICK. 1972*a*. Fine structure and contraction of isolated muscle actomyosin. I. Evidence for a sliding mechanism by means of oligomeric myosin. *Z. Zellforsch. mikrosk. Anat.*, **134,** 411–426.

D'HAESE J. and H. KOMNICK. 1972*b*. Fine structure and contraction of isolated muscle actomyosin. II. Formation of myosin filaments and their effect on contraction. *Z. Zellforsch. mikrosk. Anat.* **134,** 427–434.

DI PRAMPERO, P. E. 1972. Énergétique de l'exercise musculaire. *J. Physiol., Paris,* **65,** 51A–86A.

DORN, A. 1969. Studien zur Skeletmuskelentwicklung biem Meerschweinchen. I. Elektronenmikroskopische Untersuchungen. *Anat. Anz.*, **124,** 513–550.

DOUGHERTY, W. J. and M. M. LEE. 1970. Electron microscopic observations on glycerol-extracted rabbit muscles treated with dialyzed iron at low pH. *J. Ultrastruct. Res.*, **31,** 1–15.

DOW, J. and A. STRACHER. 1971. Identification of the essential light chain of myosin. *Proc. natn. Acad. Sci. U.S.A.*, **68,** 1107–1110.

EATON, B. L. and F. A. PEPE. 1974. Myosin filaments showing a 430 Å axial repeat periodicity. *J. molec. Biol.*, **82,** 421–423.

EBASHI, S., A. KODAMA and F. EBASHI. 1968. Troponin. I. Preparation and physiological function. *J. Biochem.*, **64,** 465–477.

EBASHI, S. and F. LIPMANN. 1962. Adenosine triphosphate-linked concentration of calcium ions in a particulate fraction of rabbit muscle. *J. Cell Biol.*, **14,** 389–400.

FINCK, H. 1965. Immunochemical studies on myosin. III. Immunochemical comparison of myosins from chicken skeletal heart and smooth muscles. *Biochem. biophys. Acta.*,**111,** 231–238.

FREYGANG, W. H. JR., S. I. RAPOPORT and L. D. PEACHEY. 1967. Some relations between changes in the linear electrical properties of striated muscle fibers and changes in ultrastructure. *J. gen. Physiol.*, **50,** 2437–2458.

GALEY, F. R. 1964. Local contraction patterns of striated muscle. *J. Ultrastruct. Res.*, **11,** 389–400.

GILËV, V. P. 1964. The ultrastructure of myofilaments. I. Application of negative staining to sectioned material. *Biochem. biophys. Acta.*, **79,** 364–370.

GILËV, V. P. 1966. On the fine structure of 'myosin' protofibrils of cross striated muscle fiber. *Biofizika*, **11,** 312–317.

HAGOPIAN, M. 1970. Contraction bands at short sarcomere length in chick muscle. *J. Cell Biol.*, **47,** 790–796.

HANSON, J. 1968. Recent X-ray diffraction studies of muscle. *Q. Rev. Biophys.*, **1,** 177–216.

HANSON, J. 1973. Evidence from the electron microscope studies on actin paracrystals concerning the origin of the cross-striation in the thin filaments of vertebrate skeletal muscle. *Proc. R. Soc. Ser. B*, **183,** 39–58.

HANSON, J. and H. E. HUXLEY. 1955. The structural basis of contraction in striated muscle. In *Fibrous Proteins and Their Biological Significance.* Symposia of the Society of Experimental Biology, No. 9. Cambridge University Press. 228–264.

HANSON, J., V. LEDNEV, E. J. O'BRIEN and P. M. BENNETT. 1973. Structure of the actin-containing filaments in vertebrate skeletal muscle. In *The Mechanism of Muscle Contraction. Cold Spring Harb. Symp. quant. Biol.*, **37,** 311–318.

HANSON, J. and J. LOWY. 1963. The structure of F-actin and of actin filaments isolated from muscle. *J. molec. Biol.*, **6,** 46–60.

HANSON, J. and J. LOWY. 1964. The structure of actin filaments and the origin of the axial periodicity in the I-substance of vertebrate striated muscle. *Proc. R. Soc. Ser. B*, **160**, 449–458.

HANSON, J., E. J. O'BRIEN and P. M. BENNETT. 1971. Structure of the myosin-containing filament assembly (A-segment) separated from frog skeletal muscle. *J. molec. Biol.*, **58,** 865–871.

HARDWICKE, P. M. D. and J. HANSON. 1971. Separation of thick and thin myofilaments. *J. molec. Biol.*, **59,** 509–516.

HARRINGTON, W. F., M. BURKE and J. S. BARTON. 1973. Association of myosin to form contractile systems. In *The Mechanism of Muscle Contraction. Cold Spring Harb. Symp. quant. Biol.*, **37,** 77–86.

HARRISON, R. G., S. LOWEY and C. COHEN. 1971. Assembly of myosin. *J. molec. Biol.*, **59,** 531–535.

HARTSHORNE, D. J. and P. DREIZEN. 1973. Studies on the subunit composition of troponin. In *The Mechanism of Muscle Contraction. Cold Spring Harb. Symp. quant. Biol.*, **37,** 225–234.

HASELGROVE, J. C. 1973. X-ray evidence for a conformational change in the actin-containing filaments of vertebrate striated muscle. In *The Mechanism of Muscle Contraction. Cold Spring Harb. Symp. quant. Biol.*, **37,** 341–352.

HAYASHI, T., R. B. SILVER and D. S. SMITH. 1972. *In vitro* association of actin and myosin filaments. *J. Cell Biol.*, **55,** 109a.

HITCHCOCK, S. E., H. E. HUXLEY and A. G. SZENT-GYÖRGYI. 1973. Calcium sensitive binding of troponin to actin-tropomyosin: A two-site model for troponin action. *J. molec. Biol.*, **80,** 825–836.

HODGE, A. J. 1956. The fine structure of striated muscle. A comparison of insect flight muscle with vertebrate and invertebrate skeletal muscle. *J. biophys. biochem. Cytol.*, **2,** Suppl., 131–142.

HUXLEY, A. F. 1957. Muscle structure and theories of contraction. *Prog. Biophys. biophys. Chem.*, **7,** 255–318.

HUXLEY, A. F. 1973. A note suggesting that the cross-bridge attachment during muscle contraction may take place in two stages. *Proc. R. Soc. Ser. B*, **183,** 83–86.

HUXLEY, A. F. and R. NIEDERGERKE. 1954. Interference microscopy of living muscle fibres. Structural changes in muscle during contraction. *Nature, Lond.*, **173,** 971–973.

HUXLEY, A. F. and L. D. PEACHEY. 1961. The maximum length for contraction in vertebrate striated muscle. *J. Physiol., Lond.*, **156,** 150–165.

HUXLEY, H. E. 1957. The double array of filaments in cross-striated muscle. *J. biophys. biochem. Cytol.*, **3,** 631–648.

HUXLEY, H. E. 1960. Muscle Cells. In *The Cell: Biochemistry, Physiology, Morphology*. Vol. 4. J. Brachet and A. E. Mirsky (eds.). Academic Press, New York. 365–481.

HUXLEY, H. E. 1963. Electron microscope studies on the structure of natural and synthetic protein filaments from striated muscle. *J. molec. Biol.*, **7,** 281–308.

HUXLEY, H. E. 1964*a*. Structural evidence concerning the mechanism of contraction in striated muscle. In *Muscle*. W. M. Paul, E. E. Daniel, C. H. Key and G. Monckton (eds.). Pergamon, New York. 3–28.

HUXLEY, H. E. 1964*b*. Structural arrangements and the contraction mechanism in striated muscle. *Proc. R. Soc. Ser. B*, **160,** 442–448.

HUXLEY, H. E. 1965. The mechanism of muscular contraction. *Scient. Am.*, **213,** 18–27.

HUXLEY, H. E. 1973. Structural changes in the actin- and myosin-containing filaments during contraction. In *The Mechanism of Muscle Contraction. Cold Spring Harb. Symp. quant. Biol.*, **37,** 361–376.

HUXLEY, H. E. and J. HANSON. 1954. Changes in cross-striations of muscle during contraction and stretch and their structural interpretation. *Nature, Lond.*, **173,** 973–976.

HUXLEY, H. E. and J. HANSON. 1959. The structural basis of the contraction mechanism in striated muscle. *Ann. N.Y. Acad. Sci.*, **81,** 403–408.

IKEMOTO, N., S. KITAGAWA, A. NAKAMURA and J. GERGELY. 1968. Electron microscopic investigations of actomyosin as a function of ionic strength. *J. Cell Biol.*, **39,** 620–629.

ISHIWATA, S. 1973. A study on the F-actin-tropomyosin-troponin complex. I. Gel-filament transformation. *Biochem. biophys. Acta.*, **303,** 77–89.

JAGENDORF-ELFVIN, M. 1967. Ultrastructure of the contraction-relaxation cycle of glycerinated rabbit psoas muscle. II. The ultrastructure of glycerinated fibers relaxed in EDT and ATP following ATP-induced contraction. *J. Ultrastruct. Res.*, **17,** 379–400.

JULIAN, F. J., K. R. SOLLINS and M. R. SOLLINS. 1973. A model for muscle contraction in which cross-bridge attachment and force generation are distinct. In *The Mechanism of Muscle Contraction. Cold Spring Harb. Symp. quant. Biol.*, **37,** 685–688.

KAWAMURA, M. and K. MARUYAMA. 1970. Electron microscopic particle length of F-actin polymerized *in vitro*. *J. Biochem., Tokyo.*, **67,** 437–457.

KENDRICK-JONES, J., E. M. SZENTKIRALYI and A. G. SZENT-GYÖRGYI. 1973. Myosin-linked regulatory systems: the role of the light chains. In *The Mechanism of Muscle Contraction. Cold Spring Harb. Symp. quant. Biol.*, **37,** 47–54.

KIELLEY, W. W. 1965. Studies on the structure of myosin. In *Molecular Biology of Muscular Contraction*. S. Ebashi, F. Oosawa, T. Sekine and Y. Tonomura (eds.). Igaku Shoin, Tokyo and Elesvier, Amsterdam. 24–32.

KISCH, B. 1962. Sarcosome-theory of muscle function. *Revue can. Biol.*, **21,** 199–205.

KORETZ, J. F., T. HUNT and E. W. TAYLOR. 1973. Studies on the mechanism of myosin and actomyosin ATPase. In *The Mechanism of Muscle Contraction. Cold Spring Harb. Symp. quant. Biol.*, **37,** 179–186.

LARSON, P. F., M. JENKINSON and P. HUDGSON. 1970. The morphological development of chick embryo skeletal muscle grown in tissue culture as studied by electron microscopy. *J. Neurol. Sci.*, **10,** 385–405.

LINDNER, E. and G. SCHAUMBURG. 1968. Zytoplasmatische Filamente in den quergestreiften Muskelzellen des kaudalen Lymphherzens von *Rana temporaria* L. *Z. Zellforsch. mikrosk. Anat.*, **84,** 549–562.

LOEWY, A. G. 1968. A theory of covalent bonding in muscle contraction *J. theor. Biol.*, **20,** 164–172.

LOWEY, S. and J. C. HOLT. 1973. An immunochemical approach to the interaction of light and heavy chains in myosin. In *The Mechanism of Muscle Contraction. Cold Spring Harb. Symp. quant. Biol.*, **37,** 19–28.

LYMN, R. W. and H. E. HUXLEY. 1973. X-ray diagrams from skeletal muscle in the presence of ATP analogs. In *The Mechanism of Muscle Contraction. Cold Spring Harb. Symp. quant. Biol.*, **37,** 449–454.

MARGOSSIAN, S. S. and C. COHEN, 1973. Troponin. Subunit interactions. *J. molec. Biol.*, **81,** 409–414.

MARGOSSIAN, S. S. and S. LOWEY. 1973*a*. Substructure of the myosin molecule. III. Preparation of single-headed derivatives of myosin. *J. molec. Biol.*, **74,** 301–311.

MARGOSSIAN, S. S. and S. LOWEY. 1973*b*. Substructure of the myosin molecule. IV. Interactions of myosin and its subfragments with adenosine triphosphate and f-actin. *J. molec. Biol.*, **74,** 313–330.

MARTINEAU, H. and I. PINSET-HÄRSTRÖM. 1969. Interactions spécifiques de l'actomyosine avec les ions Mg^{2+} et Ca^{2+} étudiées au microscope électronique. *J. Ultrastruct. Res.*, **26,** 251–261.

MATSUBARA, I. and G. F. ELLIOTT. 1972. X-ray diffraction studies on skinned single fibres of frog skeletal muscle. *J. molec. Biol.*, **72,** 657–670.

MILLMAN, B. M., G. F. ELLIOT and J. LOWY. 1967. Axial period of actin filaments. *Nature, Lond.*, **213,** 353–358.

MOMMAERTS, W. F. H. M. 1965. Muscular contraction, a subject of molecular physiology. *Archs Biol., Liege*, **76,** 355–363.

MOMMAERTS, W. F. H. M., A. J. BRADY and B. C. ABBOTT. 1961. Major problems in muscle physiology. *A. Rev. Physiol.*, **23,** 529–576.

MORIMOTO, K. and W. F. HARRINGTON. 1973. Isolation and composition of thick filaments from rabbit skeletal muscle. *J. molec. Biol.*, **77,** 165–175.

MORIMOTO, K. and W. F. HARRINGTON 1974. Substructure of the thick filament of vertebrate striated muscle. *J. molec. Biol.*, **83,** 83–97.

MORIMOTO, K. and W. F. HARRINGTON. 1974. Evidence for structural changes in vertebrate thick filaments induced by calcium. *J. molec. Biol.*, **88,** 693–710.

NAKAMURA, A., F. SRETER and J. GERGELY. 1971. Comparative studies of light meromyosin paracrystals derived from red, white and cardiac muscle myosins. *J. Cell Biol.*, **49,** 883–898.

OFFER, G. 1973. C-Protein and the periodicity in the thick filaments of vertebrate skeletal muscle. In *The Mechanism of Muscle Contraction. Cold Spring Harb. Symp. quant. Biol.*, **37,** 87–96.

OFFER, G., C. MOOS and R. STARR. 1973. A new protein of the thick filaments of vertebrate skeletal myofibrils. Extraction purification and characterization. *J. molec. Biol.*, **74,** 653–676.

PAGE, S. G. 1964. Filament lengths in resting and excited muscles. *Proc. R. Soc. Ser. B*, **160,** 460–466.

PAGE, S. G. and H. E. HUXLEY. 1963. Filament lengths in striated muscle. *J. Cell Biol.*, **19,** 369–390.

PARRY, D. A. D. and J. M. SQUIRE. 1973. Structural role of tropomyosin in muscle regulation: analysis of the X-ray diffraction patterns from relaxed and contracting muscles. *J. molec. Biol.*, **75,** 33–55.

PEPE, F. A. 1967*a*. The myosin filament. I. Structural organization from antibody staining observed in electron microscopy. *J. molec. Biol.*, **27,** 203–225.

PEPE, F. A. 1967*b*. The myosin filament. II. Interaction between myosin and actin filaments observed using antibody staining in fluorescent and electron microscopy. *J. molec. Biol.*, **27,** 227–236.

PEPE, F. A. 1971. Structure of the myosin filament of striated muscle. *Prog. Biophys. & Mol. Biol.*, **22,** 75–96.

PEPE, F. A. 1973. The myosin filament: immunochemical and ultrastructural approaches to molecular organization. In *The Mechanism of Muscle Contraction. Cold Spring Harb. Symp. quant. Biol.*, **37,** 97–108.

PEPE, F. A. and B. DRUCKER. 1972. The myosin filament. IV. Observation of the internal structural arrangement. *J. Cell Biol.*, **52,** 255–260.

PERRY, S. V. 1965. Muscle proteins in contraction. In *Muscle*. W. M. Paul, E. E. Daniel, C. M. Kay and G. Monckton (eds.). Pergamon, London. 29–42.

PERRY, S. V. 1968. The role of myosin in muscular contraction. *Symp. Soc. exp. Biol.*, **22,** 1–16.

PINSET-HÄRTSTRÖM, I. 1967. Étude de certaines proprietés de l'actomyosine en presence d'adenosine tri-phosphate à l'aide de la microscopie électronique. *J. Ultrastruct. Res.*, **17,** 278–290.

PINSET-HÄRTSTRÖM, I. 1970. Interactions spécifiques de l'actomyosine avec l'adenosine tri-phosphate étudiées au microscope électronique. *J. Ultrastruct. Res.*, **33,** 1–15.

PRINGLE, J. W. S. 1960. Models of muscle: *Symp. Soc. exp. Biol.*, **14,** 41–68.

PRINGLE, J. W. S. 1968. Mechano-chemical transformation in striated muscle. *Symp. Soc. exp. Biol.*, **22,** 67–86.

RAYNS, D. G. 1972. Myofilaments and cross bridges as demonstrated by freeze-fracturing and etching. *J. Ultrastruct. Res.*, **40,** 103–121.

REGER, J. F. 1966. The fine structure of the extensor digitorium longus. IV. Muscle of *Rana pipiens* following calcium removal via EDTA. *Expl Cell Res.*, **43,** 435–443.

RICE, R. V., A. C. BRADY, R. H. DEPUE and R. E. KELLY. 1966. Morphology of individual macromolecules and their ordered aggregates by electron microscopy. *Biochem. Z.*, **345,** 370–394.

ROME, E. 1974. Relaxation of glycerinated muscle: low-angle X-ray diffraction studies. *J. molec. Biol.*, **65,** 331–346.

ROWE, A. J. 1964. The contractile proteins of skeletal muscle. *Proc. R. Soc. Ser. B*, **160,** 437–441.

SAMOSUDOVA, N. V. and G. M. FRANK. 1971. Change in the ultrastructure of the contractile apparatus of striated muscle during tonic contraction. *Biofizika*, **16,** 250–260.

SANGER, J. W. 1971. Formation of synthetic myosin filaments: Influence of pH, ionic strength, cation substitution, dielectric constant and method of preparation. *Cytobiologie*, **4,** 450–466.

SARKAR, S., F. A. SRÉTER and J. GERGELY. 1971. Light chains of myosin from white, red and cardiac muscle. *Proc. natn. Acad. Sci. U.S.A.*, **68,** 946–950.

SCHIAFFINO, S., V. HANZLÍKOVÁ and S. PIEROBON. 1970. Relations between structure and function in rat skeletal muscle fibers. *J. Cell Biol.*, **47,** 107–119.

SJÖSTRAND, F. S. and M. JAGENDORF-ELFVIN. 1967. Ultrastructure studies of the contraction-relaxation cycle of glycerinated rabbit psoas muscle. The ultrastructure of glycerinated fibers contracted by treatment with ATP. *J. Ultrastruct. Res.*, **17,** 348–378.

SLAYTER, H. S. and S. LOWEY. 1967. Substructure of the myosin molecule as visualized by electron microscopy. *Proc. natn. Acad. Sci. U.S.A.*, **58,** 1611–1618.

SPUDICH, J. A. 1973. Effects of cytochalasin B on actin filaments. In *The Mechanism of Muscle Contraction. Cold Spring Harb. Symp. quant. Biol.*, **37,** 585–594.

SPUDICH, J. A., H. E. HUXLEY and J. T. FINCH. 1972. Regulation of skeletal muscle contraction. II. Structural studies of the interaction of the tropomyosin-troponin complex with actin. *J. molec. Biol.*, **72,** 619–632.

SQUIRE, J. M. 1971. General model for the structure of all myosin-containing filaments. *Nature, Lond.*, **233,** 457–462.

SQUIRE, J. M. 1972. General model of myosin filament structure. II. Myosin filaments and cross-bridge interactions in vertebrate striated and insect flight muscles. *J. molec. Biol.*, **72,** 125–138.

SQUIRE, J. M. 1973. General model of myosin filament structure. III. Molecular packing arrangements in myosin filaments. *J. molec. Biol.*, **77,** 291–323.

STARR, R. and G. OFFER. 1973. Polarity of the myosin molecule. *J. molec. Biol.*, **81,** 17–32.

STEPHENS, R. E. 1965. Analysis of muscle contraction by ultraviolet microbeam disruption of sarcomere structure. *J. Cell Biol.*, **25,** Suppl., 129–139.

STRACHER, A. and P. DREIZEN. 1966. Structure and function of the contractile protein myosin. In *Current Topics in Bioenergetics.* Vol. 1. D. R. Sanadi (ed.). Academic Press, New York. 153–202.

SZENT-GYÖRGYI, A. G. 1951. *Chemistry of Muscular Contraction.* 2nd edition. Academic Press, New York.

SZENT-GYÖRGYI, A. G. 1968. Role of actin-myosin in contraction. *Symp. Soc. exp. Biol.*, **22,** 17–48.

SZENT-GYÖRGYI, A. G. and W. H. JOHNSON. 1964. An alternative theory for contraction of striated muscles. In *Biochemistry of Muscle Contraction.* J. Gergely (ed.). Little, Brown & Co., Boston. 485–510.

TONOMURA, Y., S. KUBO and K. IMAMURA. 1965. A molecular model for the interaction of myosin with adenosine phosphate. In *Molecular Biology of Muscular Contraction.* S. Ebashi, F. Oosawa, T. Sekine and Y. Tonomura (eds.). Igaku Shoin, Tokyo; and Elsevier, Amsterdam. 11–23.

TROMBITÁS, K. and A. TIGYI-SEBES. 1972. Continuity of thick and thin filaments. *Acta biochem. biophys. Acad. Sci. hung.*, **7,** 193–194.

TSAO, T.-C., Y.-S. TSOU, Z.–X. LU, T.-H. KUNG, C.-H. PAN, Q.-L. LI, H.-J. KU and H.-T. TSAO. 1965. Demonstration of the existence of tropomyosin and actin in the thin filaments of striated muscle by direct isolation. *Scientia sin.*, **14,** 1707–1709.

ULLRICK, W. C. 1967. A theory of contraction for striated muscle. *J. theor. Biol.*, **15,** 53–69.

VIBERT, P. J., J. C. HASELGROVE, J. LOWY and F. R. POULSEN. 1972. Structural changes in actin-containing filaments of muscle. *J. molec. Biol.*, **71,** 757–767.

WALCOTT, B. and E. B. RIDGWAY. 1967. The ultrastructure of myosin-extracted striated muscle fibers. *Am. Zool.*, **7,** 499–504.

WALKER, S. M. and G. R. SCHRODT. 1974. I. Segment lengths and thin filament periods in skeletal muscle fibers of the rhesus monkey and the human. *Anat. Rec.*, **178,** 63–82.

WEBER, M. and A. WEBER. 1974. The cooperative action of muscle proteins. *Scient. Am.*, **230,** 58–83.

WEEDS, A. G. and G. FRANK. 1973. Structural studies on the light chains of myosin. In *The Mechanism of Muscle Contraction. Cold Spring Harb. Symp. quant. Biol.*, **37,** 9–13.

WEEDS, A. G. and S. LOWEY. 1971. Substructure of the myosin molecule. II. The light chains of myosin. *J. molec. Biol.*, **61,** 701–725.

YOUNG, M., M. V. KING, D. S. O'HARA and P. J. MOLBERG. 1973. Studies on the structure and assembly pattern of the light meromyosin section of the myosin rod. In *The Mechanism of Muscle Contraction. Cold Spring Harb. Symp. quant. Biol.*, **37,** 65–76.

YU, L. C., R. M. DOWBEN and K. KORNACKER.

1970. The molecular mechanism of force generation in striated muscle. *Proc. natn. Acad. Sci. U.S.A.*, **66,** 1199–1205.

ZOBEL, C. R. 1967. An electron-microscopic investigation of heavy meromyosin. *Biochem. biophys. Acta*, **140,** 222–230.

ZOBEL, C. R., R. J. BASKIN and S. L. WOLFE. 1967. Electron microscope observations on thick filaments isolated from striated muscle. *J. Ultrastruct. Res.*, **18,** 637–650.

Vertebrate cardiac muscle

ALPERT, N. R. (ed.) 1971. *Cardiac Hypertrophy.* Academic Press, New York.

BÁRÁNY, M., E. GAETJENS, K. BÁRÁNY and E. KARP. 1964. Comparative studies of rabbit cardiac and skeletal myosins. *Archs. Biochem. Biophys.*, **106,** 280–293.

BURLINGTON, R. F., W. D. BOWERS, R. C. DAUM JR., and P. ASHBAUGH. 1972. Ultrastructural changes in heart tissue during hibernation. *Cryobiology*, **9,** 224–228.

CARNEY, J. A. and A. L. BROWN, JR. 1965. Human cardiac myosin: electron microscopic observations. *Circulation Res.*, **17,** 336–339.

CARNEY, J. A. and A. L. BROWN, JR. 1966. An electron microscope study of canine cardiac myosin and some of its aggregates. *J. Cell Biol.*, **28,** 375–389.

HATT, P. Y. and B. SWYNGHEDAUW. 1968. Electron microscopic study of myocardium in experimental heart insufficiency. In *Herzinsuffizienz Pathophysiologie und Klinik.* H. Reindell, J. Keul and E. Doll (eds.). George Thieme, Stuttgart. 19–40.

HUXLEY, H. E. 1961. The contractile structure of cardiac and skeletal muscle. *Circulation*, **24,** 328–335.

MUELLER, H., J. FRANZEN, R. V. RICE and R. E. OLSON. 1964. Characterization of cardiac myosin from the dog. *J. biol. Chem.*, **239,** 1447–1456.

NAKAMURA, A., F. SRETER and J. GERGELY. 1971. Comparative studies of light meromyosin paracrystals derived from red, white and cardiac muscle myosins. *J. Cell Biol.*, **49,** 883–898.

NAYLOR, W. G. and N. C. R. MERRILLEES. 1964. Some observations on the fine structure and metabolic activity of normal and glycerinated ventricular muscle of toad. *J. Cell Biol.*, **22,** 533–550.

NIEMEYER, G. and W. G. FORSSMANN. 1971. Comparison of glycerol treatment in frog skeletal muscle and mammalian heart. An electrophysiological and morphological study. *J. Cell Biol.*, **50,** 288–299.

PURDY, J. E., M. LIEBERMAN, A. E. ROGGEVEEN and R. G. KIRK. 1972. Synthetic strands of cardiac muscle. Formation and ultrastructure. *J. Cell Biol.*, **55,** 563–578.

ROUILLER, CH. and W. G. FORSSMANN. 1965. Notions actuelles sur l'ultrastructure du muscle squelettique et cardiaque. *Verh. schweiz. naturf. Ges.*, **145,** 171–178.

SANTER, R. M. 1972. An electron microscopical study of the development of the teleost heart. *Z. Anat. EntwGesch.*, **139,** 93–105.

SCHIEBLER, T. H. and H. H. WOLFF. 1966. Elektronenmikroskopische Untersuchungen am Herzmuskel der Ratte während der Entwicklung. *Z. Zellforsch. mikrosk. Anat.*, **69,** 22–40.

SOMMER, J. R. and M. S. SPACH. 1964. Electron microscopic demonstration of adenosine triphosphatase in myofibrils and sarcoplasmic membranes of cardiac muscle of normal and abnormal dogs. *Am. J. Path.*, **44,** 491–506.

SONNENBLICK, E. H., D. SPIRO and T. S. COTTRELL. 1963. Fine structural changes in heart muscle in relation to the length-tension curve. *Proc. natn. Acad. Sci. U.S.A.*, **49,** 193–200.

SONNENBLICK, E. H., D. SPIRO and H. M. SPOTNITZ. 1964. The ultrastructural basis of Starling's law of the heart. The role of the sarcomere in determining ventricular size and stroke volume. *Am. Heart J.*, **68,** 336–346.

SONNENBLICK, E. H., H. M. SPOTNITZ and D. SPIRO. 1964. Role of the sarcomere in ventricular function and the mechanism of heart failure. *Circulation Res.*, **15,** Suppl. II, 70–80.

SPIRO, D. and E. H. SONNENBLICK. 1964. Comparison of the ultra-structural basis of the contractile process in heart and skeletal muscle. *Circulation Res.*, **15,** Suppl. II, 14–37.

SPIRO, D. and E. H. SONNENBLICK. 1965. The structural basis of the contractile process in heart muscle under physiological and pathological conditions. *Prog. cardiovasc. Dis.*, **7,** 295–335.

SPOTNITZ, H. M., E. H. SONNENBLICK and D. SPIRO. 1966. Relation of ultrastructure to function in the intact heart: sarcomere structure relative to pressure volume curves of intact left ventricles of dog and cat. *Circulation Res.*, **18,** 49–66.

TICE, L. W. and R. J. BARRNETT. 1962. Fine structural localization of adenosinetriphosphatase activity in heart muscle myofibrils. *J. Cell Biol.*, **15,** 401–416.

Vertebrate smooth muscle

BOIS, R. M. 1973. The organization of the contractile apparatus of vertebrate smooth muscles. *Anat. Rec.*, **177,** 61–78.

BOIS, R. M. and D. C. PEASE. 1974. Electron microscopic studies of the state of myosin aggregation in the vertebrate smooth muscle cell. *Anat. Rec.*, **180,** 465–480.

BREMEL, R. D. 1974. Myosin linked calcium regulation in vertebrate smooth muscle. *Nature, Lond.*, **252,** 405–407.

BÜSSOW, H. and U. WULFHEKEL. 1972. Die Feinstruktur der glatten Muskelzellen in der grossen muskulären Arterien der Vögel. *Z. Zellforsch. mikrosk. Anat.*, **125,** 339–352.

CAMPBELL, G. R., Y. UEHARA, G. MARK and G. BURNSTOCK. 1971. Fine structure of smooth muscle cells grown in tissue culture. *J. Cell Biol.*, **49,** 21–34.

CARSTEN, M. E. 1971. Uterine smooth muscle: Troponin. *Archs. Biochem. Biophys.*, **147,** 353–357.

CHOI, J. K. 1962. Fine structure of the smooth muscle of the chicken's gizzard. *Proc. 5th Int. Congr. Electron Microscopy*, Philadelphia. S. S. Breese (ed.). Academic Press, New York.

COOKE, P. H., R. H. CHASE and J. M. CORTES. 1970. Thick filaments resembling myosin in electrophoretically-extracted vertebrate smooth muscle. *Expl Cell Res.*, **60,** 237–246.

COOKE, P. H. and F. S. FAY. 1972. Correlation between fiber length, ultrastructure, and the length-tension relationship of mammalian smooth muscle. *J. Cell Biol.*, **52,** 105–116.

COOKE, P. H. and F. S. FAY. 1972. Thick myofilaments in contracted and relaxed mammalian smooth muscle cells. *Expl Cell Res.*, **71,** 265–272.

DEVINE, C. E. and A. P. SOMLYO. 1971. Thick filaments in vascular smooth muscle. *J. Cell Biol.*, **49,** 636–649.

ELFORD, B. C. and C. A. WALTER. 1972. Effects of electrolyte composition and pH on the structure and function of smooth muscle cooled to −79°C in unfrozen media. *Cryobiology*, **9,** 82–100.

ELLIOTT, G. F. 1967. Variations of the contractile apparatus in smooth and striated muscles. X-ray diffraction studies at rest and in contraction. *J. gen. Physiol.*, **50,** Suppl., 174–184.

FAY, F. S. and P. H. COOKE. 1973. Reversible disaggregation of myofilaments in vertebrate smooth muscle. *J. Cell Biol.*, **56,** 399–411.

FAY, F. S. and C. M. DELISE. 1973. Contraction of isolated smooth-muscle cells: structural changes. *Proc. natn. Acad. Sci. U.S.A.*, **70,** 641–645.

GANSLER, H. 1960. Phasenkontrast -und elektronenmikroskopische Untersuchungen zur Morphologie und Funktion der glatten Muskulatur. *Z. Zellforsch. mikrosk. Anat.*, **52,** 60–92.

GARAMVÖLGYI, N., E. S. VIZI and J. KNOLL. 1971. The regular occurrence of thick filaments in stretched mammalian smooth muscle. *J. Ultrastruct. Res.*, **34,** 135–143.

HAMOIR, G. and L. LASZT. 1962. Tonomyosin of arterial muscle. *Nature, Lond.*, **193,** 682–684.

HANSON, J. and J. LOWY. 1964. The problem of the location of myosin in vertebrate smooth muscle. *Proc. R. Soc. Ser. B*, **160,** 523–524.

HEUMANN, H.-G. 1969. Gibt es in glatten Vertebratenmuskeln dicke Filamente? Elektronenmikroskopische Untersuchungen an der Darmmuskulatur der Hausmaus. *Zool. Anz. Supp.*, **33,** *Verh. Zool. Ges.*, 416–424.

HEUMANN, H.-G. 1971. Über die Funktionsweise glatter Muskelfasern Elektronenmikroskopische Untersuchungen an der Darmmuskulatur der Hausmaus. *Cytobiologie*, **3,** 259–281.

JAISLE, F. 1965. Die Isolierung der Contractilen und Strukturproteine aus dem Myometrium beim Menschen. *Arch. Gynaek.*, **200,** 421–427.

KAMINER, B. 1969. Synthetic myosin filaments from vertebrate smooth muscle. *J. molec. Biol.*, **39,** 257–264.

KAMINER, B., E. SZONYI and C. D. BELCHER. 1976. 'Hybrid' myosin filaments from smooth and striated muscle. *J. molec. Biol.*, **100,** 379–386.

KELLY, R. E. and J. W. ARNOLD. 1972. Myofilaments of the papillary muscles of the iris fixed *in situ*. *J. Ultrastruct. Res.*, **40,** 532–545.

KELLY, R. E and R. V. RICE. 1968. Localization of myosin filaments in smooth muscle. *J. Cell Biol.*, **37,** 105–116.

KELLY, R. E. and R. V. RICE. 1969. Ultrastructural studies on the contractile mechanism of smooth muscle. *J. Cell Biol.*, **42,** 683–694.

KENDRICK-JONES, J., A. G. SZENT-GYÖRGYI and C. COHEN. 1971. Segments from vertebrate smooth muscle myosin rods. *J. molec. Biol.*, **59,** 527–529.

KEYSERLINGK, D. GRAPH 1970. Ultrastruktur glycerinextrahierter Dünndarmmuskelzellen der Ratte vor und nach Kontraktion. *Z. Zellforsch. mikrosk. Anat.*, **111,** 559–571.

KRISTENSEN, B. I., L. E. NIELSEN and J. ROSTGAARD. 1971. A two-filament system and interaction of heavy meromyosin (HMM) with thin filaments in smooth muscle. *Z. Zellforsch. mikrosk. Anat.*, **122,** 350–356.

LANE, B. P. 1965. Alterations in the cytologic detail of intestinal smooth muscle cells in various stages of contraction. *J. Cell Biol.*, **27,** 199–213.

LOWY, J. and J. V. SMALL. 1970. The organization of myosin and actin in vertebrate smooth muscle. *Nature, Lond.*, **227,** 46–51.

MALLIN, M. L. 1966. Actomyosin of human vascular smooth muscle. *Nature, Lond.*, **210,** 951–952.

MIURA, S. 1969*a*. Electron microscope studies on intestinal smooth muscle. I. Conformational changes in cytologic details, especially dense bodies in contracted and relaxed cell. *Sapporo med. J.*, **35,** 407–421.

MIURA, S. 1969*b*. Electronmicroscope studies on intestinal smooth muscle. II. Changes of dense bodies and dense patches caused by various biochemical treatments. *Sapporo med. J.*, **35,** 422–433.

NEEDHAM, D. M. and C. F. SHOENBERG. 1964. Proteins of the contractile mechanism of mammalian smooth muscle and their possible location in the cell. *Proc. R. Soc. Ser. B*, **160,** 517–524.

NONOMURA, Y. 1968. Myofilaments in smooth muscle of guinea pig's taenia coli. *J. Cell Biol.*, **39,** 741–745.

PANNER, B. J. and C. R. HONIG. 1967. Filament ultrastructure and organization in vertebrate smooth muscle. Contraction hypothesis based on localization of actin and myosin. *J. Cell Biol.*, **35,** 303–321.

PANNER, B. J. and C. R. HONIG. 1970. Locus and state of aggregation of myosin in tissue sections of vertebrate smooth muscle. *J. Cell Biol.*, **44,** 52–61.

PEASE, D. C. 1968. Structural features of unfixed mammalian smooth and striated muscle prepared by glycol dehydration. *J. Ultrastruct. Res.*, **23,** 280–303.

POPESCU, L. M. and N. IONESCU. 1970*a*. On the equivalence between dense bodies and Z-bands. *Experientia*, **26,** 642–643.

POPESCU, L. M. and N. IONESCU. 1970*b*. Electron microscope studies on the nature of the dense bodies in smooth muscle fibers. *Z. mikrosk.-anat. Forsch.*, **82,** 67–75.

RHODIN, J. A. G. 1962. Fine structure of vascular walls in mammals with special reference to smooth muscle component. *Physiol. Rev.*, **42,** Suppl. 5, 48–81.

RICE, R. V. and A. C. BRADY. 1973. Biochemical and ultrastructural studies on vertebrate smooth muscle. In *The Mechanism of Muscle Contraction. Cold Spring Harb. Symp. quant. Biol.*, **37,** 429–438.

RICE, R. V., G. M. MCMANUS, C. E. DEVINE and A. P. SOMLYO. 1971. Regular organization of thick filaments in mammalian smooth muscle. *Nature, Lond.*, **231,** 242–243.

RICE, R. V., J. A. MOSES, G. M. MCMANUS, A. C. BRADY and L. M. BLASIK. 1970. The organization of contractile filaments in a mammalian smooth muscle. *J. Cell Biol.*, **47,** 183–196.

ROSENBLUTH, J. 1965. Smooth muscle: an ultrastructural basis for the dynamics of its contraction. *Science, N.Y.*, **148,** 1337–1339.

ROSENBLUTH, J. 1971. Myosin-like aggregates in trypsin-treated smooth muscle cells. *J. Cell Biol.*, **48,** 174–188.

ROSENBLUTH, J. 1972. Unphysiological conditions favoring the aggregation of smooth muscle myosin *in situ*. *J. Cell Biol.*, **55,** 220a.

SANGER, J. W. and R. B. HILL. 1972. Disposition of thick and thin filaments in smooth muscle as a function of length and tension. *J. Cell Biol.*, **55,** 255a.

SCHIRMER, R. H. 1965. Die Besonderheiten des contractilen Proteins der Arterien. *Biochem. Z.*, **343,** 269–282.

SCHLÖTE, F.-W. 1960. Die Kontraktion glatter Muskulatur auf Grund von Torsionsspannungen in den Myofilamenten. *Z. Zellforsch. mikrosk. Anat.*, **52,** 362–395.

SEIDEL, D. and H. H. WEBER. 1967. Die Aktomyosinstruktur im glatten muskel der Vertebraten. *Pflügers Arch. ges. Physiol.*, **297,** 1–9.

SHOENBERG, C. F. 1962. Some electron microscope observation on the contraction mechanism in vertebrate smooth muscle. In *5th Int. Congr. Electron Microscopy*. Vol. 2. S. S. Breese (ed.). Academic Press, New York.

SHOENBERG, C. F. 1969. An electron microscope study of the influence of divalent ions on myosin filament formation in chicken gizzard extracts and homogenates. *Tissue & Cell*, **1,** 83–96.

SHOENBERG, C. F., P. J. GOODFORD, M. W. WOLOWYK and G. S. WOOTON. 1973. Ionic changes during smooth muscle fixation for electron microscopy. *J. Mechanochem. Cell Motility*, **2,** 69–82.

SHOENBERG, C. F., J. C. RÜEGG, D. M. NEEDHAM, R. H. SCHIRMER and H. NEMETCHEK-GANSLER. 1966. A biochemical and electron microscope study of the contractile proteins in vertebrate smooth muscle. *Biochem. Z.*, **345,** 255–266.

SMALL, J. V. and A. SOBIESZEK. 1973. The core component of the myosin-containing elements of vertebrate smooth muscle. In *The Mechanism of Muscle Contraction. Cold Spring Harb. Symp. quant. Biol.*, **37,** 117–149.

SMALL, J. V. and J. M. SQUIRE. 1972. Structural basis of contraction in vertebrate smooth muscle. *J. molec. Biol.*, **67,** 117–149.

SOBIESZEK, A. 1972. Cross bridges on self-assembled smooth muscle myosin filaments. *J. molec. Biol.*, **70,** 741–744.

SOBIESZEK, A. and J. V. SMALL. 1973*a*. The assembly of ribbon-shaped structures in low ionic strength extracts obtained from vertebrate smooth muscle. *Phil. Trans. R. Soc. Ser. B*, **265,** 203–212.

SOBIESZEK, A. and J. V. SMALL. 1973*b*. Filaments from purified muscle myosin. In *The Mechanism of Muscle Contraction. Cold Spring Harb. Symp. quant. Biol.*, **37,** 109–112.

SOMLYO, A. P., C. E. DEVINE and A. V. SOMLYO. 1971. Thick filaments in unstretched mammalian smooth muscle. *Nature, New Biology*, **23,** 218–219.

SOMLYO, A. P., A. V. SOMLYO, C. E. DEVINE and R. V. RICE. 1971. Aggregation of thick filaments into ribbons in mammalian smooth muscle. *Nature, New Biology*, **231,** 243–246.

TAKAHASHI, T., H. YABU and E. MIYAZAKI. 1968. Effects of glycerination on the respiratory activity and ultrastructure of smooth muscle fibers. *Sapporo med. J.*, **33,** 352–358.

TREGEAR, R. T. and J. M. SQUIRE. 1973. Myosin content and filament structure in smooth and striated muscle. *J. molec. Biol.*, **77,** 279–290.

WALTER C. A. 1970. Ultrastructural and functional changes in smooth muscle associated with freezing and thawing. In *The Frozen Cell*, Ciba Foundation Symposium. G. E. W. Wolstenholme and M. O'Connor (eds.). J. & A. Churchill, London. 271–290.

WEBER, H. H. and J. C. RÜEGG. 1966. The contractile fine structure of vertebrate smooth muscle. *Med. Coll. Virginia Quart.* **2,** 72–77.

VIZI, E. S., N. GARAMVÖLGYI and J. KNOLL. 1973. Thick filaments in guinea-pig vas deferens smooth muscle. *Acta Biol. Hellen.*, **8,** 73–76.

WACHSBERGER, P. R. and F. A. PEPE. 1974. Purification of uterine myosin and synthetic filament formation. *J. molec. Biol.*, **88,** 385–392.

Invertebrate muscle

ABBOTT, R. H. and R. A. CHAPLAIN. 1966. Preparation and properties of the contractile element of insect fibrillar muscle. *J. Cell Sci.*, **1,** 311–330.

ALLÉRA, A., R. BECK and K. E. WOHLFARTH-BOTTERMANN. 1971. Weitreichende fibrilläre Protoplasma-differenzierungen und ihre Bedeutung für die Protoplasmaströmung. VIII. Identifizierung der Plasmafilamente von *Physarum polycephalum* als F-Actin durch Anlagerung von heavy meromyosin *in situ*. *Cytobiologie*, **4,** 437–449.

ALLÉRA, A. and K. E. WOHLFARTH-BOTTERMANN. 1972. Weitreichende fibrilläre Protoplasmadifferenzierungen und ihre Bedeutung für die Protoplasmaströmung. IX. Aggregationszustände des Myosins und Bedingungen zur Entstehung von Myosinfilamenten in den Plasmodien von *Physarum polycephalum*. *Cytobiologie*, **6,** 261–286.

ARMITAGE, P., A. MILLER, C. D. RODGER and R. T. TREGEAR. 1973. The structure and function of insect muscle. In *The Mechanism of Muscle Contraction. Cold Spring Harb. Symp. quant. Biol.*, **37,** 379–388.

ARONSON, J. 1963. Observations on the variations in size of the A region of arthropod muscle. *J. Cell Biol.*, **19,** 359–367.

AUBER, J. 1964. Les premiers stades de la myofibrillogenèse dans les muscles du vol de *Calliphora erythrocephala* (Mg.) (Insecte Diptère). *C.r. hebd. Séanc. Acad. Sci., Paris*, **258,** 708–710.

AUBER, J. 1967*a*. Particularités ultrastructurales des myofibrilles des muscles du vol chez des Lépidoptères. *C.r. hebd. Séanc. Acad. Sci., Paris*, **264,** Série D, 621–624.

AUBER, J. 1967*b*. Distribution of the two kinds of myofilaments in insect muscles. *Am. Zool.*, **7,** 451–456.

AUBER, M. 1963. Remarques sur l'ultrastructure des myofibrilles chez des scorpions. *J. Microsc. (Fr.)*, **2,** 233–236.

BEAR, R. S. and C. C. SELBY. 1956. The structure of paramyosin fibrils according to X-ray diffraction. *J. biophys. biochem. Cytol.*, **2,** 55–85.

BECK, R., H. HINSSEN, H. KOMNICK, W. STOCKEM and K. E. WOHLFARTH-BOTTERMANN. 1970. Weitreichende fibrilläre Protoplasma-differenzierungen und ihre Bedeutung für die Protoplasmaströmung. V. Kontraktion, ATP-ase-Aktivität und Freinstruktur isolierter Actomyosin-Fäden von *Physarum polycephalum*. *Cytobiologie*, **2,** 259–274.

BECK, R., H. KOMNICK, W. STOCKEM and K. E. WOHLFARTH-BOTTERMANN. 1970. Weitreichende fibrilläre Protoplasmadifferenzierungen und ihre Bedeutung für die Protoplasmaströmung. VI. Vergleichende Untersuchungen an isolierten Actomyosin-Fäden schräggestreifter und glatter Muskeln. *Cytobiologie*, **2,** 413–428.

BEINBRECH, G. 1970. Zur Funktion der Mikrotubuli beim Wachstum der Myofibrillen von Insektenflugmuskeln. *Z. Zellforsch. mikrosk. Anat.*, **109,** 138–146.

BIENZ-ISLER, G. 1968*a*. Elektronenmikroskopische Untersuchungen über die imaginale Struktur der dorsolongitudinalen Flugmuskeln von *Antheraea pernyi* Guer. (Lepidoptera). *Acta anat.*, **70,** 416–433.

BIENZ-ISLER, G. 1968*b*. Elektronenmikroskopische Untersuchungen über die Entwicklung der dorsolongitudinalen Flugmuskeln von *Antheraea pernyi* Guer. (Lepidoptera). *Acta anat.*, **70,** 524–553.

BOCHÁROVA-MESSNER, O. M. and K. A. YANCHUK. 1966. Izmenenie ul'trastruktury krylovykh myshts v. ontogeneze domovogo sverchka (*Acheta domestica* L.). *Dokl. Acad. Nauk SSSR.* **170,** 948–951.

BOULIGAND, Y. 1964. Les ultrastructures musculaires des copépodes. III. Nature de la bande de contraction C_M des sarcomères. *J. Microsc. (Fr.)*, **3,** 697–710.

BOULIGAND, Y. 1966. La disposition des myofilaments chez une annélide polychète. *J. Microsc. (Fr.)*, **5,** 305–322.

BRANDT, P. W., J. P. REUBEN, L. GIRARDIER and H. GRUNDFEST. 1965. Correlated morphological and physiological studies on isolated single muscle fibers. I. Fine structure of the crayfish muscle fiber. *J. Cell Biol.*, **25,** Suppl. 2, 233–260.

BULLARD, B. and M. K. REEDY. 1973. How many myosins per cross-bridge? II. Flight muscle myosin from the blowfly, *Sarcophaga bullata*. In *The Mechanism of Muscle Contraction. Cold Spring Harb. Symp. quant. Biol.*, **37,** 423–428.

CAMATINI, M. 1971. Osservazioni sulla muscolatura del volo degli insetti a bassa

frequenza di contrazione. *Ist Lombardo Accad. Sci. Lett. Rend. Sci. Biol. Med. B*, **105,** 107–123.
CHAPLAIN, R. A. and R. T. TREGEAR. 1966. The mass of myosin per cross-bridge in insect fibrillar flight muscle. *J. molec. Biol.*, **21,** 275–280.
COBB, J. L. S. and M. S. LAVERACK. 1966. The lantern of *Echinus esculentes* (L). III. The fine structure of the lantern retractor muscle and its innervation. *Proc. R. Soc. Ser. B*, **164,** 651–658.
COHEN, C., A. G. SZENT-GYÖRGYI and J. KENDRICK-JONES. 1971. Paramyosin and the filaments of molluscan 'catch' muscles. I. Paramyosin: structure and assembly. *J. molec Biol.*, **56,** 223–237.
DEWEY, M. M., R. J. C. LEVINE and D. E. COLFLESH. 1973. Structure of *Limulus* striated muscle: the contractile apparatus at various sarcomere lengths. *J. Cell Biol.*, **58,** 574–593.
ELLIOTT, A. and J. LOWY. 1970. A model for the coarse structure of paramyosin filaments. *J. molec. Biol.*, **53,** 181–203.
ELLIOTT, G. F. 1964. Electron microscope studies of the structure of the filaments in the opaque adductor muscle of the oyster *Crassostrea angulata*. *J. molec. Biol.*, **10,** 89–104.
FOH, E. 1969. Die Auswirkung passiver Dehnungen auf die Struktur des glatten *Musculus retractor penis* von *Helix pomatia* L. *Z. Zellforsch. mikrosk. Anat.*, **93,** 414–433.
FRANZINI-ARMSTRONG, C. 1970. Natural variability in the length of thin and thick filaments in single fibres from a crab, *Portanus depurator*. *J. Cell Sci.*, **6,** 559–592.
GARAMVÖLGYI, N. 1965*a*. The arrangement of the myofilaments in the insect flight muscle. I. *J. Ultrastruct. Res.*, **13,** 409–424.
GARAMVÖLGYI, N. 1965*b*. The arrangement of the myofilaments in the insect flight muscle. II. *J. Ultrastruct. Res.*, **13,** 425–434.
GARAMVÖLGYI, N. 1969. The structural basis of the elastic properties in the flight muscle of the bee. *J. Ultrastruct. Res*, **27,** 462–471.
GARAMVÖLGYI, N. 1972. Forces acting between muscle filaments. I. Filament lattice spacing in bee flight muscle. *Acta biochim. biophys. Acad. Sci. Hung.*, **7,** 157–164.
GARAMVÖLGYI, N. and J. BELÁGYI. 1968. Mechanical properties of the flight muscle of the bee. I. Resting elasticity and its ultrastructural interpretation. *Acta Biochem. Biophys. Acad. Sci. Hung.*, **3,** 195–204.
GICQUAUD, C. R. and P. COUILLARD. 1972. Preservations des mouvements dans le cytoplasme démembrané d'*Amoeba proteus*. II. Mise en evidence de filaments de type myosine dans les preparations. *Cytobiologie*, **5,** 139–145.
GILAI, A. and I. PARNAS. 1972. Electromechanical coupling in tubular muscle fibers. I. The organization of tubular muscle fibers in the scorpion *Leiurus quinquestriatus*. *J. Cell Biol.*, **52,** 626–638.
GILËV, V. P. 1966. The ultrastructure of myofilaments. II. Further investigation of the thick filaments of crab muscles. *Biochim. biophys. Acta*, **112,** 340–345.
GILMOUR, D. and P. M. ROBINSON. 1964. Contraction in glycerinated myofibrils of an insect (*Orthoptera acrididae*). *J. Cell Biol.*, **21,** 385–396.
GONZALEZ-AGUILAR, F. 1972. Non-oblique myofilament arrangement in the dorsal muscle of *Sabellastarte magnifica*. *Z. Zellforsch. mikrosk. Anat.*, **129,** 11–19.
HAGOPIAN, M. 1966. The myofilament arrangement in the femoral muscle of the cockroach, *Leucophaea maderae* Fabricius. *J. Cell Biol.*, **28,** 545–562.
HAGOPIAN, M. and D. SPIRO. 1968. The filament lattice of cockroach thoracic muscle. *J. Cell Biol.*, **36,** 433–442.
HALVARSON, M. and B. A. AFZELIUS. 1969. Filament organization in the body muscles of the arrow worm. *J. Ultrastruct. Res*, **26,** 289–295.
HANSON, J. 1956. Studies on the cross-striation of the indirect flight myofibrils of the blowfly *Calliphora*. *J. biophys. biochem. Cytol.*, **2,** 691–710.
HAYES, D., M. HUANG and C. R. ZOBEL. 1971. Electron microscope observations on thick filaments in striated muscle from the lobster *Homarus americanus*. *J. Ultrastruct. Res.*, **37,** 17–30.
HEHN, G. VON. 1967. Die Muskulatur des Eileiters von *Carausius morosus*. I. Mitteilung. Histologische Untersuchungen. *Z. Zellforsch. mikrosk. Anat.*, **78,** 511–545.

HEUMANN, H.-G. 1973. Substructure of paramyosin filaments prepared by freeze-substitution technique. *Experientia*, **29,** 469–471.

HEUMANN, H.-G. and J. C. RÜEGG. 1968. Aggregation von Paramyosin-Filamenten in tonischen Muskeln von Mollusken während des Sperrtonus. *Pflügers Arch. ges. Physiol.*, **300,** R87.

HEUMANN, H.-G. and E. ZEBE. 1967. Über Feinbau und Funktionsweise der Fasern aus dem Hautmuskelschlauch des Regenwurms, *Lumbricus terrestris* L. *Z. Zellforsch. mikrosk. Anat.*, **78,** 131–150.

HEUMANN, H.-G. and E. ZEBE. 1968. Über die Funktionsweise glatter Muskelfasern. Elektronenmikroskopische Untersuchungen am Byssusretraktor (ABRM) von *Mytilus edulis*. *Z. Zellforsch. mikrosk. Anat.*, **85,** 534–551.

HINSSEN, H. 1970. Synthetische Myosinfilamente von Schleimpilz-Plasmodien. *Cytobiologie*, **2,** 326–331.

HODGE, A. J. 1955. Studies on the structure of muscle. III. Phase contrast and electron microscopy of dipteran flight muscle. *J. biophys. biochem. Cytol.*, **1,** 361–380.

HOFFMEISTER, H. 1961. Morphologische Beobachtungen an erschöpften indirekten Flugmuskeln der Wespe. *Z. Zellforsch. mikrosk. Anat.*, **54,** 402–420.

HOFFMEISTER, H. 1962. Beobachtungen an indirekten Flugmuskeln der Wespe nach Erholung von Erschöpfendem Dauerflug. *Z. Zellforsch. mikrosk. Anat.* **56,** 809–818.

HOYLE, G., J. H. McALEAR and A. SELVERSTON. 1965. Mechanism of supercontraction in a striated muscle. *J. Cell Biol.*, **26,** 621–640.

HOYLE, G. and P. A. McNEILL. 1968. Correlated physiological and ultrastructural studies on specialized muscles. Ib. Ultrastructure of white and pink fibers of the levator of the eyestalk of Podophthalmus vigil (Weber). *J. exp. Zool.*, **167,** 487–522.

HOYLE, G., P. A. McNEILL and A. A. SELVERSTON. 1973. Ultrastructure of barnacle giant muscle fibers. *J. Cell Biol.*, **56,** 74–91.

HOYLE, G. and T. SMYTH. 1963. Giant muscle fibers in a barnacle *Balanus nubilus* Darwin. *Science, N.Y.*, **139,** 49–50.

JAHROMI, S. S. and H. L. ATWOOD. 1971. Structural and contractile properties of lobster leg-muscle fibers. *J. exp. Zool.*, **176,** 475–486.

JOHNSON, W. H., J. S. KAHN and A. G. SZENT-GYÖRGYI. 1959. Paramyosin and contraction of 'catch muscles'. *Science, N.Y.*, **130,** 160–161.

KALAMKAROVA, M. B. and M. YE. KRYUKOVA. 1966. Ultrastructural organization and features of the protein components of contractile apparatus of the anodcnta adductor. *Biofizika*, **11,** 61–68.

KAWAGUTI, S. and N. IKEMOTO. 1959. Electron microscopic patterns of earthworm muscle in relaxation and contraction induced by glycerol and adenosinetriphosphate. *Biol. J. Okayama Univ.*, **5,** 57–72.

KNAPP, M. F. and P. J. MILL. 1971. The contractile mechanism in obliquely striated body wall muscle of the earthworm, *Lumbricus terrestris*. *J. Cell Sci.*, **8,** 413–426.

KOMINZ, D. R., F. SAAD and K. LAKI. 1958. Chemical characteristics of annelid, mollusc and arthropod tropomyosins. In *Conference on the Chemistry of Muscular Contraction, 1957*. Igaku Shoin, Tokyo. 66–75.

KOMNICK, H. and K. E. WOHLFARTH-BOTTERMANN. 1965. Das Grundplasma und die Plasmafilamente der Amöbe *Chaos chaos* nach enzymatischer Behandlung der Zellmembran. *Z. Zellforsch. mikrosk. Anat.*, **66,** 434–456.

KUNG, T.-H. and T.-C. TSAO. 1965. Electron microscopical studies of tropomyosin and paramyosin. III. Fibrils. *Scientia sin.*, **14,** 1383–1385.

LEVINE, R. J. C., M. M. DEWEY and D. E. COLFLESH. 1973. Unusual striated thick filaments in *Limulus* skeletal muscle. *J. Cell Biol.*, **57,** 591–593.

LEVINE, R. J. C., M. M. DEWEY and G. W. de VILLAFRANCA. 1972. Immunohistochemical localization of contractile proteins in *Limulus* striated muscle. *J. Cell Biol.*, **55,** 221–235.

LOWY, J. and B. M. MILLMAN. 1963. The contractile mechanism of the anterior byssus retractor muscle of *Mytilus edulis*. *Phil. Trans. R. Soc. Ser. B*, **246,** 105–148.

LOWY, J. and P. J. VIBERT. 1973. Studies of

the low-angle X-ray pattern of a molluscan smooth muscle during tonic contraction and rigor. In *The Mechanism of Muscle Contraction. Cold Spring Harb. Symp. quant. Biol.*, **37,** 353–360.

McNEILL, P. A. and G. HOYLE. 1967. Evidence for superthin filaments. *Am. Zool.*, **7,** 483–498.

MATTISSON, A. G. M. and J. A. ARVIDSSON. 1966. Some effects of electrical stimulation and exogenous metabolites on the contractile activity and the ultrastructure of the radula-muscle of *Buccinum undatum*. *Z. Zellforsch. mikrosk. Anat.*, **73,** 37–55.

MEINRENKEN, W., J. C. RÜEGG and E. ZEBE. 1967. Superkontraktion extrahierter fibrillärer Insektenmuskeln. *Helv. Physiol. pharmac. Acta.*, **25,** CR 205–207.

MILL, P. J. and M. F. KNAPP. 1970. The fine structure of obliquely striated body muscles in the earthworm, *Lumbricus terrestris* L.. *J. Cell Sci.*, **7,** 233–261.

MILLER, A. and R. TREGEAR. 1971. X-ray studies on the structure and function of vertebrate and invertebrate muscle. In *Contractility of Muscle Cells and Related Processes*. R. J. Podolsky, ed. Prentice-Hall, Englewood Cliffs, N.J. 205–228.

MILLER, A. and R. T. TREGEAR. 1972. Structure of insect fibrillar flight muscle in the presence and absence of ATP. *J. molec. Biol.*, **70,** 85–104.

NACHMIAS, V. T. 1968. Further electron microscope studies on fibrillar organisation of the ground cytoplasm of *Chaos chaos*. *J. Cell Biol.*, **38,** 40–50.

NACHMIAS, V. T. 1972. Electron microscope observations on myosin from *Physarum polycephalum*. *J. Cell Biol.*, **52,** 648–663.

NACHMIAS, V. T. 1973. Physarum myosin: two new properties. In *The Mechanism of Muscle Contraction. Cold Spring Harb. Symp. quant. Biol.*, **37,** 607–612.

NACHMIAS, V. T., H. E. HUXLEY and D. KESSLER. 1970. Electron microscope observations on actomyosin and actin preparations from *Physarum polycephalum* and on their interaction with heavy meromyosin subfragment I from muscle myosin. *J. molec. Biol.*, **50,** 83–90.

NONOMURA, Y. 1974. Fine structure of the thick filament in molluscan catch muscle. *J. molec. Biol.*, **88,** 445–456.

OSBORNE, M. P. 1967. Supercontraction in the muscles of the blowfly larva: an ultrastructural study. *J. Insect Physiol.*, **13,** 1471–1482.

PENG, C.-M., T.-H. KUNG, L.-M. HSIUNG and T.-C. TSAO. 1965. Electron microscopical studies of tropomyosin and paramyosin. II. Molecules. *Scientia sin.*, **14,** 219–228.

PETERSON, R. P. 1963. A note on the structure of crayfish myofilaments. *J. Cell Biol.*, **18,** 213–219.

PHILPOTT, D. E., M. KAHLBROCK and A. G. SZENT-GYÖRGYI. 1960. Filamentous organization of molluscan muscles. *J. Ultrastruct. Res.*, **3,** 254–269.

POLLARD, T. D. and E. D. KORN. 1971. Filaments of *Amoeba proteus*. II. Binding of heavy meromyosin by thin filaments in motile cytoplasmic extracts. *J. Cell Biol.*, **48,** 216–219.

REEDY, M. 1967. Cross-bridges and periods in insect flight muscle. *Am. Zool.*, **7,** 465–481.

REEDY, M. K. 1968. Ultrastructure of insect flight muscle. I. Screw sense and structural grouping in the rigor cross-bridge lattice. *J. molec. Biol.*, **31,** 155–176.

REEDY, M. K., G. F. BAHR and D. A. FISCHMAN. 1973. How many myosins per cross-bridge? I. Flight muscle myofibrils from the blowfly, *Sacrophaga bullata*. In *The Mechanism of Muscle Contraction. Cold Spring Harb. Symp. quant. Biol.*, **37,** 397–422.

REGER, J. F. 1967. A comparative study on sub-filament organization in primary myofilaments of basalar direct flight and tibial extensor muscles of the lepidopteran, *Achalarus lyciades*. *Z. Zellforsch. mikrosk. Anat.*, **81,** 361–365.

REGER, J. F. 1967. A comparative study on striated muscle fibers of the first antenna and the claw muscle of the crab, *Pinnixia* sp.. *J. Ultrastruct. Res.*, **20,** 72–82.

REGER, J. F. and D. P. COOPER. 1967. A comparative study on the fine structure of the basalar muscle of the wing and the tibial extensor muscle of the leg of the lepidopteran, *Achalarus lyciades*. *J. Cell Biol.*, **33,** 531–542.

RICE, M. J. 1970. Supercontracting and

non-supercontracting visceral muscles in the tsetse fly, *Glossina austeni*. *J. Insect Physiol.*, **16,** 1109–1122.

ROSENBLUTH, J. 1965. Ultrastructural organization of obliquely striated muscle fibers in *Ascaris lumbricoides*. *J. Cell Biol.*, **25,** 495–515.

ROSENBLUTH, J. 1967. Obliquely striated muscle. III. Contraction mechanism of *Ascaris* body muscle. *J. Cell Biol.*, **34,** 15–33.

ROSENBLUTH, J. 1968. Obliquely striated muscle. IV. Sarcoplasmic reticulum, contractile apparatus, and endomysium of the body muscle of a polychaete, *Glycera*, in relation to its speed. *J. Cell Biol.*, **36,** 245–259.

RÜEGG, J. C. 1964. Tropomyosin-paramyosin system and 'prolonged contraction' in a molluscan smooth muscle. *Proc. R. Soc. Ser. B*, **160,** 536–542.

RÜEGG, J. C. 1968. Contractile mechanisms of smooth muscle. *Symp. Soc. exp. Biol.*, **22,** 45–66.

RÜEGG, J. C. 1971. Smooth muscle tone. *Physiol. Rev.*, **51,** 201.

SCHAEFER, G. W., J. P. VANDERBERG and J. RHODIN. 1967. The fine structure of mosquito midgut muscle. *J. Cell Biol.*, **34,** 905–911.

SCHIPP, R. and A. SCHÄFER. 1969. Vergleichende elektronenmikroskopische Untersuchungen an den zentralen Herzorganen von Cephalopoden (*Sepia officinalis*) die Feinstruktur des Herzens. *Z. Zellforsch. mikrosk. Anat.*, **98,** 576–598.

SCHLÖTE, F.-W. 1968. Die dicken Myofilamente der glatten Muskelfasern von *Helix pomatia*. *Z. Zellforsch. mikrosk. Anat.*, **92,** 503–508.

SHAFIQ, S. A. 1963*a*. Electron microscopic studies on the indirect flight muscles of *Drosophila melanogaster*. I. Structure of the myofibrils. *J. Cell Biol.*, **17,** 351–362.

SHAFIQ, S. A. 1963*b*. Electron microscopic studies on the indirect flight muscles of *Drosophila melanogaster*. II. Differentiation of myofibrils. *J. Cell Biol.*, **17,** 363–373.

SMITH, D. S. 1961. The organization of the flight muscle in a dragonfly, *Aeshna* sp.. (Odonata). *J. biophys. biochem. Cytol.*, **11,** 119–145.

SMITH, D. S. 1962. Cytological studies on some insect muscles. *Revue can. Biol.*, **21,** 279–301.

SMITH, D. S. 1963. The structure of flight muscle sarcomeres in the blowfly, *Calliphora erythrocephala* (Diptera). *J. Cell Biol.*, **19,** 115–138.

SMITH, D. S. 1965. The organization of flight muscle in an aphid, *Megoura viciae* (Homoptera). With a discussion on the structure of synchronous and asynchronous striated muscle fibers. *J. Cell Biol.*, **27,** 379–393.

SMITH, D. S. 1966*a*. The organization of flight muscle fibers in the Odonata. *J. Cell Biol.*, **28,** 109–126.

SMITH, D. S. 1966*b*. The structure of intersegmental muscle fibers in an insect *Periplaneta americana* L. *J. Cell Biol.*, **29,** 449–459.

SMITH, D. S., B. L. GUPTA and U. SMITH. 1966. The organization and myofilament array of insect visceral muscles. *J. Cell Sci.*, **1,** 49–58.

SMITH, J. R. 1963. Observations on the ultrastructure of the myocardium of the common lobster (*Homarus americanus*), especially of the myofibrils. *Anat. Rec.*, **145,** 391–400.

SOBIESZEK, A. 1973. The fine structure of the contractile apparatus of the anterior byssus retractor muscle of *Mytilus edulis*. *J. Ultrastruct. Res.*, **43,** 313.

STEIN, R. J., W. R. RICHTER, R. A. ZUSSMAN and G. BRYNJOLFSSON. 1966. Ultrastructural characterisation of *Daphnia* heart muscle. *J. Cell Biol.*, **29,** 168–170.

SWANSON, C. J. 1971. Occurrence of paramyosin among the nematomorpha. *Nature, New Biology*, **232,** 122–123.

SZENT-GYÖRGYI, A. G., C. COHEN and J. KENDRICK-JONES. 1971. Paramyosin and the filaments of molluscan 'catch' muscles. II. Native filaments: isolation and characterization. *J. molec. Biol.*, **56,** 239–258.

SZENT-GYÖRGYI, A. G., E. M. SZENTKIRALYI and J. KENDRICK-JONES. 1973. The light chains of scallop myosin as regulatory subunits. *J. molec. Biol.*, **74,** 179–203.

TAKAHASHI, A., D. E. PHILPOTT and J. MIQUEL. 1970. Electron microscope studies on aging *Drosophila melanogaster*. 3. Flight muscle. *J. Geront.*, **25,** 222–228.

TICE, L. W. and D. S. SMITH. 1965. The localization of myofibrillar ATPase activity in the flight muscles of the blowfly, *Calliphora erythrocephala*. *J. Cell Biol.*, **25,** 121–136.

TSAO, T.-C., T.-H. KUNG, C.-M. PENG, Y.-S. CHANG and Y.-S. TSOU. 1965. Electron microscopical studies of tropomyosin and paramyosin. I. Crystals. *Scientia sin.*, **14,** 91–105.

TWAROG, B. M. 1967. The regulation of catch in molluscan muscle. *J. gen. Physiol.*, **50,** Suppl., 157–169.

TWAROG, B. M. 1968. Structure and function in smooth and obliquely striated invertebrate muscles. *XXIV Int. Congr. Physiol. Sci. Proc.*, **1,** 152–153.

TWAROG, B. M., M. M. DEWEY and T. HIDAKA. 1973. The structure of *Mytilus* smooth muscle and the electrical constants of the resting muscle. *J. gen. Physiol.*, **61,** 207–221.

VILLAFRANCA, G. W. DE and D. E. PHILPOTT. 1961. The ultrastructure of striated muscle from *Limulus polyphemus*. *J. Ultrastruct. Res.*, **5,** 151–165.

WEBER, W. 1970. Zur Ultrastruktur der Chromatophorenmuskelzellen von *Loligo vulgaris*. *Z. Zellforsch. mikrosk. Anat.*, **108,** 446–456.

WRAY, J. S., P. J. VIBERT and C. COHEN. 1974. Cross-bridge arrangements in *Limulus* muscle. *J. molec. Biol.*, **88,** 343–348.

ZEBE, E. and W. RATHMAYER. 1968. Elektronenmikroskopische Untersuchungen an Spinnenmuskeln. *Z. Zellforsch. mikrosk. Anat.*, **92,** 377–387.

ZS.-NAGY, I., J. SALÁNKI and N. GARAMVÖLGYI. 1971. The contractile apparatus of the adductor muscles in *Anodonta cygnea* L. (Mollusca, Pelecypoda). *J. Ultrastruct. Res*, **37,** 1–16.

Z-Disc, I-Band, M-Line, etc.

ASHHURST, D. E. 1967. Z-line of the flight muscle of belastomatid water bugs. *J. molec. Biol.*, **27,** 385–389.

ASHHURST, D. E. 1971. The Z-line in insect flight muscle. *J. molec. Biol.*, **55,** 283–285.

AUBER, J. and R. COUTEAUX. 1963. Ultrastructure de la strie Z dans des muscles de diptères. *J. Microsc. (Fr.)*, **2,** 309–324.

BARRNETT, R. J. and G. E. PALADE. 1959. Enzymatic activity in the M band. *J. biophys. biochem. Cytol.*, **6,** 163–170.

BUSCH, W. A., M. H. STROMER, D. E. GOLL and A. SUZUKI. 1972. Ca^{2+}-specific removal of Z lines from rabbit skeletal muscle. *J. Cell Biol.*, **52,** 367–381.

CARLSEN, F. and G. G. KNAPPEIS. 1962. The fine structure of the Z disc in skeletal muscle revealed by electron microscopy. *Danish med. Bull.*, **9,** 18.

CARLSEN, F. and G. G. KNAPPEIS. 1963. Further investigations of the ultrastructure of the Z disc in skeletal muscle. *Acta physiol. scand.*, **59,** Suppl. 213, 27.

CÔTÉ, G., S. M. MOHIUDDIN and P. E. ROY. 1970. Occurrence of Z-band widening in human atrial cells. *Exp. & Mol. Pathol.*, **13,** 307–318.

EATON, B. L. and F. A. PEPE. 1972. M band protein. Two components isolated from chicken breast muscle. *J. Cell Biol.*, **55,** 681–695.

EDGE, M. B. and S. M. WALKER. 1970. Evidence for a structural relationship between sarcoplasmic reticulum and Z lines in dog papillary muscle. *Anat. Rec.*, **166,** 51–66.

ETLINGER, J. D. and D. A. FISCHMAN. 1973. M and Z band components and the assembly of myofibrils. In *The Mechanism of Muscle Contraction. Cold Spring Harb. Symp. quant. Biol.*, **37,** 511–522.

FAWCETT, D. W. 1968. The sporadic occurrence in cardiac muscle of anomalous Z bands exhibiting a periodic structure suggestive of tropomyosin. *J. Cell Biol.*, **36,** 266–269.

FRANZINI-ARMSTRONG, C. 1970. Details of the I band structure as revealed by the localization of ferritin. *Tissue & Cell*, **2,** 327–338.

FRANZINI-ARMSTRONG, C. and K. R. PORTER. 1964. The Z-disc of skeletal muscle fibrils. *Z. Zellforsch. mikrosk. Anat.* **61,** 661–672.

FRANZINI-ARMSTRONG, C. 1973. The structure of a simple Z-line. *J. Cell Biol.*, **58,** 630–642.

FREUDENBERG, N. and E. BERTRAM. 1974. Ultrastructural investigation of human atrial myocardium in cardiac malformation with special regard to Z-band alterations. *Beitr. Path. Bd.*, **151,** 157–168.

GARAMVÖLGYI, N. 1965. Inter-Z bridges in the flight muscles of the bee. *J. Ultrastruct. Res.*, **13,** 435–443.

GARAMVÖLGYI, N., G. METZGER-TÖRÖK and A. TIGYI-SEBES. 1962. The Z- and M-formations of striated muscle. *Acta physiol. hung.*, **22,** 223–233.

HAGOPIAN, M. and D. SPIRO. 1970. Derivation of the Z line in the embryonic chick heart. *J. Cell Biol.*, **44,** 683–687.

HARSÁNYI, V. and N. GARAMVÖLGYI. 1969. On the Z-substance of striated muscle. *Acta Biochim. Biophys. Acad. Sci. Hung.*, **4,** 259–264.

HENDERSON, D. W., D. E. GOLL and M. H. STROMER. 1970. A comparison of shortening and Z line degradation in post-mortem bovine, porcine, and rabbit muscle. *Am. J. Anat.*, **128,** 117–136.

KARNOVSKY, M. J. and K. HUG. 1963. The nature of the M band enzyme in rat ventricular muscle. *J. Cell Biol.*, **19,** 255–260.

KATCHBURIAN, E., A. M. C. BURGESS and F. R. JOHNSON. 1973. The effect of tilting ultrathin sections on the image of the Z-disc of skeletal muscle. *Experientia*, **29,** 1020–1022.

KELLY, D. E. 1967. Models of muscle Z-band fine structure based on a looping filament configuration. *J. Cell Biol.*, **34,** 827–840.

KELLY, D. E. 1969. Myofibrillogenesis and Z-band differentiation. *Anat. Rec.*, **163,** 403–426.

KELLY, D. E. and M. A. CAHILL. 1972. Filamentous and matrix components of skeletal muscle Z-disks. *Anat. Rec.*, **172,** 623–642.

KNAPPEIS, G. G. and F. CARLSEN. 1962. The ultrastructure of the Z disc in skeletal muscle. *J. Cell Biol*, **13,** 323–335.

KNAPPEIS, G. G. and F. CARLSEN. 1968. The ultrastructure of the M line in skeletal muscle. *J. Cell Biol.*, **38,** 202–211.

KUNORAT, E. and F. A. PEPE. 1971. The M band. Studies with fluorescent antibody staining. *J. Cell Biol.*, **48,** 340–347.

LANDON, D. N. 1970*a*. The fine structure of the Z disc of rat striated muscle. *J. Anat.*, **106,** 172–173.

LANDON, D. N. 1970*b*. The influence of fixation upon the fine structure of the Z-disk of rat striated muscle. *J. Cell Sci.*, **6,** 257–276.

MACDONALD, R. D. and A. G. ENGEL. 1970. Observations on organization of Z-disk components and on rod-bodies of Z-disk origin. *J. Cell Biol.*, **48,** 431–436.

MARKWALD, R. R. 1973. Distribution and relationship of precursor Z material to organizing myofibrillar bundles in embryonic rat and hamster ventricular myocytes. *J. Mol. & Cell. Cardiology*, **5,** 341–350.

MASAKI, T., O. TAKAITI and S. EBASHI. 1968. 'M-substance', a new protein constituting the M-line of myofibrils. *J. Biochem., Toyko*, **64,** 909–910.

MUNNELL, J. F. and R. GETTY. 1968. Canine myocardial Z-disc alterations resembling those of nemaline myopathy. *Lab. Invest.*, **19,** 303–308.

POPESCU, L. M. and N. IONESCU. 1970*a*. On the equivalence between dense bodies and Z-bands. *Experientia*, **26,** 642–643.

POPESCU, L. M. and N. IONESCU. 1970*b*. Electron microscope studies on the nature of the dense bodies in smooth muscle fibres. *Z. mikrosk.-anat. Forsch.*, **82,** 67–75.

RASH, J. E., J. W. SHAY and J. J. BIESELE. 1968. Urea extraction of Z bands, intercalated disks, and desmosomes. *J. Ultrastruct. Res.*, **24,** 181–189.

ROWE, R. W. [D.] 1971. Ultrastructure of the Z-line of skeletal muscle fibers. *J. Cell Biol.*, **51,** 674–685.

ROWE, R. W. D. 1973. The ultrastructure of Z disks from white, intermediate, and red fibers of mammalian striated muscles. *J. Cell Biol.*, **57,** 261–271.

ROWE, R. W. D. and D. J. MORTON. 1971. Faults in the square lattice of mammalian skeletal muscle Z-disks. *J. Cell Sci.*, **9,** 139–145.

SCHOLLMEYER, R. J. VAN, D. E. GOLL, M. H. STROMER, W. DAYTON, I. SINGH and R. ROBSON. 1974. Studies on the composition of the Z disk. *J. Cell Biol.*, **63,** 303a.

STROMER, M. H. and D. E. GOLL. 1972. Studies on purified α-actinin. II. Electron microscopic studies on the competitive binding of α-actinin and tropomyosin to Z-line extracted myofibrils. *J. molec. Biol.*, **67,** 489–494.

STROMER, M. H., D. J. HARTSHORNE, H. MUELLER and R. V. RICE. 1969. The effect of various

protein fractions on Z- and M-line reconstitution. *J. Cell Biol.*, **40,** 167–178.
STROMER, M. H., D. J. HARTSHORNE and R. V. RICE. 1967. Removal and reconstruction of Z-line material in a striated muscle. *J. Cell Biol.*, **35,** C23–C28.
VILLAFRANCA, G. W. DE 1961. The A and I band lengths in stretched or contracted horseshoe crab skeletal muscle. *J. Ultrastruct. Res.*, **5,** 109–115.
VILLAFRANCA, G. W. DE and C. E. MARSCHHAUS. 1963. Contraction of the A band. *J. Ultrastruct. Res.*, **9,** 156–165.
YAROM, R. and V. MEIRI. 1971. N lines in striated muscle: a site of intracellular Ca^{2+}. *Nature, New Biology*, **234,** 254–256.

D Intermediate (100 Angstrom) filaments

In addition to thin actin-containing filaments and thick myosin-containing filaments in the sarcoplasm of vertebrate skeletal, cardiac and smooth muscle, another filament is present, 8–11 nm in diameter, called the '*intermediate*' or 100 Å *filament*'.

Filaments of a similar appearance have been observed in a variety of different cell types such as endothelial cells, fibroblasts, epithelial cells and macrophages. These filaments do not bind heavy meromyosin and are therefore considered not to contain actin. It has been suggested that these filaments are involved in the mechanism of cell motility because of their changes in location in cultured fibroblasts during cell movement.

Mitotic inhibitors such as colcimide and colchicine, markedly increase the number of intermediate (100 Å) filaments in skeletal muscle. When added to presumptive myoblasts (*myoblasts* are mononucleated cells that have withdrawn from the mitotic cycle and are committed to the production of myosin, actin, etc.) *myosacs* may be induced. *Myosacs* are modified myotubes (multinucleate developing muscle cells) containing from 2 to 100 nuclei, and with large areas of intermediate (100 Å) filaments within the sarcoplasm.

Intermediate (100 Å) filaments in smooth muscle are uniform in appearance in longitudinal section, and in transverse section they have a smooth profile, occasionally exhibiting a less electron-opaque core.

They are almost invariably preserved under a variety of fixation procedures and appear to be randomly orientated throughout the cytoplasm, although they do show some consistent relationships. For example they appear to be associated with *dark bodies* in smooth muscle.

Dark bodies are diffuse structures 20–50 nm in diameter and up to 400 nm in length usually found associated with myofilaments in smooth muscle. These are similar in appearance to the *dense areas* which alternate with plasmalemmal vesicles along the muscle cell membrane. Extraction experiments with KCl have shown that both the intermediate (100 Å) filaments and the dark bodies differ in composition from the myofilaments. The dark bodies consist of a hollow filamentous structure, possibly formed of a recently discovered muscle protein termed 'mesosin' and α-actinin, together with intermediate (100 Å) filaments. An equivalence between *dark bodies* of smooth muscle and striated muscle Z-discs, has been suggested, but so far attempts to prove this have been inconclusive.

Plate 47

Intermediate (100 Å) filaments (arrows) can be identified among the myofilaments and are either arrayed in small groups or scattered singly. The number of these filaments varies in different smooth muscle cells in different animals. They are a particularly prominent feature in cultured and developing smooth muscle cells. In this micrograph, thick myofilaments exhibiting an irregular profile are greater in number than thin myofilaments.

Intermediate (100 Å) filaments in vertebrate smooth muscle: finch ureter. Transverse section. OsO_4-glutaraldehyde-OsO_4 fixation. ×85 000. (Reproduced from Y. Uehara, G. R. Campbell and G. Burnstock, 1971, *J. Cell. Biol.* **50,** 484.)

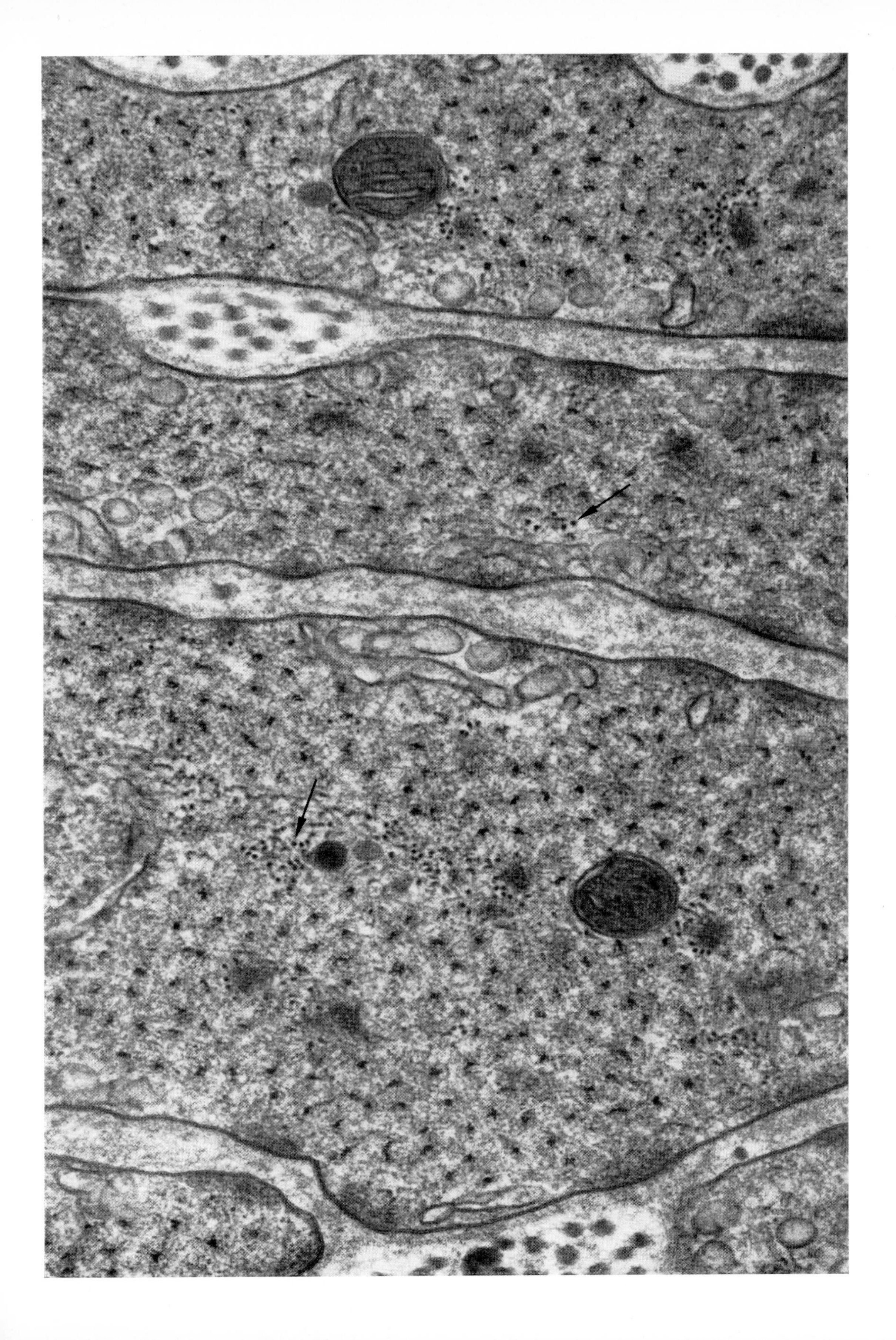

Plate 48

An accumulation of intermediate (100 Å) filaments is often seen in the nuclear region and in relation to accumulations of organelles, such as mitochondria. The profile of these filaments is quite uniform and some show an electron-transparent central core.

Intermediate (100 Å) filaments in vertebrate smooth muscle: guinea-pig ureter. Transverse section. Glutaraldehyde fixation. ×240 000. (Reproduced from Y. Uehara, G. R. Campbell and G. Burnstock, 1971, *J. Cell Biol.*, **50,** 484.)

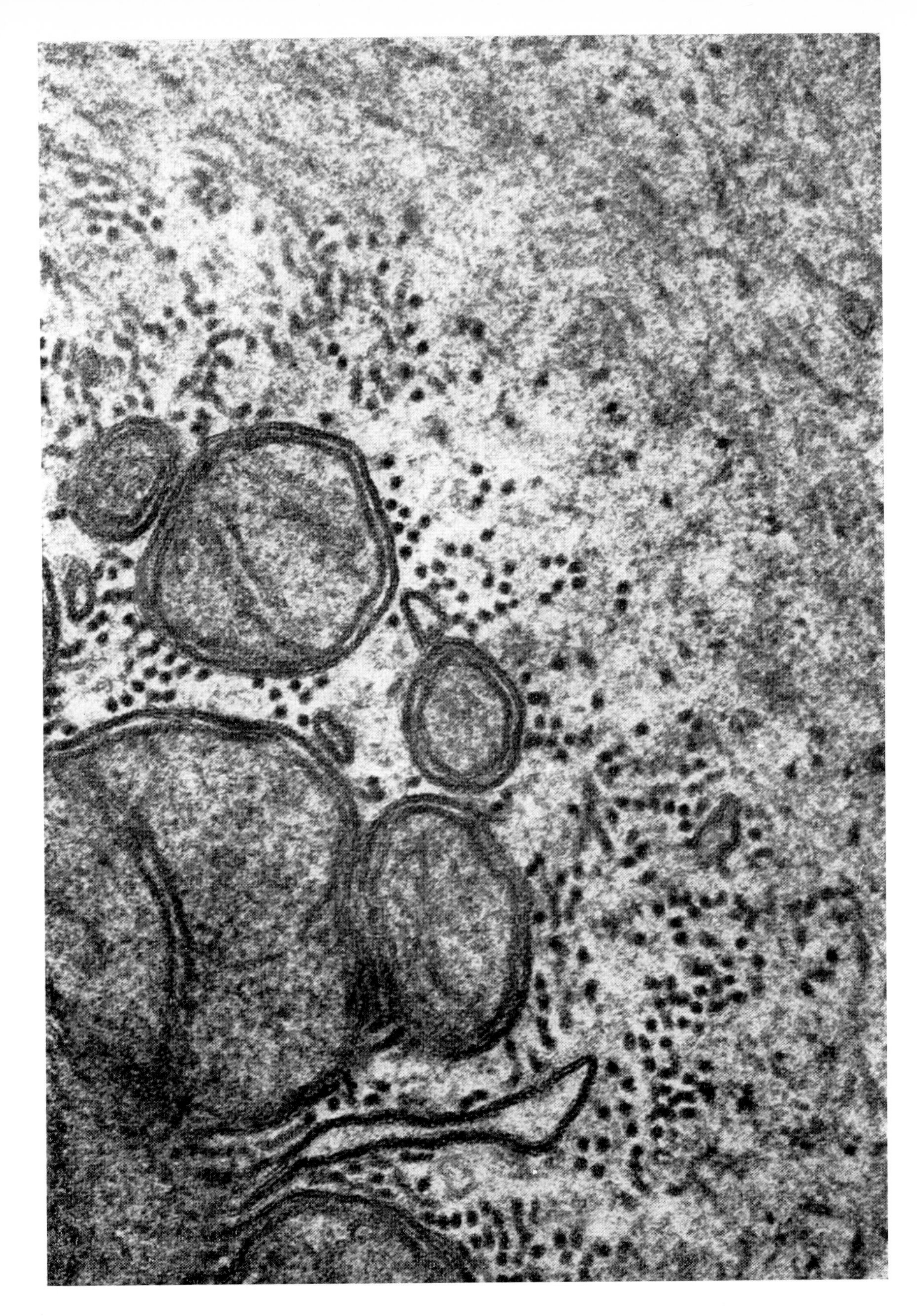

Plate 49

Intermediate (100 Å) filaments are closely associated with dark bodies sometimes giving them the appearance of having longitudinal striations within their matrices. Thin myofilaments are often also seen in their vicinity. The relationship of intermediate filaments to dark bodies is particularly prominent in developing smooth muscles.

Relation of intermediate (100 Å) filaments to 'dark bodies' in cultured smooth muscle: 10 day chicken gizzard, 5 days *in vitro*. Longitudinal section. Glutaraldehyde fixation. × 100 000. (Reproduced from Y. Uehara, G. R. Campbell and G. Burnstock, 1971, *J. Cell Biol.*, **50,** 484.)

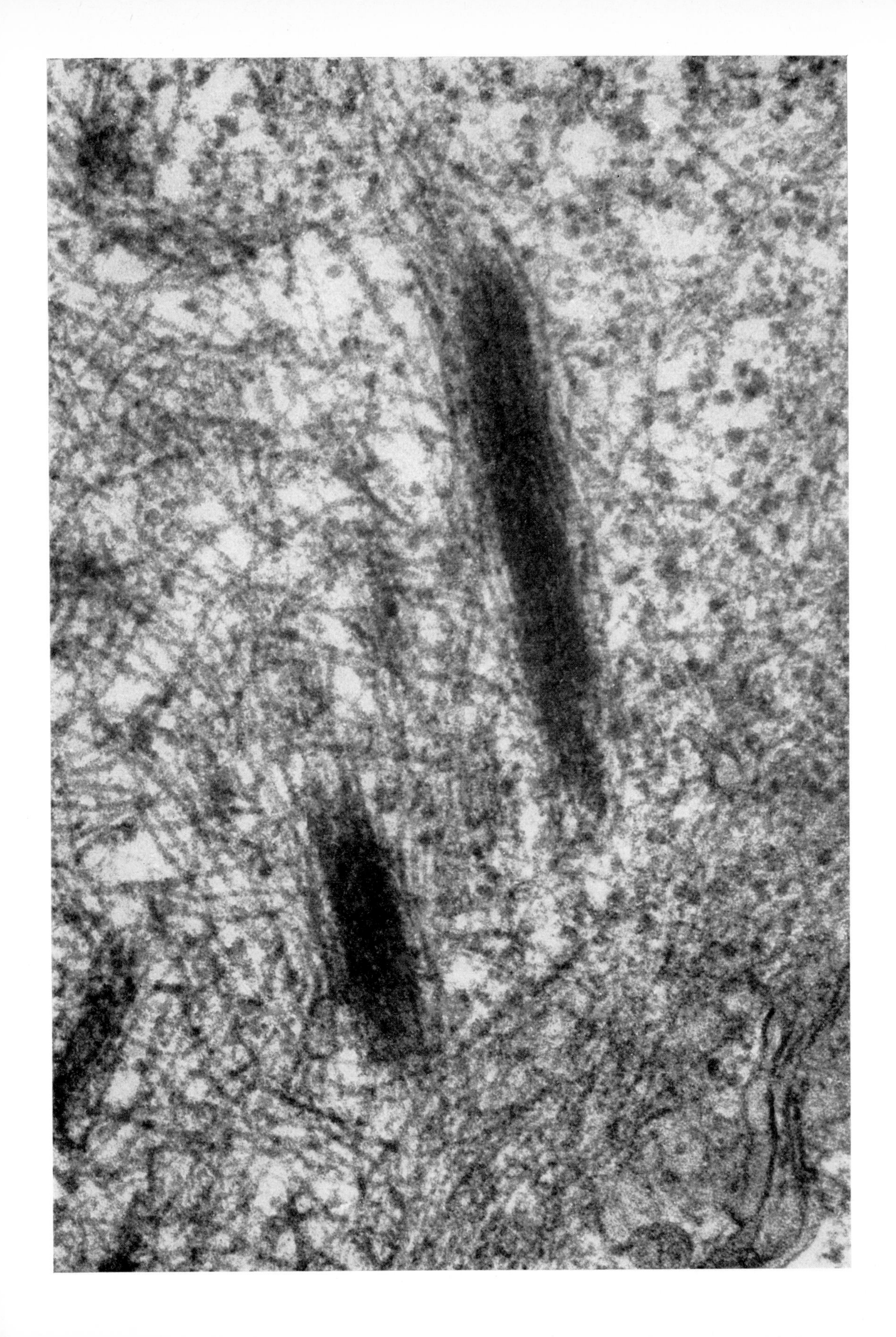

Plate 50

Intermediate (100 Å) filaments (arrows) in developing skeletal muscle appear to be associated with the Z-disc and could be taken as evidence for their involvement in the formation of the Z-disc. A comparable relationship of intermediate (100 Å) filaments to dark bodies in developing smooth muscle cells is illustrated in Plate 49. These filaments have been described in both developing and adult skeletal and cardiac muscle.

Intermediate (100 Å) filaments in developing vertebrate striated muscle: 20-day foetal rat sternothyroid muscle. Longitudinal section. Glutaraldehyde-formaldehyde fixation. ×48 500.

Plate 51

Bundles of thin filaments can be seen towards the periphery of the developing intrafusal muscle fibre. Intermediate (100 Å) filaments (arrows) are scattered in groups throughout the organelles and do not appear to have any spatial relation to the myofilaments. Similar filaments found in many non-myogenic cells do not bind heavy meromyosin and their number increases markedly in maturing muscle after exposure to colchicine. Mv, multivesicular body.

Intermediate (100 Å) filaments in developing vertebrate striated muscle: 18-day foetal rat sternothyroid muscle. Transverse section. Glutaraldehyde–formaldehyde fixation. ×71 000.

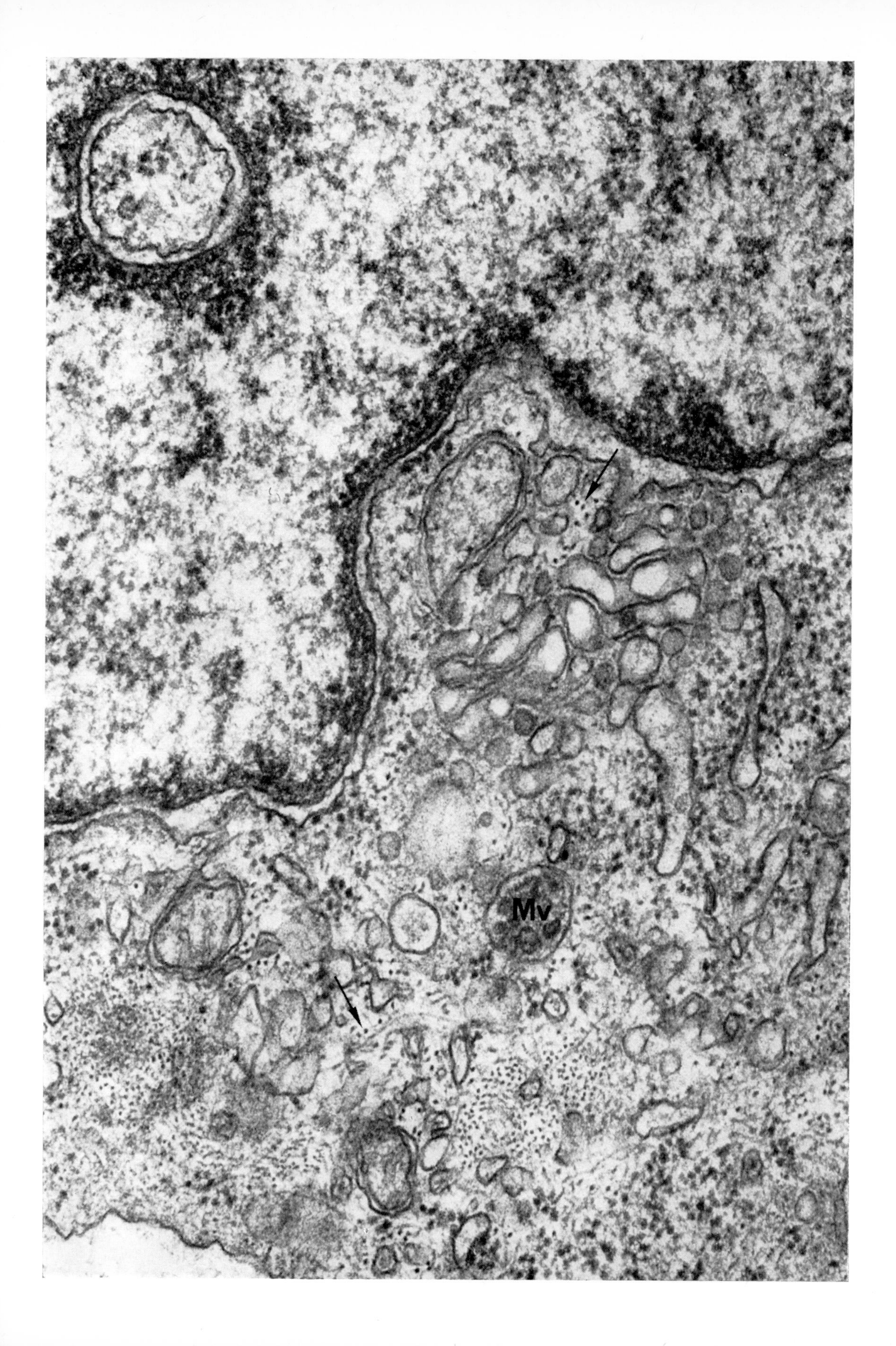
Mv

Selected Articles

CAMPBELL, G. R., Y. UEHARA, G. MARK and G. BURNSTOCK. 1971. Fine structure of smooth muscle cells grown in tissue culture. *J. Cell Biol.*, **49,** 21–34.

CLONEY, R. A. 1972. Cytoplasmic filaments and morphogenesis: Effects of cytochalasin B on contractile epidermal cells. *Z. Zellforsch. mikrosk. Anat.*, **132,** 167–192.

COOKE, P. H. and R. H. CHASE. 1971. Potassium chloride-insoluble myofilaments in vertebrate smooth muscle cells. *Expl Cell Res.*, **66,** 417–425.

FERRANS, V. J. and W. G. ROBERTS. 1973. Structural features of cardiac myxomas: histology, histochemistry and electron microscopy. *Human Pathol.*, **4,** 111–146.

FRANKS, L. M., P. N. RIDDLE and P. SEAL. 1969. Actin-like filaments and cell movements in human ascites tumour cells: an ultrastructural and cinemicrographic study. *Expl Cell Res.*, **54,** 157–162.

ISHIKAWA, H., R. BISCHOFF and H. HOLTZER. 1968. Mitosis and intermediate-sized filaments in developing skeletal muscle. *J. Cell Biol.*, **38,** 538–555.

MENDELL, J. R., R. I. ROELOFS and W. K. ENGEL. 1972. Ultrastructural development of explanted human skeletal muscle in tissue culture. *J. Neuropath. exp. Neurol.*, **31,** 433–446.

RASH, J. E., J. J. BIESELE and G. O. GEY. 1970. Three classes of filaments in cardiac differentiation. *J. Ultrastruct. Res.*, **33,** 408–435.

RASH, J. E., J. W. SHAY and J. J. BIESELE. 1970. Preliminary biochemical investigations of the intermediate filaments. *J. Ultrastruct. Res.*, **33,** 399–407.

UEHARA, Y., G. R. CAMPBELL and G. BURNSTOCK. 1971. Cytoplasmic filaments in developing and adult vertebrate smooth muscle. *J. Cell Biol.*, **50,** 484–497.

YOHRO, T. and G. BURNSTOCK. 1973. Filament bundles and contractility of endothelial cells in coronary arteries. *Z. Zellforsch. mikrosk. Anat.*, **138,** 85–95.

E Smooth endoplasmic reticulum (including sarcoplasmic reticulum) and T-tubules

Smooth endoplasmic reticulum is a common organelle in cells actively engaged in synthetic activity, such as the hormone-secreting cells of the cortex of the adrenal gland. In such cells, autoradiographic and other studies have shown the involvement of the smooth endoplasmic reticulum in four functions: triglyceride synthesis, phospholipid synthesis, some aspects of glycogen metabolism and the transport of various substances such as proteins and lipids to the Golgi apparatus. Smooth endoplasmic reticulum in this form is a relatively uncommon feature of the more differentiated muscle cell types, such as adult vertebrate skeletal muscle, as is the Golgi and rough endoplasmic reticulum. However, in some smooth muscle cells, smooth endoplasmic reticulum is a prominent feature (see Plate 63).

The smooth endoplasmic reticulum is highly developed and specialized in striated muscle cells to form the longitudinally orientated sarcoplasmic reticulum, which is involved in the process of excitation–contraction coupling. The sarcoplasmic reticulum in vertebrate smooth muscle has generally been reported to be poorly developed relative to striated muscle. However, recent studies suggest that an organized sarcoplasmic reticulum is present in some smooth muscles.

The *sarcoplasmic reticulum* in skeletal muscle is a system of membrane limited tubules that extend longitudinally throughout the sarcoplasm and form a network around the myofibrils (Fig. 14). At regular intervals along the length of these myofibrils, the longitudinal tubules of this sarcoplasmic reticulum expand to form elaborate ramifications in the H-zone and transversely orientated channels of larger calibre, the *terminal cisternae* (see Plate 53). Pairs of parallel terminal cisternae run transversely across the myofibrils in close apposition to slender intermediate elements, the *T-tubules*. These three associated transverse structures constitute the so-called *triads* of muscle, which are involved in the process of excitation–contraction coupling. In fish, amphibian and bird skeletal muscle,

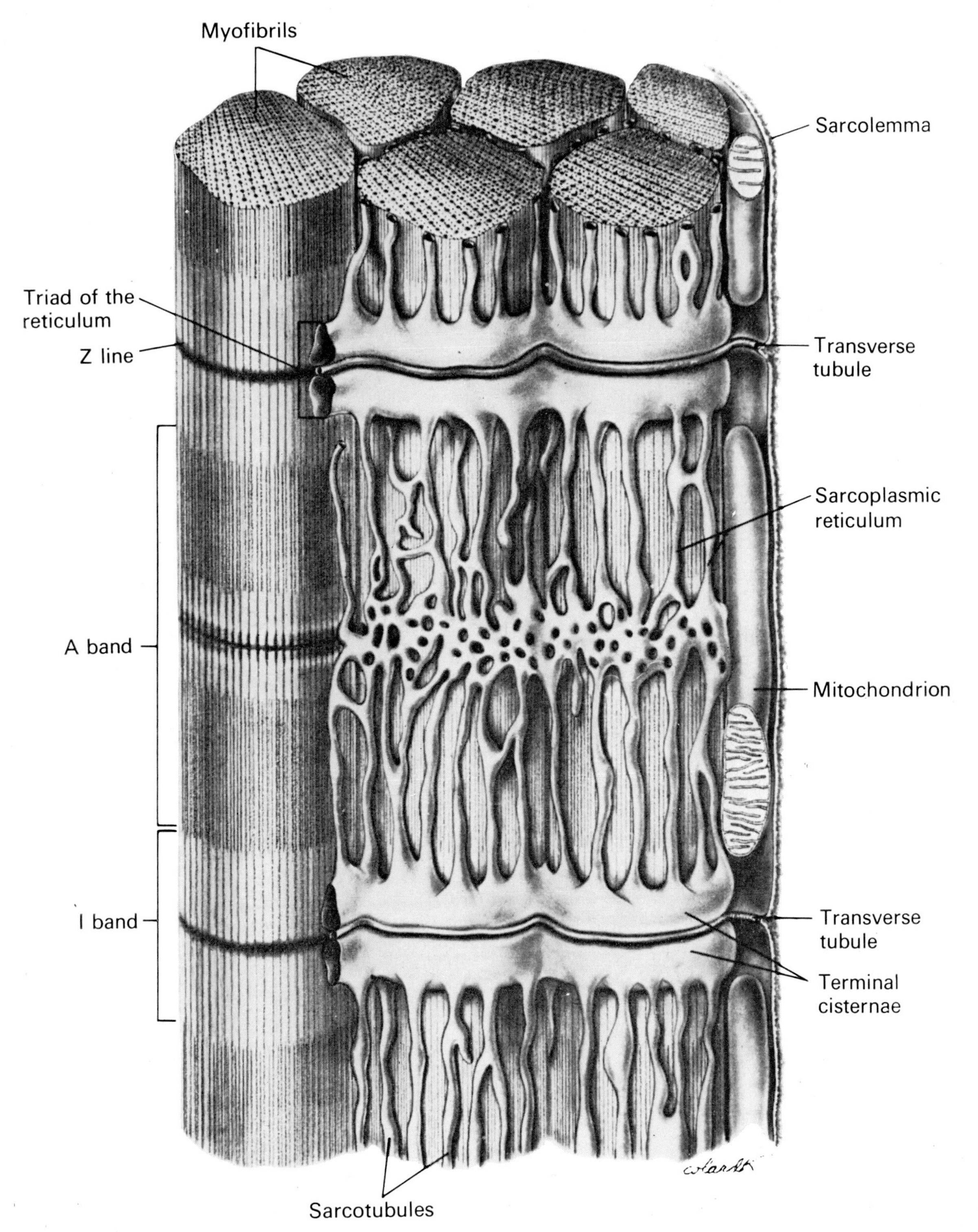

Fig. 14 Schemic representation of the distribution of the sarcoplasmic reticulum around the myofibrils of skeletal muscle. (Courtesy W. Bloom and D. W. Fawcett, 1968, *A Textbook of Histology*, W. B. Saunders Company, London.)

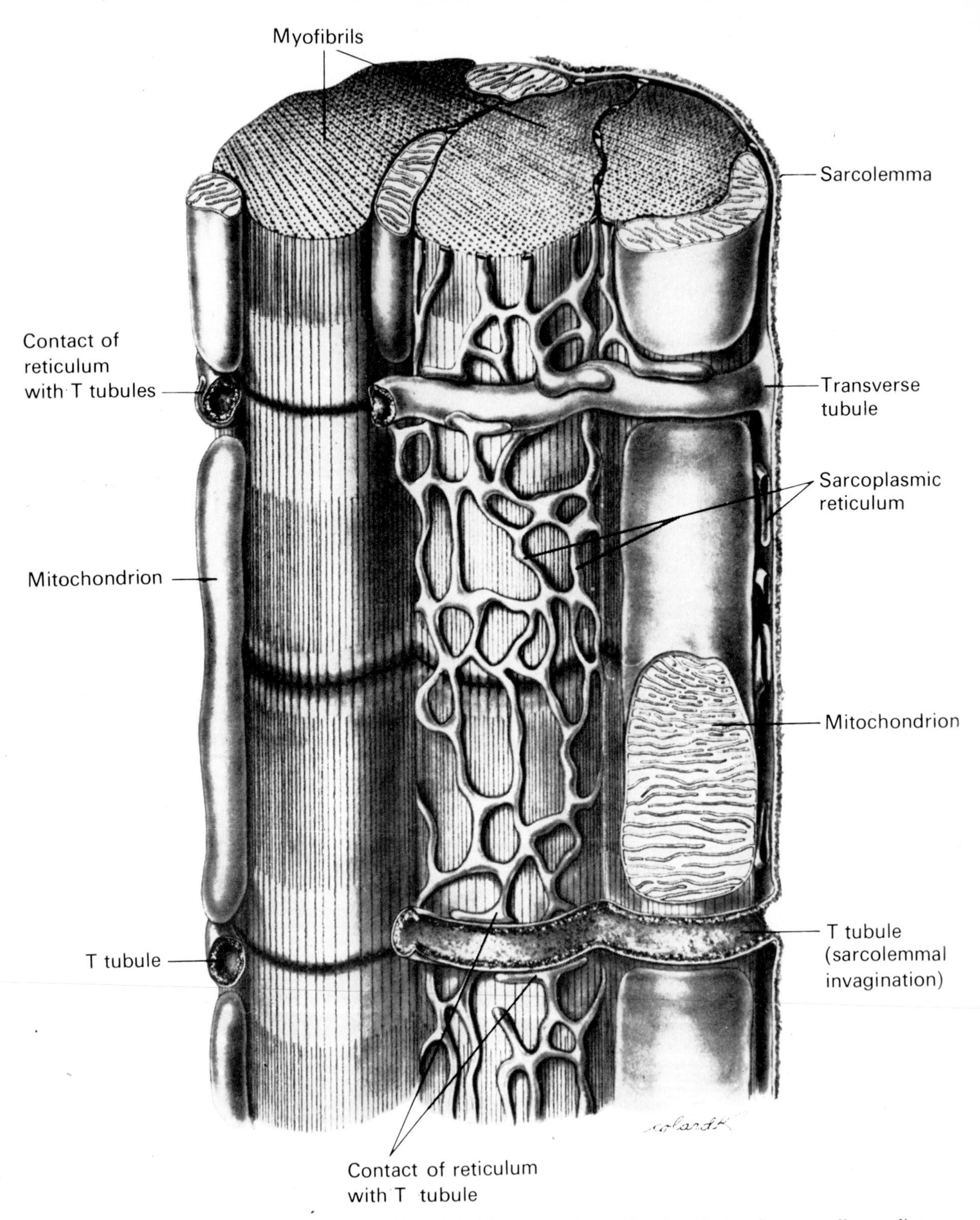

Fig. 15 Schemic representation of the disposition of the T-system and sarcoplasmic reticulum in mammalian cardiac muscle. (Courtesy W. Bloom and D. W. Fawcett, 1968, *A Textbook of Histology*, W. B. Saunders Company, London.)

triads are usually at the level of the Z-discs, but in fast acting mammalian muscles there are two triads per sarcomere, situated at or near the junction of the A- and I-bands.

In the mammalian heart the sarcoplasmic reticulum is not as extensive as in skeletal muscle, and consists of a simple plexus of tubules which do not ramify in the region of the H-zone (see Fig. 15 and Plate 54). In the region of the I-band, flattened saccular expansions of sarcotubules can be observed in close contact with the T-tubules forming a modified triad. These flattened saccular expansions have been termed '*foot plates*', by some authors and when seen in close proximity to the sarcolemma they are termed *subsarcolemmal cisternae*.

Most invertebrate striated muscles do not have two elements of sarcoplasmic reticulum in contact with their T-tubules (triad) but only one, thus producing *dyads* (Plate 57) in contrast to the triads commonly observed in vertebrates. The number and position of the dyads varies but there are often up to four dyads per sarcomere.

Another type of tubule, the Z-tubules, has also been described in some mammalian cardiac muscles and in some invertebrate striated muscles. In the heart of the ox and the ferret these Z-tubules encircle the myofibrils at the level of the Z-disc and communicate with sarcotubules of the reticulum and Z-tubules of other fibrils. Certain crustacean muscles also contain these tubules; however, here the Z-tubules do not themselves form dyadic contacts, but give rise to tubules which run longitudinally to form dyads.

The lumen of the T-tubule is usually considered not to open into the terminal cisternae of the sarcoplasmic reticulum (although this has been contested). Its limiting membrane is continuous with the sarcolemma and its lumen communicates with the extracellular space at the cell surface.

The T-tubule is the path by which the action potential is conveyed rapidly to all the myofibrils inside the muscle fibre. As a result of depolarization of the membranes of the transverse tubules Ca^{2+} is released from the terminal cisternae of the sarcoplasmic reticulum. Ca^{2+} is required for the ATPase activity of the myosin necessary for filament sliding and muscle contraction (see Chapter 2C). Ca^{2+} is taken up again by the sarcoplasmic reticulum during relaxation. Thus, the sarcoplasmic reticulum is specialized for uptake, storage and release of Ca^{2+} and contains an active transport system. Characterization of the proteins involved in this system is the subject of much research. As many as seven proteins are thought to be involved of which two are an *ATPase* thought to be the Ca^{2+} transport enzyme and *calsequestrin* which is thought to sequester Ca^{2+} on the interior of the sarcoplasmic reticulum for passage to the exterior.

Cultured muscle cells often show an elaborate three-dimensional network of a membranous system, and these are regarded as a special morphological elaboration of T-system tubules (see Plates 66, 67). Myotubes often show a number of micropinocytotic vesicles or sarcolemmal vesicles linked together. A mechanism of T-tubule formation has been suggested in which the T-system tubule first appears as an inpocketing of the sarcolemmal vesicles; further vesicles are formed in close association to these primary vesicles and they coalesce. This procedure is repeated until a long tube, the T-tubule, is formed.

Plate 52

In transverse section the sarcoplasmic reticulum (SR) appears as an elaborate network of tubules, 40–70 nm in diameter, distributed in the interfibrillar sarcoplasm. Thus, the sarcoplasmic reticulum together with the mitochondria and glycogen granules delineate the myofibrils.

Sarcoplasmic reticulum in vertebrate striated muscle: guinea-pig extra-ocular muscle. Transverse section. Glutaraldehyde fixation. ×57 800.

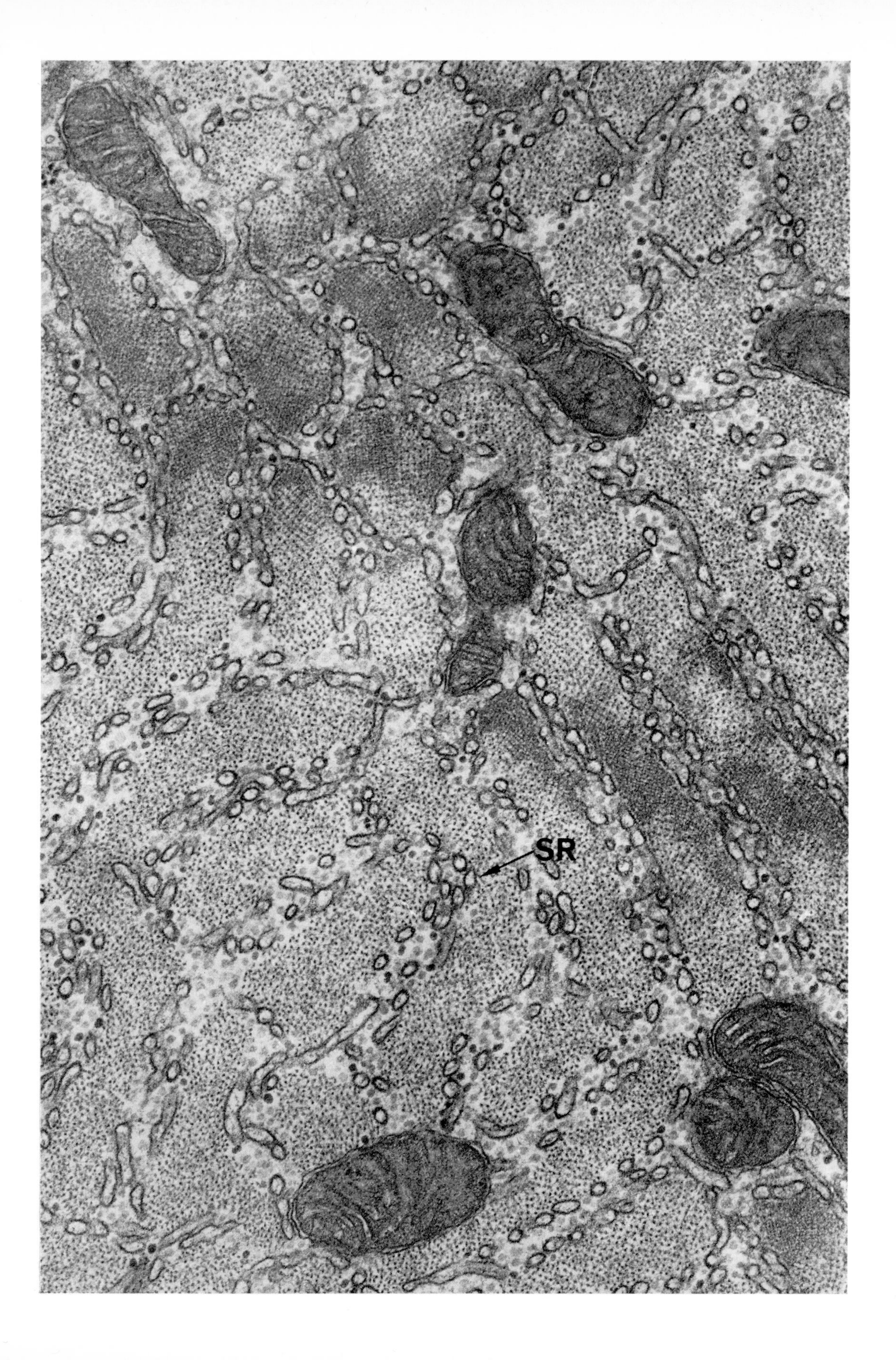
SR

Plate 53

A highly ordered organization of sarcoplasmic reticulum and T-tubules occurs regularly along skeletal muscle myofibrils. In the fish muscle illustrated, the sarcoplasmic reticulum consists of longitudinally disposed tubules at the A-band level. At the H-zone level, the longitudinal tubules fuse to form a flattened sac which contains pores or fenestrations (f) of about 30 nm in diameter.

At the level of I-band (or A–I junction in most of mammalian muscles), longitudinal elements of sarcoplasmic reticulum join together again to form an expanded sac, called the terminal cistern.

The cisternae are closely related to transversely aligned T-tubules (about 40 nm in diameter) (T) to form the triads. The gap between the membranes of the terminal cisternae and the T-tubules is 12–13 nm and contains electron dense globular structures about 10 nm in diameter. Z, Z-disc.

Relationship between sarcoplasmic reticulum and T-tubules to form triads in vertebrate skeletal muscle: goldfish pinnae pectoralis muscle. Longitudinal section. Glutaraldehyde fixation. ×78 300.

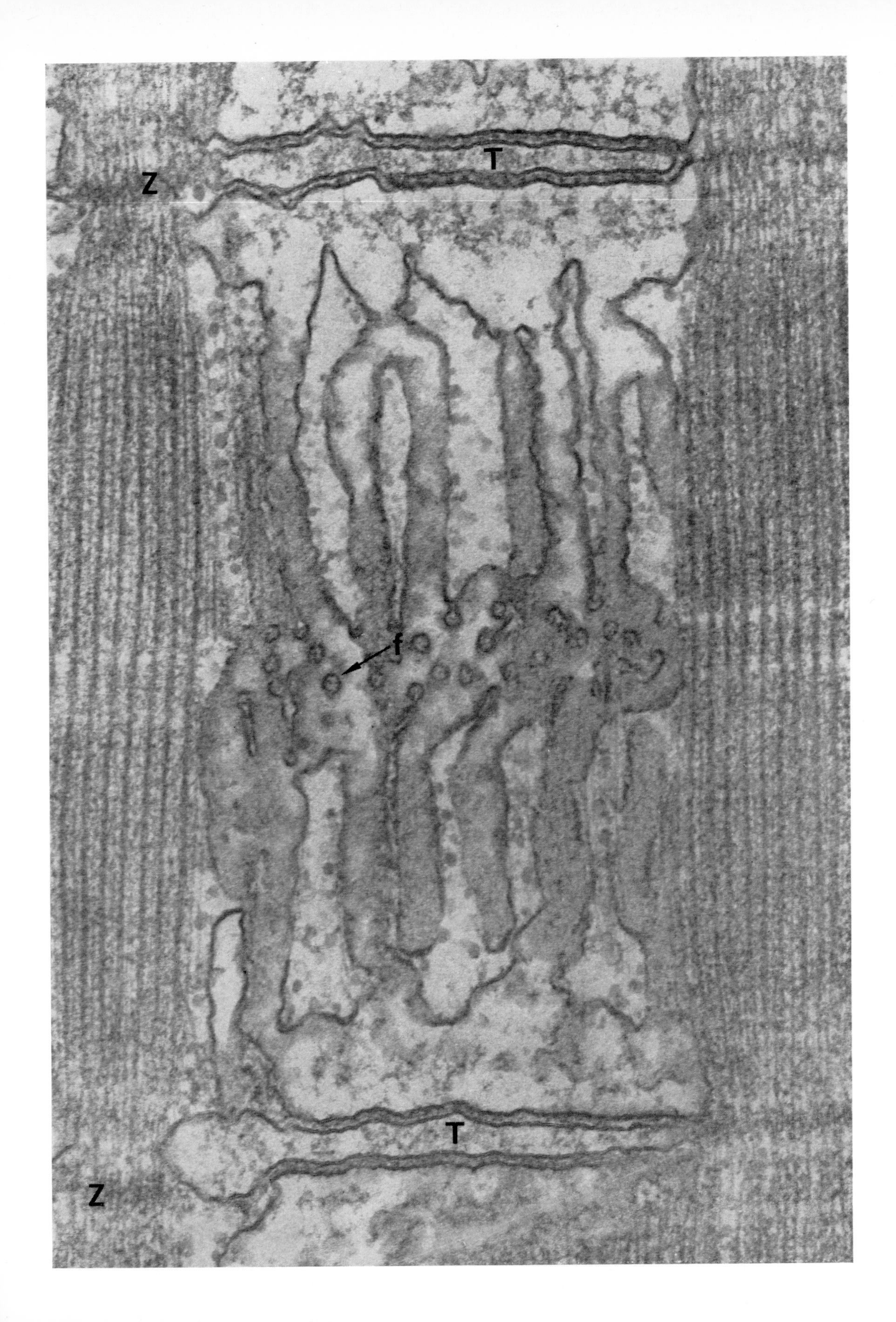
T
Z
f
T
Z

Plate 54

The sarcoplasmic reticulum of cardiac muscle differs from that of skeletal muscle being a simple plexiform type (compare Figs. 14 and 15, pp. 159–60). T-tubules are present in the I-band and are much larger (150–200 nm in diameter) than those of skeletal muscle (40 nm). Cardiac muscle sarcoplasmic reticulum is a simple plexus of tubules of rather uniform calibre which freely anastomose at all levels of the myofibril cross-banding pattern. Instead of large terminal cisternae, small saccular expansions of the reticulum are in contact with the T-tubules. The sarcoplasmic reticulum often continues over the Z-disc and the A-band with no local specialization being apparent.

Sarcoplasmic reticulum in vertebrate cardiac muscle: rat ventricle. Longitudinal section. Glutaraldehyde fixation. ×91 000.

Plate 55

There is a considerable variation in the organization and distribution of sarcoplasmic reticulum and T-tubules with different striated muscles. Most vertebrate skeletal muscles and some invertebrate muscles contain highly ordered, well developed sarcoplasmic reticulum and regularly occurring T-tubules (see Plate 53). Generally, fast-acting fibres are characterized by a prominent system of T-tubules and the presence of triads or dyads which are arranged in a precise relationship to the banding pattern of the myofibrils. Slow-acting muscles usually lack T-tubules. However, the amount of sarcoplasmic reticulum does not appear to differ greatly between slow and fast-acting types of muscle. There is variation in the sarcoplasmic reticulum in different fast-acting invertebrate striated muscles. For example, the asynchronous flight muscle in insect almost completely lacks sarcoplasmic reticulum. In contrast, the grasshopper leg muscle fibres shown here, contain a well developed sarcoplasmic reticulum which appears as an elaborate network of tubules between the myofibrils.

Relationship between sarcoplasmic reticulum and T-tubules in an invertebrate striated muscle: leg muscle of grasshopper. Longitudinal section. Glutaraldehyde fixation. ×65 000.

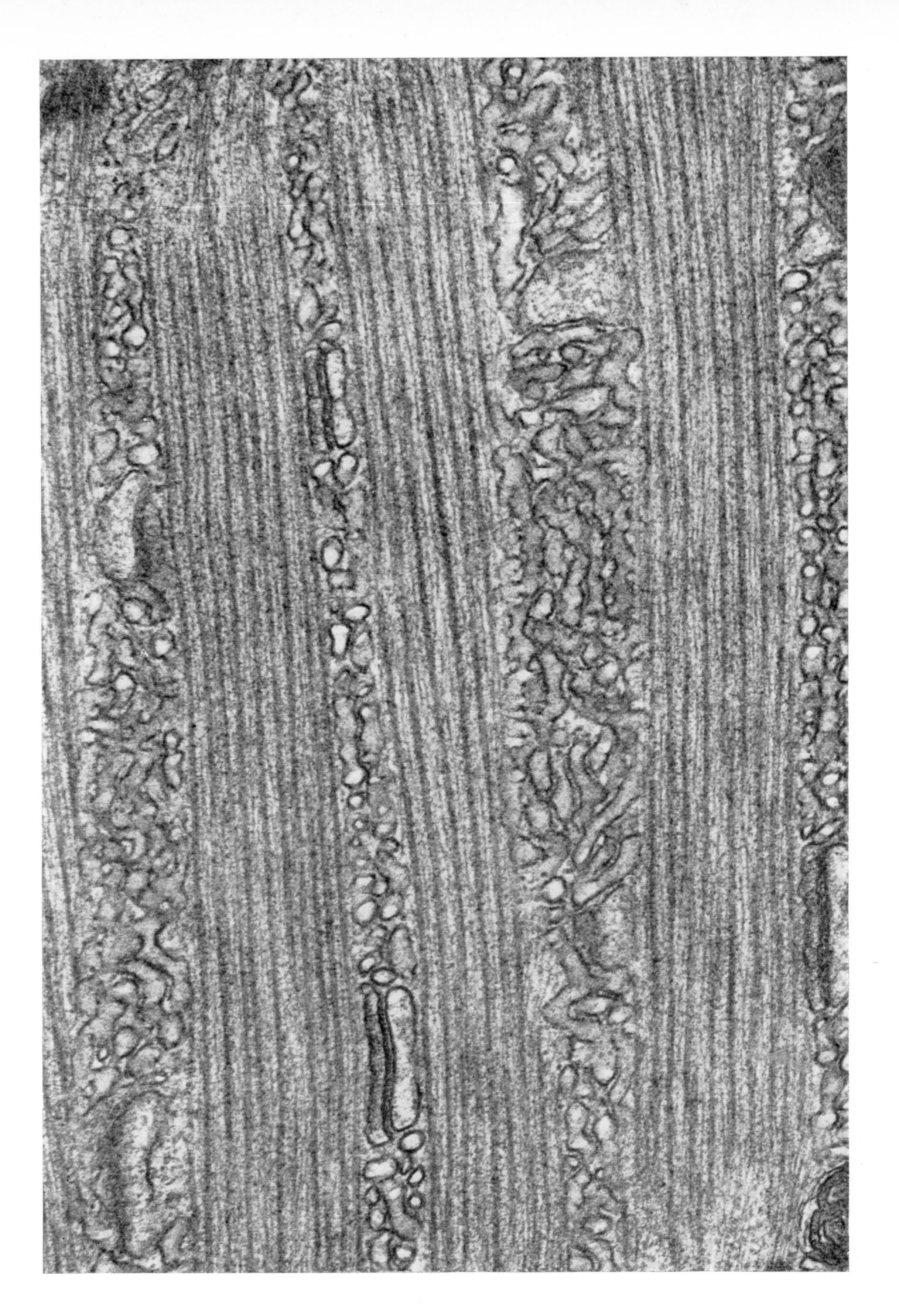

Plate 56

The sarcoplasmic reticulum is well developed in the spider leg muscle. It consists of an irregular network of tubular elements surrounding the myofibrils and frequently crossing the Z-discs. When viewed in transverse section through the A-band region, enlarged elements (80 nm in diameter) of the sarcoplasmic reticulum can be seen, as illustrated. In contrast, when viewed in transverse section through the A–I junction, elements of the T-tubules are also present and form dyads with flattened elements of the sarcoplasmic reticulum. This is illustrated in the next plate (57).

Sarcoplasmic reticulum in an invertebrate striated muscle: spider leg muscle. Transverse section through A-band. Glutaraldehyde fixation. × 162 000.

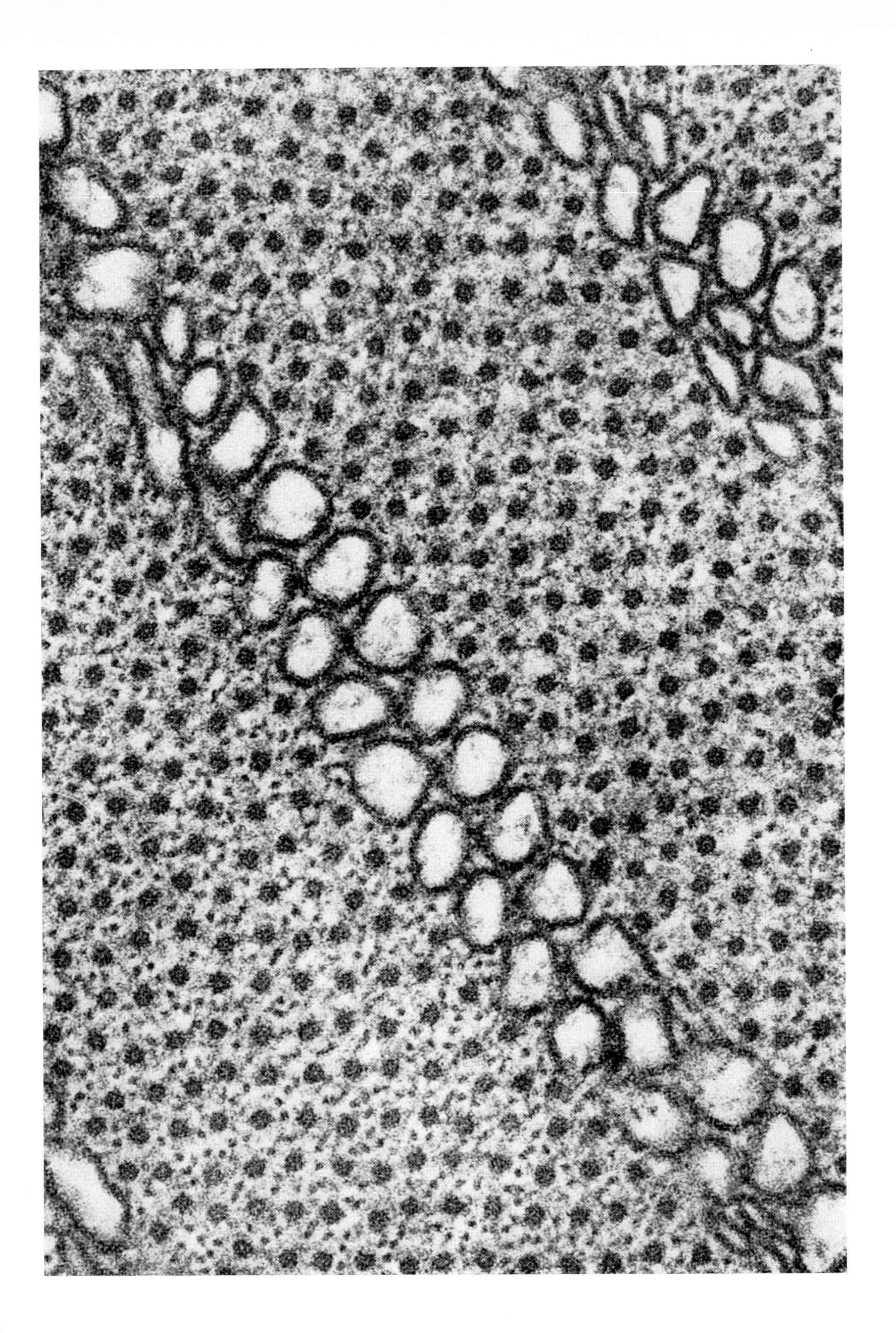

Plate 57

Dyads (arrows), which are equivalent to the triads seen in vertebrate striated muscle (see Plate 53), consist of flattened intracellular cisternae applied to the sarcolemma at the cell surface and along the length of the T-tubules. This micrograph demonstrates T-tubules passing across the cells with a series of regularly spaced dyads on alternate sides. The space between the limiting membranes of the cisternae and of the T-system is occupied by a layer of peg-shaped densities which is referred to as the subsarcolemmal lamina.

A section through the A-band region of the same muscle is illustrated in Plate 56.

Relation between sarcoplasmic reticulum and T-tubules to form dyads in an invertebrate striated muscle: spider leg muscle. Transverse section through A–I junction. Glutaraldehyde fixation. × 126 000.

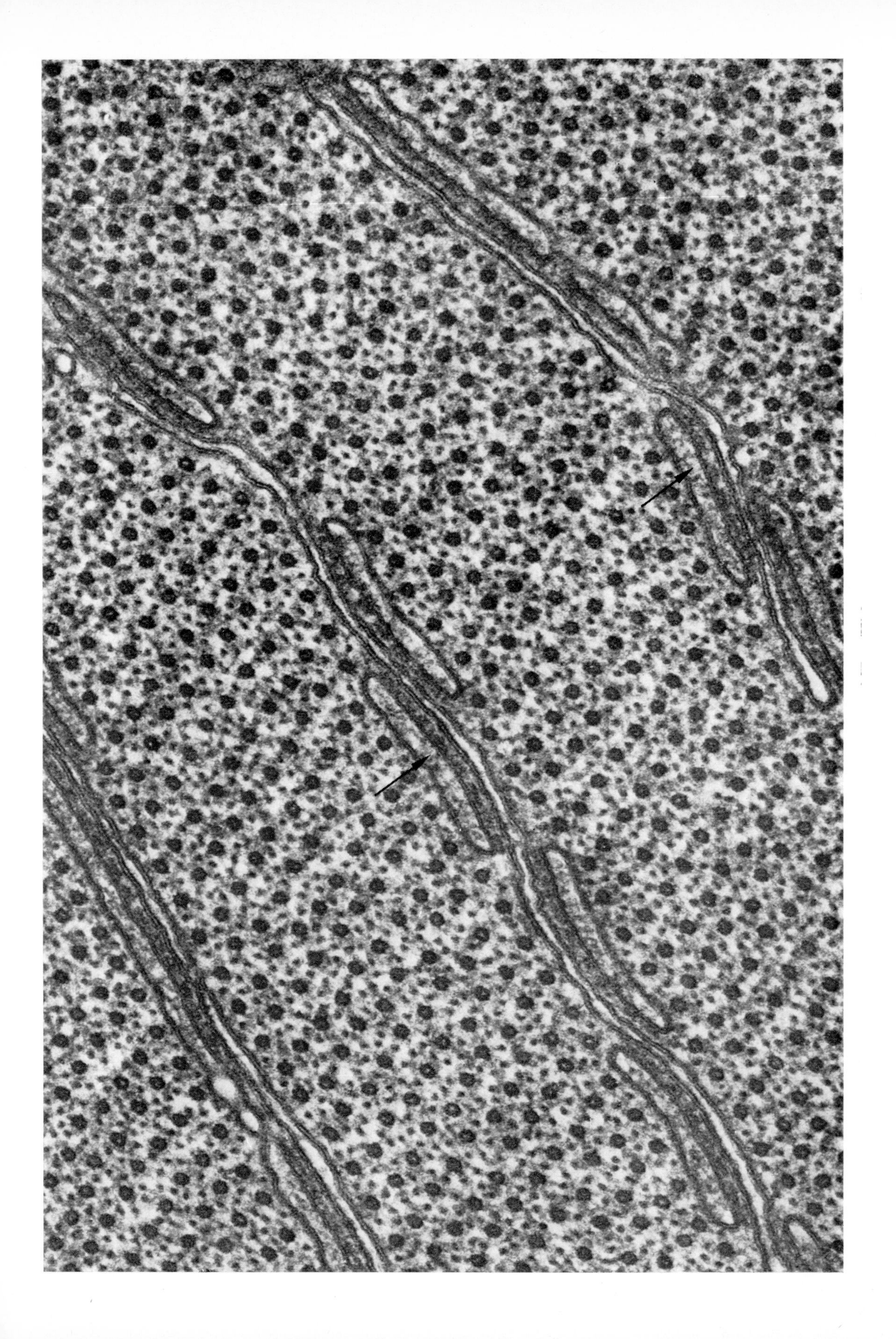

Plate 58

The T-system is continuous with the extracellular space in all vertebrate and invertebrate striated muscles. Since they have narrow openings in most muscles, it is often difficult to demonstrate them in electronmicroscope sections. However in some invertebrate muscles, like the one illustrated, the T-tubules appear to open into depressions of the sarcolemma and are therefore easier to visualize (arrows).

T-system in an invertebrate striated muscle: millipede gut. Transverse section. Glutaraldehyde fixation. ×26 000.

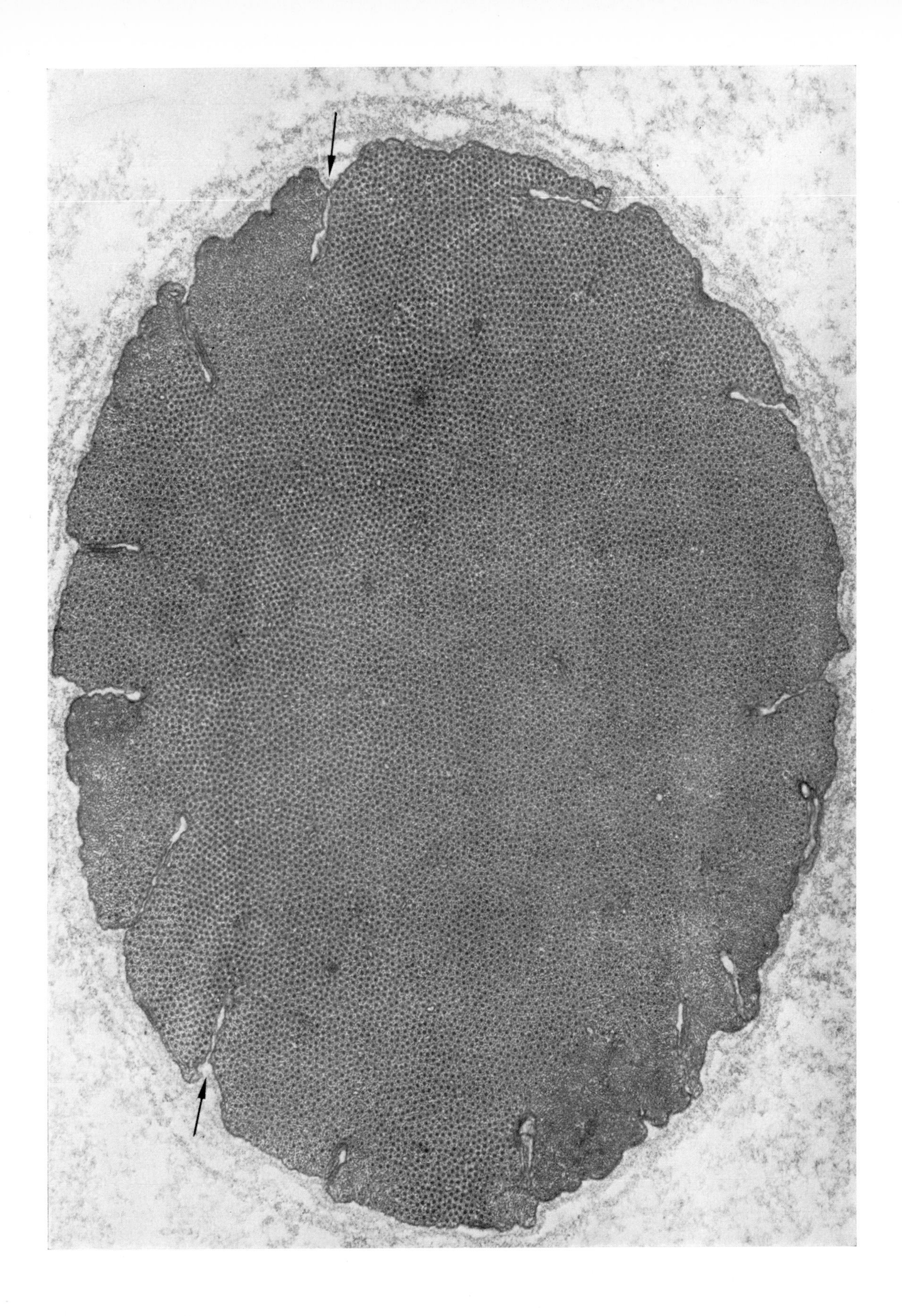

Plate 59

Several techniques have been used to establish that the T-tubules communicate with the extracellular space but do not open into the sarcoplasmic reticulum. For example, the direct diffusion of ferritin, horseradish peroxidase, and lanthanum nitrate has been used to follow the extracellular space into the fibre, and ruthenium red has been used to stain a mucopolysaccharide that invests the surface of the T-tubules. In this plate, ruthenium red, which is an electron dense material, clearly demonstrates the presence of the T-tubules, both at the triad and in other regions.

Communication of T-tubule with extracellular space in vertebrate striated muscle: rat rectus femoris muscle. Longitudinal section. Glutaraldehyde fixation. ×51 000.

Plate 60

Horseradish peroxidase has been used as a tracer to demonstrate the T-system (arrows). The peroxidase completely surrounds the cells and penetrates plasmalemmal vesicles at the periphery. The T-system is not as extensive in cardiac muscle as in skeletal muscle (see also Plate 54).

Communication of T-tubule with extracellular space in vertebrate cardiac muscle: ventricle of dog. Longitudinal section. Glutaraldehyde fixation. ×7700. (Courtesy of Nayler, W. G. and Merillees, N. C. R., 1971, Cellular exchange of calcium, in *Calcium and the Heart* P. Harris and L. H. Opie (ed.). London, Academic Press. 24.)

Plate 61

In earthworm somatic muscle, fibres appear to lack T-tubules and an expanded part of the sarcoplasmic reticulum is closely applied to the sarcolemma. The expanded part of the sarcoplasmic reticulum corresponds to the terminal cistern (t) in other animals (see Fig. 16, page 182). The sarcoplasmic reticulum (SR) can be traced to the centre of the cell. The walls of the terminal cisternae are juxtaposed to the sarcolemma and the material between the two membranes is electron dense (double headed arrow). The single headed arrows indicate the extra cellular space. A similar situation has also been reported in vertebrates and other invertebrates.

Relationship between sarcoplasmic reticulum and sarcolemma in an invertebrate obliquely striated muscle: earthworm somatic muscle. Transverse section. Glutaraldehyde fixation. ×200 000.

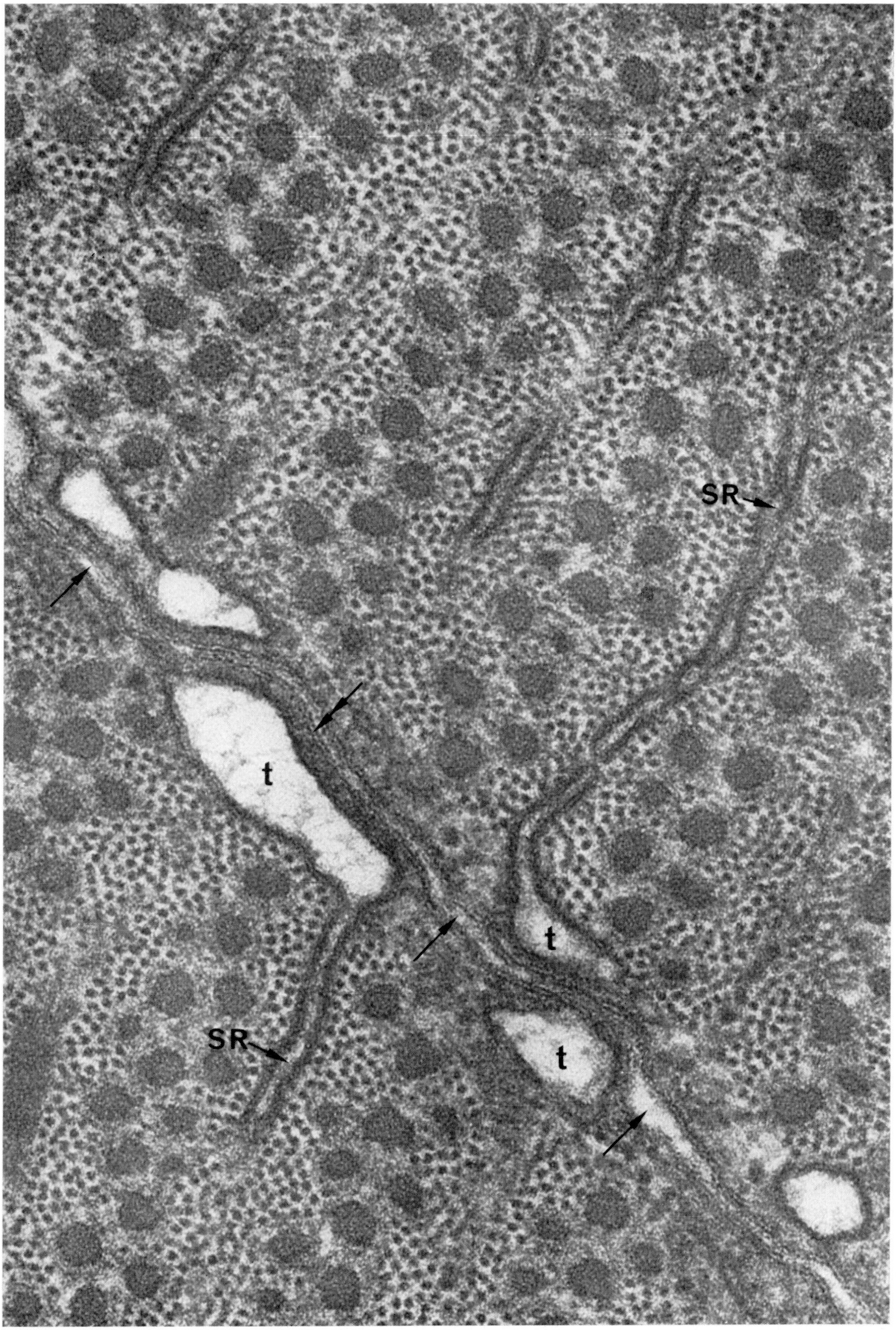

SR
t
t
SR
t

Plate 62

Some vertebrate smooth muscle cells contain smooth endoplasmic reticulum (arrows) in appreciable amounts. There is often a close relationship between part of this reticulum and plasmalemmal vesicles and plasma membrane (see Plates 64 and 96). It has been suggested that these components of smooth endoplasmic reticulum may be equivalent to sarcoplasmic reticulum of striated muscle and also that plasmalemmal vesicles may be equivalent to the T-tubules of skeletal muscle since they are open to the extracellular space and may be electrically coupled to the adjacent sarcoplasmic reticulum. If this is so, the sarcoplasmic reticulum may be the intracellular site of storage and release of Ca^{2+} and play a similar role in excitation–contraction coupling as it does in striated muscle.

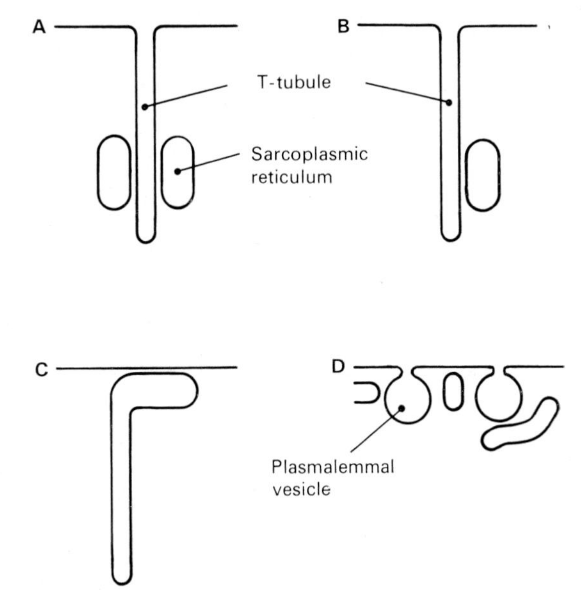

Fig. 16 Relationship between sarcoplasmic reticulum and the cell surface of various muscle types.

A, Triad of vertebrate skeletal muscle (Plate 53);
B, Dyad of invertebrate striated muscle (Plate 57);
C, Enlarged sarcoplasmic reticulum at cell surface in earthworm obliquely striated muscle (Plate 61);
D, Relationship of sarcoplasmic reticulum and plasmalemmal vesicles in vertebrate smooth muscle.

Smooth endoplasmic (sarcoplasmic) reticulum in vertebrate smooth muscle: guinea-pig iris. Transverse section. Glutaraldehyde fixation. ×23 700.

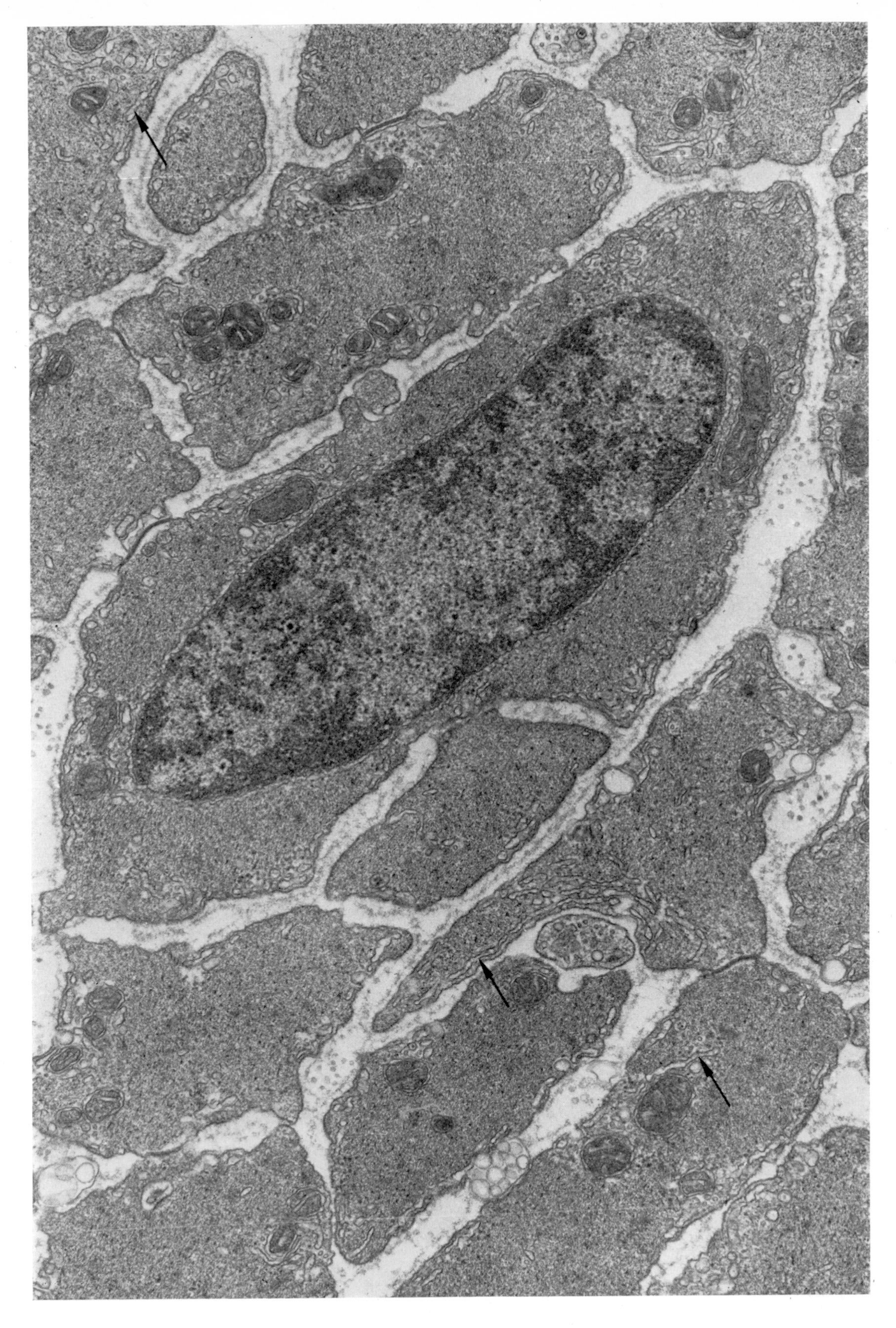

M I—G

Plate 63

Some smooth muscle cells such as those of the iris (and vascular smooth muscle in some species) are unusual in that they contain large areas of smooth endoplasmic reticulum. In the iris muscle illustrated here, this may be because these muscle cells are neuroectodermal in origin and not mesenchymal like most other smooth muscles. The presence of large amounts of smooth endoplasmic reticulum suggests that these cells have functions related to synthesis as well as contractile properties.

Smooth endoplasmic reticulum in vertebrate smooth muscle: guinea-pig iris. Transverse section. Glutaraldehyde fixation. ×51 000.

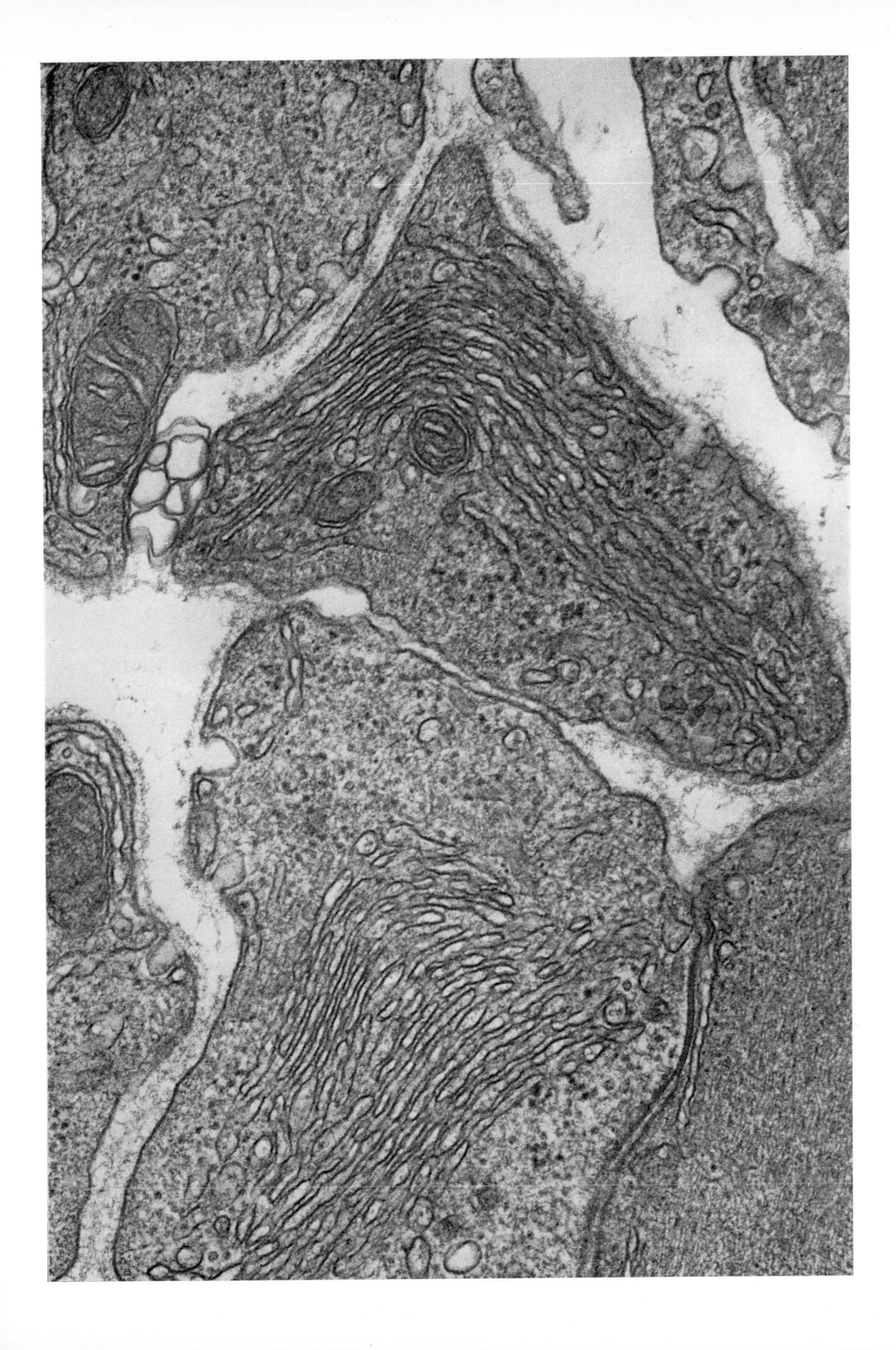

Plate 64

During normal development, smooth endoplasmic reticulum appears to be derived from rough endoplasmic reticulum. This is why in a number of instances the two are continuous. Autoradiographic studies have shown that during intensive smooth endoplasmic formation, rough endoplasmic reticulum is first formed and then the ribosomes are later detached. Arrows indicate the lumen of the rough endoplasmic reticulum.

Continuity between smooth and rough endoplasmic reticulum in vertebrate smooth muscle: guinea-pig iris. ×135 000.

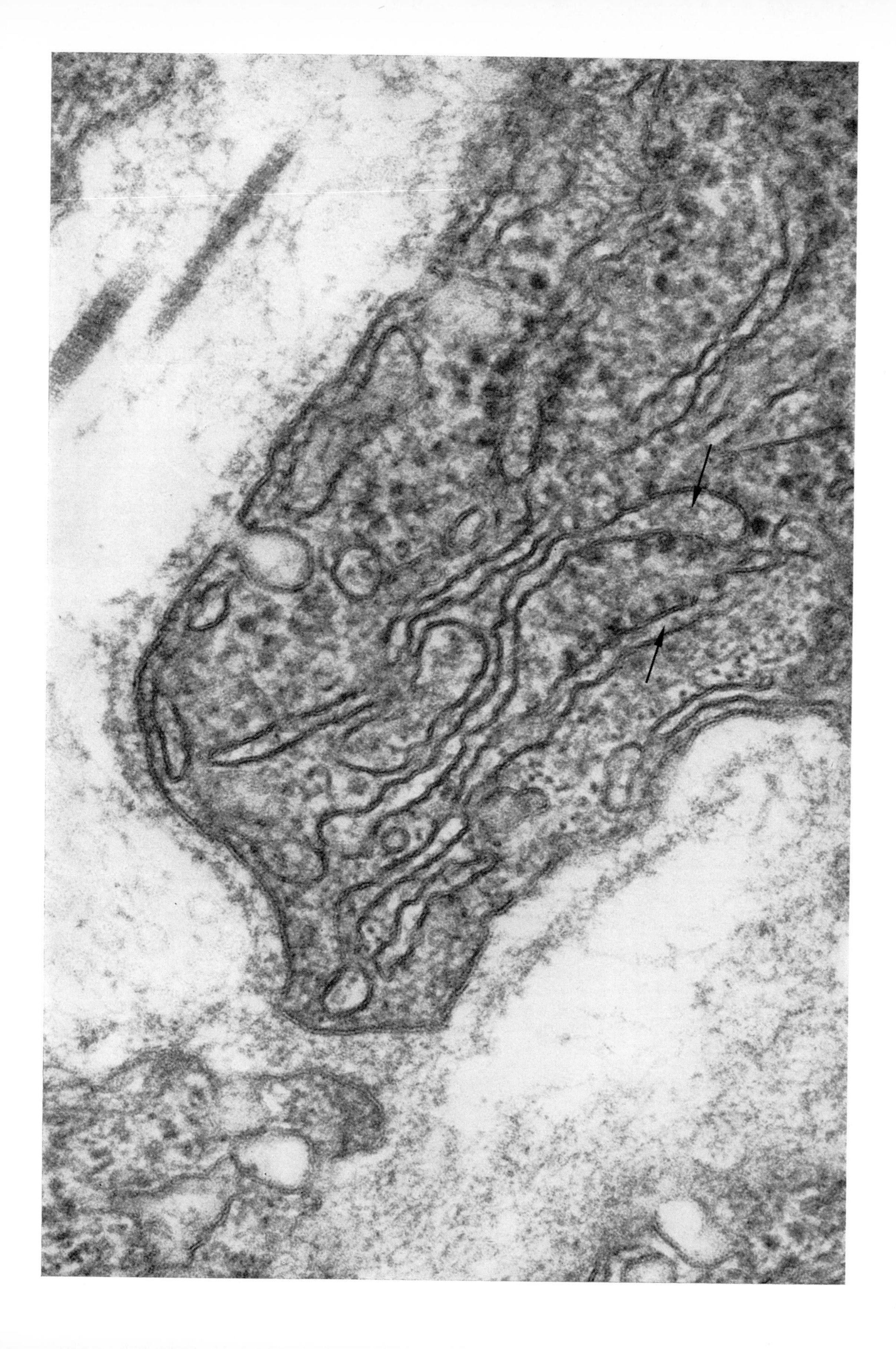

Plate 65

It has been suggested that the T-system of skeletal muscle develops from invaginations of the sarcolemma of the myotube. In contrast, the sarcoplasmic reticulum is derived from the granular endoplasmic reticulum. Therefore, the T-system and the sarcoplasmic reticulum develop independently and may become apposed at a later date. The T-system (Tr) in the embryonic and early postnatal period usually runs in a longitudinal or oblique direction within the muscle cells. As a result, triads in muscle at this stage exhibit a longitudinal rather than transverse orientation.

T-system in developing skeletal muscle: 18-day rat sternothyroid muscle. Longitudinal section. Glutaraldehyde fixation. ×109 000.

Tr

Plate 66

Elaborate, three-dimensional networks of a membranous system (Et) are sometimes apparent in striated muscle. One network illustrated here is seen in the interfibrillar space deep inside the fibre. Another is close to the surface. Ferritin, an extracellular tracer substance, is capable of penetrating this system, suggesting that it is continuous with the extracellular space and therefore perhaps an elaboration of the T-system.

Elaborate membrane system in vertebrate intrafusal muscle: finch rectus femoris. Transverse section. Glutaraldehyde fixation. ×53 000.

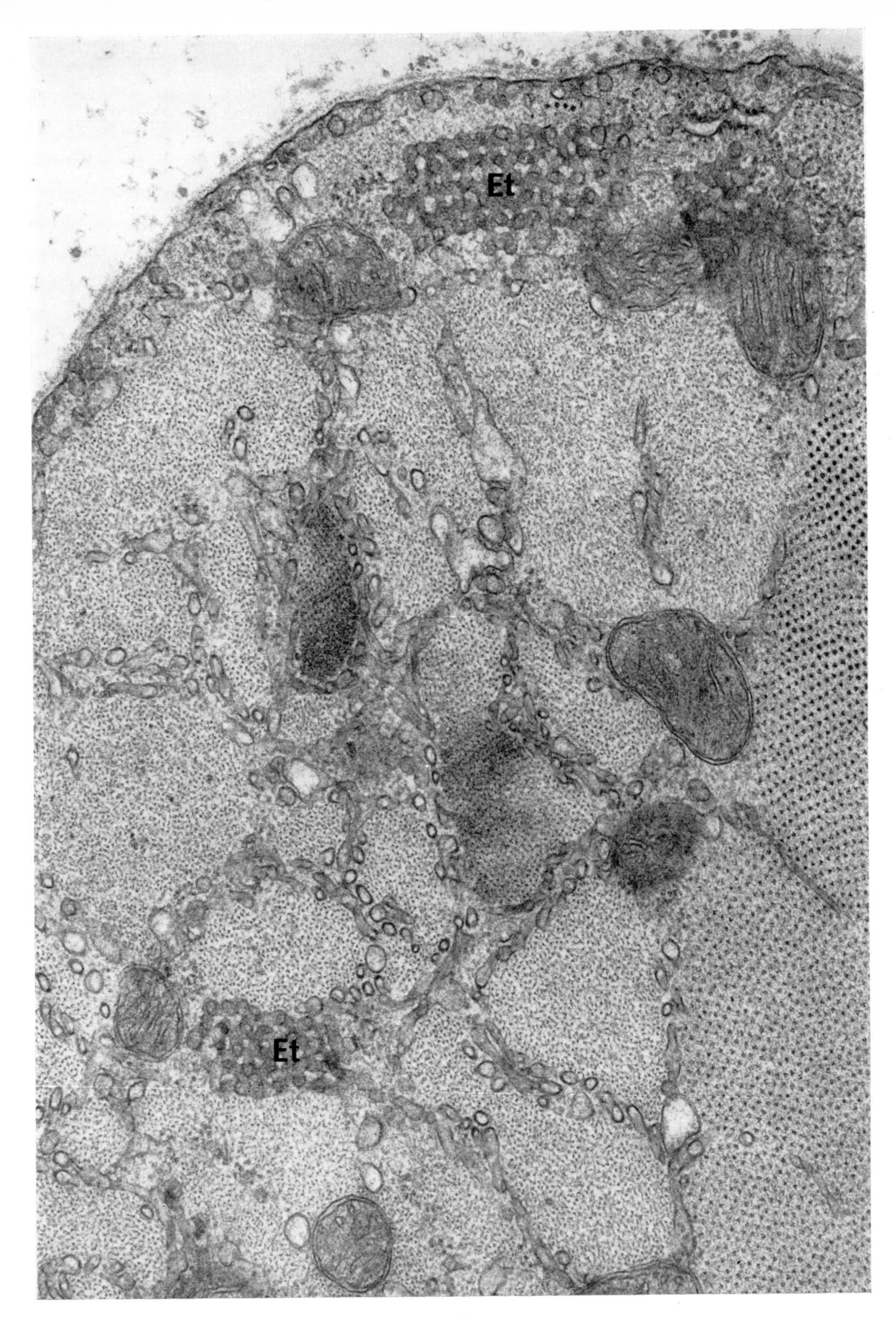
Et
Et

Plate 67

(*a*) The membranous network in some skeletal muscles consists of tubular units which have a diameter of about 50 nm and are regularly arranged in an approximate hexagonal pattern (see Fig. 17).

(*b*) Most smooth muscle does not appear to have a T-system. However, some cultured smooth muscle cells contain a membranous network of tubules, comparable to but not as well organized as in skeletal muscle. Experiments using tracer substances such as ferritin have not been used to determine whether these networks in cultured smooth muscle are connected to the extracellular space. Comparable networks of tubules can be induced by drugs in smooth muscle and a number of other cell types, such as luteal cells. Networks of a similar nature have also been observed in denervated skeletal muscle.

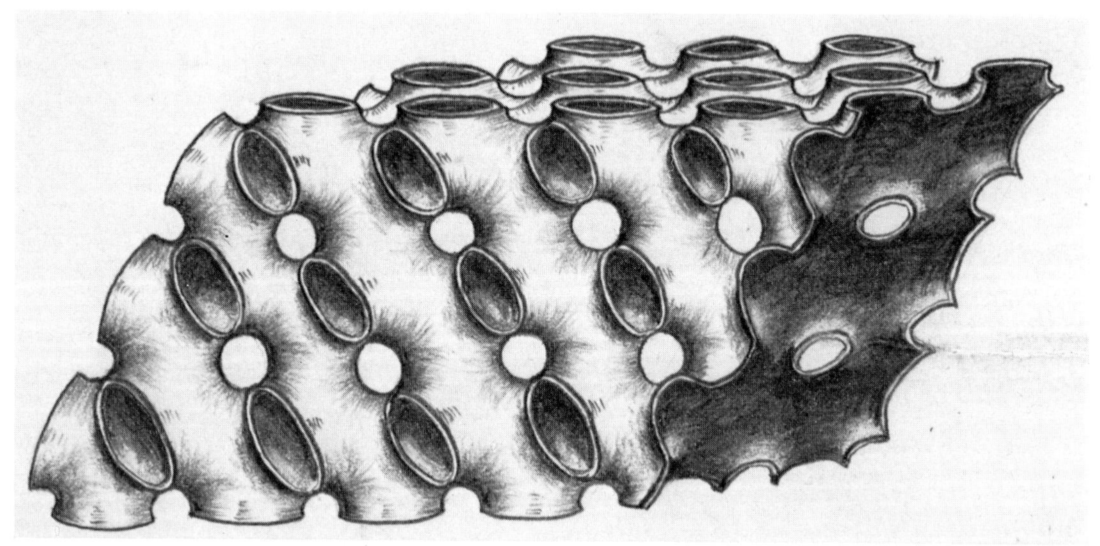

Fig. 17 Three-dimensional reconstruction of the hexagonal T-system network. Dark areas on the right represent the interior surface of the network tubules. The network is arranged in successive planes in which the tubular units form a hexagonal pattern. The 'vertical' tubular units connecting the successive 'horizontal' planes themselves form a plane, which is inclined about 60° from the horizontal planes. Thus, any plane with the typical hexagonal pattern intersects other such planes at 60°. (Courtesy of H. Ishikawa, 1968, *J. Cell. Biol.*, **38,** 51.)

(*a*) Elaborate membrane system in vertebrate intrafusal muscle: rat sternothyroid. Transverse section. Osmium fixation. × 47 000.

(*b*) Elaborate membrane system in vertebrate cultured smooth muscle: 10-day chicken gizzard, 4 days in culture. Glutaraldehyde fixation. × 137 000.

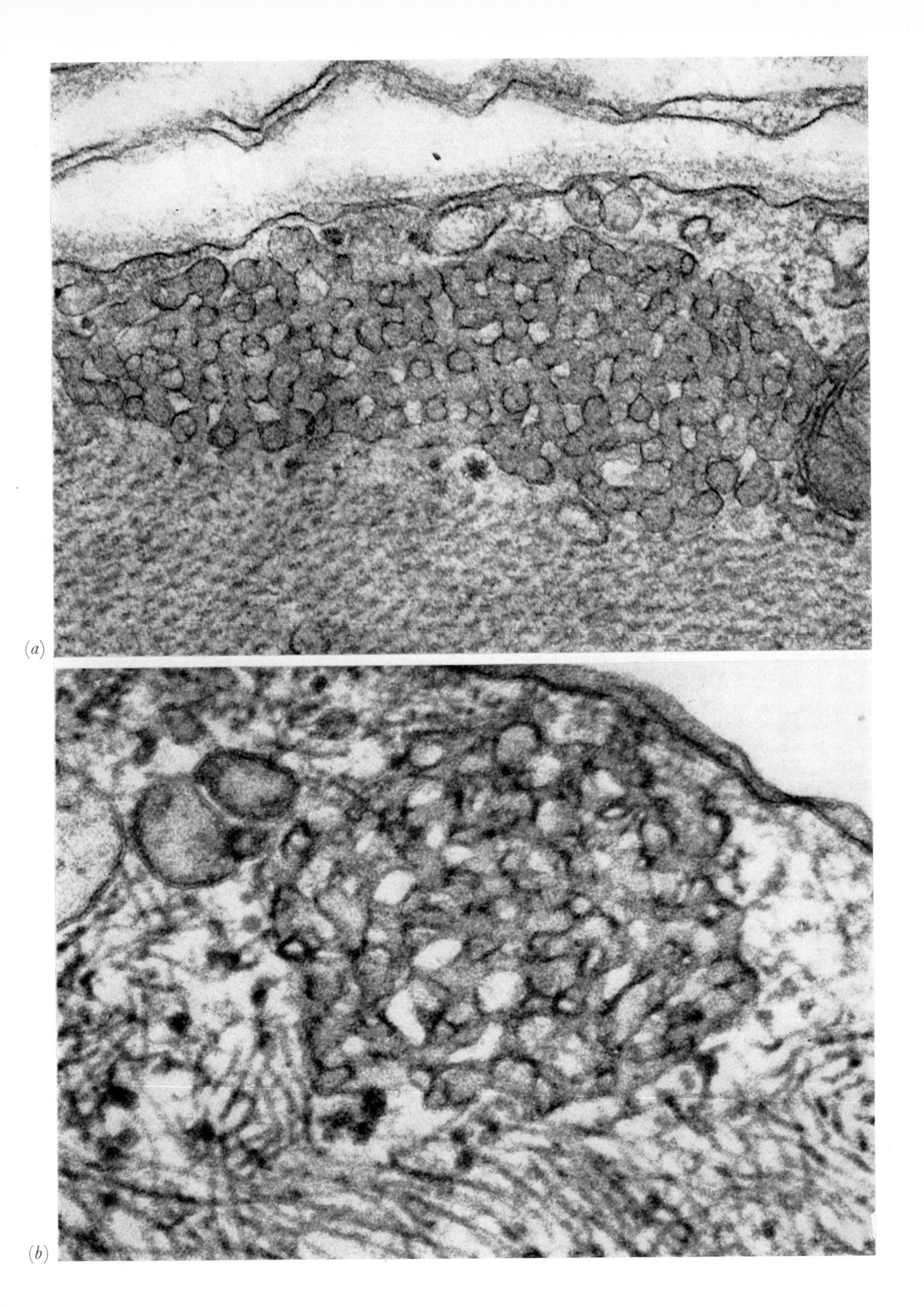
(a)
(b)

Selected articles

Vertebrate skeletal muscle

ANDERSSON-CEDERGREN, E. 1959. Ultrastructure of motor end plate and sarcoplasmic components of mouse skeletal muscle fiber as revealed by three-dimensional reconstructions from serial sections. *J. Ultrastruct. Res.*, Supplement 1.

ANDERSSON-CEDERGREN, E. and U. MUSCATELLO. 1963. The participation of the sarcotubular system in glycogen metabolism. *J. Ultrastruct. Res.*, **8,** 391–401.

BIANCHI, C. P. 1969. Pharmacology of excitation–contraction coupling in muscle. Introduction: statement of the problem. *Fedn Proc.*, **28,** 1624–1627.

BIRKS, R. I. 1964. The sarcoplasmic reticulum of twitch fibres in the frog sartorius muscle. In *Muscle*. W. M. Paul, E. E. Daniel, E. M. Kay and G. Monckton (eds.). Pergamon Press, Oxford. 199–216.

BIRKS, R. I. and D. F. DAVEY. 1969. Osmotic responses demonstrating the extracellular character of the sarcoplasmic reticulum. *J. Physiol., Lond.*, **202,** 171–188.

BIRKS, R. I. and D. F. DAVEY. 1972. An analysis of volume changes in the T-tubes of frog skeletal muscle exposed to sucrose. *J. Physiol., Lond.*, **222,** 95–111.

BOYDE, A. and J. C. P. WILLIAMS. 1968. Surface morphology of frog striated muscle as prepared for and examined in the scanning electron microscope. *J. Physiol., Lond.*, **197,** 10P–11P.

BUSS, W. C. and G. B. FRANK. 1969. Calcium and excitation–contraction coupling in mammalian skeletal muscle. *Archs int. Pharmacodyn. Ther.*, **181,** 15–26.

CARVALHO, A. P. 1972. Binding and release of cations by sarcoplasmic reticulum before and after removal of lipid. *Eur. J. Biochem.*, **27,** 491–502.

COSTANTIN, L. L., C. FRANZINI-ARMSTRONG and R. J. PODOLSKY. 1965. Localization of calcium-accumulating structures in striated muscle fibers. *Science, N.Y.*, **147,** 158–159.

CÔTÉ, M. G., E. B. SANDBORN and P. BOIS. 1966. Continuité entre le système 'T' et le sarcolemme dans la fibre squelettique du rat. *Revue can. Biol.*, **25,** 221–223.

DEAMER, D. W. and R. J. BASKIN. 1969. Ultrastructure of sarcoplasmic reticulum preparations. *J. Cell Biol.*, **42,** 296–307.

DRABIKOWSKI, W., M. G. SARZAŁA, A. WRONISZEWSKA, E. ŁAGWINSKA and B. DRZEWIECKA. 1972. Role of cholesterol in the Ca^{2+} uptake and ATPase activity of fragmented sarcoplasmic reticulum. *Biochim. biophys. Acta*, **274,** 158–170.

EBASHI, S. 1972. Calcium ions and muscle contraction. *Nature, Lond.*, **240,** 217–218.

EDWARDS, G. A., H. RUSKA, P. SOUZA SANTOS and A. VALLEJO-FREIRE. 1956. Comparative cytophysiology of striated muscle with special reference to the role of the endoplasmic reticulum. *J. biophys. biochem. Cytol.*, **2,** Suppl., 143–156.

EISENBERG, B. and R. S. EISENBERG. 1968*a*. Transverse tubular system in glycerol-treated skeletal muscle. *Science, N.Y.*, **160,** 1243–1244.

EISENBERG, B. and R. S. EISENBERG. 1968*b*. Selective disruption of the sarcotubular system in frog sartorius muscle. A quantitative study with exogenous peroxidase as a marker. *J. Cell Biol.*, **39,** 451–467.

ENDO, M. 1966. Entry of fluorescent dyes into the sarcotubular system of the frog muscle. *J. Physiol., Lond.*, **185,** 224–238.

ENDO, M. 1973. Length dependence of activation of skinned muscle fibers by calcium. In *The Mechanism of Muscle Contraction. Cold Spring Harb. Symp. quant. Biol.*, **37,** 505–510.

ENDO, M., M. TANAKA and Y. OGAWA. 1970. Calcium induced release of calcium from the sarcoplasmic reticulum of skinned skeletal muscle fibres. *Nature, Lond.*, **228,** 34–36.

ENGEL, W. K., D. W. BISHOP and G. G. CUNNINGHAM. 1970. Tubular aggregates in type II muscle fibers: ultrastructural and histochemical correlation. *J. Ultrastruct. Res.*, **31,** 507–525.

FAHRENBACH, W. H. 1964. A new configuration of the sarcoplasmic reticulum. *J. Cell Biol.*, **22,** 477–481.

FARHENBACH, W. H. 1965. Sarcoplasmic reticulum: ultrastructure of the triadic junction. *Science, N.Y.*, **147,** 1308–1310.

FAWCETT, D. W. and J. P. REVEL. 1961. The

sarcoplasmic reticulum of a fast-acting fish muscle. *J. biophys. biochem. Cytol.*, **10,** 89–110.

FIEHN, W. and J. B. PETER. 1971. Properties of the fragmented sarcoplasmic reticulum from fast twitch and slow twitch muscles. *J. clin. Invest.*, **50,** 570–573.

FRANK, G. B. 1964. Calcium and the initiation of contraction. *Circulation Res.*, **15,** Suppl. 2, 54–63.

FRANZINI-ARMSTRONG, C. 1963. Pores in the sarcoplasmic reticulum. *J. Cell Biol.*, **19,** 637–641.

FRANZINI-ARMSTRONG, C. 1964. Fine structure of sarcoplasmic reticulum and transverse tubular system in muscle fibers. *Fedn Proc.*, **23,** 887–895.

FRANZINI-ARMSTRONG, C. 1970. Studies of the triad. I. Structure of the junction in frog twitch fibers. *J. Cell Biol.*, **47,** 488–499.

FRANZINI-ARMSTRONG, C. 1971. Studies of the triad. II. Penetration of tracers into the junctional gap. *J. Cell Biol.*, **49,** 196–204.

FRANZINI-ARMSTRONG, C. 1972. Studies of the triad. III. Structure of the junction in fast twitch fibers. *Tissue & Cell*, **4,** 469–478.

FRANZINI-ARMSTRONG, C. 1973. Studies of the triad. IV. Structure of the junction in frog slow fibers. *J. Cell Biol.*, **56,** 120–128.

FRANZINI-ARMSTRONG, C. and K. R. PORTER. 1964. Sarcolemmal invaginations constituting the T system in fish muscle fibers. *J. Cell Biol.*, **22,** 675–696.

FREYGANG, W. H., JR., D. A. GOLDSTEIN, D. C. HELLAM and L. D. PEACHEY. 1964. The relation between the late after-potential and the size of the transverse tubular system of frog muscle. *J. gen. Physiol.*, **48,** 235–263.

GAGE, P. W. and R. S. EISENBERG. 1969. Action potentials, after potentials and excitation–contraction coupling in frog sartorius fibers without transverse tubules. *J. gen. Physiol.*, **53,** 298–310.

GOLDSTEIN, M. A. 1969. A morphological and cytochemical study of sarcoplasmic reticulum and T system of fish extraocular muscle. *Z. Zellforsch. mikrosk. Anat.*, **102,** 31–39.

GORI, Z. 1972. Proliferations of the sarcoplasmic reticulum and the T-system in denervated muscle fibers. *Virchows Arch. Abt. B. Zellpath.* **11,** 147–160.

HAGOPIAN, M. and NUNEZ, E. A. 1972. Sarcolemmal scalloping at short sarcomere lengths with incidental observations on the T tubules. *J. Cell Biol.*, **53,** 252–257.

HASSELBACH, W. 1964. Relaxing factor and the relaxation of muscle. *Progr. Biophys. mol. Biol.*, **14,** 167–222.

HASSELBACH, W. 1966. Structural and enzymatic properties of the calcium transporting membranes of the sarcoplasmic reticulum. *Ann. N.Y. Acad. Sci.*, **137,** 1041–1048.

HASSELBACH, W. and L.-G. ELFVIN. 1967. Structural and chemical asymmetry of the calcium-transporting membranes of the sarcotubular system as revealed by electron microscopy. *J. Ultrastruct. Res.*, **17,** 598–622.

HASSELBACH, W. and M. MAKINOSE. 1964. The calcium pump of the relaxing vesicles and the production of a relaxing substance. In *Biochemistry of Muscle Contraction.* J. Gergely (ed.). Little, Brown & Co., Boston. 247–269.

HASSELBACH, W. and H. H. WEBER. 1965. Die intracelluläre Regulation der Muskelaktivität. *Naturwissenschaften*, **52,** 121–128.

HEUSON-STIENNON, J.-A., J.-C. WANSON and P. DROCHMANS. 1972. Isolation and characterization of the sarcoplasmic reticulum of skeletal muscle. *J. Cell Biol.*, **55,** 471–488.

HIKIDA, R. S. 1972. The structure of the sarcotubular system in avian muscle. *Am. J. Anat.*, **134,** 481–496.

HOYLE, G., P. A. MCNEILL and B. WALCOTT. 1966. Nature of invaginating tubules in *Felderstruktur* muscle fibers of the garter snake. *J. Cell Biol.*, **30,** 197–201.

HUXLEY, A. F. 1964. The links between excitation and contraction. *Proc. R. Soc. Ser. B.*, **160,** 486–488.

HUXLEY, A. F. and R. E. TAYLOR. 1958. Local activation of striated muscle fibers. *J. Physiol., Lond.*, **144,** 426–441.

HUXLEY, H. E. 1964. Evidence for continuity between the central elements of the triads and extracellular space in frog sartorius muscle. *Nature, Lond.*, **202,** 1067–1071.

HUXLEY, H. E., S. PAGE and D. R. WILKIE. 1963. An electron-microscopic study of muscle in hypertonic solutions. *J. Physiol., Lond.*, **169,** 312–329. Appendix of Dydyńska, M. and D. R. Wilkie.

INESI, G., M. MILLMAN and S. ELETR. 1973. Temperature induced transitions of function and structure in sarcoplasmic reticulum membranes. *J. molec. Biol.*, **81,** 483–504.

JAMES, N. T. and G. A. MEEK. 1973. Studies on the sarcoplasmic reticulum of rat, cat and sheep intrafusal fibres. *J. Anat.*, **116,** 219–226.

JASPER, D. 1967. Body muscles of the lamprey. Some structural features of the T system and sarcolemma. *J. Cell Biol.*, **32,** 219–227.

KARNOVSKY, M. J. 1965. Vesicular transport of exogenous peroxidase across capillary endothelium into the T-system of muscle. *J. Cell Biol.*, **27,** 49A–50A.

KELLY, D. E. 1969. The fine structure of skeletal muscle triad junctions. *J. Ultrastruct. Res.*, **29,** 37–49.

KILARSKI, W. 1964. The organization of the sarcoplasmic reticulum in skeletal muscles of fishes. Part I. The sarcoplasmic reticulum of striated muscles of the swim-bladder in the burbot (*Lota lota* L.). *Acta Biol. Cracov. Serie zoologique*, **7,** 161–168.

KILARSKI, W. 1965. The organization of the sarcoplasmic reticulum in skeletal muscles of fishes. Part II. The perch (*Perca fluviatilus* L.). *Acta Biol. Cracov. Serie zoologique*, **8,** 51–57.

KILARSKI, W. 1966. The organization of the sarcoplasmic reticulum in skeletal muscles of fishes. Part III. Pike (*Esox lucius* L.). *Bull. Acad. pol. Sci.*, **8,** 576–580.

KILARSKI, W. 1967. Preliminary report of observations on the organization of the sarcoplasmic reticulum in the ocular muscles in fish. *Acta med. Pol. VIII*, **4,** 339–402.

KILARSKI, W. 1973. Cytomorphometry of sarcoplasmic reticulum in extrinsic eye muscles of the teleost (*Tinca tinca* L.). *Z. Zellforsch. mikrosk. Anat.*, **136,** 535–544.

KULCZYCKY, S. and G. W. MAINWOOD. 1972. Evidence for a functional connection between the sarcoplasmic reticulum and the extracellular space in frog sartorius muscle. *Can. J. Physiol. Pharmacol.*, **50,** 87–98.

McCALLISTER, L. P. and R. HADEK. 1970. Transmission electron microscopy and stereo ultrastructure of the T system in frog skeletal muscle. *J. Ultrastruct. Res.*, **33,** 360–368.

MacLENNAN, D. H., C. C. YIP, G. H. ILES and P. SEEMAN. 1973. Isolation of sarcoplasmic reticulum proteins. In *The Mechanism of Muscle Contraction. Cold Spring Harb. Symp. quant. Biol.*, **37,** 469–478.

MARTONOSI, A. 1968. Sarcoplasmic reticulum. V. The structure of sarcoplasmic reticulum membranes. *Biochim. biophys. Acta.*, **150,** 694–704.

MARTONOSI, A., R. BOLAND and R. A. HALPIN. 1973. The biosynthesis of sarcoplasmic reticulum membranes and the mechanism of calcium transport. In *The Mechanism of Muscle Contraction. Cold Spring Harb. Symp. quant. Biol.*, **37,** 455–468.

MEISSNER, G. 1973. ATP and Ca^{2+} binding by Ca^{2+} pump protein of sarcoplasmic reticulum. *Biochem. biophys. Acta*, **298,** 906–926.

MENDELL, J. R. 1971. Unusual features of the T-system of the pectoralis muscle of the chicken. *J. Ultrastruct. Res.*, **37,** 383–387.

MUSCATELLO, U. and E. ANDERSSON-CEDERGREN. 1962. Function of sarcotubular system in relation to biosynthesis of muscle proteins. *Revue can. Biol.*, **21,** 207–218.

MUSCATELLO, U., E. ANDERSSON-CEDERGREN, G. F. AZZONE and A. VON DER DECKEN. 1961. The sarcotubular system of frog skeletal muscle. A morphological and biochemical study. *J. Biochem, biophys. Cytol.*, **10,** Suppl., 201–218.

PAGE, S. 1968. Structure of the sarcoplasmic reticulum in vertebrate muscles. *Br. med. Bull.*, **24,** 170–173.

PEACHEY, L. D. 1961. Structure of the longitudinal body muscles of *Amphioxus*. *J. biophys. biochem. Cytol.*, **10,** Suppl., 159–176.

PEACHEY, L. D. 1965. The sarcoplasmic reticulum and transverse tubules of the frog's sartorius. *J. Cell Biol.*, **25,** 209–231.

PEACHEY, L. D. 1973. Electrical events in the T-system of frog skeletal muscle. In *The Mechanism of Muscle Contraction. Cold Spring Harb. Symp. quant. Biol.*, **37,** 479–488.

PEACHEY, L. D. and R. F. SCHILD. 1968. The distribution of the T-system along the sarcomeres of frog and toad sartorius muscles. *J. Physiol., Lond.*, **194,** 249–258.

PEASE, D. C., D. J. JENDEN and J. N. HOWELL. 1965. Calcium uptake in glycerol-extracted rabbit psoas muscle fibers. II. Electron microscopic localization of uptake sites. *J. cell. comp. Physiol.*, **65,** 141–153.

PETER, J. B., W. FIEHN and R. F. DUNN. 1970. Biochemistry and morphology of fragmented sarcoplasmic reticulum. In *Electron Microscopy*, 1970. C. J. Arceneaux (ed.). Claitor's Publications, Baton Rouge, La.

PODOLSKY, R. J. and L. L. COSTANTIN. 1966. The internal membrane system and muscle activation. *Ann. N.Y. Acad. Sci.*, **137,** 1038–1040.

PORTER, K. R. 1956. The sarcoplasmic reticulum in muscle cells of *Amblystoma* larvae. *J. biophys. biochem. Cytol.*, **2,** Suppl. 4, 163–170.

PORTER, K. R. 1961. The sarcoplasmic reticulum. Its recent history and present status. *J. biophys. biochem. Cytol.*, **10,** Suppl., 219–226.

PORTER, K. R. and G. E. PALADE. 1957. Studies on the endoplasmic reticulum. III. Its form and distribution in striated muscle cells. *J. biophys. biochem. Cytol.*, **3,** 269–300.

RAPOPORT, S. I., L. D. PEACHEY and D. A. GOLDSTEIN. 1969. Swelling of the transverse tubular system in frog sartorius. *J. gen. Physiol.*, **54,** 166–177.

RAYNS, D. G., F. O. SIMPSON and W. S. BERTAUD. 1968. Surface features of striated muscle. II. Guinea-pig skeletal muscle. *J. Cell Sci.*, **3,** 475–482.

REVEL, J. P. 1962. The sarcoplasmic reticulum of the bat cricothyroid muscle. *J. Cell Biol.*, **12,** 571–588.

RUBIO, R. and N. SPERELAKIS. 1972. Penetration of horseradish peroxidase into the terminal cisternae of frog skeletal muscle fibers and blockade of caffeine contracture by Ca^{++} depletion. *Z. Zellforsch. mikrosk. Anat.*, **124,** 57–71.

SCHOTLAND, D. L. 1968. Ultrastructural abnormalities in myotonic dystrophy including an unusual T system alteration. *J. Neuropathol. exp. Neurol.*, **27,** 109–110.

SOMMER, J. R. and W. HASSELBACH. 1967. The effect of glutaraldehyde and formaldehyde on the calcium pump of the sarcoplasmic reticulum. *J. Cell Biol.*, **34,** 902–905.

STEFANI, E. and A. STEINBACH. 1968. Persistence of excitation contraction coupling in 'slow' muscle fibres after a treatment that destroys transverse tubules in 'twitch' fibres. *Nature, Lond.*, **218,** 681–682.

TROMBITÁS, K. 1971. The submicroscopic transversal structure of striated fibril. *Acta biochim. biophys. Acad. Sci. hung.* **6,** 419–426.

VAN DER KLOOT, W. 1969. Calculated effects of SR thickness on sarcoplasmic calcium concentration. Appendix to Mendelson J. *J. Cell Biol.*, **42,** 562–563.

VERATTI, E. (Translated from the Italian) 1961. Investigations on the fine structure of striated muscle fiber. *J. biophys. biochem. Cytol.*, **10,** Suppl. 4, 3–59.

WALKER, S. M. and G. R. SCHRODT. 1965. Continuity of the T-system with the sarcolemma in rat skeletal muscle fibers. *J. Cell Biol.*, **27,** 671–677.

WALKER, S. M. and G. R. SCHRODT. 1966. Connections between the T system and sarcoplasmic reticulum. *Anat. Rec.*, **155,** 1–10.

WALKER, S. M. and G. R. SCHRODT. 1966. Evidence for connections between mitochondria and the sarcoplasmic reticulum and evidence for glycogen granules within the sarcoplasmic reticulum. *Am. J. Phys. Med.*, **45,** 25-43.

WARREN, R. H. 1973*a*. Interaction of the sarcoplasmic reticulum with Z-lines during myogenesis in amphibian skeletal muscle. *Anat. Rec.*, **177,** 225–242.

WARREN, R. H. 1973*b*. Association of the sarcoplasmic reticulum with developing Z-lines of *Rana pipiens*. *Anat. Rec.*, **175,** 464.

WAUGH, R. A., T. L. SPRAY and J. R. SOMMER. 1973. Fenestrations of sarcoplasmic reticulum. Delineation by lanthanum acting as a fortuitous tracer and *in situ* negative stain. *J. Cell Biol.*, **59,** 254–60.

WEIBEL, E. R. 1972. A stereological method for estimating volume and surface of sarcoplasmic reticulum. *J. Microsc.* (*Oxf.*), **95,** 229–242.

WINEGRAD, S. 1970. The intracellular site of calcium activation of contraction in frog skeletal muscle. *J. gen. Physiol.*, **55,** 77–88.

Vertebrate cardiac muscle

BASKIN, R. J. and D. W. DEAMER. 1969. Comparative ultrastructure and calcium transport in heart and skeletal muscle microsomes. *J. Cell Biol.*, **43,** 610–617.

CARSTEN, M. E. and M. K. REEDY. 1971. Cardiac sarcoplasmic reticulum: chemical and electron microscope studies of calcium accumulation. *J. Ultrastruct. Res.*, **35,** 554–574.

DREIFUSS, J. J., L. GIRARDIER and W. G. FORSSMANN. 1966. Étude de la propagation de l'excitation dans la ventricule de rat au moyen de solutions hypertoniques. *Pflügers Arch. ges. Physiol.*, **292,** 13–33.

EDGE, M. B. and S. H. WALKER. 1970. Evidence for a structural relationship between sarcoplasmic reticulum and Z lines in dog papillary muscle. *Anat. Rec.*, **166,** 51–66.

EDMAN, K. A. P., D. W. GRIEVE and E. NILSSON. 1966. Studies of the excitation–contraction mechanism in the skeletal muscle and the myocardium. *Pflügers Arch. ges. Physiol.*, **290,** 320–334.

EPLING, G. P. 1965. Electron microscopy of bovine cardiac muscle: the transverse sarco-tubular system. *Amer. J. vet. Res.*, **26,** 224–238.

FABIATO, A. and F. FABIATO. 1972. Excitation–contraction coupling of isolated cardiac fibers with disrupted or closed sarcolemmas. Calcium dependent cyclic and tonic contractions. *Circulation Res.*, **31,** 293–307.

FANBURG, B., R. M. FINKEL and A. MARTONOSI. 1964. The role of calcium in the mechanism of relaxation of cardiac muscle. *J. biol. Chem.*, **239,** 2298–2306.

FAWCETT, D. W. 1961. The sarcoplasmic reticulum of skeletal and cardiac muscle. *Circulation*, **24,** 336–348.

FAWCETT, D. W. 1962. Physiologically significant specializations of the cell surface. *Circulation*, **26,** 1105–1125.

FAWCETT, D. W. 1965. Observations on the T-system and the cell-to-cell contacts in cardiac muscle. *VIII. Intern. Anatomenkongr. Wiesbaden*. 1965. *Zus. fass. d. Vortr. S.* 37–38. George Thieme, Stuttgart.

FORBES, M. S. and N. SPERELAKIS. 1971. Ultrastructure of lizard ventricular muscle. *J. Ultrastruct. Res.*, **34,** 439–451.

FORBES, M. S. and N. SPERELAKIS. 1972. (Na^+, K^+)-ATPase activity in tubular systems of mouse cardiac and skeletal muscles. *Z. Zellforsch. mikrosk. Anat.*, **134,** 1–11.

FORBES, M. S. and N. SPERELAKIS. 1973. A labyrinthine structure formed from a transverse tubule of mouse ventricular myocardium. *J. Cell Biol.*, **56,** 865–869.

FORBES, M. S. and N. SPERELAKIS. 1974. Spheroidal bodies in the junctional sarcoplasmic reticulum of lizard myocardial cells. *J. Cell Biol.*, **60,** 602–616.

FORSSMANN, W. G. and L. GIRARDIER. 1966. Untersuchungen zur Ultrastruktur des Rattenherzmuskels mit besonderer Berücksichtigung des sarcoplasmatischen Retikulums. *Z. Zellforsch. mikrosk. Anat.*, **72,** 249–275.

FORSSMANN, W. G. and L. GIRARDIER. 1970. A study of the T system in rat heart. *J. Cell Biol.*, **44,** 1–19.

GIRARDIER, L. 1965. The problem of the inward spread of excitation in skeletal and heart muscle cells. In *Electrophysiology of the Heart*. B. Taccardi and G. Marchetti (eds.). Pergamon Press, Oxford. 53–70.

GIRARDIER, L., J. J. DREIFUSS and W. G. FORSSMANN, 1967. Micropinocytose de ferritine dans les cellules myocardiques de tortue et de rat. *Acta anat.*, **68,** 251–257.

HIRAKOW, R. 1970. Ultrastructural characteristics of the mammalian and sauropsidan heart. *Am. J. Cardiol.*, **25,** 195–203.

JEWETT, P. H., S. D. LEONARD and J. R. SOMMER. 1973. Chicken cardiac muscle. Its elusive extended junctional sarcoplasmic reticulum and sarcoplasmic reticulum fenestrations. *J. Cell Biol.*, **56,** 595–599.

JEWETT, P. H., J. R. SOMMER and E. A. JOHNSON. 1971. Cardiac muscle. Its ultrastructure in the finch and hummingbird with special reference to the sarcoplasmic reticulum. *J. Cell Biol.*, **49,** 50–65.

LANGER, G. A. 1968. Ion fluxes in cardiac excitation and contraction and their relation to myocardial contractility. *Physiol. Rev.*, **48,** 708–757.

LEGATO, M. J., D. SPIRO and G. A. LANGER. 1968. Ultrastructural alterations produced in mammalian myocardium by variation in perfusate ionic composition. *J. Cell Biol.*, **37,** 1–12.

LEAK, L. V. 1970. Fractured surfaces of myocardial cells. *J. Ultrastruct. Res.*, **31,** 76–94.

LÜTTGAU, M. C. 1965. The role of calcium ions

in excitation–contraction coupling. In *Electrophysiology of the Heart.* B. Taccardi and G. Marchetti (eds.). Pergamon Press, Oxford. 87–95.

MCNUTT, N. S. and D. W. FAWCETT. 1967. A comparison of the T system and sarcoplasmic reticulum in atrial and ventricular heart muscle. *J. Cell Biol.*, **35,** 90A.

NAYLOR, E. and N. C. R. MERRILLEES. 1971. Cellular exchange of calcium. In *Calcium and the Heart.* P. Harris and L. H. Opie (eds.). Academic Press, London. 24–65.

NELSON, D. A. and E. S. BENSON. 1963. On the structural continuities of the transverse tubular system of rabbit and human myocardial cells. *J. Cell Biol.*, **16,** 297–313.

OKITA, S. 1971. The fine structure of the ventricular muscle cells of the soft-shelled turtle heart (*Amyda*), with special reference to the sarcoplasmic reticulum. *J. Electron Microsc.*, **20,** 107–119.

ORBER, V. and W. S. BERTAUD. 1971. Cellular surfaces of amphibian atrial muscle. *J. Cell Sci.*, **9,** 427–434.

PAGE, E. 1967. Tubular systems in Purkinje cells of the cat heart. *J. Ultrastruct. Res.*, **17,** 72–83.

PAGE, E. 1968. Correlations between electron microscopic and physiological observations in heart muscle. *J. gen. Physiol.*, **51,** 211s–220s.

PAGE, E., L. P. MCCALLISTER and B. POWER. 1971. Stereological measurements of cardiac ultrastructures implicated in excitation–contraction coupling. *Proc. natn. Acad. Sci. U.S.A.*, **68,** 1465–1466.

PAGE, E., B. POWER, H. A. FOZZARD and D. A. MEDDOFF. 1969. Sarcolemmal evaginations with knob-like or stalked projections in Purkinje fibers of the sheep's heart. *J. Ultrastruct. Res.*, **28,** 288–300.

PAGE, S. G. and R. NIEDERGERKE. 1972. Structures of physiological interest in the frog heart ventricle. *J. Cell Sci.*, **11,** 179–203.

PAGER, J. 1971*a*. Étude morphométrique du système tubulaire transverse du myocarde ventriculaire de rat. *J. Cell Biol.*, **50,** 233–236.

PAGER, J. 1971*b*. Comparative study on physicochemical properties of the T-system and sarcoplasmic reticulum in two types of striated muscle fibers. The fast muscle fiber of the frog and the myocardial fiber of the rat ventricle. *Z. Zellforsch. mikrosk. Anat.*, **119,** 227–243.

RAYNS, D. G., F. O. SIMPSON and W. S. BERTAUD. 1968. Surface features of striated muscle. I. Guinea-pig cardiac muscle. *J. Cell Sci.*, **3,** 467–474.

ROSTGAARD, J. and O. BEHNKE. 1965. Fine structural localization of adenosine nucleoside phosphatase activity in the sarcoplasmic reticulum and the T-system of rat myocardium. *J. Ultrastruct. Res.*, **12,** 579–591.

ROY, P. E. and P. J. MORIN. 1972. Dilatations of transverse tubules and of the intercalated disk in human cardiac muscle. *J. Mol. & Cell. Cardiol.*, **4,** 337–343.

RUBIO, R. and N. SPERELAKIS. 1971. Entrance of colloidal ThO_2 tracer into the T tubules and longitudinal tubules of the guinea pig heart. *Z. Zellforsch. mikrosk. Anat.*, **116,** 20–36.

RUSKA, M. 1965. Electron microscopy of the heart. (With special reference to structures involved in regulation of frequency, formation and conduction of excitation, triggering of contraction and relaxation.) In *Electrophysiology of the Heart.* B. Taccardi and G. Marchetti (eds.). Pergamon Press, Oxford. 1–19.

SIMPSON, F. O. 1965. The transverse tubular system in mammalian myocardial cells. *Am. J. Anat.*, **117,** 1–17.

SIMPSON, F. O. and S. J. OERTELIS. 1962. The fine structure of sheep myocardial cells; sarcolemmal invaginations and the transverse tubular system. *J. Cell Biol.*, **12,** 91–100.

SIMPSON, F. O. and D. G. RAYNS. 1968. The relationship between the transverse tubular system and other tubules at the Z disc levels of myocardial cells in the ferret. *Am. J. Anat.*, **122,** 193–207.

SIMPSON, F. O., D. G. RAYNS and W. S. BERTAUD. 1969. The structural basis for excitation–contraction coupling in mammalian myocardial cells. *Israel J. Med. Sci.*, **5,** 488–490.

SOMMER, J. R. and E. A. JOHNSON. 1968. Purkinje fibers of the heart examined with the peroxidase reaction. *J. Cell Biol.*, **37,** 570–574.

SOMMER, J. R. and M. S. SPACH. 1964. Electron microscopic demonstration of adenosine triphosphatase in myofibrils and sarcoplasmic membranes of cardiac muscle of normal and abnormal dogs. *Am. J. Path.*, **44,** 491–505.

SPERELAKIS, N. and R. RUBIO. 1972. Ultrastructural changes produced by hypertonicity in cat cardiac muscle. *J. Mol. & Cell. Cardiol.*, **3,** 139–156.

STALEY, N. A. and E. S. BENSON. 1968. The ultrastructure of frog ventricular cardiac muscle and its relationship to mechanisms of excitation–contraction coupling. *J. Cell Biol.*, **38,** 79–114.

VIRÁGH, S. and C. E. CHALLICE. 1969. Variation in filamentous and fibrillar organization, and associated sarcolemmal structure, in cells of the normal mammalian heart. *J. Ultrastruct. Res.*, **28,** 321–334.

WALKER, S. M., G. R. SCHRODT and M. B. EDGE. 1970. Electron-dense material within sarcoplasmic reticulum apposed to transverse tubules and to the sarcolemma in dog papillary muscle fibres. *Am. J. Anat.*, **128,** 33–44.

WALKER, S. M., G. R. SCHRODT and M. B. EDGE. 1971. The density attached to the inside surface of the apposed sarcoplasmic reticular membrane in vertebrate cardiac and skeletal muscle fibres. *J. Anat.*, **108,** 217–230.

Vertebrate smooth muscle

BOHR, D. F., C. SEIDEL and J. SOBIESKI. 1969. Possible role of sodium–calcium pumps in tension development of vascular smooth muscle. *Microvasc. Res.*, **1,** 335–343.

BOZLER, E. 1969. Role of calcium in initiation of activity of smooth muscle. *Am. J. Physiol.*, **216,** 671–674.

BURNSTOCK, G. 1970. Structure of smooth muscle and its innervation. In *Smooth Muscle.* E. Bülbring, A. Brading, A. Jones and T. Tomita (eds.). Edward Arnold, London. 1–69.

CARSTEN, M. E. 1969. Role of calcium binding by sarcoplasmic reticulum in the contraction and relaxation of uterine smooth muscle. *J. gen. Physiol.*, **53,** 414–426.

DANIEL, E. E. 1965. Attempted synthesis of data regarding divalent ions in muscle function. In *Muscle.* W. M. Paul, E. E. Daniel, C. M. Kay and G. Monckton (eds.). Pergamon Press, London. 295–313.

DEVINE, C. E., F. O. SIMPSON and W. S. BERTAUD. 1971. Surface features of smooth muscle cells from the mesenteric artery and vas deferens. *J. Cell Sci.*, **8,** 427–443.

DEVINE, C. E., A. V. SOMLYO and A. P. SOMLYO. 1972. Sarcoplasmic reticulum and excitation–contraction coupling in mammalian smooth muscles. *J. Cell Biol.*, **52,** 690–718.

GABELLA, G. 1971. Caveolae intracellulares and sarcoplasmic reticulum in smooth muscle. *J. Cell Sci.*, **8,** 601–609.

GOODFORD, P. J. 1965. The distribution of calcium in intestinal smooth muscle. In *Muscle.* W. M. Paul, E. E. Daniel, C. M. Kay and G. Monckton (eds.). Pergamon Press, London. 219–227.

HURWITZ, L., D. F. FITZPATRICK, G. DEBBAS and E. J. LANDON. 1973. Location of calcium pump activity in smooth muscle. *Science, N.Y.*, **179,** 384–386.

IMAI, S. and K. TAKEDA. 1967. Calcium and contraction of heart and smooth muscle. *Nature, Lond.*, **213,** 1044–1045.

LANE, B. P. 1967. Localization of products of ATP hydrolysis in mammalian smooth muscle cells. *J. Cell Biol.*, **34,** 713–720.

MARSHALL, J. M. 1965. Calcium and uterine smooth muscle membrane potentials. In *Muscle.* W. M. Paul, E. E. Daniel, C. M. Kay and G. Monckton (eds.). Pergamon Press, Oxford. 229–285.

MUGGLI, R. and H. R. BAUMGARTNER. 1972. Pattern of membrane invaginations at the surface of smooth muscle cells of rabbit arteries. *Experientia*, **28,** 1212–1214.

NISHIHARA, H. 1970. Some observations on the fine structure of the guinea-pig taenia coli after incubation in hypertonic solutions. *J. Anat.*, **107,** 101–114.

ROGERS, D. C. 1964. I. Comparative electron-microscopy of smooth muscle and its innervation. II. Cytology of the amphibian carotid labyrinth and reptilian epithelial body. Ph.D. Thesis, University of Melbourne.

SOMLYO, A. P., C. E. DEVINE, A. V. SOMLYO and S. R. NORTH. 1971. Sarcoplasmic reticulum and the temperature-dependent contraction of smooth muscle in calcium-free solutions. *J. Cell Biol.*, **51,** 722–741.

Invertebrate muscle

ATWOOD, H. L. 1971. Z and T tubules in stomach muscles of the spiny lobster. *J. Cell Biol.*, **50,** 264–268.

BASKIN, R. J. 1971. Ultrastructure and calcium transport in crustacean muscle microsomes. *J. Cell Biol.*, **48,** 49–60.

BRANDT, P. W., J. P. REUBEN and H. GRUNDFEST. 1968. Correlated morphological and physiological studies on isolated single muscle fibres. II. The properties of the crayfish transverse tubular system: localisation of the sites of reversible swelling. *J. Cell Biol.*, **38,** 115–129.

FAHRENBACH, W. H. 1963. The sarcoplasmic reticulum of striated muscle of a cyclopoid copepod. *J. Cell Biol.*, **17,** 629–640.

FORBES, M. S., R. RUBIO and N. SPERELAKIS. 1972. Tubular systems of *Limulus* myocardial cells investigated by use of electron-opaque tracers and hypertonicity. *J. Ultrastruct. Res.*, **39,** 580–597.

GILAI, A. and I. PARNAS. 1972. Electromechanical coupling in tubular muscle fibers. I. The organization of tubular muscle fibers in the scorpion *Leiurus quinquestriatus*. *J. Cell Biol.*, **52,** 626–638.

HAGOPIAN, M. and D. SPIRO. 1967. The sarcoplasmic reticulum and its association with the T-system in an insect. *J. Cell Biol.*, **32,** 535–545.

HEUMANN, H.-G. 1969. Calciumakkumulierende Strukturen in einem glatten Wirbellosenmuskel. *Protoplasma*, **67,** 111–115.

HOYLE, G. 1965. Nature of the excitatory sarcoplasmic reticular junction. *Science, N.Y.*, **149,** 70–72.

HUDDART, H. and K. OATES. 1970. Ultrastructure of stick insect and locust skeletal muscle in relation to excitation–contraction coupling. *J. Insect Physiol.*, **16,** 1467–1483.

LAVALLARD, R. 1960. Étude au microscope électronique au reticulum endoplasmique dans des fibres musculaires du crabe bleu. *J. biophys. biochem. Cytol.*, **7,** 399–402.

OLIPHANT, L. W. and R. A. CLONEY. 1972. The ascidian myocardium: sarcoplasmic reticulum and excitation–contraction coupling. *Z. Zellforsch. mikrosk. Anat.*, **129,** 395–412.

PASQUALI-RONCHETTI, I. 1969. The organization of the sarcoplasmic reticulum and T system in the femoral muscle of the housefly, *Musca domestica*. *J. Cell Biol.*, **40,** 269–273.

PEACHEY, L. D. 1967. Membrane systems of crab fibres. *Am. Zool.*, **7,** 505–513.

PUCCI, I. and B. A. AFZELIUS. 1962. An electron microscope study of sarcotubules and related structures in the leech muscle. *J. Ultrastruct. Res.*, **7,** 210–224.

PETERSON, R. P. 1962. Continuities between the plasma membrane and the sarcoplasmic reticulum in crayfish stretch receptor muscle as revealed by reconstructions from serial sections. *Am. J. Anat.*, **111,** 89–110.

PETERSON, R. P. and F. A. PEPE. 1962. The relationship of the sarcoplasmic reticulum to sarcolemma in crayfish stretch receptor muscle. *Am. J. Anat.*, **110,** 277–298.

REGER, J. F. 1961. The fine structure of neuromuscular junctions and the sarcoplasmic reticulum of extrinsic eye muscles of *Fundulus heteroclitus*. *J. biophys. biochem. Cytol.*, **10,** Suppl., 111–121.

REGER, J. F. 1967. The organization of sarcoplasmic reticulum in direct flight muscle of the lepidopteran *Achalarus lyciades*. *J. Ultrastruct. Res.*, **18,** 595–599.

ROSENBLUTH, J. 1968. Obliquely striated muscle. IV. Sarcoplasmic reticulum, contractile apparatus and endomysium of the body muscle of a polychaete, *Glycera*, in relation to its species. *J. Cell Biol.*, **36,** 245–259.

ROSENBLUTH, J. 1969*a*. Sarcoplasmic reticulum of an unusually fast-acting crustacean muscle. *J. Cell Biol.*, **42,** 534–547.

ROSENBLUTH, J. 1969*b*. Ultrastructure of dyads in muscle fibers of *Ascaris lumbricoides*. *J. Cell Biol.*, **42,** 817–825.

SELVERSTON, A. 1967. Structure and function of the transverse tubular system in crustacean muscle fibres. *Amer. Zool.*, **7,** 515–525.

SHAFIQ, S. A. 1964. An electron microscopical study of the innervation and sarcoplasmic reticulum of the fibrillar flight muscle of *Drosophilla melanogaster. Q. Jl microsc. Sci.*, **105,** 1–6.

SMITH, D. S. 1961. The structure of insect fibrillar flight muscle: a study made with special reference to the membrane systems of the fiber. *J. biophys. biochem. Cytol.*, **10,** Suppl., 123–158.

SMITH, D. S. 1966*a*. The organization and function of the sarcoplasmic reticulum and T-system of muscle cells. In *Progress in Biophysics and Molecular Biology*. Vol. 16. J. A. V. Butler and H. E. Huxley (eds.). Pergamon Press, Oxford. 107–142.

SMITH, D. S. 1966*b*. The organization of flight muscle fibers in the Odonata. *J. Cell Biol.*, **28,** 109–126.

SMITH, D. S. and H. C. ALDRICH. 1971. Membrane systems of freeze-etched striated muscle. *Tissue & Cell*, **3,** 261–281.

SMITH, D. S. and M. E. ANDERSON. 1972. The disposition of membrane systems in cardiac muscle of a lobster, *Homarus americanus. Tissue & Cell*, **4,** 629–645.

TWAROG, B. and Y. MUNEOKA. 1973. Calcium and the control of contraction and relaxation in a molluscan catch muscle. In *The Mechanism of Muscle Contraction. Cold Spring Harb. Symp. quant. Biol.*, **37,** 489–504.

WONG, Y. C. and J. C. HWANG. 1974. Coexistence of dyads and triads in an adult striated muscle. *Am. J. Anat.*, **139,** 285–292.

Other cell types

BLACK, V. H. 1972. The development of smooth-surfaced endoplasmic reticulum in adrenal cortical cells of fetal guinea pigs. *Am. J. Anat.*, **135,** 381–418.

DAEMS, W. TH., M. VAN DER PLOEG, J.-P. PERSIJN and P. VAN DUIJN. 1964. Demonstration with the electron microscope of injected peroxidase in rat liver cells. *Histochemie*, **3,** 561–564.

DALLNER, G., P. SIEKEVITZ and G. E. PALADE. 1966. Biogenesis of endoplasmic reticulum membranes. I. Structural and chemical differentiation in developing rat hepatocyte. *J. Cell Biol.*, **30,** 73–96.

HIGGINS, J. A. and R. J. BARRNETT. 1972. Studies on the biogenesis of smooth endoplasmic reticulum membranes in livers of phenobarbital-treated rats. I. The site of activity of acyltransferases involved in synthesis of the membrane phospholipid. *J. Cell Biol.*, **55,** 282–298.

JONES, A. L. and D. W. FAWCETT. 1966. Hypertrophy of the agranular endoplasmic reticulum in hamster liver induced by phenobarbital (with a review on the functions of this organelle in liver). *J. Histochem. Cytochem.*, **14,** 215–232.

LESKES, A., P. SIEKEVITZ and G. E. PALADE. 1971*a*. Differentiation of endoplasmic reticulum in hepatocytes. I. Glucose-6-phosphate distribution *in situ. J. Cell Biol.*, **49,** 264–287.

LESKES, A., P. SIEKEVITZ and G. E. PALADE. 1971*b*. Differentiation of endoplasmic reticulum in hepatocytes. II. Glucose-6-phosphatase in rough microsomes. *J. Cell Biol.*, **49,** 288–302.

Development

EDGE, M. B. 1970. Development of apposed sarcoplasmic reticulum at the T system and sarcolemma and the change in orientation of triads in rat skeletal muscle. *Devl. Biol.*, **23,** 634–650.

EZERMAN, E. B. and H. ISHIKAWA. 1967. Differentiation of the sarcoplasmic reticulum and T-system in developing chick skeletal muscle *in vitro. J. cell. Biol.*, **35,** 405–420.

ISHIKAWA, H. 1968. Formation of elaborate networks cf T-system tubules in cultured skeletal muscle with special reference to the T-system formation. *J. cell. Biol.*, **38,** 51–66.

KELLY, A. M. 1971. Sarcoplasmic reticulum and T tubules in differentiating rat skeletal muscle. *J. Cell Biol.*, **49,** 335–344.

LOUGH, J. W., M. L. ENTMAN, E. H. BOSSEN and J. L. HANSEN. 1972. Calcium accumulation by isolated sarcoplasmic reticulum of skeletal muscle during development in tissue culture. *J. cell. Physiol.*, **80,** 431–436.

LUFF, A. R. and H. L. ATWOOD. 1971. Changes in the sarcoplasmic reticulum and transverse tubular system of fast and slow skeletal muscles of the mouse during postnatal development. *J. Cell Biol.*, **51,** 369–383.

SCHIAFFINO, S. and A. MARGRETH. 1969. Coordinated development of the sarcoplasmic reticulum and T-system during postnatal differentiation of rat skeletal muscle. *J. Cell Biol.*, **41,** 855–875.

WALKER, S. M. and M. B. EDGE. 1971. The sarcoplasmic reticulum and development of Z lines in skeletal muscle fibers of foetal and postnatal rats. *Anat. Rec.*, **169,** 661–678.

WALKER, S. M. and G. R. SCHRODT. 1968. Triads in skeletal muscle fibres of 19-day foetal rats. *J. Cell Biol.*, **37,** 564–569.

WALKER, S. M., G. R. SCHRODT and M. BINGHAM. 1968. Electron microscope study of the sarcoplasmic reticulum at the Z-line level in skeletal fibers of fetal and newborn rats. *J. Cell Biol.*, **39,** 469–475.

F Rough endoplasmic reticulum and free ribosomes

Ribosomes appear under the electron microscope as spherical or ellipsoidal granules about 12–15 nm in diameter consisting of two distinct subunits of *ribosomal ribonucleic acid* (rRNA). These two subunits differ both in size and molecular weight, the larger being one third more than the size of the other. During activity, the *messenger ribonucleic acid* (mRNA) becomes situated between these two subunits, but closely associated with the small subunit. Newly synthesized protein becomes associated with the larger subunit as it forms.

Ribosomes are frequently associated in groups and occasionally form recurrent patterns called *polyribosomes* or *polysomes*. These are the sites of protein production within the cell. The genetic code on the *deoxyribose nucleic acid* (DNA) is transcribed into mRNA in the nucleus. mRNA then moves across the nuclear membrane to the ribosomes in the sarcoplasm. It becomes attached and amino acids are carried to the appropriate sites on the mRNA by *transfer ribonucleic acid* (tRNA), where linkage occurs. Thus ribosomes act as a site where mRNA can be bound, enabling the correct sequence of amino acids to be formed into a protein.

Experiments with isolated muscle polyribosomes have shown that the heavy subunit of myosin is synthesized on a class of polyribosomes which contain 50–60 ribosomes, while the lower molecular weight subunits of myosin are synthesized on a separate class of polysomes containing fewer ribosomes. Thus, these two units are produced separately and completion of the whole molecule occurs at a later stage within the sarcoplasm. Similarly, actin and tropomyosin have also been shown to be produced by different classes of polysomes. Since ribosomes and polysomes have been implicated in the production of myofilaments, it is not surprising that a greater number of these are present at certain stages of differentiation; ribosomes are densely packed within the cytoplasm of myoblasts, giving these cells a basophilic appearance under the light microscope. The appearance of the myosin-synthesizing polysomes parallels myofilament production within the myotube.

Ribosomes are also observed attached to the outer or cytoplasmic surface of the endoplasmic reticulum, which is then termed *rough* (or *granular*) *endoplasmic reticulum.* This also plays a role in protein synthesis. The bound ribosomes, which attach to the endoplasmic reticulum by their larger subunit, form polysomes with mRNA and transfer newly synthesized protein into the interior of the endoplasmic reticulum.

Plate 68

Rough endoplasmic reticulum is not a prominent feature of the adult smooth muscle cell, with the exception of some vascular smooth muscles and the uterus under the influence of oestrogen and some other steroid hormones. It is however, prominent in developing muscle. The smooth muscle cells illustrated here are in the process of differentiating following transplantation into the anterior eye chamber of a guinea-pig. There is a great abundance of free ribosomes (R) and rough endoplasmic reticulum (ER).

Ribosomes and rough endoplasmic reticulum in differentiating vertebrate smooth muscle: guinea-pig vas deferens. Glutaraldehyde fixation. ×9500. (Reproduced from G. R. Campbell, Y. Uehara, T. Malmfors and G. Burnstock, 1971, *Z. Zellforsch. mikrosk. Anat.*, **177,** 155.)

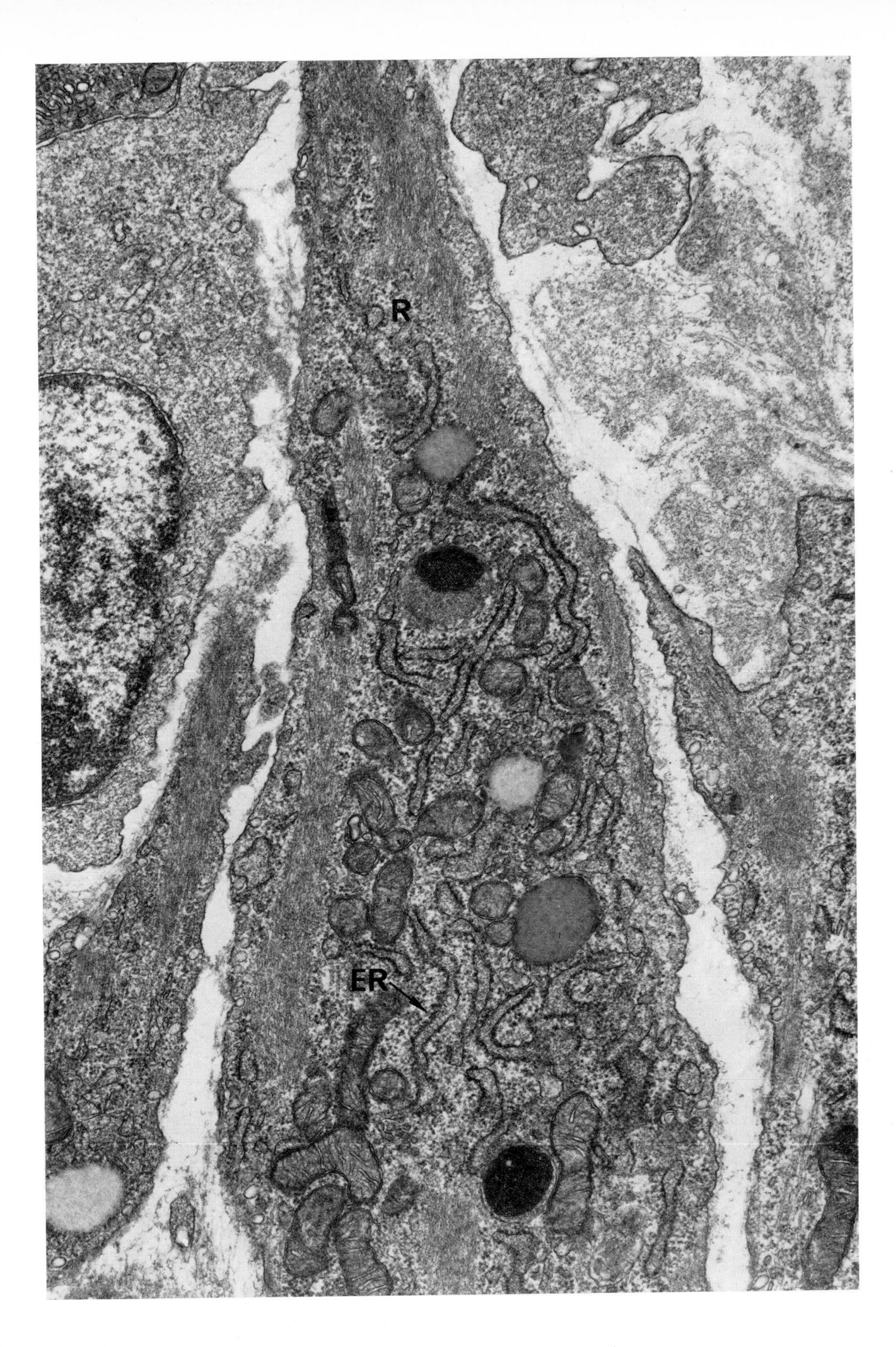
R
ER

Plate 69

Rough endoplasmic reticulum is a prominent feature in smooth muscle cells developing in culture. In the cell illustrated, it is dilated and contains an electron dense flocculent material. A number of free ribosomes are present. Ribosomes are often found on the cytoplasmic side of the nuclear envelope and the outermost membrane is often continuous with the endoplasmic reticulum (arrows); this provides evidence that the nuclear envelope is part of the endoplasmic reticulum. It has been shown that smooth muscle cells can synthesise collagen and elastin; rough endoplasmic reticulum is involved in this process.

Rough endoplasmic reticulum and ribosomes in cultured smooth muscle: new born guinea-pig vas deferens, 6 days in culture. Glutaraldehyde fixation. ×470 000. (Reproduced from J. H. Chamley, G. R. Campbell and G. Burnstock, 1974, *J. Emb. and Exp. Morph.*, **32,** 297.)

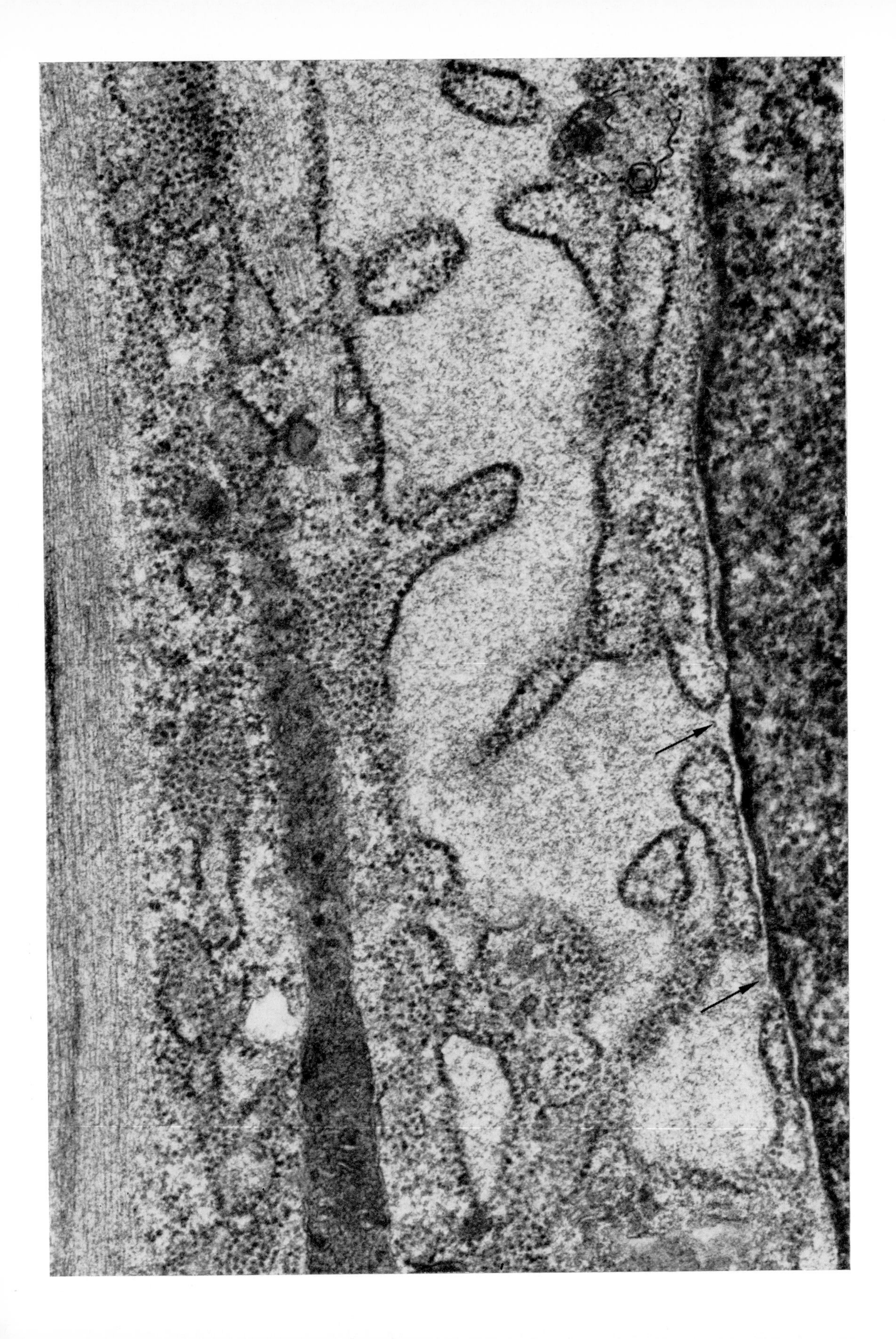

Plate 70

Polyribosomes in smooth muscle consist of a number of ribosomes which often show a helical arrangement, with a centre-to-centre distance between adjacent ribosomes of about 22 nm. Polyribosomes are particularly abundant in developing smooth and striated muscle in close association with myofilament bundles. Few are present in adult tissue. Groups of ribosomes have also been shown to be involved in protein synthesis, the ribosomes of the group being held together with a thin strand interpreted as messenger RNA. These features suggest that polysomes may be involved in myofibrillogenesis.

Polyribosomes in vertebrate smooth muscle: 10-day chicken gizzard, 4 days in culture. Glutaraldehyde fixation. ×253 000.

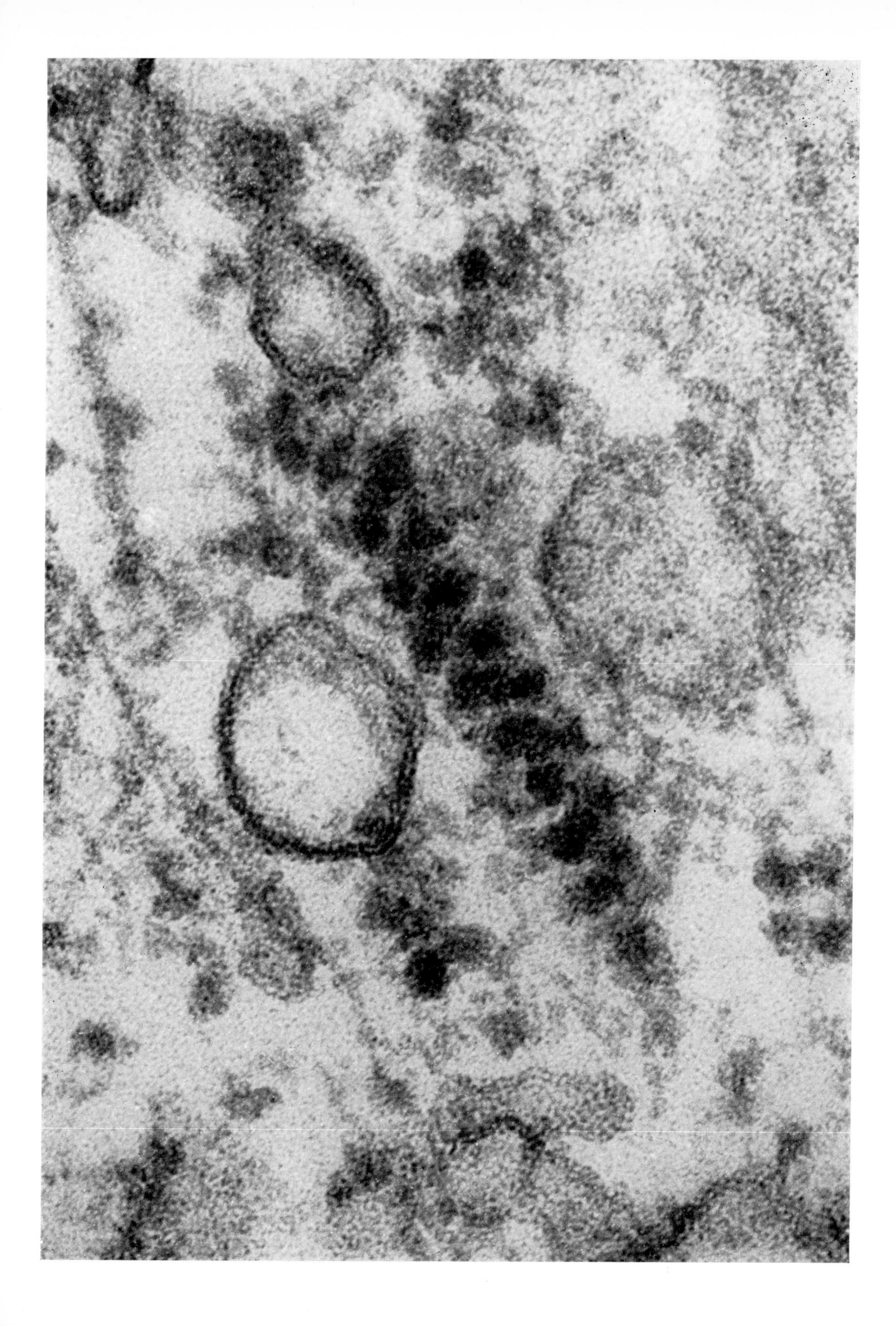

Selected articles

ANDERSSON-CEDERGREN, E. and U. KARLSSON. 1967. Polyribosomal organization in intact intrafusal muscle fibers. *J. Ultrastruct. Res.*, **19,** 409–416.

BURNSTOCK, G. and N. C. R. MERRILLEES. 1964. Structural and experimental studies on autonomic nerve endings in smooth muscle. In *Pharmacology of Smooth Muscle. Proc. of 2nd Int. Pharmacol. Meeting Prague.* Pergamon Press, Oxford. 1–17.

CAMPBELL, G. R., Y. UEHARA, T. MALMFORS and G. BURNSTOCK. 1971. Degeneration and regeneration of smooth muscle transplants in the anterior eye chamber: An ultrastructural study. *Z. Zellforsch. mikrosk. Anat.*, **117,** 155–175.

CAMPBELL, G. R., Y. UEHARA, G. MARK and G. BURNSTOCK. 1971. Fine structure of smooth muscle cells grown in tissue culture. *J. Cell Biol.*, **49,** 21–34.

GALAVAZI, G. 1971. Identification of helical polyribosomes in sections of mature skeletal muscle fibers. *Z. Zellforsch. mikrosk. Anat.*, **121,** 531–547.

GALAVAZI, G. and J. A. SZIRMAI. 1971*a*. Cytomorphometry of skeletal muscle: the influence of age and testosterone on the rat M. levator ani. *Z. Zellforsch. mikrosk. Anat.*, **121,** 507–530.

GALAVAZI, G. and J. A. SZIRMAI. 1971*b*. The influence of age and testosterone on the ribosomal population in the M. levator ani and a thigh muscle of the rat. *Z. Zellforsch. mikrosk. Anat.*, **121,** 548–560.

GARRETT, R. A. and H. G. WITTMAN. 1973. Structure and function of the ribosome. *Endeavour*, **32,** 8–14.

GAUTHIER, G. F. and S. F. SCHAEFFER. 1974. Ultrastructural and cytochemical manifestations of protein synthesis in the peripheral sarcoplasm of denervated and newborn skeletal muscle fibres. *J. Cell Sci.*, **14,** 113–137.

GOLDBERG, A. L. 1968. Protein synthesis during work-induced growth of skeletal muscle. *J. Cell Biol.*, **36,** 653–657.

HEUSON-STIENNON, J.-A. 1964. Intervention de polysomes dans la synthése des myofilaments du muscle embryonnaire du rat. *J. Microsc. (Fr.)*, **3,** 229–232.

HEYWOOD, S. M., R. M. DOWBEN and A. RICH. 1967. The identification of polyribosomes synthesizing myosin. *Proc. natn. Acad. Sci. U.S.A.*, **57,** 1002–1009.

HEYWOOD, S. M., R. M. DOWBEN and A. RICH. 1968. A study of muscle polyribosomes and the coprecipitation of polyribosomes with myosin. *Biochemistry, N.Y.*, **7,** 3289–3296.

KABAT, D. and A. RICH. 1969. The ribosomal subunit–polyribosome cycle in protein synthesis of embryonic skeletal muscle. *Biochemistry, N. Y.*, **8,** 3742–3749.

LARSON, P. F., J. J. FULTHORPE and P. HUDGSON. 1973. The alignment of polysomes along myosin filaments in developing myofibres. *J. Anat.*, **116,** 327–334.

LARSON, P. F., P. HUDGSON and J. N. WALTON. 1969. Morphological relationship of polyribosomes and myosin filaments in developing and regenerating skeletal muscle. *Nature, Lond.*, **222,** 1168–1169.

LEESON, C. R. and T. S. LEESON. 1965. An unusual arrangement of ribosomes in mesenchymal cells. *J. Cell Biol.*, **24,** 324–327.

THORNELL, L.-E. 1972. Myofilament–polyribosome complexes in the conducting system of hearts from cow, rabbit and cat. *J. Ultrastruct. Res.*, **41,** 579–596.

WOODING, F. B. P. 1968. Ribosome helices in mature cells. *J. Ultrastruct. Res.*, **24,** 157–164.

G Mitochondria

Mitochondria, a large source of energy rich adenosine triphosphate (ATP), are most frequently found in close contact with the myofibrils, since it is the breakdown of ATP to ADP (adenosine diphosphate) which provides the energy requirement for the processes of muscle contraction. Other processes in the muscle cells which require the breakdown of ATP are: a number of synthetic reactions, such as protein synthesis and the formation of glycogen; and active transport mechanisms, such as Ca^{2+} exchange in the sarcoplasmic reticulum during excitation–contraction coupling. Energy is provided as a result of the *citric acid* or *tricarboxylic acid cycle* (TCA) which occurs in the mitochondria. A detailed account of the biochemistry of this process can be found in standard texts.

Mitochondria also contain small amounts of DNA (deoxyribose nucleic acid) and RNA (ribose nucleic acid), which are thought to be involved in the production of a few of the mitochondrial proteins and the mitochondrial replication process. The mechanism of mitochondrial self-replication is still not fully understood, but of the three main theories for mitochondrial genesis, namely formation from other membranous structures in the cell, *de novo* synthesis from submicroscopic precursors, and growth and division of pre-existing mitochondria, the last appears to be the most widely supported.

Plate 71

Mitochondria of slow-contracting striated muscle cells are relatively numerous compared to fast-contracting muscles and are usually found between myofibrils, often conforming to their shape. Their size and number varies considerably in different muscles and even at different levels of the sarcomere. In contrast, the mitochondria in smooth muscle cells tend to be situated either at the periphery of the cell or in the perinuclear region (see Plate 3).

Mitochondria are bounded by a smooth contoured outer membrane (about 7 nm thick). Within this membrane and separated from it by a space of about 8 nm is an inner membrane. This inner membrane has numerous infoldings or *cristae* that project into the cavity of the mitochondria. The area enclosed by the inner membrane is called the mitochondrial *matrix*. The inner membrane is thinner (5–7 nm) than most unit membranes and negative staining techniques have shown the presence of small spheres (8 nm in diameter) attached by small stalks to the side facing the matrix.

Mitochondria in vertebrate skeletal muscle: ilio-tibialis muscle of a lizard. Transverse section. OsO_4–glutaraldehyde–OsO_4 fixation. ×62 000.

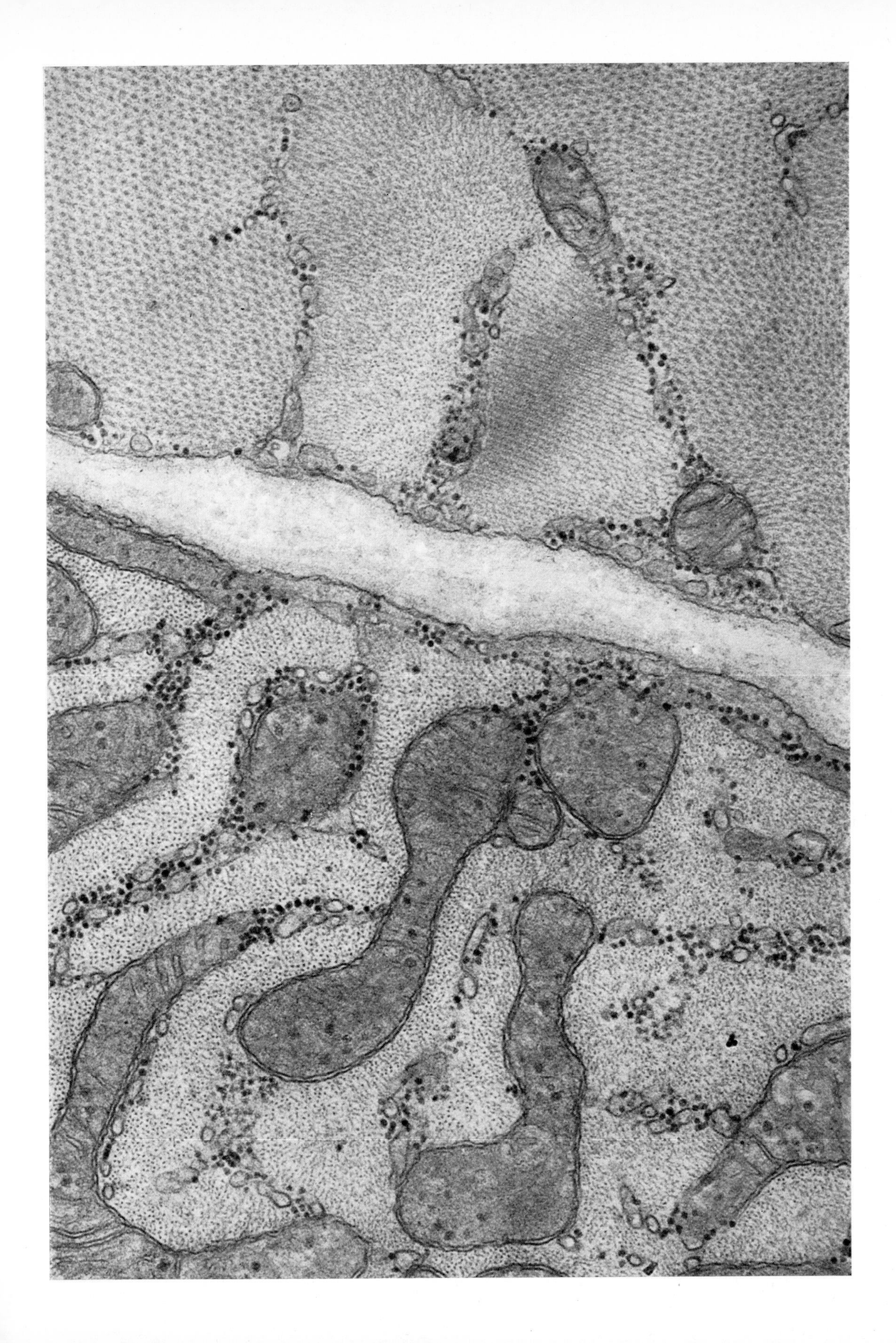

Plate 72

In fast-contracting vertebrate skeletal muscle, the mitochondria often conform to the shape of the myofibrils at the I-band and are wrapped around them. Occasionally the mitochondria envelop the myofibril, as illustrated here. All the mitochondria are intercalated in a more or less continuous field of myofilaments so that most of their surface is in direct contact with the surrounding myofilaments.

Mitochondria in vertebrate skeletal muscle: guinea-pig anterior tibtalis muscle. Transverse section. Glutaraldehyde fixation. ×66 000.

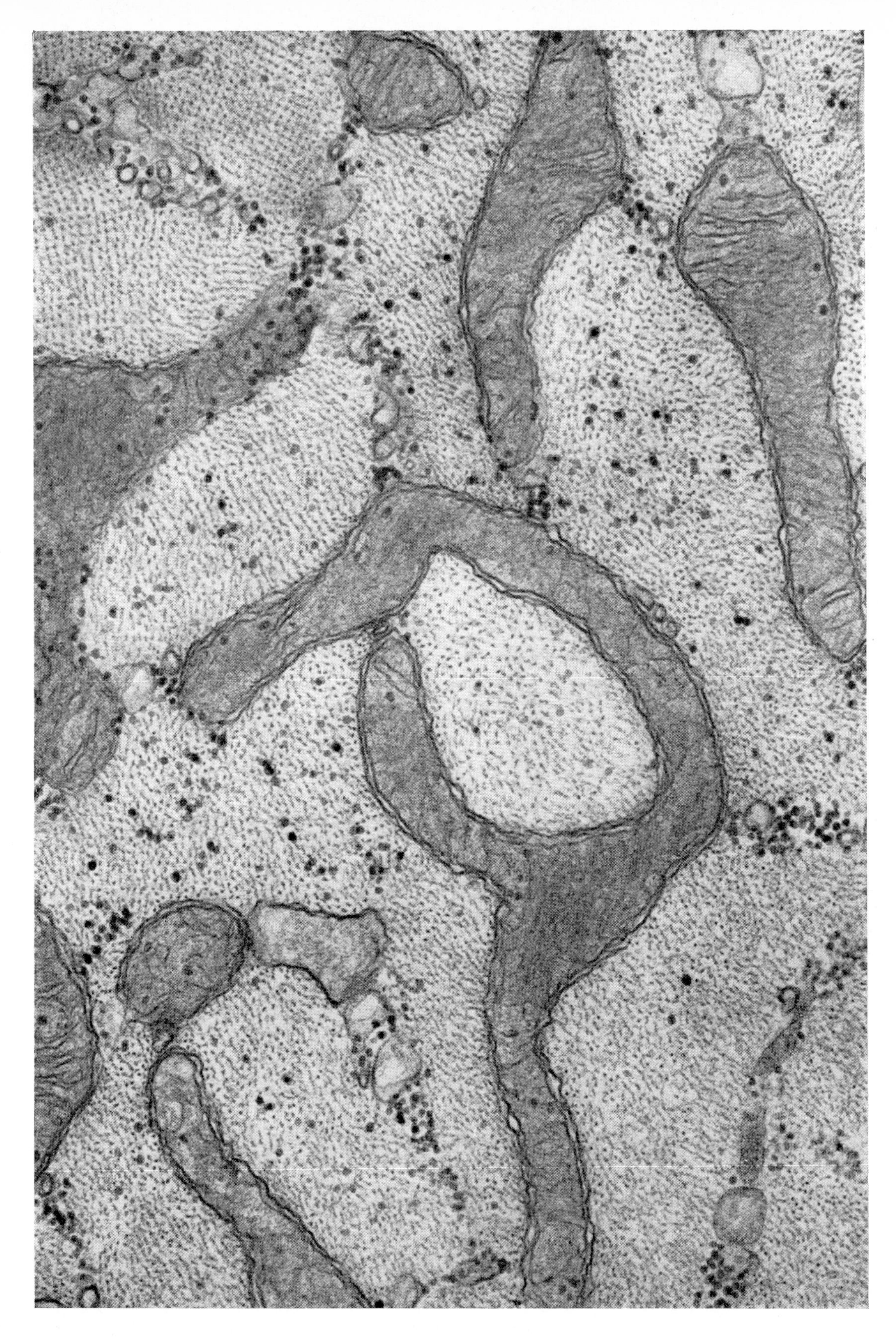

Plate 73

In cardiac muscle, the cristae in mitochondria often exhibit sharp angulations of their membranes which occur at regular intervals. These angulations alternate in direction, occurring first on one leaf of the crista and then on the other, giving the crista a zig-zag appearance. Cristae of this configuration can be changed by the action of certain drugs. This suggests that they may also be capable of altering their form with changes in metabolic activity.

Mitochondria in vertebrate cardiac muscle: finch ventricle. Longitudinal section. Glutaraldehyde fixation. ×86 000.

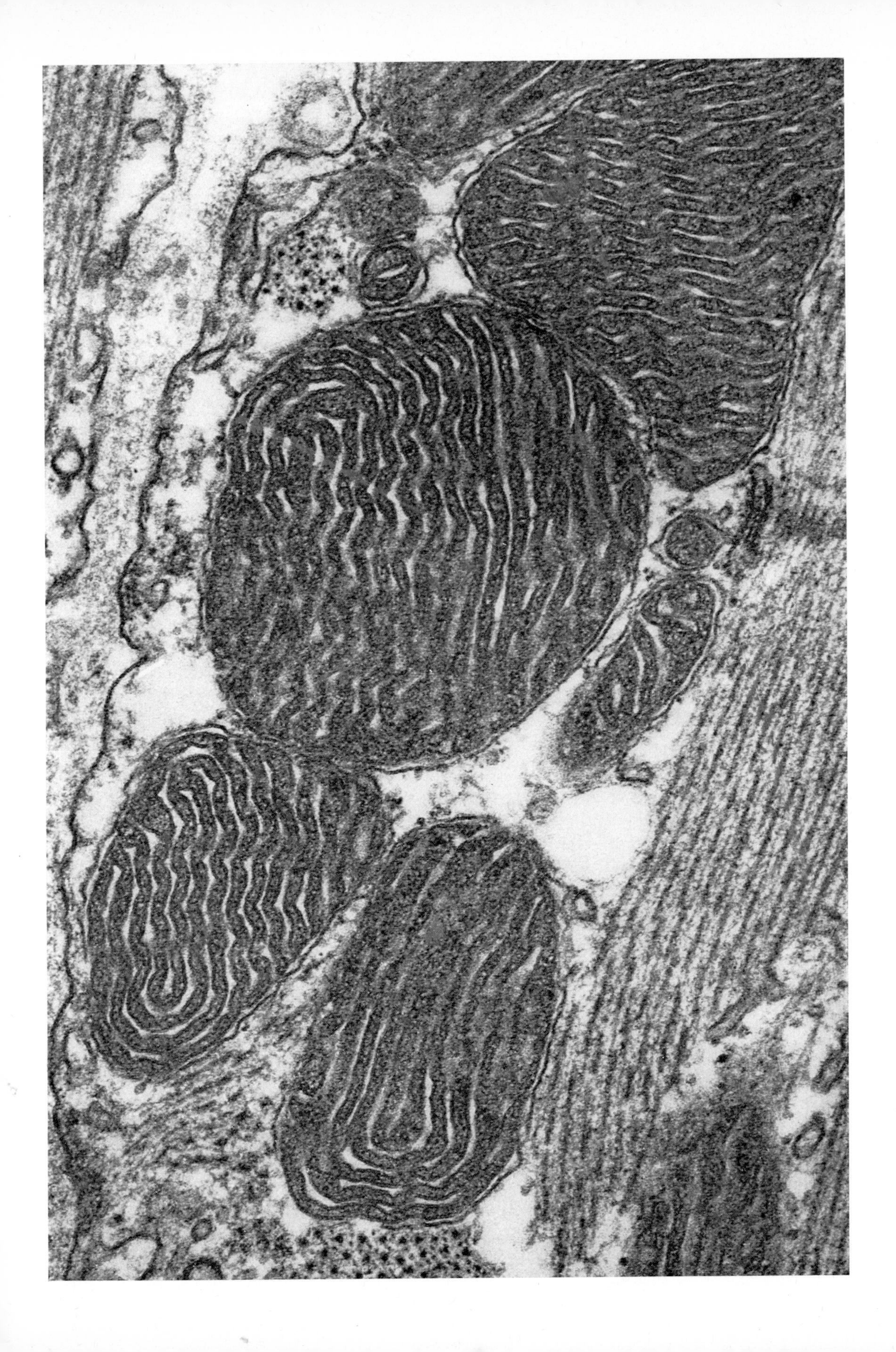

Plate 74

Some muscle fibres, such as mammalian intrafusal fibres, contain unusually large mitochondria which often exceed 5 μm in diameter, compared to most mitochondria found in striated muscles which are less than 1 μm in diameter. These giant mitochondria contain many thin lamellar cristae with fenestrations.

The induction of giant mitochondria in certain tissues by riboflavin deficiency or the addition of copper-chelating agents such as cuprizone has been demonstrated. These mitochondria can be rapidly restored to normal dimensions by a process involving mitochondrial division after the injection of vitamin B_{12}. In the fibrillar flight muscles of the house fly, they appear to arise by the fusion of smaller mitochondria and by growth related to adult maturation.

Mitochondrial granules, about 30 nm in diameter, are present in numbers which vary from tissue to tissue and have been suggested to be a site for storage of Ca^{2+} and Mg^{2+}. However, only about 20% of the total mitochondrial Ca^{2+} is concentrated in these structures. Lipid may also be present in mitochondrial granules.

Giant mitochondrion in striated muscle: intrafusal fibre rat sternothyroid muscle. OsO_4–glutaraldehyde–OsO_4 fixation. ×48 000.

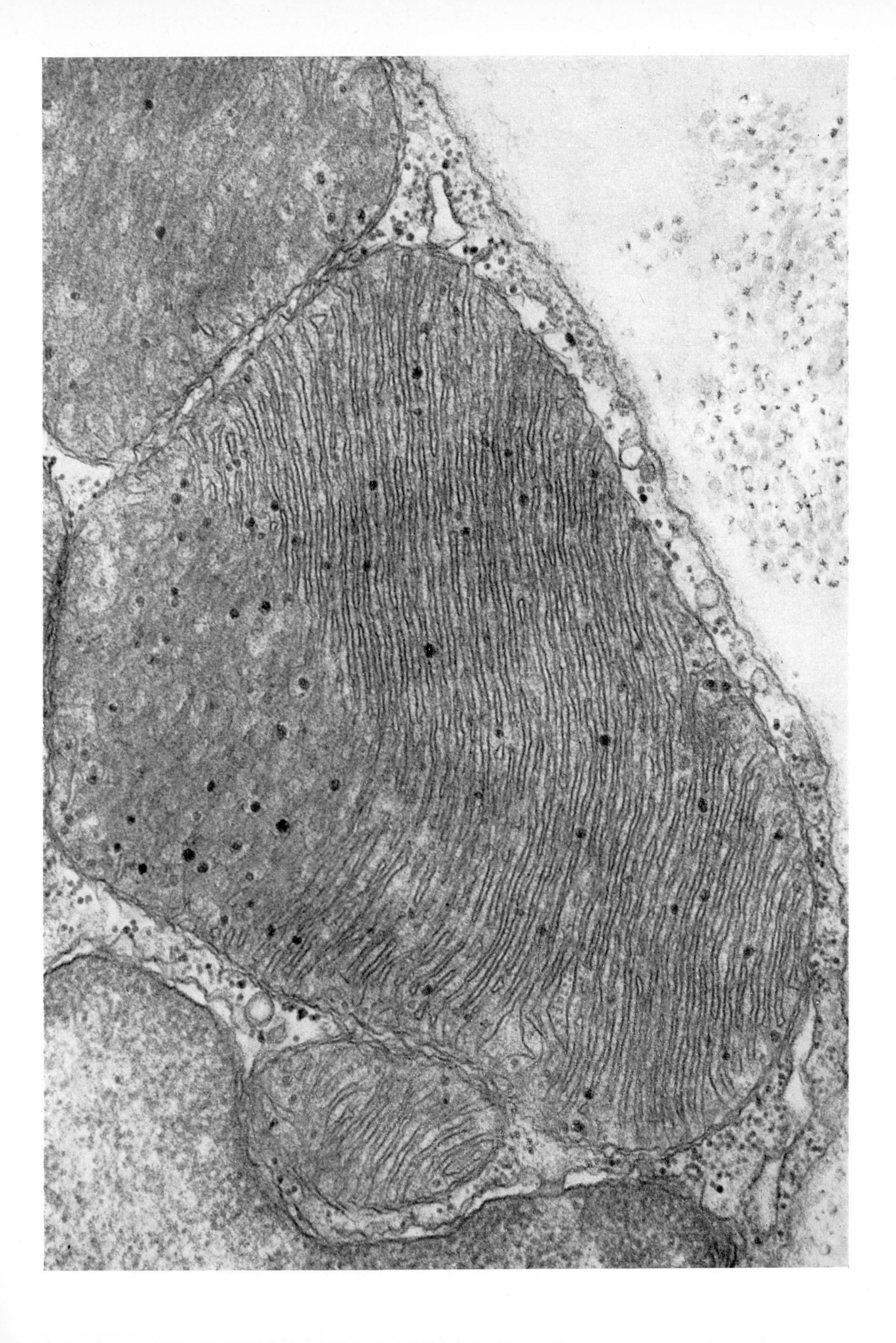

Plate 75

The form of crystalline inclusions varies considerably in different tissues. The intracrystalline rods in the accompanying plate appear as electron opaque lines running the length of a crista with electron-lucent regions on the other side. Similar inclusions have also been noted in beef heart muscle mitochondria. The significance of the mitochondrial crystalline inclusions is unknown.

Crystalline inclusions in mitochondria: intrafusal muscle fibre, rat sternothyroid muscle. Glutaraldehyde fixation. ×104 000.

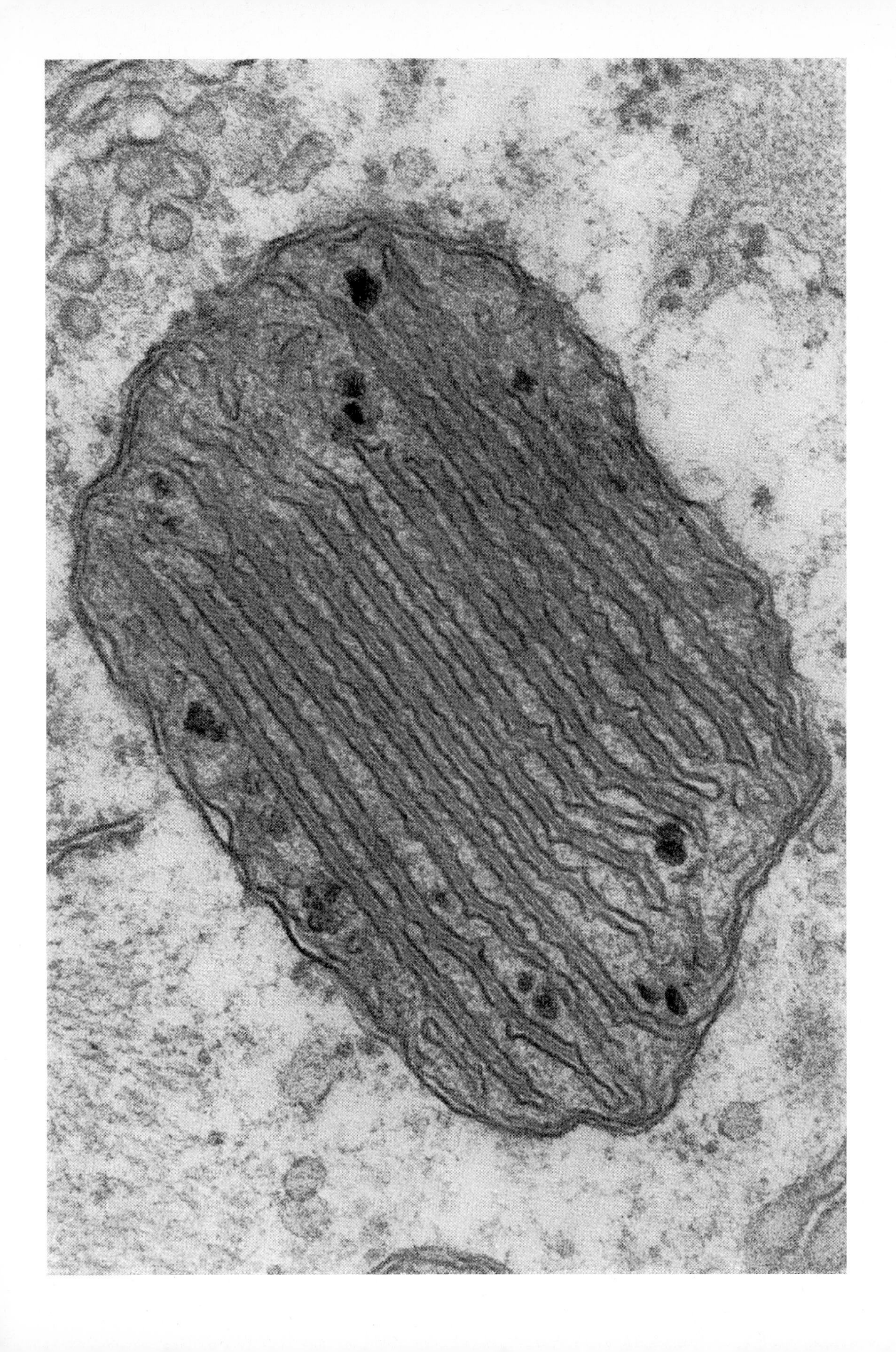

Plate 76

The rosettes of glycogen in the mitochondrial inclusion illustrated are composed of clusters of α-particles which range in size from 50–200 nm. These in turn are composed of particles of β-glycogen, which are 20–35 nm in diameter (see Chapter 3A). Glycogen particles are usually found free in the cytoplasm, but have also been reported to occur within lysosomes, nuclei, cisternae of endoplasmic reticulum as well as in mitochondria.

In some cell types, such as the spinal neurons of frogs, glycogen accumulates in mitochondria as the result of normal physiological states. However, in muscle, intramitochondrial glycogen has been found only under pathological conditions.

Intramitochondrial glycogen: intrafusal muscle fibre rat sternothyroid muscle. Transverse section. Glutaraldehyde fixation. ×134 000.

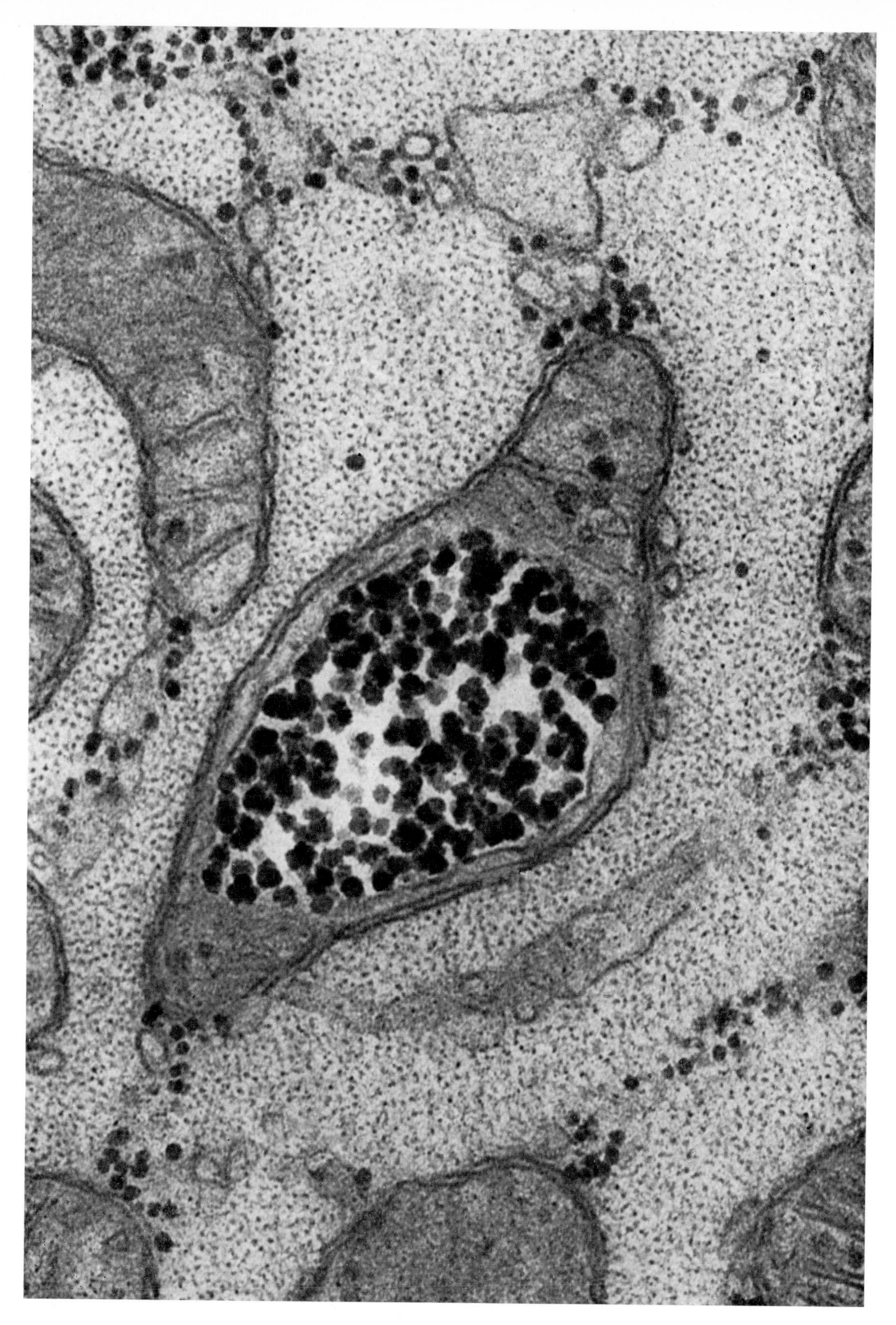

Selected reviews

KLINGENBERG, M. 1964. Muskelmitochondrien. *Ergebn. Physiol.*, **55,** 131–189.

LEHNINGER, A. L. 1964. *The Mitochondrion. Molecular Basis of Structure and Function.* W. A. Benjamin, New York.

MUNN, E. A. 1969. Ultrastructure of mitochondria. In *Handbook of Molecular Cytology*. A. Lima-de-faria (ed.) North Holland, Amsterdam. 875–913.

NOVIKOFF, A. B. 1961. Mitochondria. In *The Cell*. Vol. 2. J. Brachet and A. E. Mirsky (eds.). Academic Press, New York. 299–421.

RABINOWITZ, M. and H. SWIFT. 1970. Mitochondrial nucleic acids and their relation to the biogenesis of mitochondria. *Physiol. Rev.*, **50,** 376–427.

Selected articles

ALBRING, M., K. RADSAK, H.-J. RUMPELT and W. THOENES. 1973. Giant mitochondria. III. Cycloheximide dependant persistance of cuprizone-induced megamitochondria. *Cytobiologie*, **8,** 168–174.

AUMÜLLER, G. and W. G. FORSSMANN. 1973. Riesenmitochondrien im Übergangsepithel der Harnblase des Maulwurfs. *Z. Zellforsch. mikrosk. Anat.*, **137,** 421–434.

BLANCHAER, M. C. 1964. Respiration of mitochondria of red and white muscle. *Am. J. Physiol.*, **206,** 1015–1020.

BUJAL, M., V. J. FERRANS and S. LEVITSKY. 1972. Occurrence of intramitochondrial glycogen in canine myocardium after prolonged anoxic cardiac arrest. *J. Mol. & Cell. Cardiol.*, **4,** 237–254.

BULTMANN, H. and C. D. LAIRD. 1973. Mitochondrial DNA from *Drosophila melanogaster*. *Biochim. biophys. Acta.*, **299,** 196–209.

CARAFOLI, E., P. PATRIARCA and C. S. ROSSI. 1969. A comparative study of the role of mitochondria and the sarcoplasmic reticulum in the uptake and release of Ca^{2+} by the rat diaphragm. *J. cell. Physiol.*, **74,** 17–30.

DAEMS, W. TH. and E. WISSE. 1966. Shape and attachment of the cristae mitochondriales in mouse hepatic cell mitochondria. *J. Ultrastruct. Res.*, **16,** 123–140.

DESHPANDE, P. D., D. D. HICKMAN and R. W. VON KORFF. 1961. Morphology of isolated rabbit heart muscle mitochondria and the oxidation of extramitochondrial reduced diphosphopyridine nucleotide. *J. Cell Biol.*, **11,** 77–94.

DIETERT, S. E. 1969. The occurrence of tubular intramitochondrial inclusions in the post-mortem zona fasciculata of the rat adrenal. *Anat. Rec.*, **165,** 41–54.

FERNÁNDEZ-MORÁN, H., T. ODA, P. V. BLAIR and D. E. GREEN. 1964. A macromolecular repeating unit of mitochondrial structure and function. Correlated electron microscopic and biochemical studies of isolated mitochondria and submitochondrial particles of beef heart muscle. *J. Cell Biol.*, **22,** 63–100.

FLEISCHER, S., B. FLEISCHER and W. STOECKENIUS. 1967. Fine structure of lipid-depleted mitochondria. *J. Cell Biol.*, **32,** 193–208.

GUSTAFSSON, R., J. R. TATA, O. LINDBERG and L. ERNSTER. 1965. The relationship between the structure and activity of rat skeletal muscle mitochondria after thyroidectomy and thyroid hormone treatment. *J. Cell Biol.*, **26,** 555–578.

HACKENBROCK, C. R. 1966. Ultrastructural bases for metabolically linked mechanical activity in mitochondria. I. Reversible ultrastructural changes with change in metabolic steady state in isolated liver mitochondria. *J. Cell Biol.*, **30,** 269–298.

HACKENBROCK, C. R. 1968. Ultrastructural bases for metabolically linked mechanical activity in mitochondria. II. Electron transport-linked ultrastructural transformations in mitochondria. *J Cell. Biol.*, **37,** 345–369.

HAGOPIAN, M. 1967. Three shapes of mitochondria in femoral muscle of the cockroach, *Leucophaea maderae* Fabricius. *J. Morph.*, **122,** 147–167.

HALL, J. D. and F. L. CRANE. 1971. Intracristal rods. A new structure in beef heart mitochondria. *J. Cell Biol.*, **48,** 420–425.

HAND, A. R. 1970. Intracristal helices in salivary gland mitochondria. *Anat. Rec.*, **168,** 565–568.

HEIDRICH, H.-G., R. STAHN and K. HANNIG. 1970. The surface charge of rat liver mitochondria and their membranes. Clarification of some controversies concerning mitochondrial structure. *J. Cell Biol.*, **46,** 137–150.

HENSON, M. M. 1973. Oxidative phosphorylation in mitochondria during embryonic development. *J. exp. Zool.*, **183,** 11–20.

HUNTER, G. R. and G. P. BRIERLEY. 1971. On the 'energized-twisted' configuration of isolated beef heart mitochondria. *J. Cell Biol.*, **50,** 250–255.

HUSZTIK, E., M. POBERAI and M. KOZMA. 1963. Ein Beitrag zur Frage der Mitochondrien in der glatten Muskulatur. *Anat. Anz.*, **113,** 462–468.

IWAYAMA, T., W. W. FLEMING and G. BURNSTOCK. 1973. Ultrastructure of mitochondria in atrial muscle associated with depression and supersensitivity produced by reserpine. *J. Pharmac. exp. Ther.*, **184,** 95–105.

JONES, M. and V. J. FERRANS. 1973 Intramitochondrial glycogen in hypertrophied infundibular muscle of patients with congenital heart diseases. *Am. J. Path.*, **70,** 69–88.

KIMBERG, D. V. and J. N. LOEB. 1972. Effects of cortisone administration on rat liver mitochondria. Support for the concept of mitochondrial fusion. *J. Cell Biol.*, **55,** 635–643.

KISTLER, A. and R. WEBER. 1973. Enzyme patterns in mitochondria of mouse liver and heart muscle. *J. exp. Zool.*, **184,** 149–156.

KUROSUMI, K., T. MATSUZAWA and N. WATARI. 1966. Mitochondrial inclusions in the snake renal tubules. *J. Ultrastruct. Res.*, **16,** 269–277.

LAGUENS, R. 1971. Morphometric study of myocardial mitochondria in the rat. *J. Cell Biol.*, **48,** 673–675.

LARSEN, W. J. 1970. Genesis of mitochondria in insect fat body. *J. Cell Biol.*, **47,** 373–383.

LEESON, C. R. and T. S. LEESON. 1969. Mitochondrial organization in skeletal muscle of the rat soft palate. *J. Anat.*, **105,** 363–370.

LYNN, W. S. JR., S. FORTNEY and R. H. BROWN. 1964*a*. Osmotic and metabolic alterations of mitochondrial size. *J. Cell Biol.*, **23,** 1–8.

LYNN, W. S. Jr., S. FORTNEY and R. H. BROWN. 1964*b*. Role of EDTA and metals in mitochondrial contraction. *J. Cell Biol.*, **23,** 9–20.

MALHOTRA, S. K. 1966. A study of structure of the mitochondrial membrane system. *J. Ultrastruct. Res.*, **15,** 14–37.

MATTISSON, A. G. M. and A. BIRCH-ANDERSEN. 1962. On the fine structure of the mitochondria and its relation to oxidative capacity in muscles in various invertebrates. *J. Ultrastruct. Res.*, **6,** 205–228.

MILEDI, R. and C. R. SLATER. 1968. Some mitochondrial changes in denervated muscle. *J. Cell Sci.*, **3,** 49–54.

MONTENECOURT, B. S., M. E. LANGSAM and D. T. DUBIN. 1970. Mitochondrial RNA from cultured animal cells. II. A comparison of the high molecular weight RNA from mouse and hamster cells. *J. Cell Biol.*, **46,** 245–251.

MORELAND, J. E. 1962. Electron microscopic studies of mitochondria in cardiac and skeletal muscle from hibernated ground squirrels. *Anat. Rec.*, **142,** 155–168.

MORGAN-HUGHES, J. A. and W. G. P. MAIR. 1973. Atypical muscle mitochondria in oculoskeletal myopathy. *Brain*, **96,** 215–224.

NASS, M. M. K. and S. NASS. 1963. Intramitochondrial fibers with DNA characteristics. I. Fixation and electron staining reactions. *J. Cell Biol.*, **19,** 593–612.

NASS, S. and M. M. K. NASS. 1963. Intramitochondrial fibers with DNA characteristics. II. Enzymatic and other hydrolytic treatments. *J. Cell Biol.*, **19,** 613–630.

PACKER, L. 1963*a*. Size and shape transformations correlated with oxidative phosphorylation in mitochondria. I. Swelling-shrinkage mechanisms in intact mitochondria. *J. Cell Biol.*, **18,** 487–494.

PACKER, L. 1963*b*. Size and shape transformations correlated with oxidative phosphorylation in mitochondria. II. Structural changes in mitochondrial membrane fragments. *J. Cell Biol.*, **18,** 495–502.

PACKER, L., J. M. WRIGGLESWORTH, P. A. G. FORTES and B. C. PRESSMAN. 1968. Expansion of the inner membrane compartment and its relation to mitochondrial volume and ion transport. *J. Cell Biol.*, **39,** 382–391.

PASQUALI-RONCHETTI, I., J. W. GREENAWALT and E. CARAFOLI. 1969. On the nature of the dense matrix granules of normal mitochondria. *J. Cell Biol.*, **40,** 565–567.

PEACHEY, L. D. 1964. Electronmicroscopic observations on the accumulation of divalent cations in intramitochondrial granules. *J. Cell Biol.*, **20,** 95–111.

PEASE, D. C. 1962. Demonstration of a highly ordered pattern upon a mitochondrial surface. *J. Cell Biol.*, **15,** 385–389.

REITH, A., D. BRDICZKA, J. NOLTE and H. W. STAUDTE. 1973. The inner membrane of mitochondria under influence of triiodothyrosine and riboflavin deficiency in rat heart muscle and liver. A quantitative electronmicroscopical and biochemical study. *Expl Cell Res.*, **77,** 1–14.

REVEL, J. P., D. W. FAWCETT and C. W. PHILPOTT. 1963. Observations on mitochondrial structure. Angular configuration of the cristae. *J. Cell Biol.*, **16,** 187–195.

SACKTOR, B. and Y. SHIMADA. 1972. Degenerative changes in the mitochondria of flight muscle from aging blowflies. *J. Cell Biol.*, **52,** 465–477.

SCHELLENS, J. P. M. and E. OSSENTJUK. 1970. Mitochondrial ultrastructure with crystalloid inclusions in an unusual type of human myopathy. *Virchows Arch. Abt. B. Zellpath.*, **4,** 21–29.

SCHOEBITZ, K., E. L. RODRIGUEZ ECHANDIA and H. CAMPOS. 1973. Complex mitochondria in the retinal cones of the teleost *Galaxia platei*. *J. Microsc. (Fr.)*, **18,** 109–114.

SCHWALBACH, G. and B. AGOSTINI. 1964. Die Beziehung zwischen Mitochondrienmorphologie und Aktivitätsdauer verschiedener Flugmuskelfasern von *Locusta migratoria* L. *Z. Zellforsch. mikrosk. Anat.*, **61,** 855–870.

SJÖSTRAND, F. S. and L. BARAJAS. 1970. A new model for mitochondrial membranes based on structural and on biochemical information. *J. Ultrastruct. Res.*, **32,** 293–306.

SLAUTTERBACK, D. B. 1965. Mitochondria in cardiac muscle cells of the canary and some other birds. *J. Cell Biol.*, **24,** 1–22.

SOHAL, R. S., J. L. MCCARTHY and V. F. ALLISON. 1972. The formation of 'giant' mitochondria in the fibrillar flight muscles of the house fly, *Musa domestica* L. *J. Ultrastruct. Res.*, **39,** 484–495.

STASNY, J. T. and F. L. CRANE. 1964. The effect of sonic oscillation on the structure and function of beef heart mitochondria. *J. Cell Biol.*, **22,** 49–62.

STOECKENIUS, W. 1963. Some observations on negatively stained mitochondria. *J. Cell Biol.*, **17,** 443–454.

STONER, C. D. and H. D. SIRAK. 1969. Osmotically induced alterations in volume and ultrastructure of mitochondria isolated from rat liver and bovine heart. *J. Cell Biol.*, **43,** 521–538.

TANDLER, B. and C. L. HOPPEL. 1972. Possible division of cardiac mitochondria. *Anat. Rec.*, **173,** 309–324.

TANDLER, B. and C. L. HOPPEL. 1973. Division of giant mitochondria during recovery from cuprizone intoxication. *J. Cell Biol.*, **56,** 266–274.

TANGUAY, R. and K. D. CHAUDHARY. 1972. Studies on mitochondria. II. Mitochondrial DNA of thoracic muscles of *Schistocerca gregaria*. *J. Cell Biol.*, **54,** 295–301.

ULRICH, F. 1959. Ion transport by heart and skeletal muscle mitochondria. *Am. J. Physiol.*, **197,** 997–1004.

WEBER, N. E. 1972. Ultrastructural studies of beef heart mitochondria. III. The inequality of gross morphological change and oxidative phosphorylation. *J. Cell Biol.*, **55,** 457–470.

WILLIAMS, M. A. 1967. More intramitochondrial bodies. *J. Cell Biol.*, **35,** 730–732.

WOLLENBERGER, A., B. KLEITKE and W. SCHULZE. 1966. Über den Status der Mitochondrien im hypertrophierten Herzen von Hunden mit allmählich entstandener Aortenstenose. *Acta biol. med. germ.*, **17,** 334–342.

WOLLENBERGER, A. and W. SCHULZE. 1961. Mitochondrial alterations in the myocardium of dogs with aortic stenosis. *J. biophys. biochem. Cytol.*, **10,** 285–288.

H Golgi complex

Discovered by Camillo Golgi in 1898, the Golg complex appears to serve a number of functions within the cell. The most important of these is the concentration and transport of materials produced in secretion. Consequently, although the Golgi complex is found in all muscle cells, it is more common in developing and regenerating muscle or in those cells capable of performing synthetic activity (such as vertebrate smooth muscle) than in the highly specialized vertebrate skeletal muscle.

Studies of non-muscle cells with radioactively labelled amino acids (H^3) have shown that these amino acids are first incorporated into proteins in the rough endoplasmic reticulum and then travel to the Golgi complex. Here they are concentrated, packaged into vesicles and transported to the cell membrane for secretion. The Golgi complex appears to play a further role in protein production, by effecting changes in their tertiary or quaternary structure. Furthermore, studies with H^3-labelled sugars or sulphur labelled precursors of some polysaccharides, indicate that the Golgi complex is not only the site of concentration of polysaccharides, but it is also involved in the synthesis of complex polysaccharides.

The elements which comprise the Golgi complex vary in form and extent with the type of cell and its metabolic state. The cisternae are bounded by smooth-surfaced membranes, are usually flattened, and most often consist of a central plate-like region (saccule) continuous with a peripheral system of tubules and vesicles. The plate-like region is typically 0.5–1 μm in diameter and is often fenestrated. The cisternae are organized into stacks. The number of cisternae in each is variable, but is usually in the range of 5–8. The hierarchy of structural organization is completed by the association of several stacks of cisternae.

Plate 77

The Golgi complex in muscle cells is usually not as extensive as in other types of cells actively involved in synthesis or secretion, apart from those muscles which are developing or regenerating. In the smooth muscle cell shown in the accompanying micrograph, the Golgi complex appears to be associated with melanin granules, perhaps indicating a role in their formation.

Golgi complex in vertebrate smooth muscle: guinea-pig iris. Glutaraldehyde fixation. ×62 500.

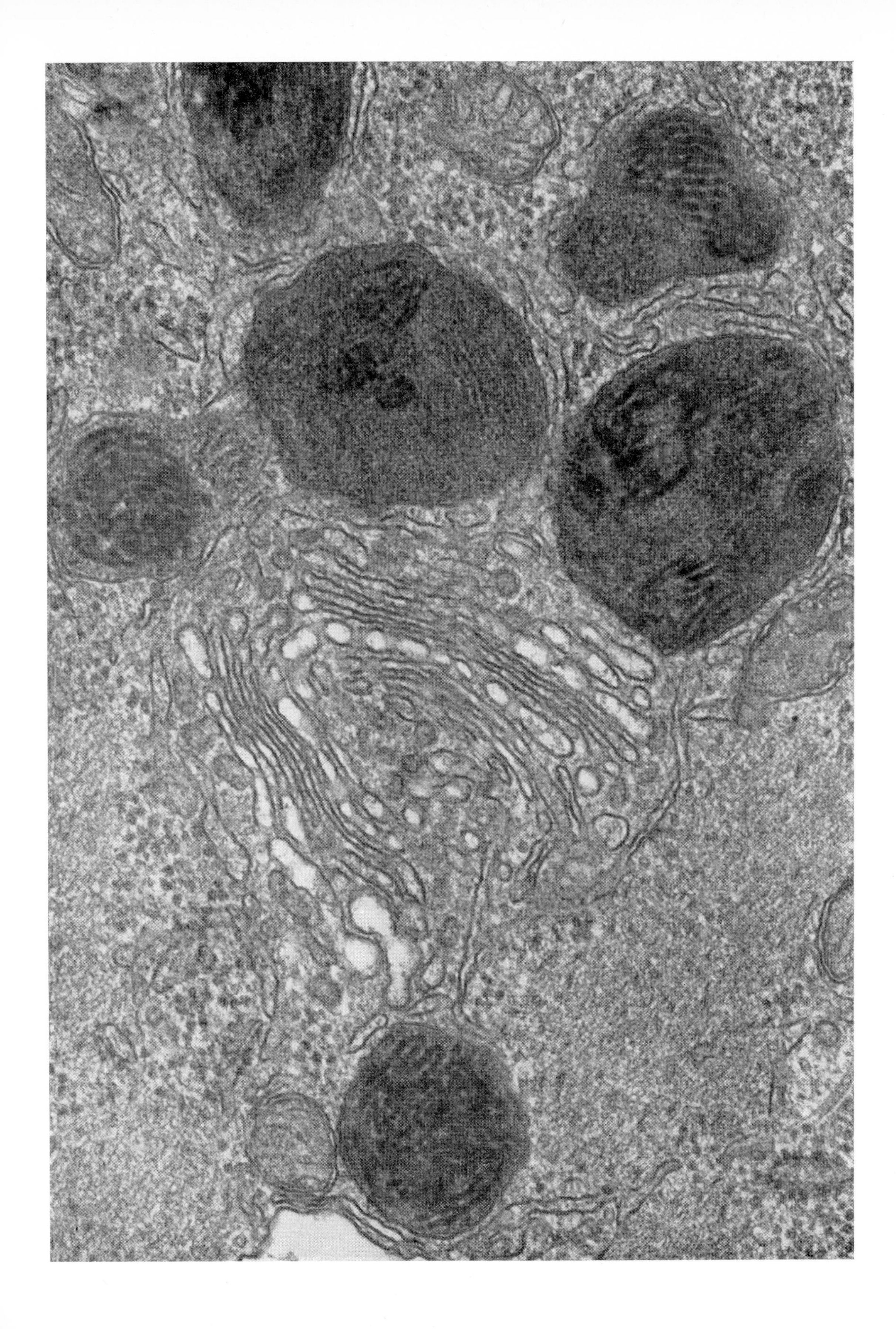

Selected articles

BEAMS, H. W. and R. G. KESSEL. 1968. The Golgi apparatus: Structure and function. *Int. Rev. Cytol.*, **23,** 209–276.

BUCCIARELLI, E. 1966. Intranuclear cisternae resembling structures of the Golgi complex. *J. Cell Biol.*, **30,** 664–666.

CARO, L. G. and G. E. PALADE. 1964. Protein synthesis, storage, and discharge in the pancreatic exocrine cell. An autoradiographic study. *J. Cell Biol.*, **20,** 473–495.

DALTON, A. J. and M. D. FELIX. 1956. A comparative study of the Golgi complex. *J. biophys. biochem. Cytol.*, **2,** Suppl., 79–83.

FLICKINGER, C. J. 1969*a*. The development of Golgi complexes and their dependence upon the nucleus in amebae. *J. Cell Biol.*, **43,** 250–262.

FLICKINGER, C. J. 1969*b*. Fenestrated cisternae in the Golgi apparatus of the epididymis. *Anat. Rec.*, **163,** 39–54.

FLICKINGER, C. J. 1971. Decreased formation of Golgi bodies in amebae in the presence of RNA and protein synthesis inhibitors. *J. Cell Biol.*, **49,** 221–225.

FRIEND, D. S. 1969. Cytochemical staining of multivesicular body and Golgi vesicles. *J. Cell Biol.*, **41,** 269–279.

FRIEND, D. S. and M. J. MURRAY. 1965. Osmium impregnation of the Golgi apparatus. *Am. J. Anat.* **117,** 135–150.

GRAY, E. G. 1970. The question of relationship between Golgi vesicles and synaptic vesicles in Octopus neurons. *J. Cell Sci.*, **7,** 189–202.

JAMIESON, J. D. and G. E. PALADE. 1966. Role of the Golgi complex in the intracellular transport of secretory proteins. *Proc. natn. Acad. Sci. U.S.A.*, **55,** 424–431.

JAMIESON, J. D. and G. E. PALADE. 1967. Intracellular transport of secretory proteins in the pancreatic exocrine cell. I. Role of the peripheral elements of the Golgi complex. *J. Cell Biol.*, **34,** 577–596.

KESSEL, R. G. 1971. Origin of the Golgi apparatus in embryonic cells of the grasshopper. *J. Ultrastruct. Res.*, **34,** 260–275.

LOESTUMBO, F. 1964. On ultrastructure of the smooth muscle fibrocell of the rat uterus. 3. Ergastoplasm. Golgi apparatus. Lysosomes. Connective tissue. Conclusive considerations. *Riv. Ostet. Ginec.*, **19,** 630–648.

MANASEK, F. J. 1969. The appearance of granules in the Golgi complex of embryonic cardiac myocytes. *J. Cell Biol.*, **43,** 605–609.

MOLLENHAUER, H. H. 1965. An intercisternal structure in the Golgi apparatus. *J. Cell Biol.*, **24,** 504–510.

NEUTRA, M. and C. P. LEBLOND. 1966. Radioautographic comparison of the uptake of galactose-H^3 and glucose-H^3 in the Golgi region of various cells secreting glycoproteins or mucopolysaccharides. *J. Cell Biol.*, **30,** 137–150.

ROBBINS, E., P. I. MARCUS and N. K. GONATAS. 1964. Dynamics of acridine orange-cell interaction. II. Dye-induced ultrastructural changes in multivesicular bodies (acridine orange particles). *J. Cell Biol.*, **21,** 49–62.

ZEIGEL, R. F. and A. J. DALTON. 1962. Speculations based on the morphology of the Golgi systems in several types of protein-secreting cells. *J. Cell Biol.*, **15,** 45–54.

I Centrioles

Centrioles usually occur in pairs and in typical mononuclear cells such as smooth muscle there is one pair per cell. Although first discovered in 1887 the precise role of the centriole is still uncertain. Many have suggested that they are foci at the poles of the mitotic-apparatus and participate directly in cell division. Their role in mitosis seems to be related to the formation of the microtubules of the spindle. It has been proposed that the centriole may regulate the synthesis and aggregation of protein monomers required for microtubule formation. The formation of flagella and cilia requires the presence of a centriole. Centrioles have been observed to arise *de novo* (by synthesis from submicroscopic precursors).

Centrioles are frequently encountered in vertebrate smooth muscles (see Plate 78) and invertebrate muscles (see Plate 14), but less often in vertebrate striated and cardiac muscle cells.

Plate 78

The centriole is usually about 0.5 μm in length and 150 nm in diameter, and is often seen in close proximity to the Golgi complex. It consists of an array of nine triplet microtubules equally spaced around the perimeter of an imaginary cylinder. The space between the triplets is filled with an amorphous, electron-dense material. The triplets are tilted in a clockwise direction so that they form an angle of approximately 40° to the radius of the centriole. The three subunit microtubules of the triplet are usually designated A, B and C with A being closest to the centre. Only the A tubule is round, the others are partial and appear to share their wall with the preceding tubule.

Centriole in vertebrate smooth muscle: guinea-pig iris. Transverse section. Glutaraldehyde fixation. ×89 500.

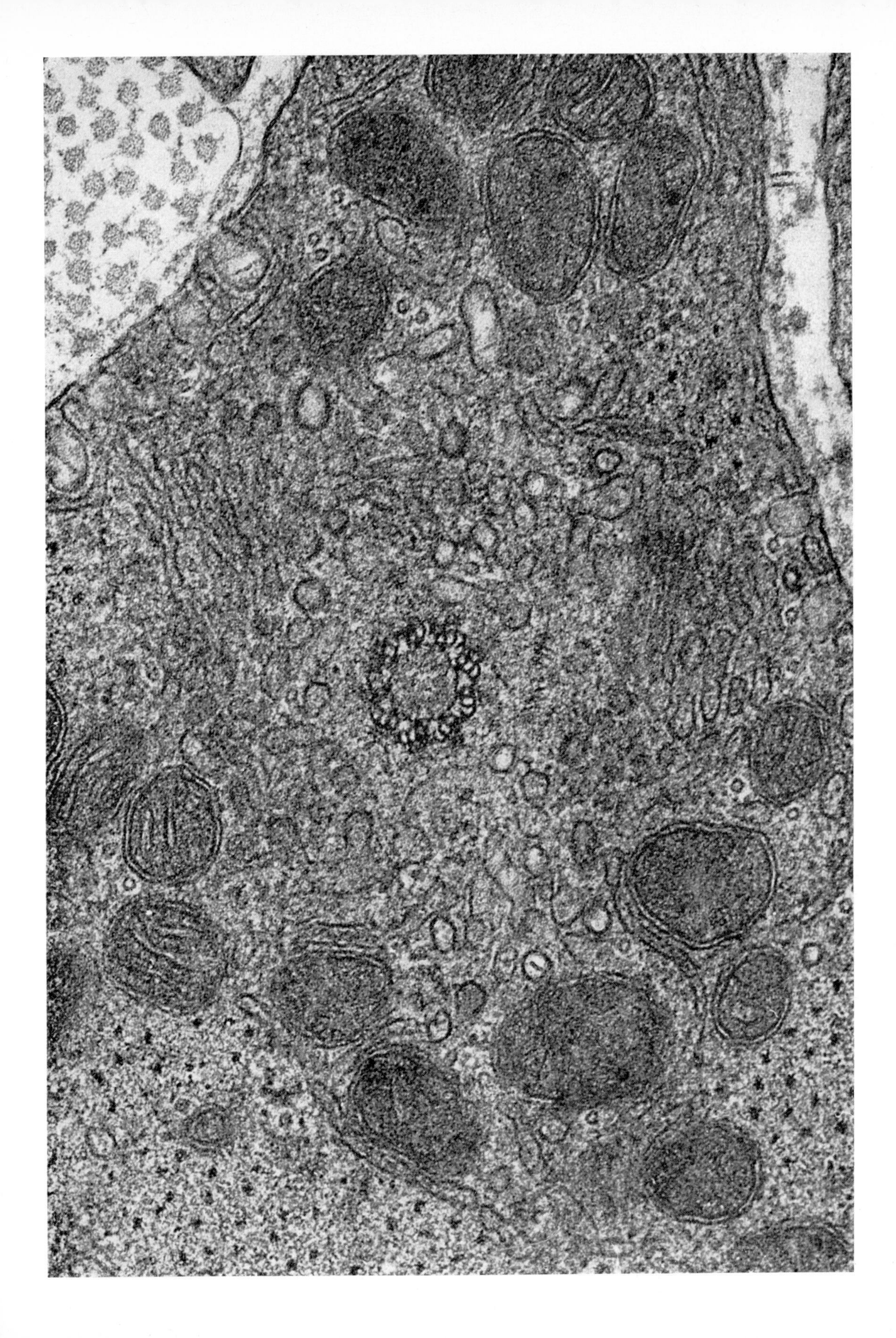

Selected articles

ANDERSON, R. G. W. and R. M. BRENNER. 1971. The formation of basal bodies (centrioles) in the rhesus monkey oviduct *J. Cell Biol.*, **50,** 10–34.

COBB, J. L. S. and T. BENNETT. 1970. An ultrastructural study of mitotic division in differentiated gastric smooth muscle cells. *Z. Zellforsch. mikrosk. Anat.*, **108,** 177–189.

KANE, R. E. 1962. The mitotic apparatus. Fine structure of the isolated unit. *J. Cell Biol.*, **15,** 279–288.

KONISHI, A., W. S. BEACHAM and C. C. HUNT. 1973. Centrioles in intrafusal muscle fibers. *J. Cell Biol.*, **59,** 749–755.

LAUWERYNS, J. M. and L. BOUSSAUN. 1973. Striated filamentous bundles associated with centrioles in pulmonary endothelial cells. *J. Ultrastruct. Res.*, **42,** 25–28.

PRZYBYLSKI, R. J. 1971. Occurrence of centrioles during skeletal and cardiac myogenesis. *J. Cell Biol.*, **49,** 214–221.

WOLFE, J. 1970. Structural analysis of basal bodies of the isolated oral apparatus of *Tetrahymena pyriformis*. *J. Cell Sci.*, **6,** 679–700.

J Lysosomes

The term *lysosome* (Greek for dissolution is *lysis* and for body is *soma*) was introduced to describe a group of membrane-bound particles isolated by cell fractionation that contain a number of *hydrolytic* enzymes. Over forty of these lysosomal enzymes have now been identified, most of which are active at an acid pH and are consequently called *acid hydrolases*. All lysosomes are related, directly or indirectly, to intracellular digestion and the material digested may be *exogenous* (*extracellular*) or *endogenous* (*intracellular*) in origin.

Autoradiographic studies have shown that the lysosome commences its life in the ribosomes with the production of lysosomal enzymes. These enzymes are then transported by the endoplasmic reticulum to the lysosomes, either directly or via the Golgi complex. Four types of lysosome have been classified on the basis of present knowledge. The *primary lysosome* appears to be produced by the Golgi complex and is the body by which the hydrolytic enzymes are carried to the *secondary lysosome*. The secondary lysosome contains both material which is to be digested and hydrolytic enzymes. The material to be digested is often a result of phagocytosis or pinocytosis of extracellular substances. Certain materials which cannot be digested are stored within the secondary lysosome, in what are called *residual bodies*. The fourth type of lysosome is the *autophagic vacuole*. This is a special case in which the lysosome contains part of its own cell in a process of digestion.

Vertebrate skeletal muscle is not normally thought of as having phagocytic properties, however, it does contain lysosomal-like particles. On the basis of histochemical and biochemical experiments it has been suggested that primary muscle lysosomes are in a morphological configuration different from that seen in other tissues. They do not exist as separate entities but as part of the sarcotubular system—the *sarcotubulo-lysosomal system*. Minimal titers of hydrolases are stored within portions of the sarcotubular elements and used to form autophagic vacuoles in response to pathological stresses. In denervated skeletal muscle for example, numerous lysosomes are observed often weeks after nerve section. However, these lysosomes do not appear to be directly involved in myofibrillar disintegration. This appears to occur as a result of extralysosomal processes, the fragmented particles then being segregated and digested further in the lysosomes.

Both cardiac and smooth muscle, in contrast to skeletal muscle contain clearly recognisable lysosomes. In the heart, these increase in number both with age and in certain pathological conditions. Although most types of lysosomes are present in cardiac muscle, residual bodies and lipofuscin granules are more common, especially in older animals. Lipofuscin granules are thought to be residual bodies which at least in part contain residues of previous autodigestive events and have lost their acid phosphatase activity. Myocardial cells are apparently unable to extrude degraded cellular material as fast as it is produced. Consequently, there is an accumulation of residual bodies with age and these can occupy up to 10% of the intracellular volume.

Invertebrate muscle cells also contain lysosomes with similar hydrolytic enzymes to those of vertebrates. The degeneration of intersegmental muscles in the silkmoth is a very specialized example of the activity of lysosomal enzymes in muscle. The intersegmental muscles of this insect persist from the larvae stage to the pupa and enable the moth to inflate its wings. Shortly after inflating the wings the muscles are rapidly broken down (complete removal of the muscles occurs in less than 24 hours), presumably as a nutritional source. Apparently the nervous system plays an important role in this breakdown as elimination of motor impulses at an earlier stage results in maintenance of the intersegmental muscles throughout life.

Plate 79

Lysosomes are bound by a single unit membrane and show wide variation in size and in their internal structure which ranges from opaque flocculent material to whorls of myelin-like membranes. This variation in appearance is dependent upon the stage of lysis of the contents.

In smooth muscle cells from guinea-pig ureter, single membrane bound bodies containing electron dense lamellar structures with fine granular material are frequently encountered. However, membrane bound bodies cannot be positively identified as lysosomes without cytochemical staining reactions for localization of acid-phosphatase activity.

Lysosomes in vertebrate smooth muscle: guinea-pig ureter (kidney end). Longitudinal section. OsO_4–glutaraldehyde –OsO_4 fixation. × 157 000.

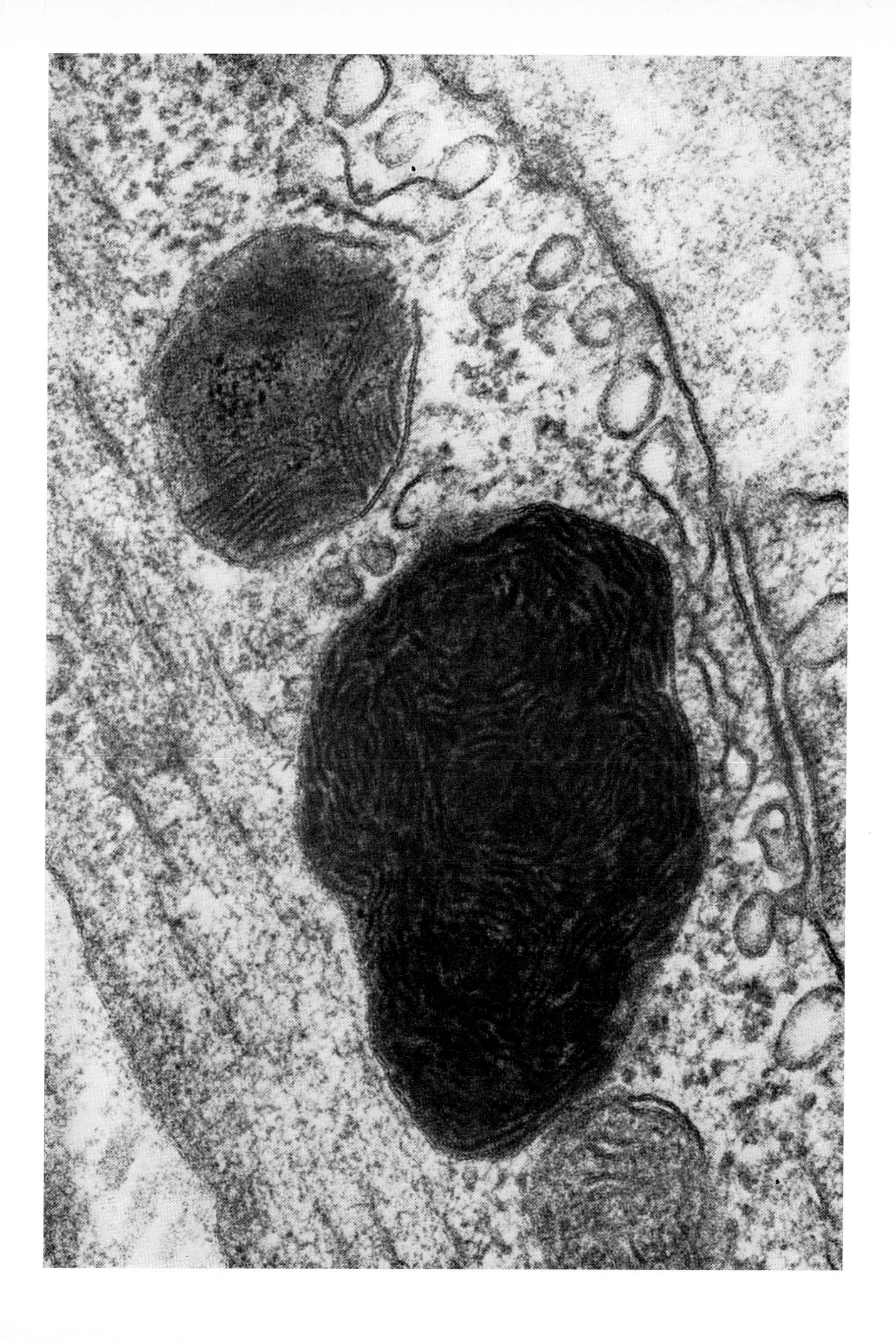

Plate 80

Under normal conditions the hydrolytic enzymes of lysosomes are contained within their enclosing membrane. Rupture of this membrane due to pathological or experimental conditions allows the enzymes to digest or lyse the cell, a process called *autolysis*.

Smooth muscle cells are capable of phagocytosis and therefore of removing cellular debris. Uterine smooth muscle cells during postpartum involution appear to be the only muscle cells ever reported to have myofilaments within autophagic vacuoles. Myofibrillar disintegration in other muscle types apparently occurs as the result of extralysosomal processes.

Lysosomes in degenerating vertebrate smooth muscle: chicken gizzard. Transverse section. Glutaraldehyde fixation. ×19 800.

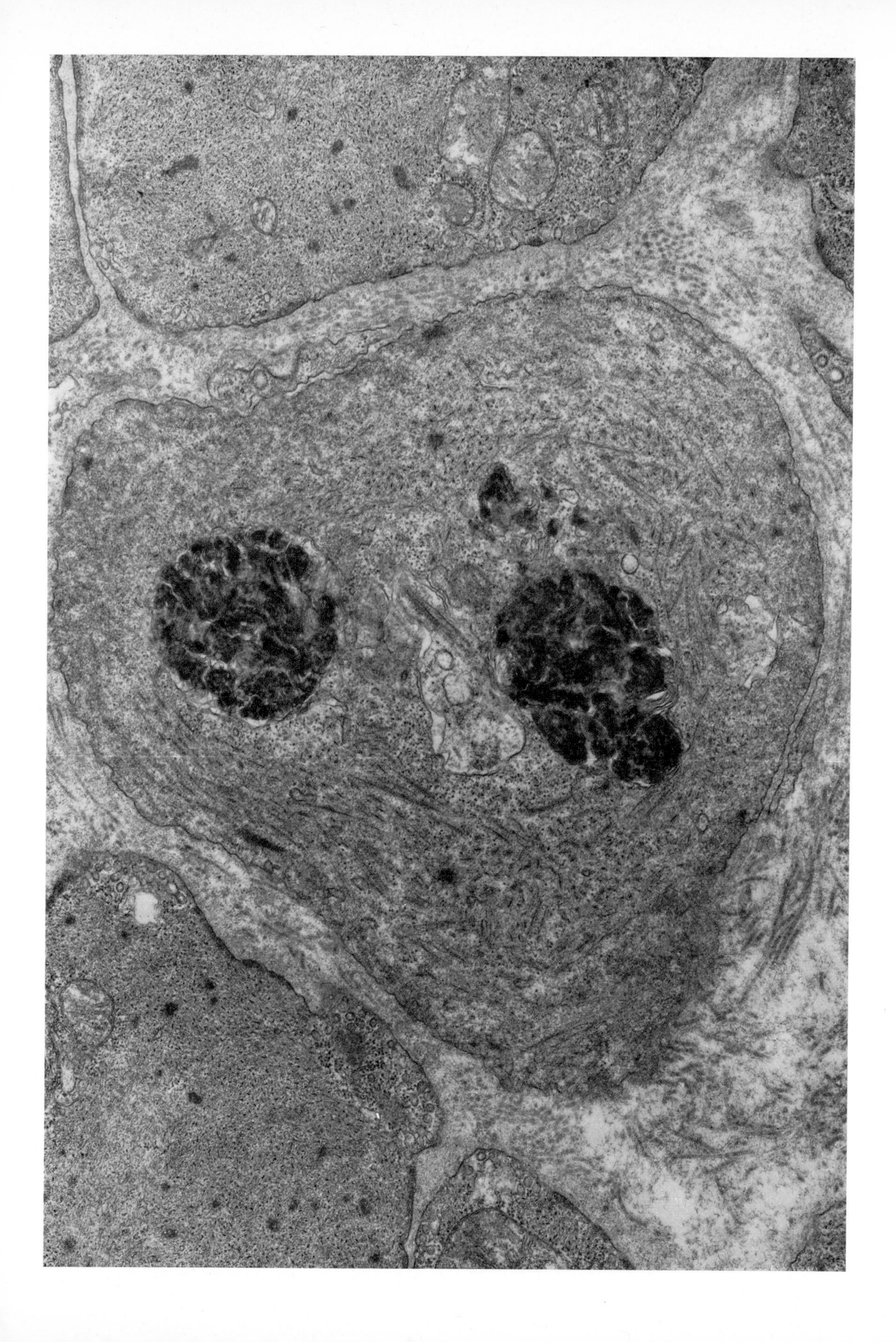

Plate 81

Another example of a physiological degeneration process in which cells are occasionally seen to degenerate for no apparent reason is illustrated here (see also Plate 80). Note the presence of lysosomes in the surrounding cell and the unusual configuration of tubular structures in the adjacent cell.

Lysosomes in degenerating invertebrate obliquely striated muscle: earthworm somatic muscle. Transverse section. Glutaraldehyde fixation. × 51 000.

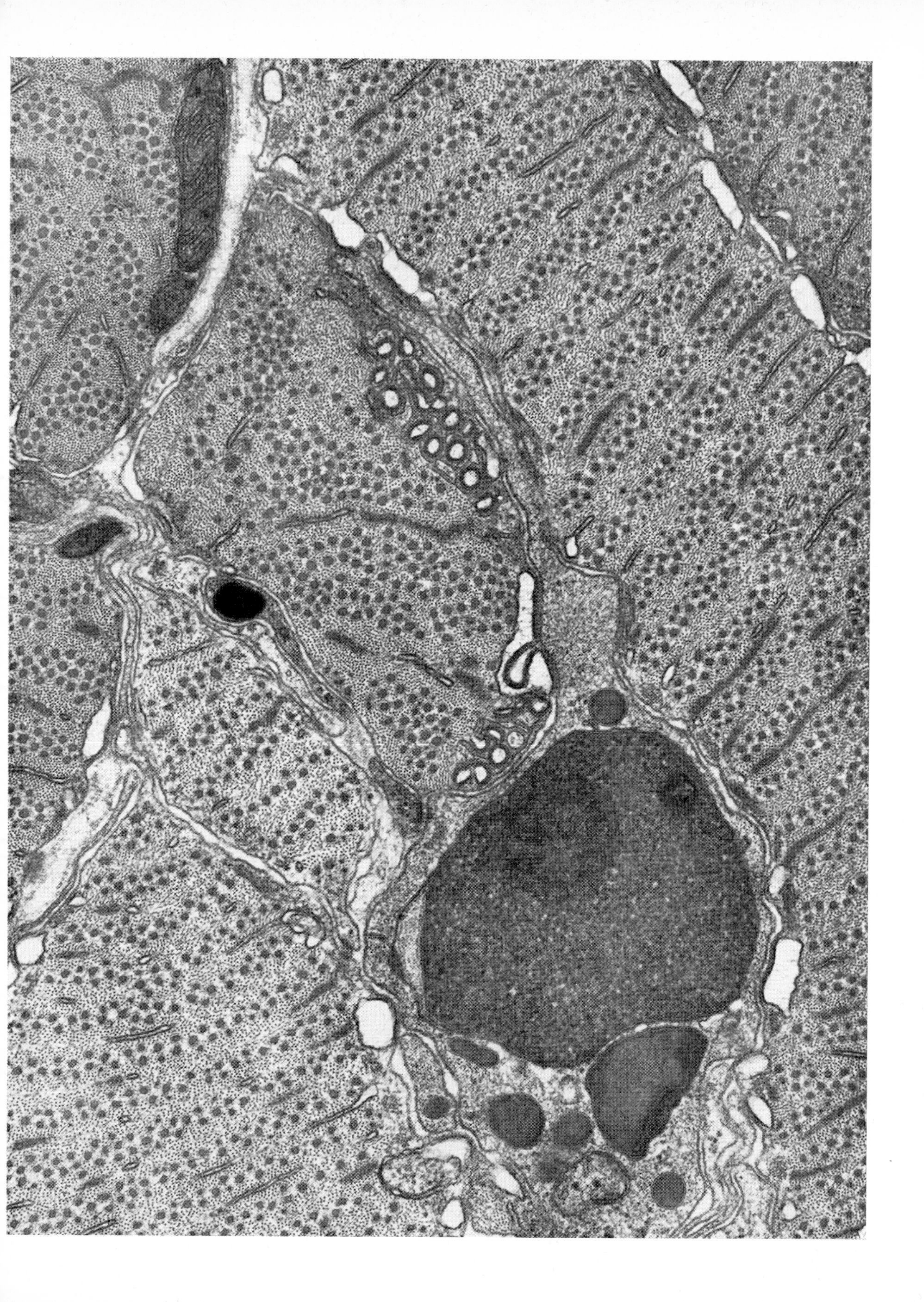

Selected articles

BRANDES, D. and E. ANTON. 1969. Lysosomes in uterine involution: intracytoplasmic degradation of myofilaments and collagen. *J. Geront.*, **24,** 55–69.

BUCHANAN, W. E. and T. B. SCHWARTZ. 1967. Lysosomal enzyme activity in heart and skeletal muscle of cortisone-treated rats. *Am. J. Physiol.*, **212,** 732–736.

CAMPBELL, G. R., Y. UEHARA, T. MALMFORS and G. BURNSTOCK. 1971. Degeneration and regeneration of smooth muscle transplants in the anterior eye chamber: an ultrastructural study. *Z. Zellforsch. mikrosk. Anat.*, **117,** 155–175.

CANONICO, P. G. and J. W. C. BIRD. 1969. The use of acridine orange as a lysosomal marker in rat skeletal muscle. *J. Cell Biol.*, **43,** 367–371.

CANONICO, P. G. and J. W. C. BIRD. 1970. Lysosomes in skeletal muscle tissue. Zonal centrifugation evidence for multiple cellular sources. *J. Cell Biol.*, **45,** 321–333.

DE DUVE, C. 1959. Lysosomes, a new group of cytoplasmic particles. In *Subcellular Particles.* T. Hayashi (ed.). Ronald Press, New York. 128–158.

DE DUVE, C. 1968. Lysosomes as targets for drugs. In *The Interaction of drugs and subcellular components in Animal cells.* P. N. Campbell (ed.). J. & A. Churchill, London. 155.

DE DUVE, C. and R. WATTIAUX. 1966. Functions of lysosomes. *A. Rev. Physiol.*, **28,** 435–492.

DINGLE, J. T. and H. B. FELL (eds.) 1969–1973. *Lysosomes in Biology and Pathology.* Vols. 1–3. North Holland, Amsterdam.

HIBBS, R. G., V. J. FERRANS, J. J. WALSH and G. E. BURCH. 1965. Electron microscopic observations on lysosomes and related cytoplasmic components of normal and pathological cardiac muscle. *Anat. Rec.*, **153,** 173–186.

HOURDRY, J. 1968. Données cytologiques et cytochemiques sur l'evolution des lysosomes. *Année biol.*, **7,** 485–512.

IMAI, H., S. K. LEE, S. J. PASTORI and W. A. THOMAS. 1970. Degeneration of arterial smooth muscle cells: ultrastructural study of smooth muscle cell death in control and cholesterol-fed animals. *Virchow Arch. Abt. A Path. Anat.*, **350,** 183–204.

LAUMONIER, R., CL. MARCHE and J. METAYER. 1971. Le lysosome en pathologie. *Annls anat. path.*, **16,** 321–334.

MANASEK, F. J. 1969. Myocardial cell death in the embryonic chick ventricle. J. *Embryol. exp. Morph.*, **21,** 271–284.

MAX, S. R., R. F. MAYER and L. VOGELSANG. 1971. Lysosomes and disuse atrophy of skeletal muscle. *Archs. Biochem. Biophys.*, **146,** 227–232.

RESIBOIS, A., M. TONDEUR, S. MOCKEL and P. DUSTIN. 1970. Lysosomes and storage diseases. *Int. Rev. Exp. Pathol.*, **9,** 93–149.

SHIAFFINO, S. and V. HANZLINKOVA. 1972. Studies on the effect of denervation in developing muscle: II. The lysosomal system. *J. Ultrastruct. Res.*, **39,** 1–14.

SOBEL, H. J., E. MARQUET and R. SCHWARZ. 1971. Granular degeneration of appendiceal smooth muscle. *Archs Path.*, **92,** 427–432.

STAGNI, N. and B. DE BERNARD. 1968. Lysosomal enzyme activity in rat and beef skeletal muscle. *Biochim. biophys. Acta.*, **170,** 129–139.

WEBB, J. N. 1972. The development of human skeletal muscle with particular reference to muscle cell death. *J. Path.*, **106,** 221–228.

WHEAT, M. W. 1965. Ultrastructure autoradiography and lysosome studies in myocardium. *J. Mt Sinai Hosp.*, **32,** 107–121.

K Leptomere fibrils

Leptomere fibrils (also termed γ-fibrils, microladders or intracellular microtendons) have been reported in various cell types. They were first described in avian striated muscle but have now been observed in the myocardium, intrafusal fibres of muscle spindles, and extraocular muscles (Plate 83). Two types of leptomere fibrils, termed types I and II, have been described in frog intrafusal muscle fibres. Type I is approximately 0.3 μm wide, and has cross striations with a periodicity of approximately $\frac{1}{10}$ the sarcomere length. Longitudinal filaments 5 nm in diameter run between these striations. The cross-striations consist of transverse discs, which appear to have a similar structure to that of Z-discs. The periodicity of the cross striations alters with the stretch of the muscle. Type II has a similar distribution and width, but the periodicity is smaller and is usually about $\frac{1}{100}$ the sarcomere length. Comparable structures have been described in endothelial cells. Leptomere fibrils appear in the vicinity of Z-discs and of the sarcolemma of muscle cells. This, together with the fact that they can be induced by cytochalasin D in myotubes has led to the suggestion that they participate as auxillary organelles in contraction, especially at the cell periphery. Another suggestion is that they act as microtendons, resisting local changes in sarcomere length.

Plate 82

The leptomere fibril illustrated is about 0.2 μm in width and exhibits periodicity of the transverse discs of approximately the same dimensions. Filaments about 5 nm in diameter pass between the transverse discs. The internal composition of each transverse disc appears similar to that of Z-discs.

Leptomere fibrils in vertebrate striated muscle: finch intrafusal fibre, rectus femoris muscle. Transverse section. Glutaraldehyde fixation. × 112 000.

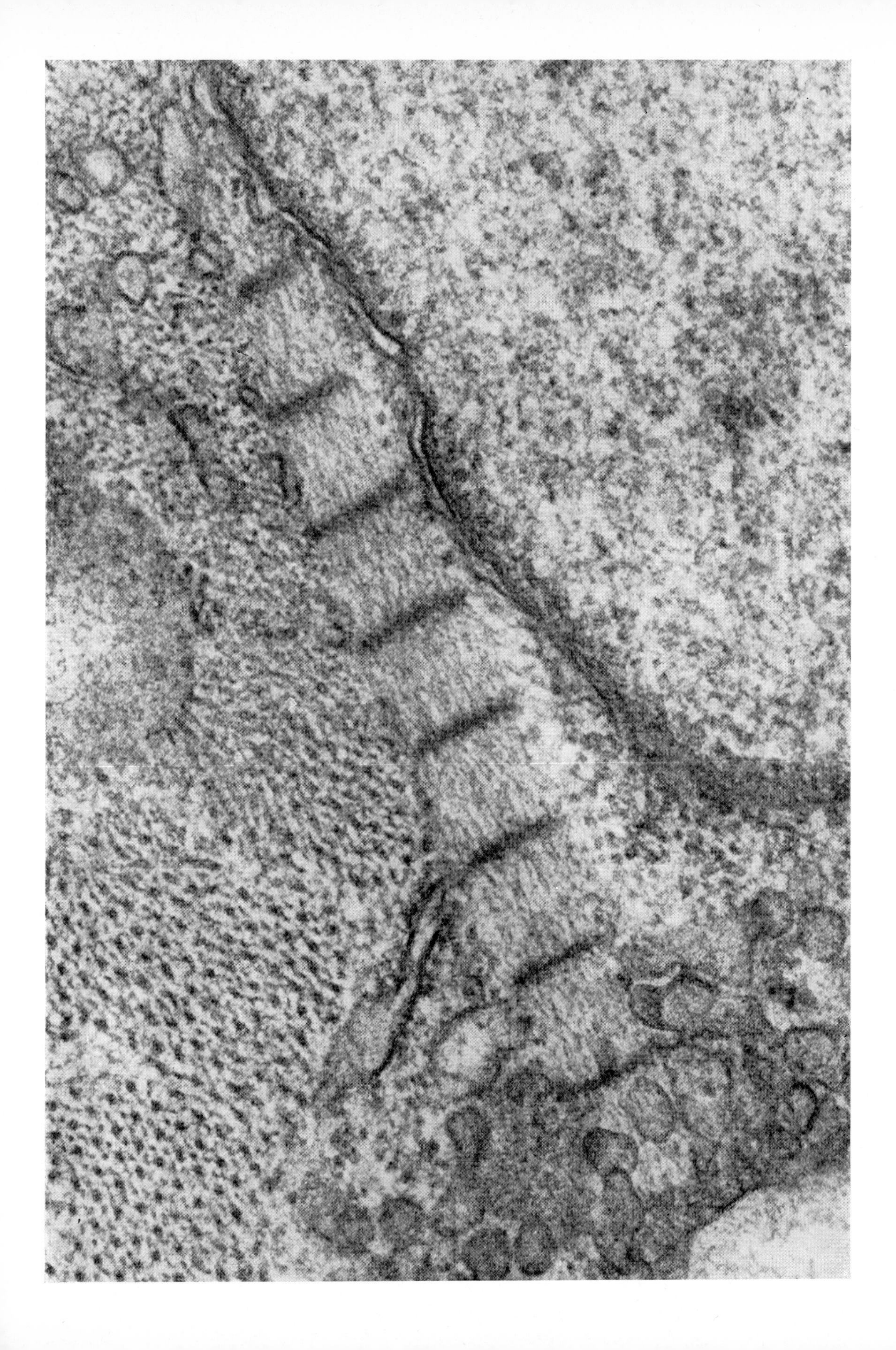

Plate 83

In the accompanying plate, a leptomere fibril (Le) is shown in a protrusion of a muscle cell, where no myofilaments appear to be present but which contains mitochondria and free ribosomes. It seems unlikely that this leptomere fibril is involved in the contraction of the whole muscle fibre.

The presence of leptomere fibrils in developing tissues originally led to the view that they were associated with growth. However, these organelles also occur in adult muscle cells so this view must be questioned.

Leptomere fibrils in vertebrate striated muscle: guinea-pig rectus superior muscle. Transverse section. Glutaraldehyde fixation. $\times$50 500.

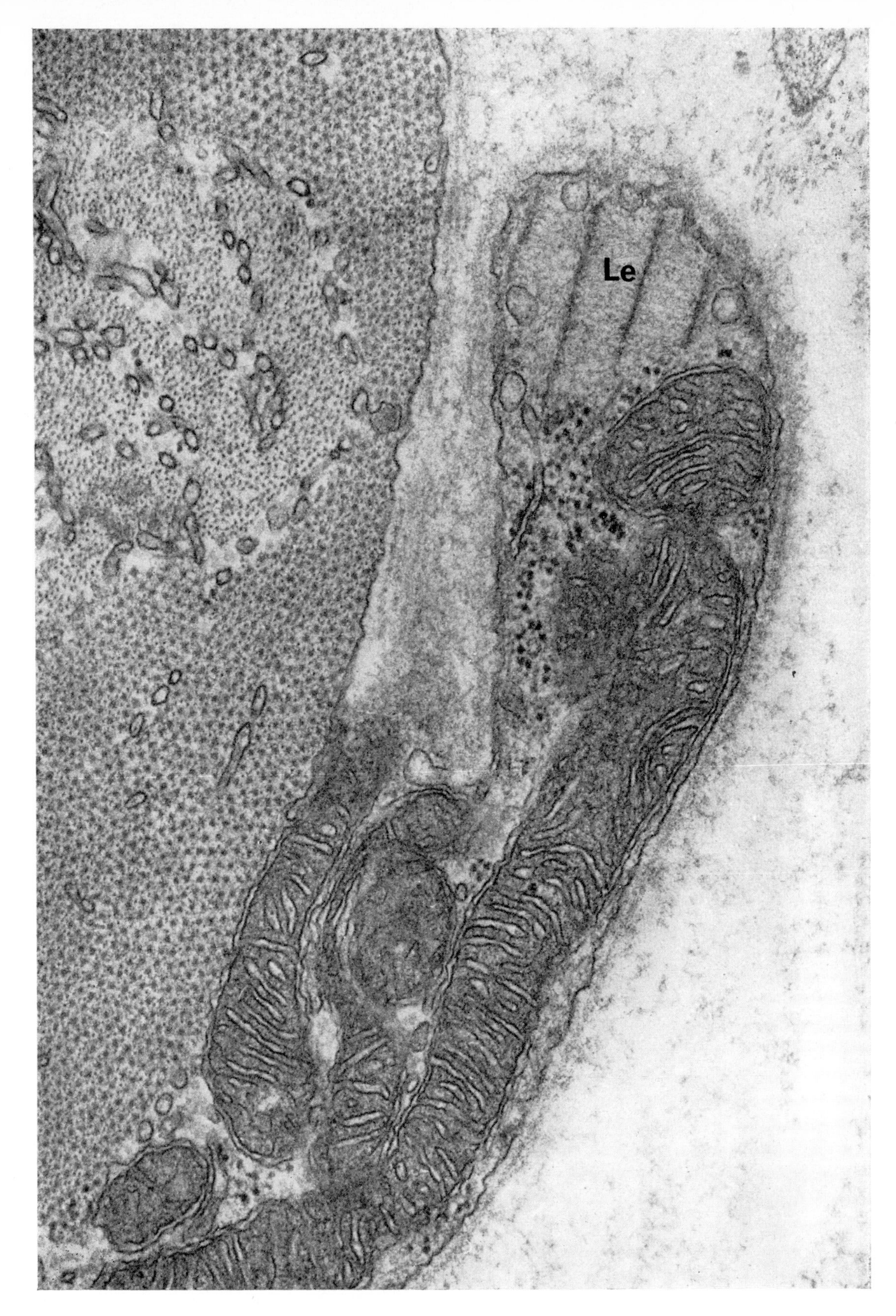
Le

Selected articles

GRUNER, J.-E. 1961. Sur un organite du fuseau neuromusculaire et sur ses relations avec les myofibrilles leptomères de Ruska. *Cr. Soc. Biol. Paris.*, **155,** 1841–1847.

KARLSSON, U. and E. ANDERSSON-CEDERGREN. 1968. Small leptomeric organelles in intrafusal muscle fibers of the frog as revealed by electron microscopy. *J. Ultrastruct. Res.*, **23,** 417–426.

MIRANDA, A. F. and G. C. GODMAN. 1973. The effects of cytochalasin D on differentiating muscle in culture. *Tissue & Cell*, **5,** 1–22.

MUKUNO, K. 1966. The fine structure of the human extraocular muscles. (1) A 'laminated structure' in the muscle fibers (in Japanese). *J. Electron Microsc.*, **15,** 227–236.

THOENES, W. and H. RUSKA. 1960. Über 'Leptomere Myofibrillen' in der Herzmuskelzelle. *Z. Zellforsch. mikrosk. Anat.*, **51,** 560–570.

3 Cell Inclusions

A Glycogen

Glycogen particles have three levels of structural organization. The largest units are called *α-particles* and are from 50–200 nm in diameter. The α-particles are composed of smaller units 20–35 nm in diameter, the *β-particles.* In turn these are composed of smaller rod shaped subunits, 30 by 20 nm, the *γ-particles.* Glycogen is the chief storage form of reserve carbohydrate within the body and is composed of a series of glucose units largely derived from the blood.

The glycogen content of mammalian skeletal muscle decreases during sustained activity as it is used to resynthesize adenosine triphosphate (ATP).

Under anaerobic conditions, the lactic acid formed by this process leaks from the muscle into the blood, from which it passes to the liver to be reconverted to glucose or to the heart where it is the preferred substrate for oxidative metabolism. When the muscle is at rest (under aerobic conditions), glycogen can be reformed from lactic acid, although this process requires energy.

During starvation, skeletal muscle glycogen is severely depleted.

Cardiac muscle, however, tends to maintain its glycogen levels at normal or elevated values during starvation. Few studies have been made of glycogen in smooth muscle, but many particles have been observed in some smooth muscle cells of lower vertebrates and in some cultured smooth muscle.

There are a number of pathological conditions in muscle in which glycogen storage is affected. Most of these conditions involve deficiencies of the various enzymes associated with the building up or breaking down of glycogen. For example, a feature of McArdle's disease is a deficiency of phosphorylase; consequently glycogen cannot be broken down and as a result it accumulates in the muscle cells.

The preservation of glycogen varies with the fixation method and may also be variable from tissue to tissue. Consequently, it is sometimes difficult to distinguish free ribosomes from poorly preserved β-particles of glycogen.

Plate 84

Cardiac muscle contains a large amount of glycogen, but not in the form of aggregates. The glycogen appears as β-particles, 15–30 nm in diameter, grouped together in close association with the mitochondria. A lipid droplet (L) is also present in the cells illustrated.

Glycogen distribution in vertebrate cardiac muscle: toad ventricle. Formaldehyde fixation. $\times$15 800. (Courtesy of P. Robinson, Department of Anatomy, University of Melbourne.)

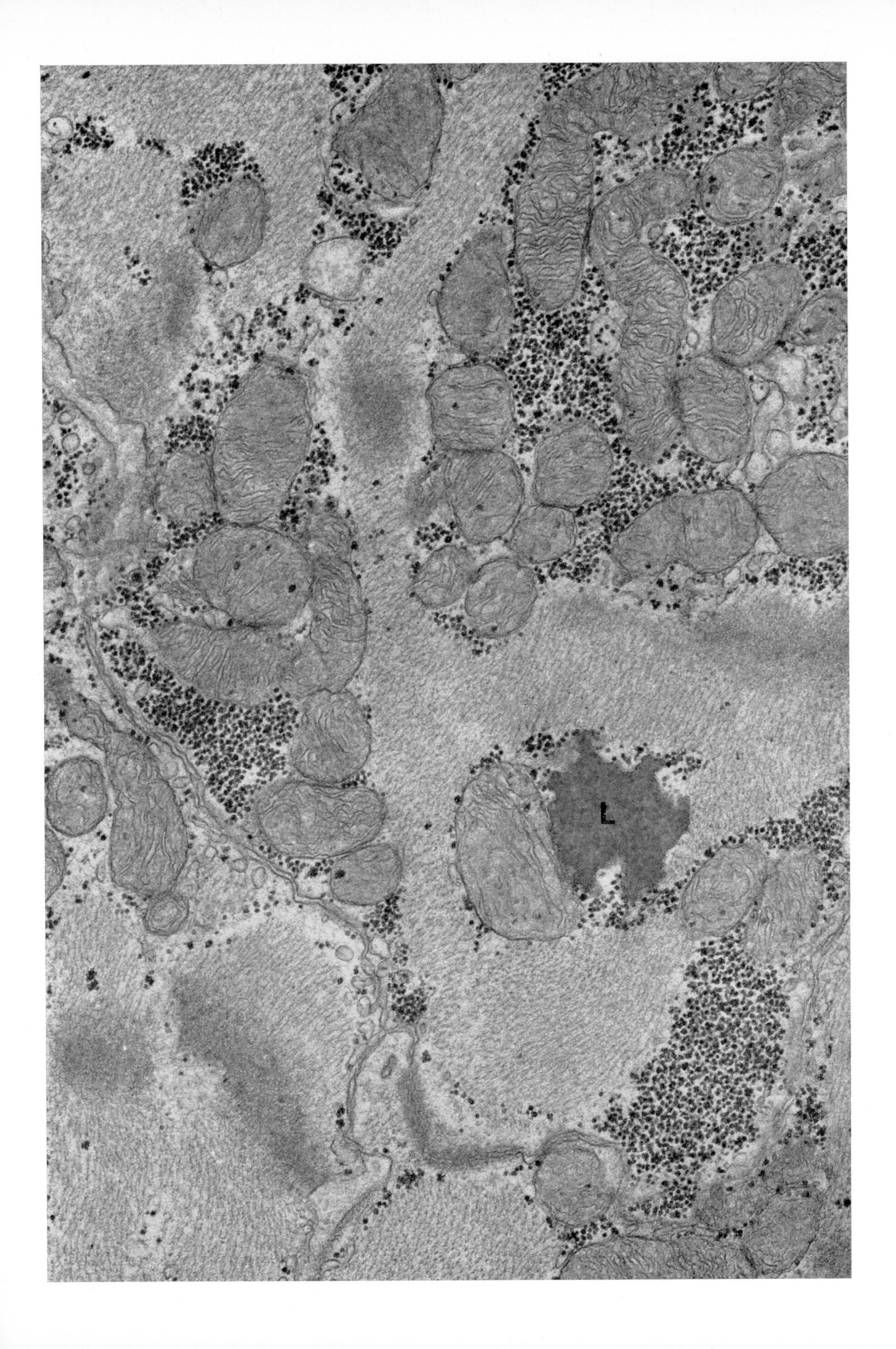
L

Plate 85

Glycogen, in the form of β-particles, is distributed between the myofibrils in many striated muscles. The close association of these particles to the sarcoplasmic reticulum has led to the suggestion that this organelle is involved in glycogenolysis.

The amount of glycogen present within striated muscle varies according to the type. In man, the white or fast twitch fibres contain relatively few mitochondria, large amounts of glycogen and little lipid, while the β red or slow twitch fibres contain little glycogen and much lipid.

Glycogen distribution in vertebrate striated muscle: rat diaphragm. Transverse section. Glutaraldehyde fixation. ×223 000.

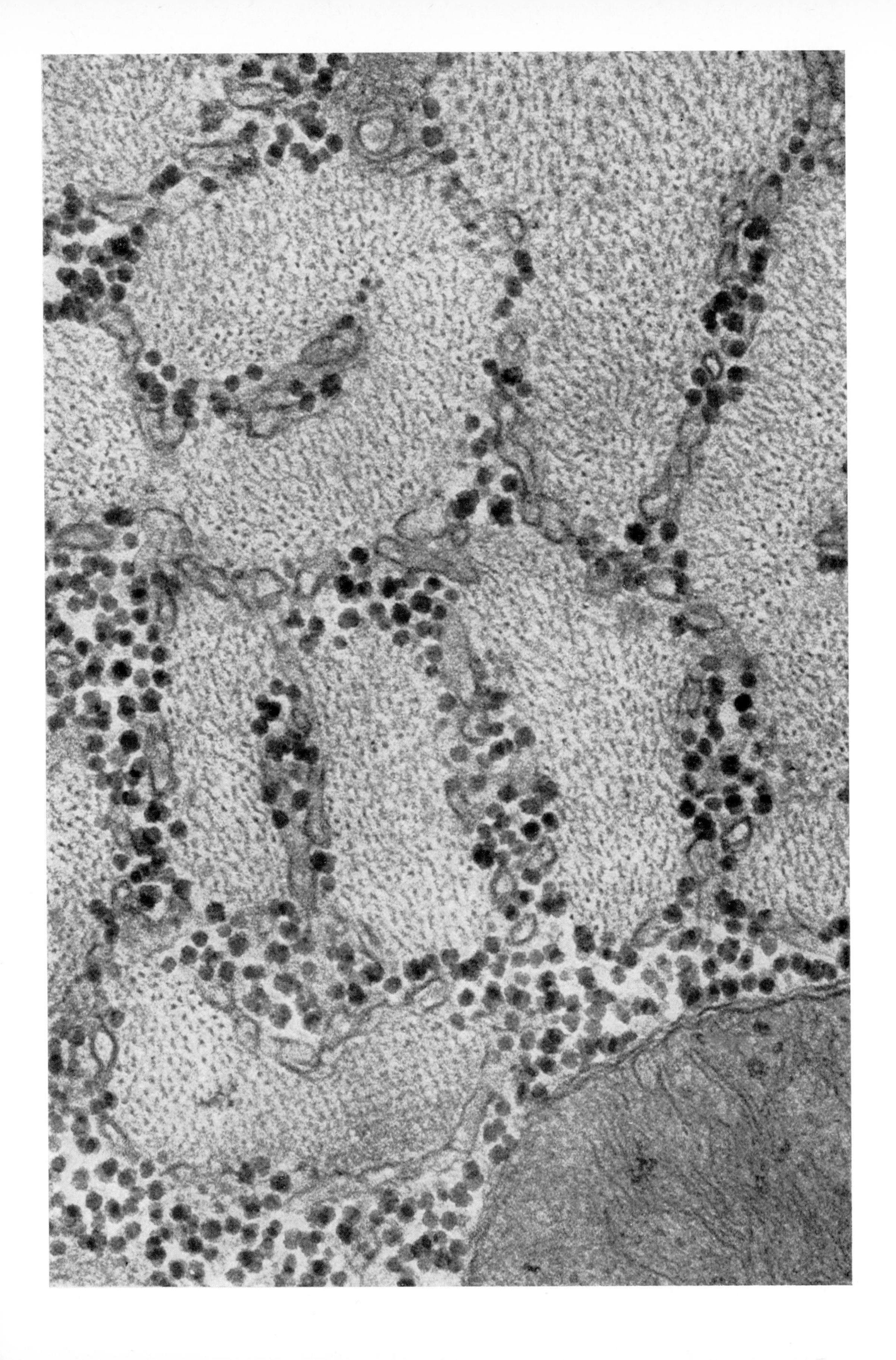

Plate 86

In this example of invertebrate smooth muscle, the glycogen is irregular in outline and is found both in the form of free *β-particles* and of aggregates, the *α-particles*, widely distributed throughout the sarcoplasm.

Glycogen distribution in an invertebrate smooth muscle: mussel anterior byssus retractor muscle. Longitudinal section. Glutaraldehyde fixation. × 138 000.

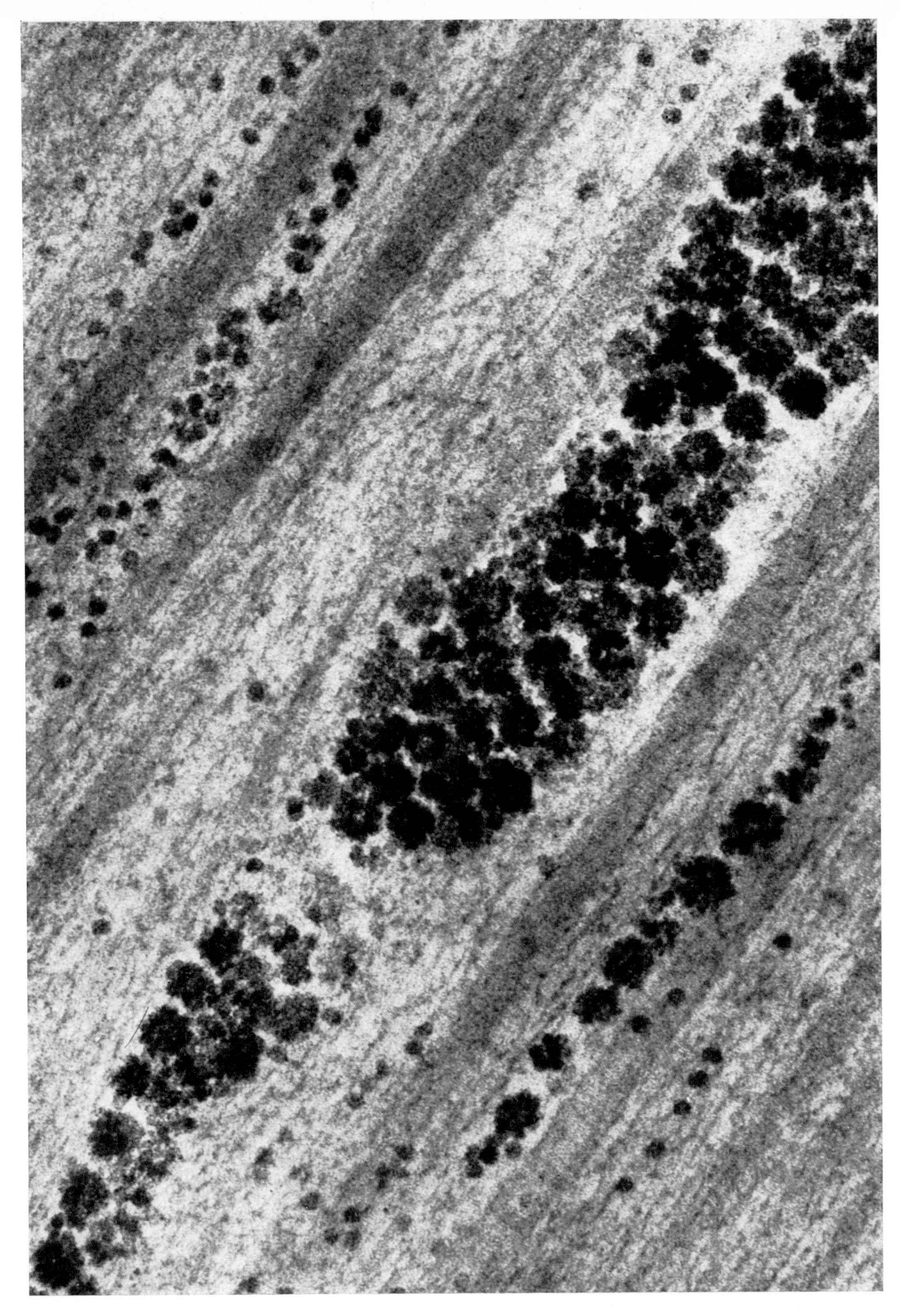

Selected articles

ABDULLAH, M. and W. J. WHELEN. 1963. Enzymatic debranching of glycogen. A new pathway in rabbit muscle for the enzymatic debranching of glycogen. *Nature, Lond.*, **197,** 979–980.

ANDERSON-CEDERGREN, E. and U. MUSCATELLO. 1963. The participation of the sarcotubular system in glycogen metabolism. *J. Ultrastruct. Res.*, **8,** 391–401.

BAUDHUIN, P., H. G. HERS and M. LOEB. 1964. An electron microscopic and biochemical study of type II glycogenosis. *Lab. Invest.*, **13,** 1139–1152.

BERGMAN, R. A. 1960. Further observations on the localization of glycogen in frog striated muscle. *Johns Hopkins Hosp. Bull.*, **107,** 307–319.

BLAKE, C. A. and R. L. HAZELWOOD. 1971. Effect of pregnancy and exercise on actomyosin, nucleic acid, and glycogen content of the rat heart. *Proc. Soc. exp. Biol. Med.*, **136,** 632–636.

BRUIJN, W. C. DE. 1973. Glycogen, its chemistry and morphologic appearance in the electron microscope. I. A modification OsO_4 fixative which selectively contrasts glycogen. *J. Ultrastruct. Res.*, **42,** 29–50.

CHILDRESS, C. C., B. SACKTOR, I. W. GROSSMAN and E. BUEDING. 1970. Isolation, ultrastructure, and biochemical characterization of glycogen in insect flight muscle. *J. Cell Biol.*, **45,** 83–90.

COIMBRA, A. 1969. Radioautographic studies of glycogen synthesis in the striated muscle of rat tongue. *Am. J. Anat.*, **124,** 361–377.

ENGEL, W. K. 1961. Cytological localization of glycogen in cultured skeletal muscle. *J. Histochem. Cytochem.*, **9,** 38–43.

GARANT, P. R. 1968. Glycogen-membrane complexes within mouse striated muscle cells. *J. Cell Biol.*, **36,** 648–652.

GILLESPIE, C. A., D. R. SIMPSON and V. R. EDGERTON. 1970. High glycogen content of red as opposed to white skeletal muscle fibers of guinea pigs. *J. Histochem. Cytochem.*, **18,** 552–558.

HULTMAN, E. 1969. Glycogen metabolism in skeletal muscle. *Lakartidningen*, **66,** 241–254.

IWAMASA, T. and T. TAKEUCHI. 1971. Macromolecular structure of glycogen in the rat liver and muscle. *J. Electron Microsc.*, **20,** 233.

LE DOUARIN, N. 1968. Synthèse du glycogène dans les hépatocytes en voie de differenciation: rôle des mésenchymes homologue et hétérologues. *Devl Biol.*, **17,** 101–114.

LIU, T. P. and D. M. DAVIES. 1971. Ultrastructural localization of glycogen in the flight muscle of the blackfly, *Simulium vittatum* Zett. *Can. J. Zool.*, **49,** 219–221.

LUCIANO, L., E. JUNGER and E. REALE. 1968. Glykogen in glatten Muskelzellen der Gefässwand von Säugetieren. Elektronenmikroskopische und spektrophotometrische Untersuchungen. *Histochemie*, **15,** 219–228.

MAUNSBACH, A. B. and C. WIRSEN. 1966. Ultrastructural changes in kidney, myocardium and skeletal muscle of the dog during excessive mobilization of free fatty acids. *J. Ultrastruct. Res.*, **16,** 35–54.

PERRY, M. M. 1967. Identification of glycogen in thin sections of amphibian embryos. *J. Cell Sci.*, **2,** 257–264.

POLINGER, I. S. 1973. Identification of cardiac myocytes *in vivo* and *in vitro* by the presence of glycogen and myofibrils. *Expl Cell Res.*, **76,** 243–252.

REVEL, J. P., L. NAPOLITANO and D. W. FAWCETT. 1960. Identification of glycogen in electron micrographs of thin tissue sections. *J. biophys. biochem. Cytol.*, **8,** 575–589.

ROSATI, G. 1967. Enzyme treatment of glycogen particles in rat liver and muscle. *J. Ultrastruct. Res.*, **18,** 444–455.

SASAKI, M., S. SUKO and T. TAKEUCHI. 1971. Intracellular distribution of polyglucose synthesized by UDP glucose glycogen glucosyltransferase in rabbit skeletal muscles. *J. Electron Microsc.*, **20,** 299–311.

VYE, M. V. and D. A. FISCHMAN. 1970. The morphological alteration of particulate glycogen by *en bloc* staining with uranyl acetate. *J. Ultrastruct. Res.*, **33,** 278–291.

VYE, M. V. and D. A. FISCHMAN. 1971. A comparative study of three methods for the ultrastructural demonstration of glycogen in thin sections. *J. Cell Sci.*, **9,** 727–750.

WANSON, J.-C. and P. DROCHMANS. 1968. Rabbit skeletal muscle glycogen. A morphological and biochemical study of glycogen β-particles isolated by the precipitation–centrifugation method. *J. Cell Biol.*, **38,** 130–150.

WANSON, J.-C. and P. DROCHMANS. 1972. Role of the sarcoplasmic reticulum in glycogen metabolism. Binding of phosphorylase, phosphorylase kinase, and primer complexes to the sarcovesicles of rabbit skeletal muscle. *J. Cell Biol.*, **54,** 206–224.

B Lipid

Lipid is usually seen in muscle cells in the form of droplets of triglycerides of fatty acids. These droplets are not membrane bound and their number and size varies considerably between different muscle types and between the same type of muscle in different areas of the body. Lipid droplets may serve as a local store of short carbon chains for the synthesis of membranes. Fatty acids can form a source of energy for muscle since they can be β-oxidized to acetyl CoA, which can then yield energy as ATP via the tricarboxylic acid cycle. As mentioned in Chapter 2E, the smooth endoplasmic reticulum plays a major role in the synthesis of triglycerides.

An unusual accumulation of lipid droplets in muscle is associated with a number of pathological conditions. One of the most striking of these is the accumulation of lipid droplets present in vascular smooth muscle cells in *atherosclerosis*. A characteristic feature of all atherosclerotic lesions is the presence of *foam cells*, so called because their cell body is almost completely filled with lipid droplets. Two points of view exist as to the origin of these cells: the first suggests foam cells develop from smooth muscle cells of the arterial media; the second maintains that most foam cells are derived from cells originating from the blood. Lipid inclusions have been demonstrated in cardiac muscle following chronic injection of reserpine.

Plate 87

Lipid droplets are frequently closely associated with mitochondria, particularly in cardiac muscles. Sometimes a lipid droplet (L) is completely encircled by a mitochondrion. This type of association has been interpreted as structural evidence for a role of mitochondria in the utilization of lipid as a source of energy for muscular contraction. Complete preservation of lipid for electron-microscopy is difficult to achieve and consequently lipid droplets vary in appearance from those with a high electron density to those with a low electron density. This is due to the composition of the lipid before fixation and to the amount extracted during dehydration.

Lipid in vertebrate cardiac muscle: guinea-pig ventricle. Longitudinal section. Glutaraldehyde fixation. ×62 300.

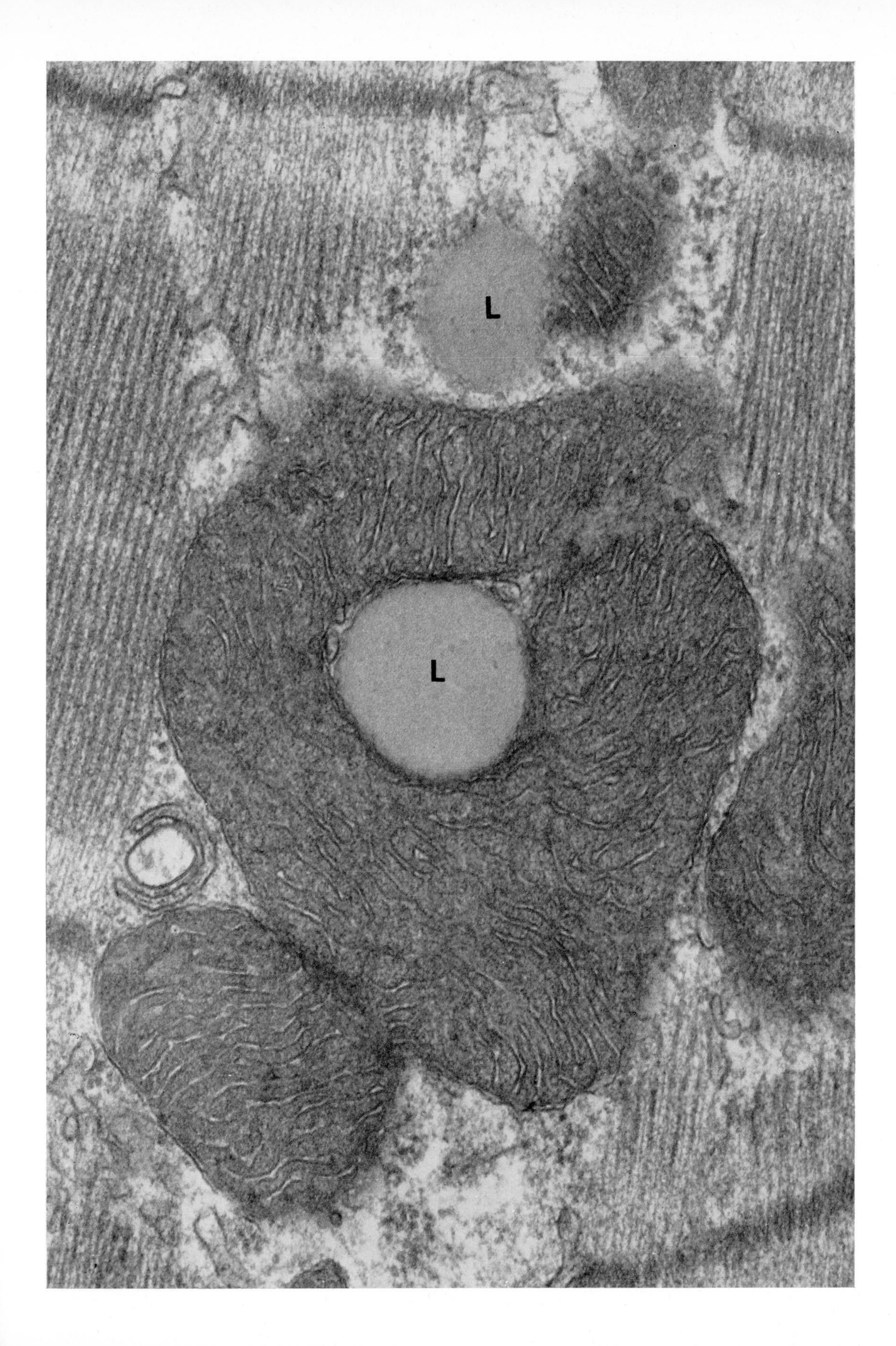
L
L

Selected articles

ASHHURST, D. E. and B. M. LUKE. 1968. Lipid inclusions in the flight muscles of belostomatid water-bugs. *Z. Zellforsch. mikrosk. Anat.*, **92,** 270–274.

CHAPMAN, D. 1965. *The Structure of Lipids.* Methuen, London.

FONT, R. L. and B. S. FINE. 1972. Ocular pathology in Fabry's disease: Histochemical and electron microscopic observations. *J. Ophthal.*, **73,** 419–430.

HESS, R. and W. STAÜBLI. 1969. Ultrastructure of vascular changes. In *Atherosclerosis: Pathology, Physiology, Aetiology, Diagnosis and Clinical Management.* F. G. Schettler and G. S. Boyd (eds.). Elsevier, Amsterdam.

KNIERIEM, H.-J. 1970. Elektronenmikroskopische Untersuchungen zur Bedeutung der glatten Muskelzellen für die Pathohistogenese der Arteriosklerose. *Beitr. path. Anat.*, **140,** 298–332.

MASORO, E. J., L. B. ROWELL and R. M. McDONALD. 1966. Intracellular muscle lipids as energy sources during muscular exercise and fasting. *Fedn Proc.*, **25,** 1421–1426.

MAUNSBACH, A. B. and C. WIRSEN. 1966. Ultrastructural changes in kidney, myocardium, and skeletal muscle of the dog during excessive mobilization of free fatty acids. *J. Ultrastruct. Res.*, **16,** 35–54.

NEWMAN, H. A. I., T. M. MURAD and J. C. GEER. 1971. Foam cells of rabbit atheromatous lesion. Identification and cholesterol uptake in isolated cells. *Lab. Invest.*, **25,** 586–595.

STEIN, O., S. EISENBERG and Y. STEIN. 1971. Morphologic and biochemical changes in smooth muscle cells of aortas in growth-restricted rats. *Lab. Invest.*, **25,** 149–157.

STEIN, O. and Y. STEIN. 1968. Lipid synthesis, intracellular transport, and storage. III. Electron microscope radioautographic study of the rat heart perfused with tritiated oleic acid. *J. Cell Biol.*, **36,** 63–77.

TAKEBAYASHI, S., I. KUBOTA, A. KAMIO and T. TAKAGI. 1972. Ultrastructural aspects of human atherosclerosis; role of the foam cells and modified smooth muscle cells. *J. Electron Microsc.*, **21,** 301–313.

WOOD, E. M. 1967. An ordered complex of filaments surrounding the lipid droplets in developing adipose cells. *Anat. Rec.*, **157,** 437–448.

C Granules

Vertebrate cardiac muscle cells contain a number of different types of membrane-bound granule. Some workers have classified these granules into two major groups on the basis of their acid-phosphatase reaction, namely *c-granules* and *specific granules.* The c-granules are usually large and irregular in shape and include such structures as lysosomal bodies (see Chapter 2J), lipofuscin granules, residual bodies and lytostoma c. They are acid-phosphatase positive. 'Specific granules' have a homogenous electron-dense core and are morphologically very similar to secretory granules in endocrine cells. For this and other reasons, it has been suggested that secretion is their function.

According to this concept, cardiac muscle would have a two-fold function—one of contraction, the other of secretion. They have been variously termed 'corps denses', microbodies, secretory granules, dense bodies, 'dichte Körper' and atrial granules. These granules are acid-phosphatase negative, do not take up ^{3}H-dopamine and do not appreciably bind ^{3}H-norepinephrine *in situ.*

Another pigment granule, *melanin* occurs in a variety of animal cell types, particularly epithelial cells of the skin and eye. Melanin pigment granules are occasionally seen within smooth muscle cells of the iris either in mature form or as promelanin granules in albino type animals. These granules are membrane bound and have a highly organized internal structure showing a regular pattern of fine density or cross striations along the length of a filamentous substructure. The pigment epithelium of the iris, which has a common origin with iris smooth muscle cells, also contains melanin and promelanin pigment.

Plate 88

Granules in the form of specific granules range from 20–40 nm in diameter in mammalian heart and contain an homogenous electron-dense core. However, in non-mammalian vertebrates comparable granules (Gr) can be up to 500 nm in diameter. They are found throughout the cell but usually in close association with other organelles such as mitochondria and Golgi complex.

Both atrial and ventricular muscle of non-mammalian vertebrates contain large numbers of specific granules. However, few 'specific granules' have been found in ventricular muscle cells of mammals.

Granules in vertebrate cardiac muscle: finch atrium. Longitudinal section. Glutaraldehyde fixation. ×51 000.

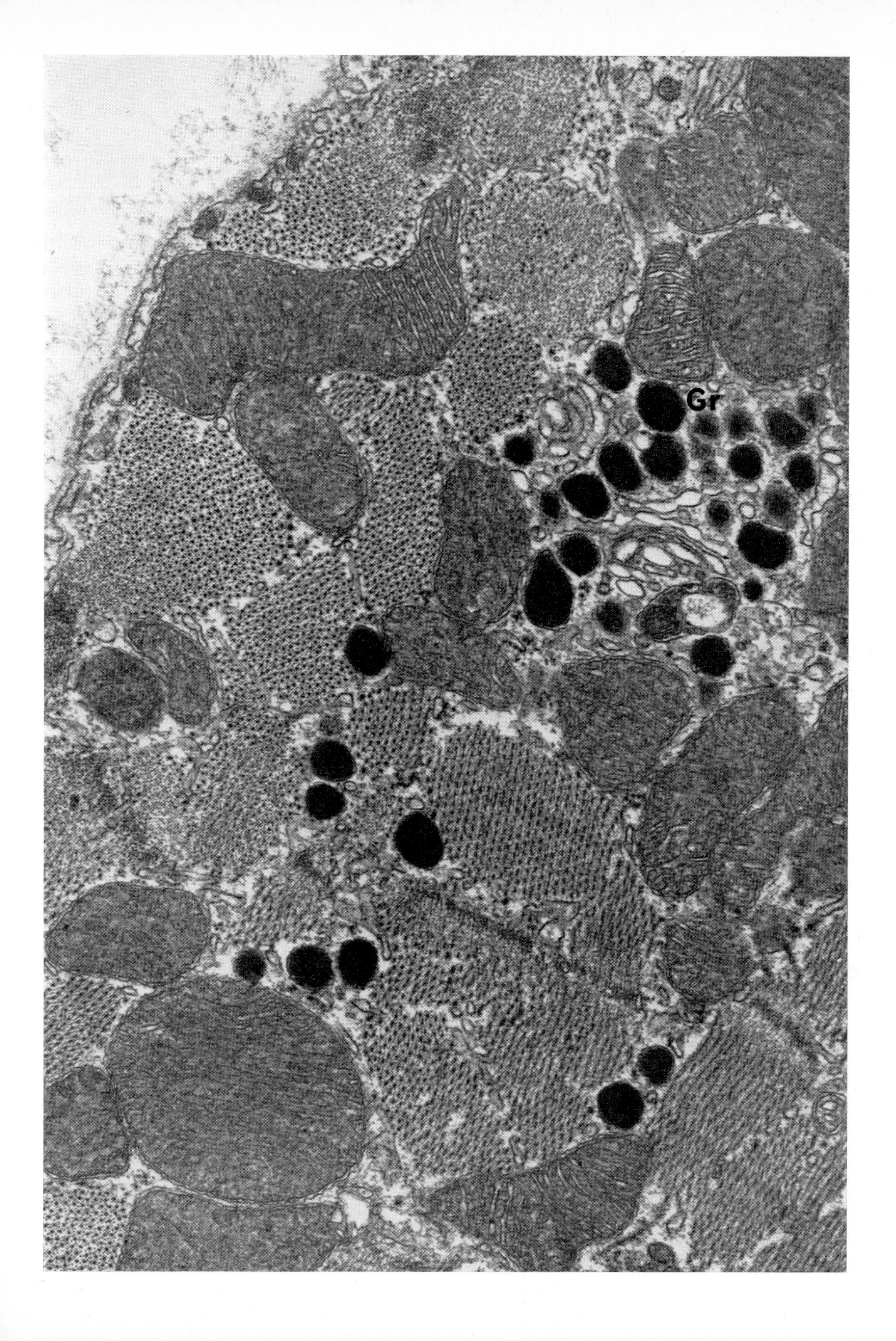
Gr

Plate 89

Granules of a similar appearance to the 'specific granules' of the vertebrate heart are found in invertebrate muscle cells. This suggests that here also other functions, such as secretion, may be combined with contraction.

Granules in an invertebrate myoendothelial cell: earthworm lateral heart. Glutaraldehyde fixation. ×65 000.

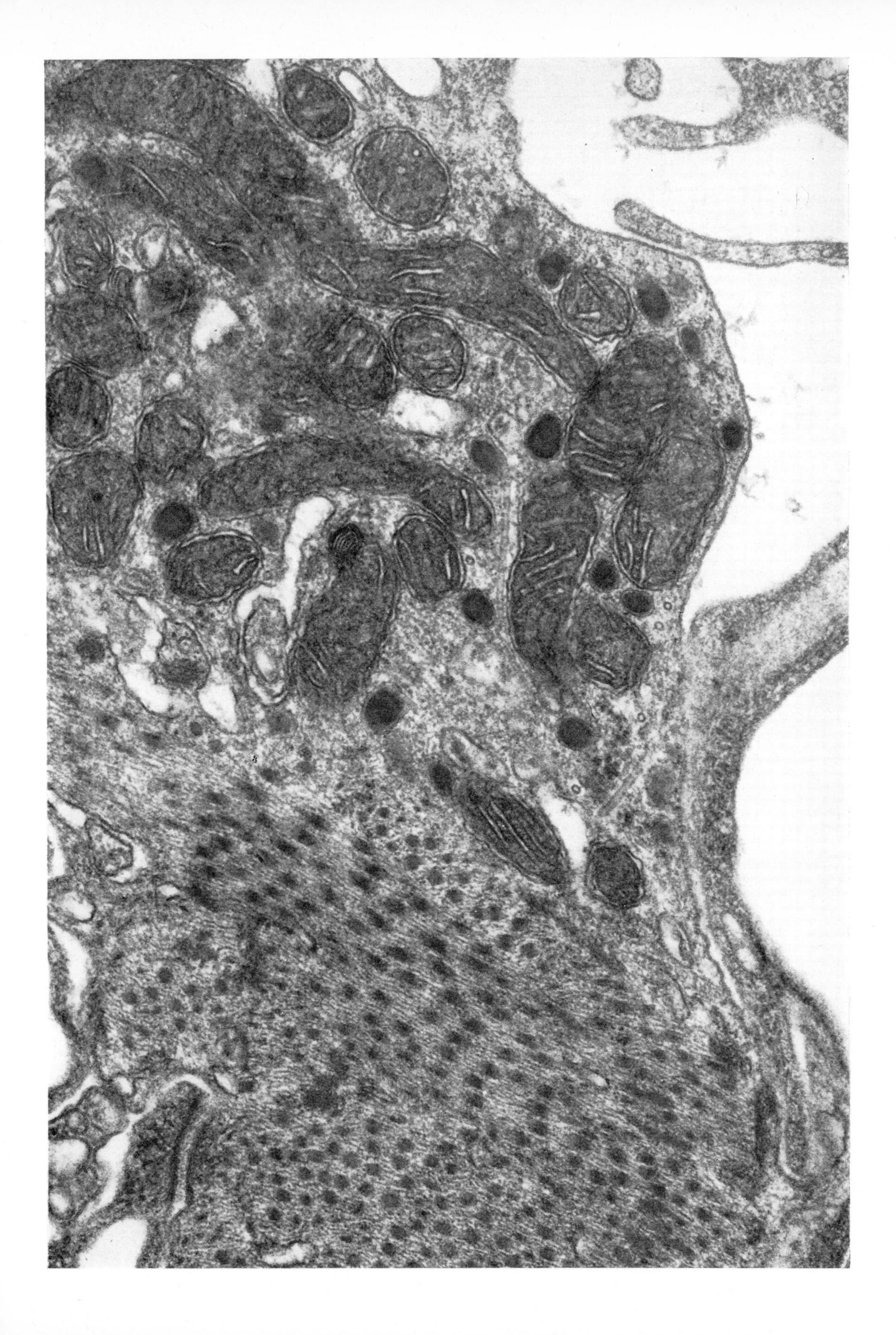

Plate 90

Promelanin pigment granules usually seen in the epithelium lining the iris are occasionally seen in smooth muscle cells of the sphincter pupillae.

Pigment in vertebrate smooth muscle: guinea-pig sphincter pupillae. Transverse section. Glutaraldehyde fixation. × 71 000.

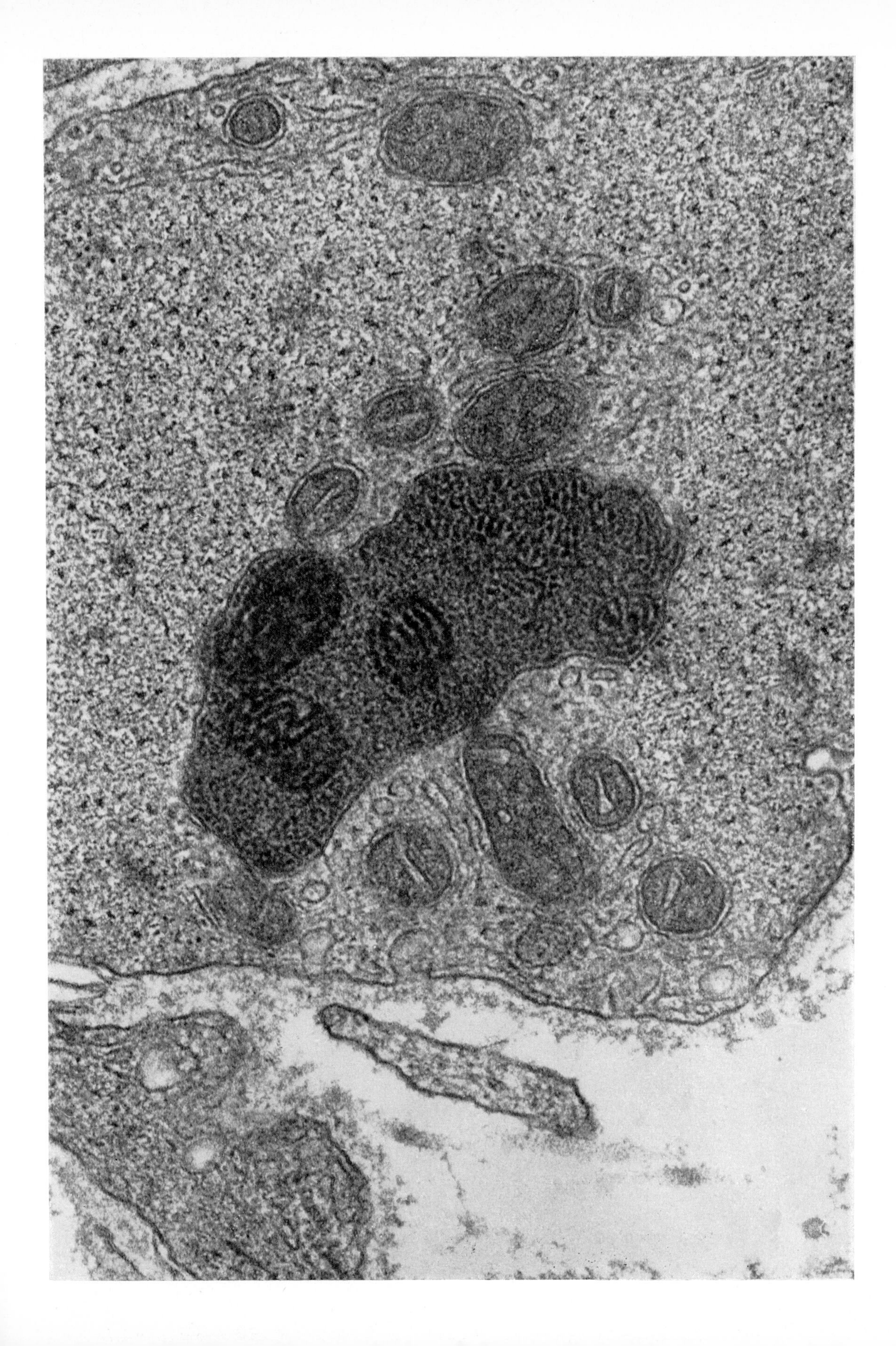

Selected articles

BAJUSZ, E. and G. RONA (eds.). 1972. *Recent Advances in Studies on Cardiac Structure and Metabolism: Myocardiology*. Vol. 1. University Park Press, Baltimore.

BICKLE, D., L. G. TILNEY and K. R. PORTER. 1966. Microtubules and pigment migration in the melanophores of *Fundulus heteroclitus* L. *Protoplasma*, **61,** 322–345.

DE BOLD, A. J. and S. A. BENCOSME. 1973*a*. Studies on the relationship between the catecholamine distribution in the atrium and specific granules present in atrial muscle cells. 1. Isolation of a purified specific granule subfraction. *Cardiovasc. Res.*, **7,** 351–363.

DE BOLD, A. J. and S. A. BENCOSME. 1973*b*. Studies on the relationship between the catecholamine distribution in the atrium and the specific granules present in atrial muscle cells. 2. Studies on the sedimentation pattern of atrial noradrenaline and adrenaline. *Cardiovasc. Res.*, **7,** 364–369.

HOFFMEISTER, H., K. LICKFIELD, H. RUSKA and B. RYBAK. 1961. Sécrétions granulaires dans le cœur branchial de *Myxine glutinosa* L. *Z. Zellforsch. mikrosk. Anat.*, **55,** 810–817.

JAMIESON, J. D. and G. E. PALADE. 1964. Specific granules in atrial muscle cells. *J. Cell Biol.*, **23,** 151–172.

MALKOFF, D. B. and B. L. STREHLER. 1963. The ultrastructure of isolated and *in situ* human cardiac age pigment. *J. Cell Biol.*, **16,** 611–616.

MANASEK, F. J. 1969. The appearance of granules in the Golgi complex of embryonic cardiac myocytes. *J. Cell Biol.*, **43,** 605–609.

OKAMOTO, H. 1969. An electron microscopic study of the specific granules in the atrial muscle cell upon the administration of agents affecting autonomic nerves. *Arch. histol. jap.*, **30,** 467–478.

PORTA, E. A. and W. S. HARTROFT. 1969. *In Pigments in Pathology*. M. Wolman (ed.). Academic Press, New York. 191–235.

STREHLER, B. L., D. D. MARK, A. S. MILDVAN and M. V. GEE. 1959. Rate and magnitude of age pigment accumulation in the human myocardium. *J. Geront.*, **14,** 430–439.

STROSBERG, A. M., B. G. KATZUNG and J. C. LEE. 1970. Demonstration of adenosine triphosphatase activity in coated dense vesicles and membranes of specific granules in mammalian myocardium. *Lab. Invest.*, **23,** 386–391.

TOMISAWA, M. 1969. Atrial specific granules in various mammals. *Arch. histol. jap.*, **30,** 449–465.

D Other inclusion bodies

A number of other inclusion bodies have been demonstrated in muscle cells. However, since these generally only appear under pathological conditions, they will not be considered in any detail in this book.

Plate 91

The inclusion body illustrated is very similar to the rod- or thread-like bodies seen in nemaline myopathy. They are not membrane bound and do not have cross striations. It has been suggested that they arise from Z-discs.

Inclusion body in vertebrate striated muscle: rat sterno-thyroid. Transverse section. Glutaraldehyde fixation. ×81 000.

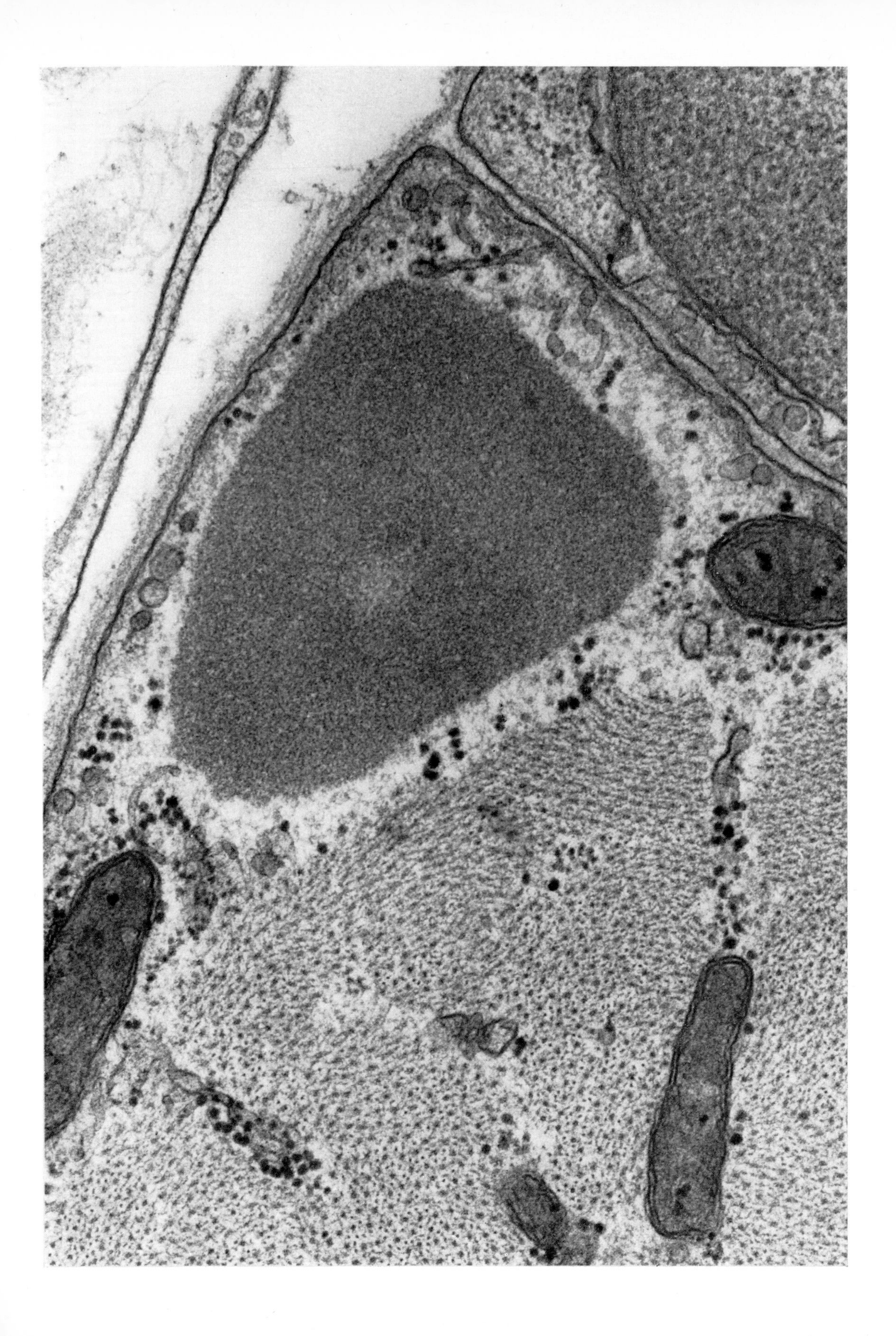

Plate 92

Cells with features of striated muscle fibres can be found in smooth muscle such as the guinea-pig sphincter pupillae. The peculiar organelles in these cells, which are very few in number, are characteristic of striated muscle fibres, although their arrangement is far less regular. They are comparable to the aggregation of triads seen in striated muscle from subjects with alcoholic neuropathy, and consist of a clear central tubule (equivalent to the T-system), on either side of which are electron-dense ellipsoidal lateral sacs (equivalent to the terminal cysternae of the sarcoplasmic reticulum). It is probably more correct to consider them as atypical striated muscle cells than as smooth muscle cells with inclusions of striated type. The origin and significance of these muscle cells in the sphincter pupillae is not known.

Aggregation of triads in an unusual vertebrate muscle: guinea-pig iris. Glutaraldehyde fixation. ×26 800.

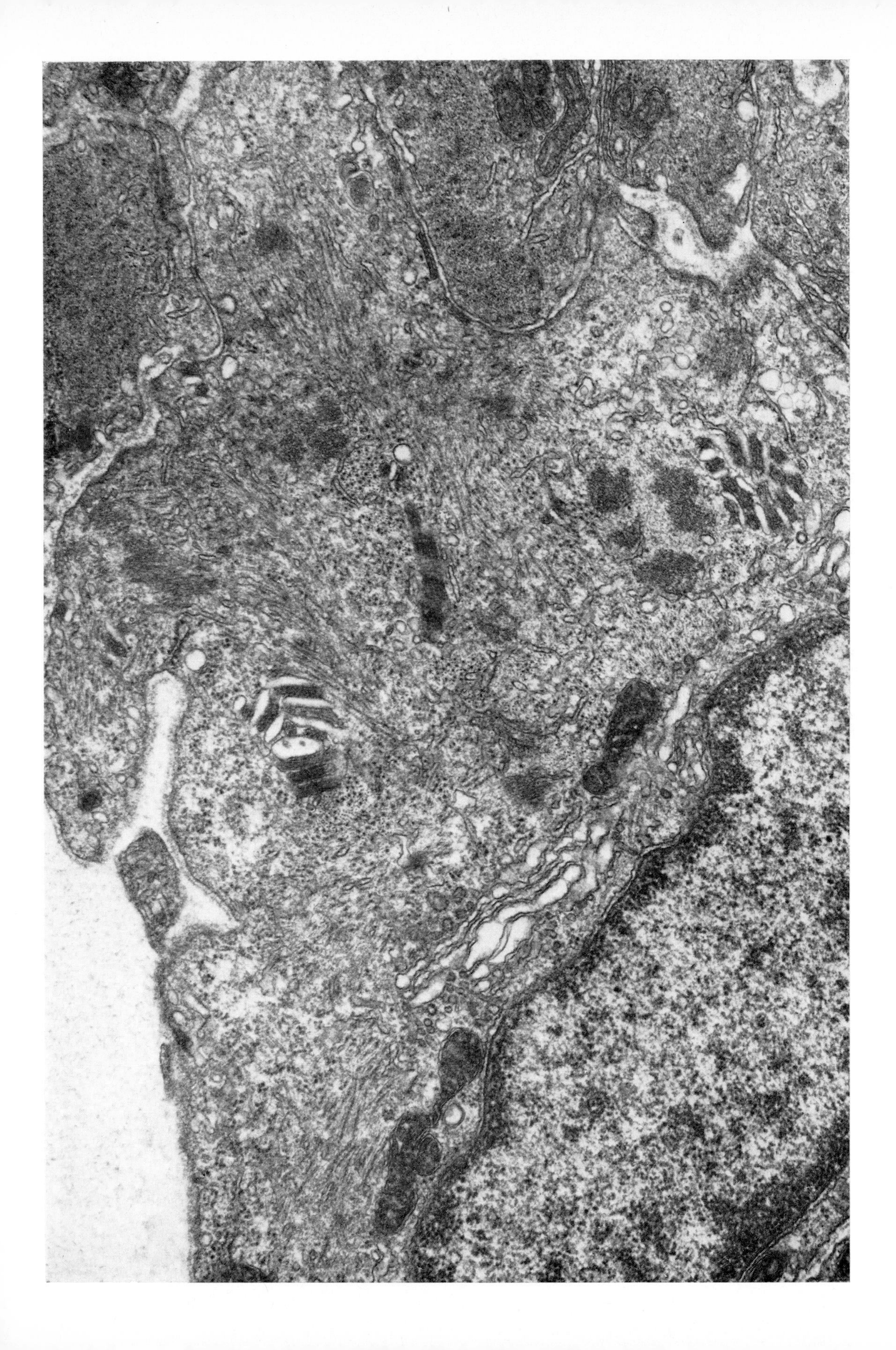

Selected articles

DAVIES, M. J., S. BALLANTINE, S. DARRACOTT and M. BRAIMBRIDGE. 1973. Nemaline bodies in the heart: anomalous Z bands with a periodic structure suggesting tropomyosin in human cardiac muscle biopsies. *Cardiovasc. Res.*, **7,** 408–411.

ENGEL, A. G. and M. R. GOMEZ. 1967. Nemaline (Z-disc) myopathy; observations on the origin, structure and solubility properties of the nemaline structures. *J. Neuropath. exp. Neurol.*, **26,** 601–619.

GABELLA, G. 1974. The sphincter pupillae of the guinea-pig: structure of muscle cells, intercellular relations and density of innervation. *Proc. R. Soc. Lond. Ser. B*, **186,** 369–386.

GONATAS, N. K. 1966. The fine structure of the rod-like bodies in nemaline myopathy and their relation to the Z-discs. *J. Neuropath. exp. Neurol.*, **25,** 409–421.

MACDONALD, R. D. and A. G. ENGEL. 1971. Observations on organisation of Z-disk components and on rod-bodies of Z-disk origin. *J. Cell Biol.*, **48,** 431–437.

PAGE, E. 1967. The occurrence of inclusions within membrane-limited structures that run longitudinally in the cells of mammalian heart muscle. *J. Ultrastruct. Res.*, **17,** 63–71.

4 Muscle Cell Surface

The muscle cell membrane (sarcolemma) is a selectively permeable barrier which separates the sarcoplasm within the cell from the extracellular fluid. Furthermore, it has permeability properties associated with excitability, and special regions for interaction with nerve and other cells. With the electron microscope the sarcolemma appears as a triple laminated structure, about 7·5 nm thick. A *basal lamina* (or basement membrane), composed largely of protein polysaccharide, is in association with the outer surface of the sarcolemma. Connective tissue elements such as collagen fibrils and elastic fibres are also associated with the muscle cell surface. Structural specializations of some muscle cell surfaces include inpocketings of the surface membrane (called plasmalemmal vesicles), cilia and desmosomes.

At least ten models have been proposed to explain both the properties and ultrastructural appearance of the unit membrane. The most widely accepted of these for many years was the Danielli–Davson model first presented in 1935. According to this hypothesis, the inner region or leaflet of the unit membrane is composed of a lipid bimolecular layer with the hydrophobic portions of the lipid molecule facing inwards. Protein in the extended β form is then attached to both of the lipid–aqueous interfaces to form the outer leaflets. Perhaps the most popular current model is that presented by Singer and Nicolson, the so called 'fluid mosaic membrane model', in which cell membranes are viewed as two-dimensional solutions of oriented globular proteins and lipids. The proteins are a heterogeneous set of globular molecules arranged with the ionic or polar groups protruding from the membrane and the nonpolar groups buried within the hydrophobic centre of the membrane (Fig. 18).

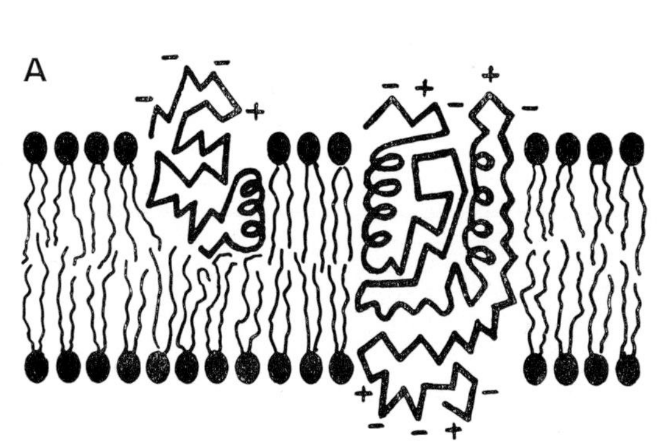

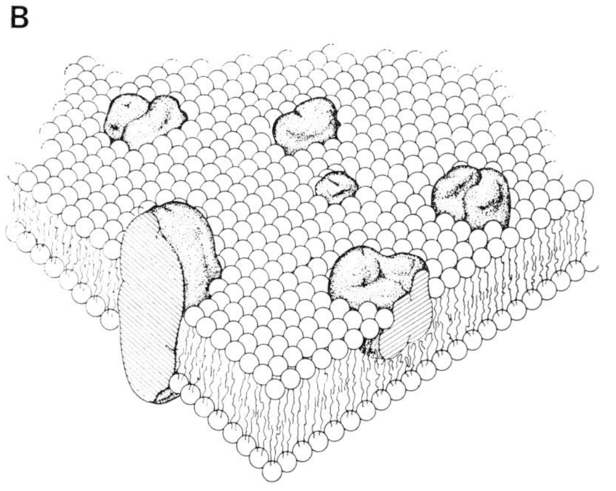

Fig. 18 The lipid-globular protein mosaic model with a lipid matrix ('the fluid mosaic model'). (Courtesy of S. J. Singer and G. L. Nicolson, 1972, *Science, N.Y.*, **175,** 720.)

A Cross-sectional view of lipid-globular protein mosaic model of membrane. The filled circles represent the ionic and polar heads of the phospholipid molecules and the wavy lines connected to these represent the fatty acid chains. The integral proteins, with the heavy lines representing the folded polypeptide chains, are shown as globular molecules partially embedded in, and partially protruding from, the membrane. The protruding parts have on their surfaces the ionic residues (— and +) of the protein, while the nonpolar residues are largely in the embedded parts.

B Three-dimensional and cross-sectional view of the lipid-globular protein mosaic model. The solid bodies with stippled surfaces represent the globular integral proteins embedded within the lipid matrix.

The selective permeability properties of the sarcolemma not only dictate what molecules can enter the muscle cell but determine specific ionic gradients which result in a potential difference across the membrane. The principle ions involved are K^+, Na^+, Ca^{2+} and Cl^-. According to the ionic hypothesis of Hodgkin, a resting potential across the muscle cell membrane is determined largely by the distribution of the ions to which it is most freely permeable, namely K^+ and Cl^-, according to the laws of Donnan equilibrium. However, an active membrane pump is also involved, the *sodium pump*, which maintains a concentration gradient of Na^+ (this is approximately 10 : 1 outside to inside in most muscles). To transport ions against an electrochemical gradient in this way, energy is required. This is provided in the form of ATP. It has been estimated that 10% of the resting metabolism of the frog skeletal muscle is used in the *active transport* of Na^+ across the sarcolemma. The resting potential for most vertebrate skeletal muscles is about 90–100 mV (inside negative), for cardiac muscle about 80–90 mV, while for vertebrate smooth muscle it varies between about 40 and 70 mV depending to some extent on whether the muscle is spontaneously active. The resting potential in most invertebrate muscles is lower than in vertebrates.

In skeletal muscles of the fast twitch type, in cardiac and in most smooth muscles, all-or-none action potentials are responsible for spread of excitation and for initiaion of excitation–contraction coupling. In most excitable tissues a special voltage-dependent sodium permeability change is responsible for the generation of the action potential (see Chapter 7A). During the action potential, there is a brief reversal of charge across the muscle membrane to about 30 mV positive inside. In many vertebrate smooth muscles and in crustacean muscles, the action potential is Ca^{2+} rather than Na^+ dependent.

In many slow-acting muscles, however, there are graded potentials which precede contractions. In some vascular smooth muscles, it has been suggested that the contractile system can be directly activated by neurohormones and other agents without involving changes in membrane potential (i.e. 'pharmaco-mechanical' coupling) as compared with the more traditional 'electro-mechanical' coupling.

Plate 93

The sarcolemma of the muscle fibre is surrounded by a *basal lamina* or basement membrane (Bm), which is associated with *collagen fibrils* (C) and *elastic fibres* (El). In contrast, *fibroblasts* (F), like most other motile cell types, do not appear to have a basal lamina.

The thickness of the basal lamina is very variable (20–80 nm) and composed of moderately dense material with a fine filamentous texture. The basal lamina is separated from the sarcolemma by an electron transparent layer, 20–40 nm thick. The word basement membrane is derived from light microscopy and is not strictly correct at the ultrastructural level since it is not a true membrane.

The collagen fibrils which are associated with the basal lamina are 20–100 nm in diameter with a cross striated repeating pattern of about 65 nm. Elastin has a coarse structure, comprising individual fibres up to 44 μm in length and 3–5 μm in diameter. It consists of outer fibrillar and inner amorphous components.

Cell surface of vertebrate skeletal muscle: chicken latissimus dorsi muscle. Glutaraldehyde fixati on. ×91 000.

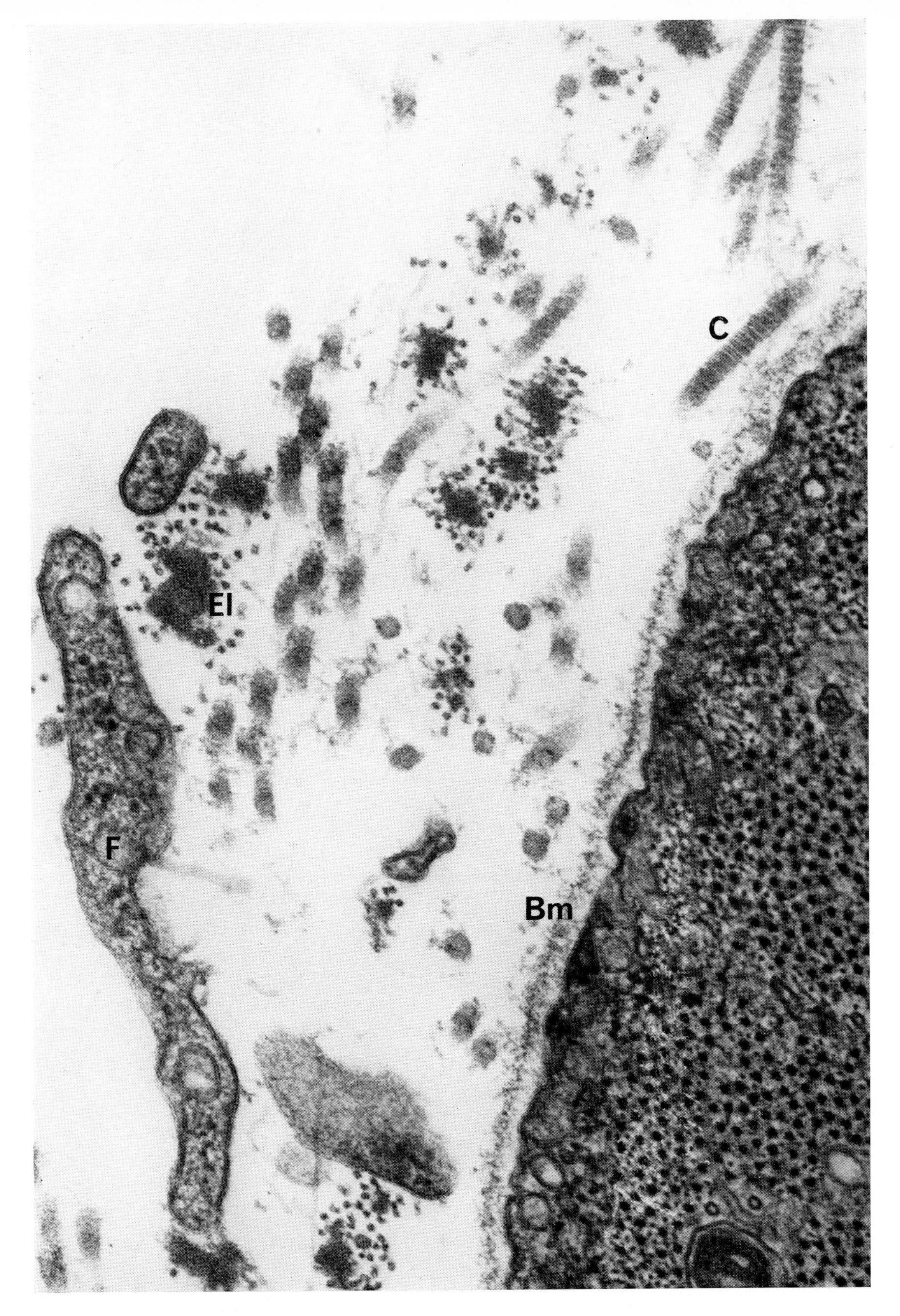
C
El
F
Bm

Plate 94

Some areas of muscle membranes are specialized to form semi-desmosomes (arrows). As the name implies a semi-desmosome (or hemi-desmosome) is half a desmosome. Consequently it has a similar structure to the desmosome (see Plate 109) except that one side is represented by a thickened basal lamina. Fine filaments are often seen to be embedded in the basal lamina at the site of the semi-desmosome. This appears to act as an attachment point of muscle fibres with surrounding connective tissue, providing adhesive strength.

Semi-desmosome in an invertebrate visceral obliquely striated muscle: earthworm intestine. Transverse section. Glutaraldehyde fixation. ×129 000.

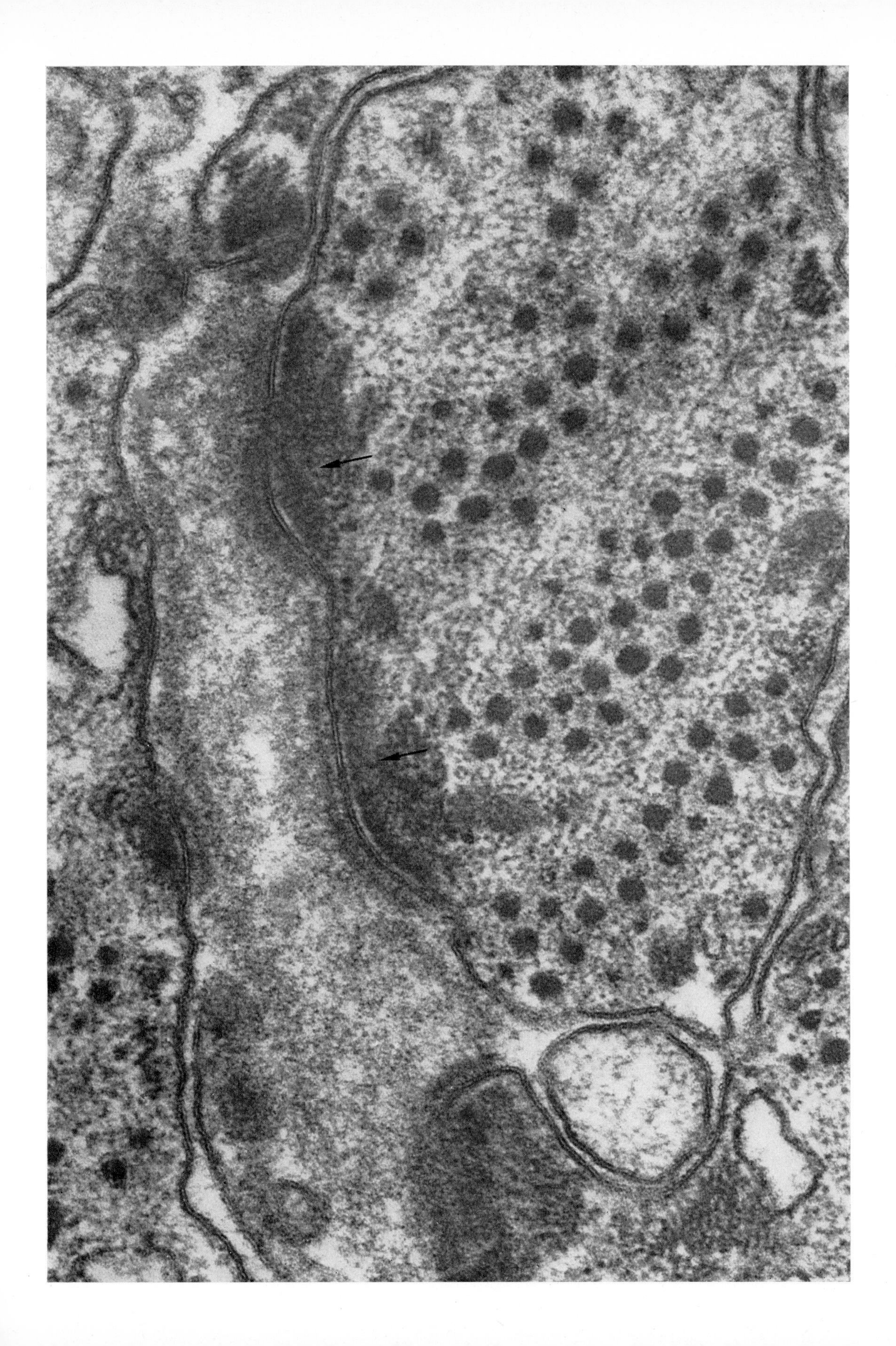

Plate 95

Plasmalemmal vesicles (micropinocytotic vesicles, caveolae intracellulares or surface vesicles) are about 70 × 250 nm in diameter, with a constricted neck opening to the extracellular space. There is often a band of electron dense material about 5–10 nm wide encircling the neck. (See also Plates 64 and 96.)

Plasmalemmal vesicles are a particularly prominent feature of smooth muscle but vary in number from tissue to tissue. They are usually grouped to form longitudinal rows, separated from each other by 'dense areas', which may be attachment sites for myofilaments, and/or 100 Å filaments.

The freeze-etch technique has been used to demonstrate the details of the arrangement of plasmalemmal vesicles in different smooth muscles.

Although the smooth-surface micropinocytotic vesicles of capillary endothelium function in the transport of material (a process which has been called *cytopempsis*), the plasmalemmal vesicles of smooth muscle, although remarkably similar in appearance, do not appear to have the same function. It has been suggested that they are sites for binding of various ions such as Na^+, K^+ and Ca^{2+}.

Plasmalemmal vesicles in vertebrate smooth muscle: guinea-pig iris. Glutaraldehyde fixation. ×118 000.

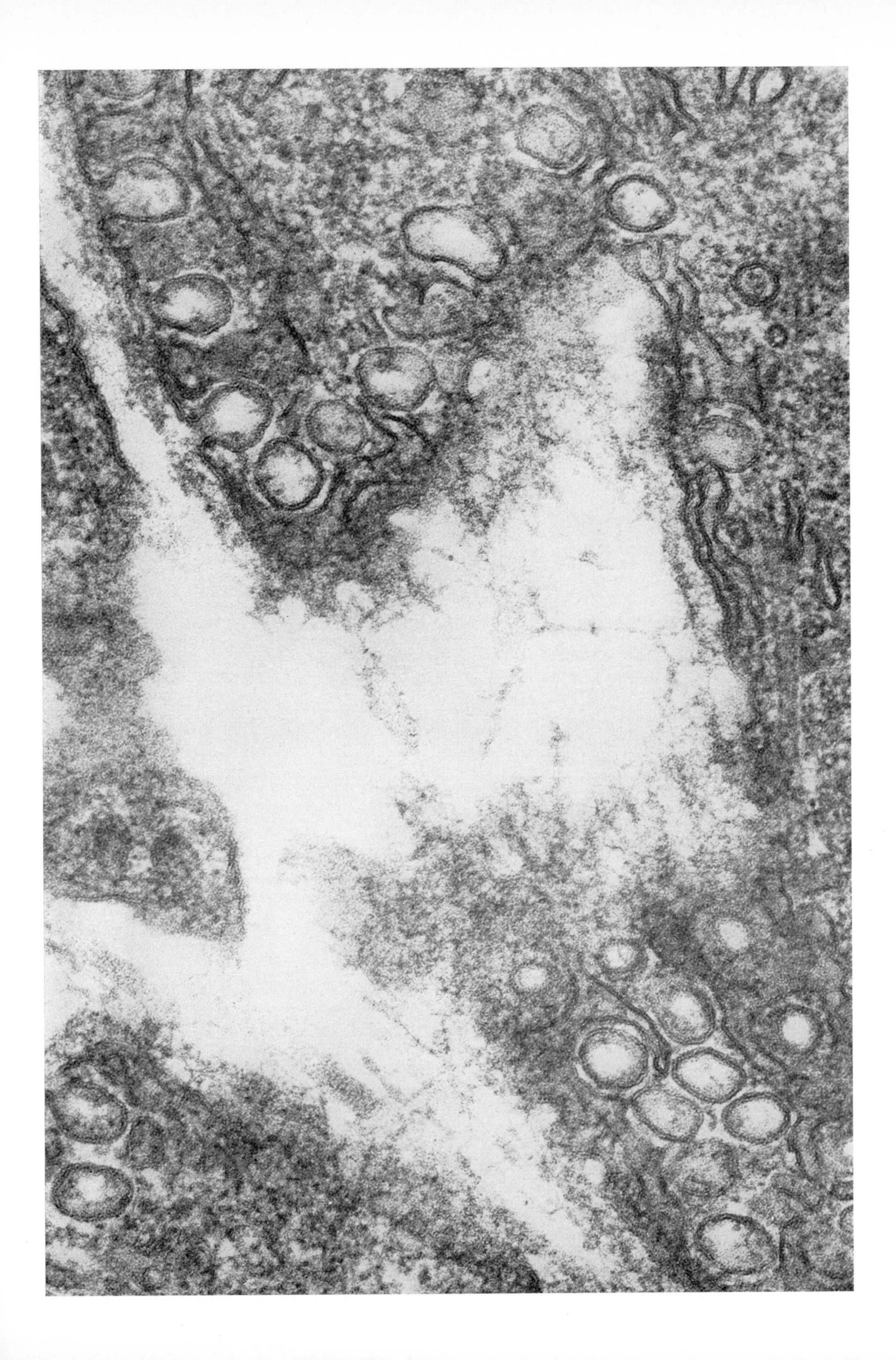

Plate 96

(*a*) Transverse section through a smooth muscle cell of the guinea-pig iris demonstrating the presence of plasmalemmal vesicles (P) and their association with the sarcotubular system (SR). The close proximity of the two organelles has led to speculation that they are involved in a similar system to that which is present in skeletal muscle concerned with excitation–contraction coupling; the plasmalemmal vesicles being considered equivalent to the T-tubules (see Chapter 2E and Plate 62).

(*b*) Section through a smooth muscle cell from the new born guinea-pig vas deferens 10 days in culture showing the association of a number of plasmalemmal vesicles (P) with an intrusion of the plasma membrane.

Relationship of plasmalemmal vesicles to sarcotubular. system in vertebrate smooth muscle: (*a*) guinea-pig iris; (*b*) new-born guinea-pig vas deferens, 10 days in culture. Glutaraldehyde fixation. (*a*) ×88 000; (*b*) ×148 000.

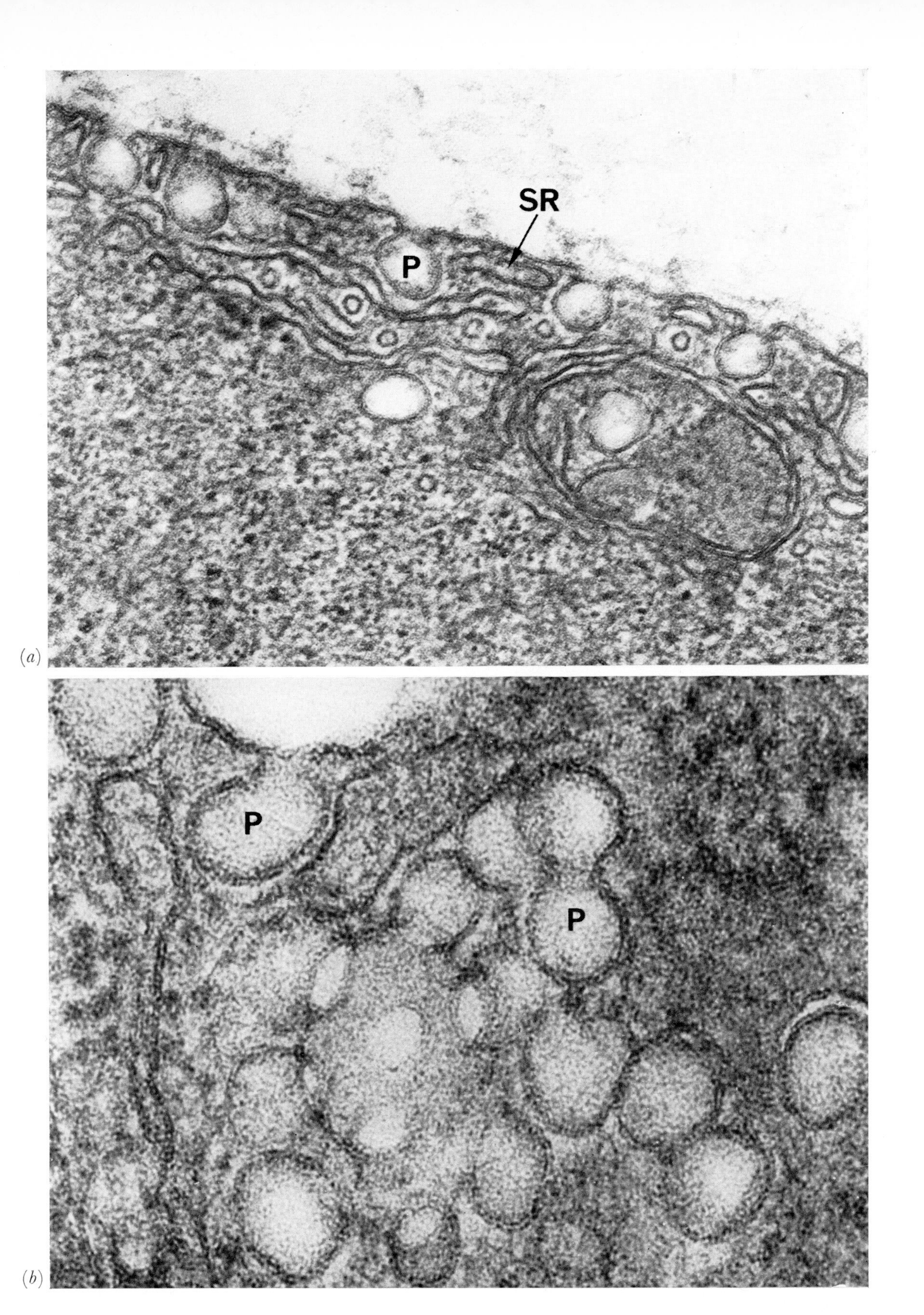
SR
P
(a)
P
P
(b)

Plate 97

Specialized vesicles, called 'coated vesicles', are characterized by the presence of an organized layer of material on the outside in the form of spherical polygonal basket work. They have been described variously as complex, bristle-coated, alveolate, dense-rimmed or 'vesicle in a basket'. Two major types of coated vesicles have been distinguished in epithelial cells. One type 100 nm or more in diameter is formed at the surface by pinocytotic invagination of the cell membrane (illustrated in smooth muscle in (*a*); the other type is 75 nm in diameter (illustrated in smooth muscle in (*b*)) and originates from the Golgi cisternae. The larger type is involved in protein uptake and transport and some of the smaller type have been shown to transport acid phosphatase. The coating about the vesicles has been suggested to play a role in the mechanism of infolding and fission of the membrane caused by the transformation of the regular hexagons of the coating into regular pentagons.

Coated vesicles in vertebrate smooth muscle: guinea-pig ureter.

(*a*) Longitudinal section demonstrating the association of two coated vesicles to the plasma membrane.

(*b*) High power electronmicrograph of a coated vesicle inside a smooth muscle cell.

Glutaraldehyde fixation. (*a*) ×123 000; (*b*) ×352 000.

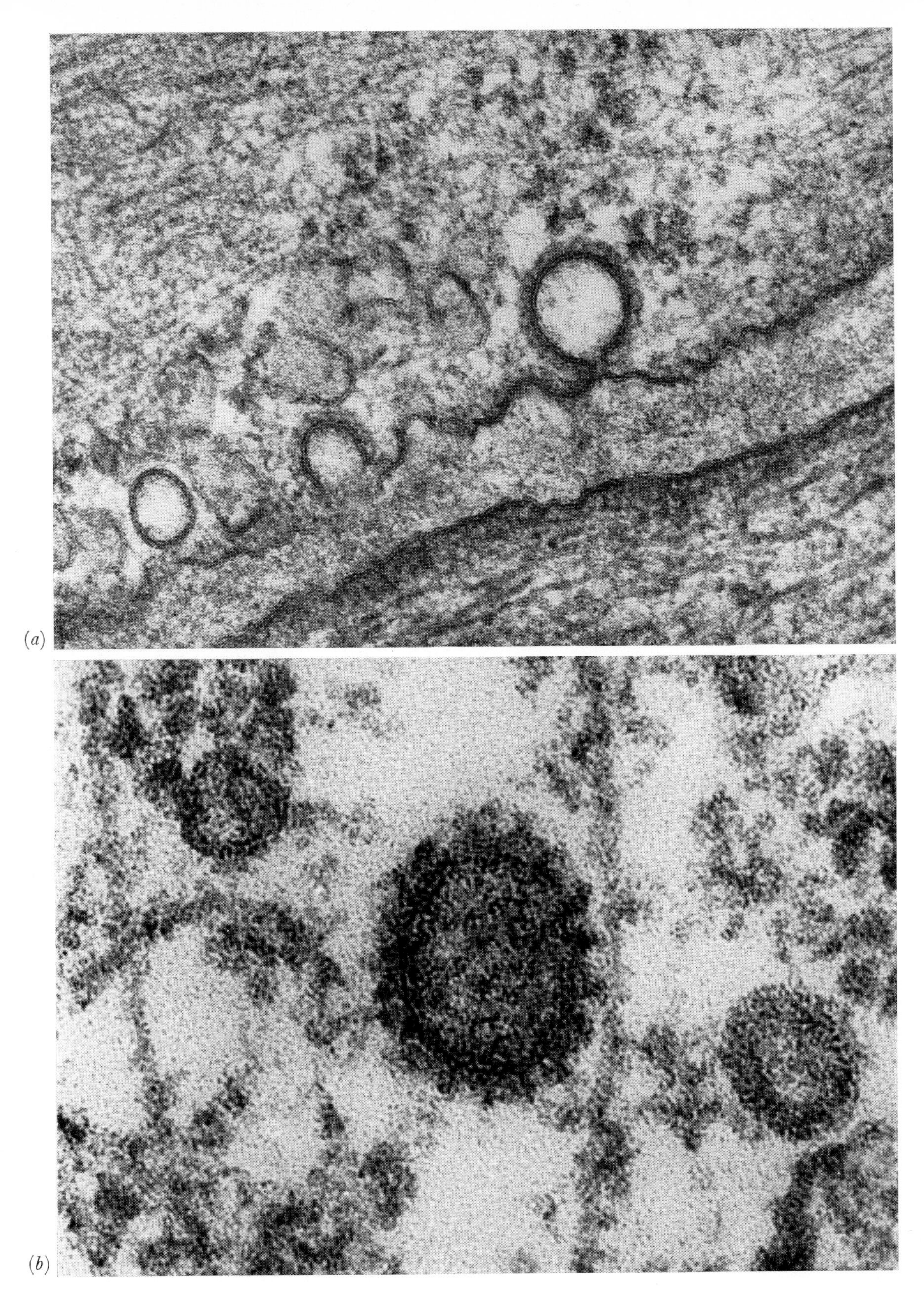
(a)
(b)

Plate 98

Cilia are conspicuous surface specializations in many cell types, including smooth muscle. The cilium, illustrated in longitudinal section, measures from 3–10 μm in length and about 250 nm in diameter and is an elongated cytoplasmic extension covered by an apical surface membrane. It originates from the basal body, a structure which closely resembles the centriole from which it, in turn, is derived. The basal body appears to provide stability for the cilium through dense *satellites* (arrows), attached to the outside. These in turn are interconnected by microtubules, which may control and coordinate ciliary activity. Another basal body is usually associated with the primary one, but its function is unknown.

Cilium in vertebrate smooth muscle: 10-day chicken gizzard, 4 days in culture. Longitudinal section. Glutaraldehyde fixation. ×149 300.

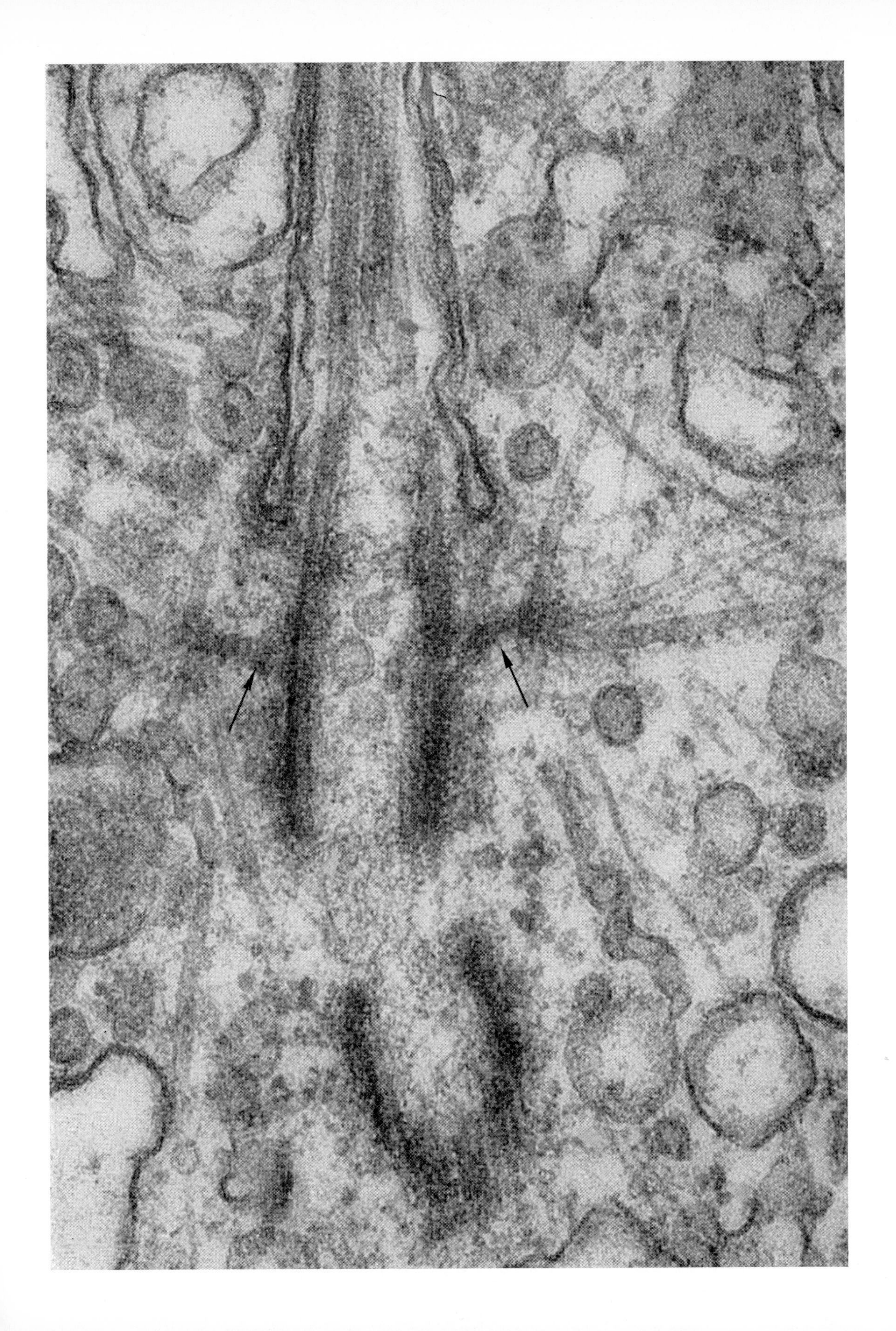

Plate 99

Cilia are cylindrical structures containing a complex array of filaments orientated longitudinally, called the *axial filament complex*. In the transverse section through the tip of a cilium illustrated, each outer fibre appears as a doublet (two joined tubules) with a figure eight configuration and bears two projections or arms that extend towards an adjacent outer fibre. Nine of these are usually evenly spaced around the periphery. In the centre there are two separate tubules, each about 24 nm in diameter. These provide the characteristic 9 + 2 pattern. However, in the cilium illustrated the centre tubules appear to be absent and the nine doublets have become rearranged. It is characteristic of the end part of a cilium that filaments are lost successively as the tip is reached. The ciliary filaments themselves do not change length as the cilium beats, but move past each other to allow the cilium to curve.

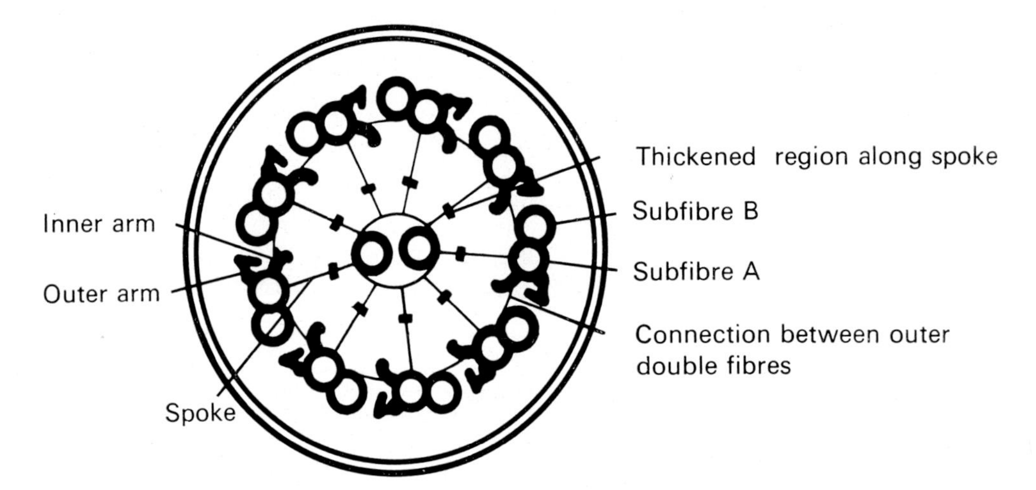

Fig. 19 Diagram of a cross section of a cilium (Courtesy of R. D. Allan, 1968, *J. Cell Biol.*, **37**, 825.)

Cilium in vertebrate smooth muscle: guinea-pig iris. Transverse section. Glutaraldehyde fixation. ×86 200.

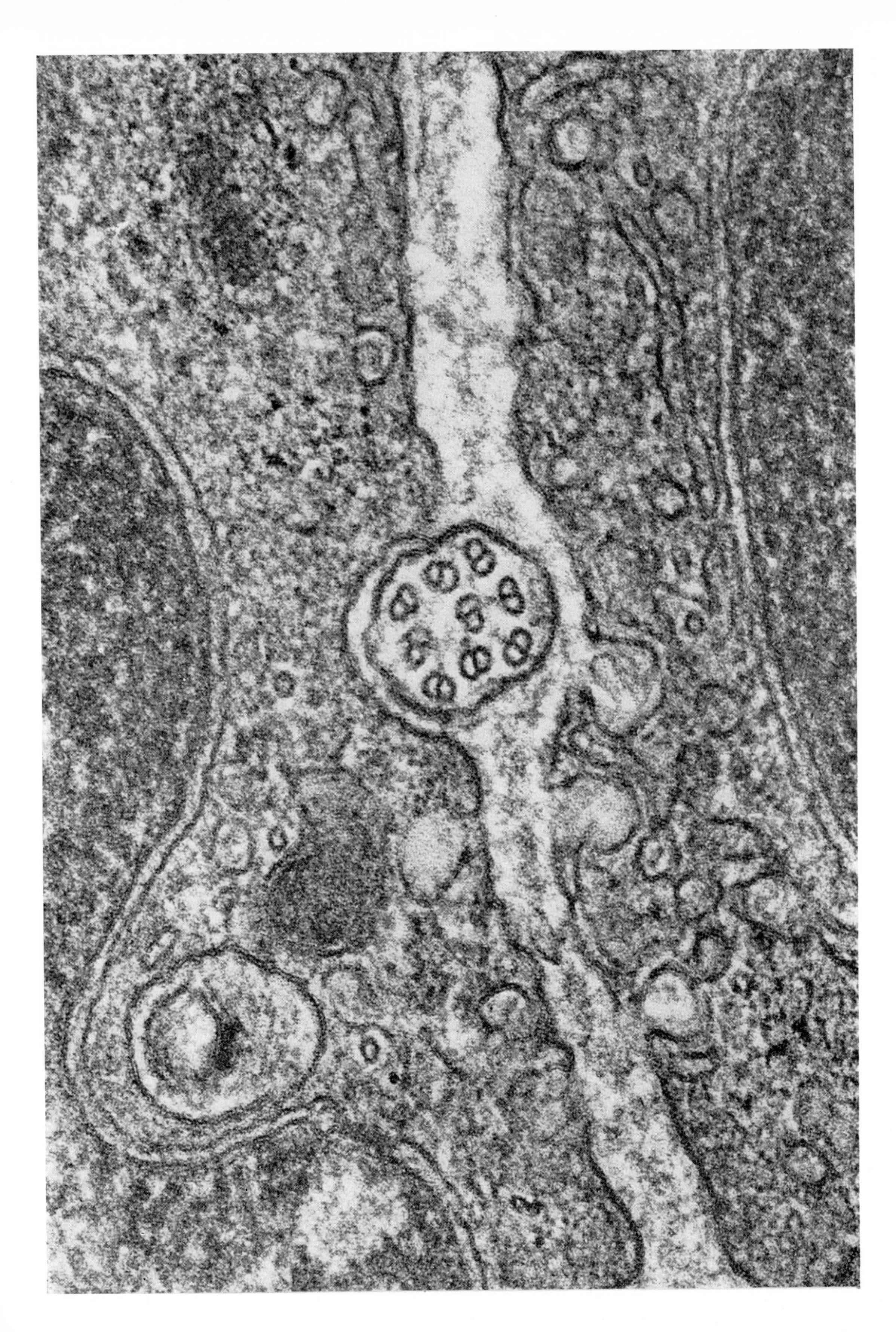

Plate 100

Interesting surface specializations of invertebrate muscle cells are the finger-like cellular projections illustrated here in earthworm visceral muscle cells. These projections are 40–100 nm in diameter, often exceed several micrometres in length and do not contain myofilaments. They extend from the cell body to interdigitate with similar processes from nearby chloragogen or yellow cells whose physiological role is suggested to be analogous to the liver of vertebrates.

Surface projections in an invertebrate visceral obliquely striated muscle: earthworm intestine. Transverse section. Glutaraldehyde fixation. ×35 000.

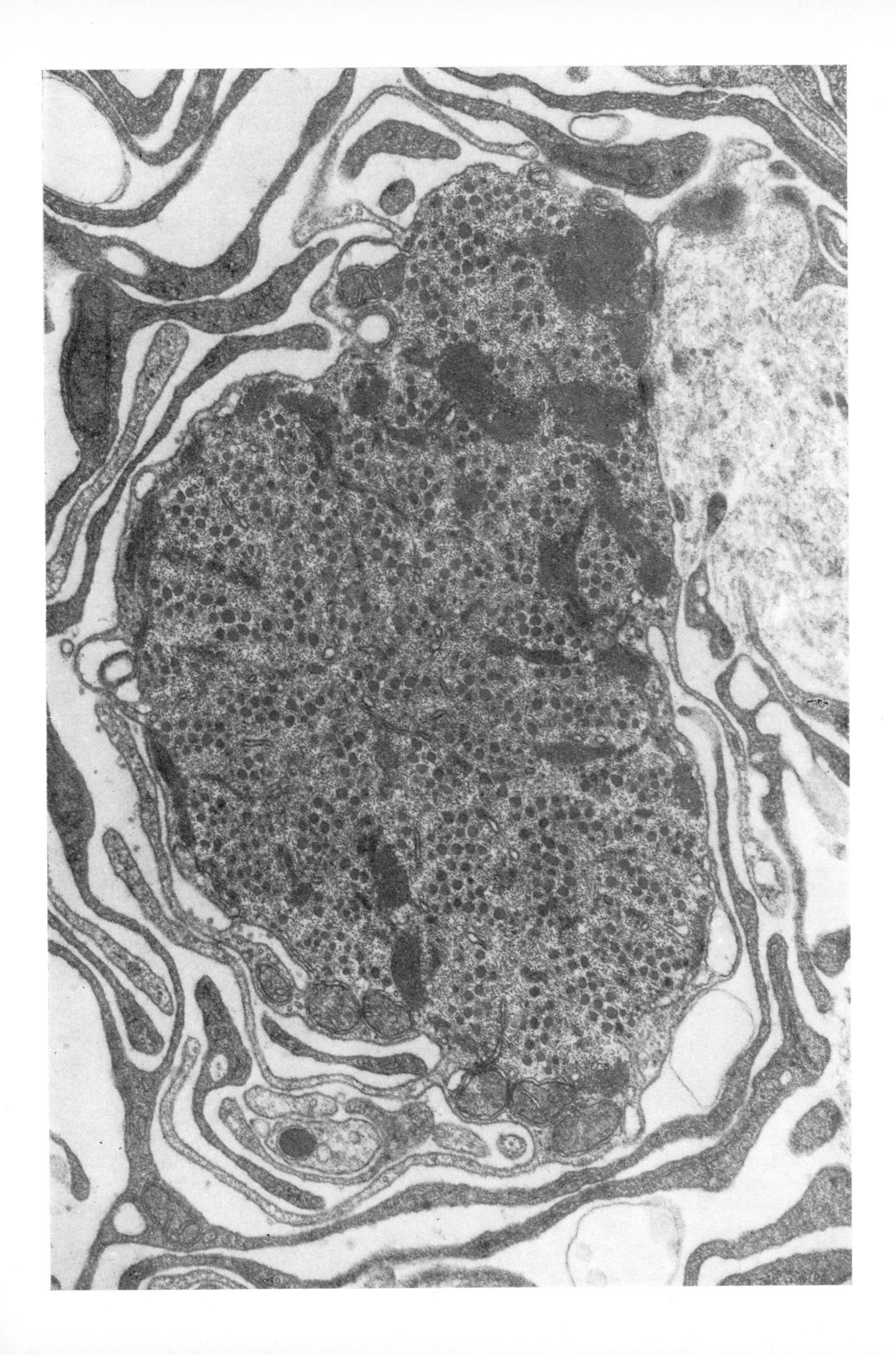

Selected reviews

ADELMAN, W. J. 1971. *Biophysics and Physiology of Excitable Membranes.* Van Nostrand Reinhold, New York.

AVERY, J. (ed.). 1973. *Membrane Structure and Mechanisms of Biological Energy Transduction.* Plenum Press, N.Y.

BOLIS, L., A. KATCHALSKY, R. D. KEGNES, W. R. LOWENSTEIN AND B. PETHICA (eds.). 1970. *Permeability and Function of Biological Membranes.* North-Holland, Amsterdam.

BOLIS, L. and B. A. PETHICA (eds.). 1968. *Membrane Models and the Formation of Biological Membranes.* John Wiley, New York.

CAPALDI, R. A. 1974. A dynamic model of cell membranes. *Scient. Am.*, **230,** 26–33.

CHANCE, B. (ed.). 1971. *Probes of Structure and Function of Macromolecules and Membranes.* 2 vols. Academic Press, New York.

CHAPMAN, D. (ed.). 1968. *Biological Membranes, Physical Fact and Function.* Academic Press, New York.

COLE, K. S. 1968. *Membranes, Ions and Impulses. A chapter of classical biophysics.* University of California Press, Berkeley.

DEWEY, M. M. and L. BARR. 1970. Some considerations about the structure of cellular membranes. In *Current Topics in Membranes and Transport.* Vol. 1. F. Bonner and A. Kleinzeller (eds.). Academic Press, New York. 1–33.

DOWBEN, R. M. (ed.). 1969. *Biological Membranes.* Little, Brown, Boston.

FOX, C. F. and A. D. KEITH. 1972. *Membrane Molecular Biology.* Sinauer, Stanford Connecticut.

GREEN, D. E. (ed.). 1972. Membrane structure and its biological applications. *Ann. N.Y. Acad. Sci.*, **195,** 5–519.

HARRIS, E. J. 1972. *Transport and Accumulation in Biological Systems.* 3rd ed. Butterworths, London.

HENDLER, R. W. 1971. Biological membrane ultrastructure. *Physiol. Rev.*, **51,** 66–97.

HOLWILL, N. 1967. Contractile mechanisms in cilia and flagella. In *Current Topics in Bioenergetics.* Vol. 2. D. R. Sanadi (ed.). Academic Press, New York. 287–333.

HÖLZL WOLLACH, D. F. and H. FISCHER (eds.). 1971. *The Dynamic Structure of Cell Membranes.* Springer-Verlag, Berlin.

HOPE, A. B. 1971. *Ion Transport and Membranes. A Biophysical Outline.* Butterworths, London.

HUBBERT, W. T. and W. J. MILLER 1974. Immunogenetic ontogeny of cellular membrane function: A review. *J. cell. Physiol.* **84,** 429–444.

JOHNSTON, P. V. and B. I. ROOTH. 1972. *Nerve Membranes.* International series of monographs in pure and applied biology. Zoology Division. Vol. 36. Pergamon Press, Oxford.

KAPLAN, D. M. and R. S. CRIDDLE. 1971. Membrane structural proteins. *Physiol. Rev.* **51,** 249–272.

KEFALIDES, N. S. 1973. Structure and biosynthesis of basement membranes. *Int. Rev. Conn. Tiss. Res.*, **6,** 63–104.

KORN, E. D. 1969. Cell membranes: structure and syntheses. *A. Rev. Biochem.*, **38,** 263–288.

LAKSHMINARAYANAIAH, N. 1969. *Transport phenomena in membranes.* Academic Press, New York.

MANSON, L. A. (ed.). 1971–1972. *Biomembranes.* 3 vols. Plenum Press, New York.

O'BRIEN, J. S. 1967. Cell membranes—composition: structure, function. *J. theor. Biol.*, **15,** 307–324.

RICHTER, G. W. and D. G. SCARPELLI (eds.). 1971. *Cell membranes. Biological and pathological aspects.* Williams & Wilkins, Baltimore.

ROSS, R. 1973. The elastic fiber. A review. *J. Histochem. Cytochem.*, **21,** 199–208.

ROTHFIELD, L. I. 1971. *Structure and function of biological membranes.* Academic Press, New York.

SCHMITT, F. O. (ed.). 1970. *Neurosciences: Second Study Program.* Rockefeller Univ. Press, New York.

SINGER, S. J. and G. L. NICOLSON, 1972. The fluid mosaic model of the structure of cell membranes. *Science, N.Y.*, **175,** 720–731.

STOECKENIUS, W. and D. M. ENGELMAN. 1969. Current models for the structure of biological membranes. *J. Cell Biol.*, **42,** 613–646.

TOSTESON, D. C. (ed.). 1969. *The molecular basis of membrane function.* Prentice-Hall, New Jersey.

VANDERKOOI, G. and D. E. GREEN. 1970. Biological membrane structures: I. The protein crystal model for membranes. *Proc. natn. Acad. Sci. U.S.A.*, **66,** 615–621.

VRACKO, R. 1974. Basal lamina scaffold—Anatomy and significance for maintenance of orderly tissue structure. *Am. J. Path.*, **77,** 314–346.

Selected articles

ALBERT, E. N. 1973. A combined fluorescent and electron microscopic stain for elastic tissue. *Histochem. J.*, **5,** 157–167.

ALLEN, R. D. 1968. A reinvestigation of cross-sections of cilia. *J. Cell Biol.*, **37,** 825–830.

ANDERSON, R. G. W. 1972. The three-dimensional structure of the basal body from the rhesus monkey oviduct. *J. Cell Biol.*, **54,** 246–265.

BACCETTI, B. 1967. Collagen of the earthworms. *J. Cell Biol.*, **34,** 885–890.

BANFIELD, W. G., C. K. LEE and C. W. LEE. 1973. Myocardial collagen of the fibrous long-spacing type. *Archs Path.*, **95,** 262–266.

BENEDETTI, E. L. and P. EMMELOT. 1965. Electron microscopic observations on negatively stained plasma membranes isolated from rat liver. *J. Cell Biol.*, **26,** 299–304.

BOUTEILLE, M. and D. C. PEASE. 1971. The tridimensional structure of native collagenous fibrils, their proteinaceous filaments. *J. Ultrastruct. Res.*, **35,** 314–338.

BRETSCHER, M. S. 1973. Membrane structure: Some general principles. *Science, N.Y.*, **181,** 622–629.

CALLEJA, G. B. and G. T. REYNOLDS. 1970. Experimental demonstration of ATP on the muscle cell surface. *Revue can. Biol.*, **29,** 395–398.

CASLEY-SMITH, J. R. 1971. The passage of cytoplasmic vesicles across endothelial and mesothelial cells. *J. Microsc. (Oxf.)*, **93,** 167–189.

CARROLL, P. M. and D. D. SEREDA. 1968. Cell membrane of uterine smooth muscle. *Nature, Lond.*, **217,** 666–667.

CLARA, M. 1961. Was ist das Sarkolemm? *Anat. Anz.*, **110,** 41–51.

DAVSON, H. and J. F. DANIELLI. 1952. *The permeability of natural membranes.* 2nd ed. Cambridge Univ. Press, Cambridge.

DePIERRE, J. W. and M. L. KARNOVSKY. 1973. Plasma membranes of mammalian cells. A review of methods for their characterization and isolation. *J. Cell Biol.*, **56,** 275–303.

FERNANDEZ-MORAN, H. 1962. Cell-membrane ultrastructure. Low temperature electron microscope and X-ray diffraction studies of lipoprotein components in lamellar systems. *Circulation*, **26,** 1039–1065.

FONTE, V. G., R. L. SEARLS and S. R. HILFER. 1971. The relationship of cilia with cell division and differentiation. *J. Cell Biol.*, **49,** 226–228.

FRASER, R. D. B., A. MILLER and D. A. D. PARRY, 1974. Packing of microfibrils in collagen. *J. molec. Biol.*, **83,** 281–284.

FRIEND, D. S. and M. G. FARQUHAR. 1967. Functions of coated vesicles during protein absorption in the rat vas deferens. *J. Cell Biol.*, **35,** 357–376.

FRIEND, D. S. and D. W. FAWCETT 1974. Membrane differentiations in freeze-fractured mammalian sperm. *J. Cell Biol.*, **63,** 641–664.

GRAY, E. G. 1972. Are the coats of coated vesicles artefacts? *J. Neurocytol.*, **1,** 363–382.

HARVEN, E. DE and W. BERNHARD. 1956. Étude au microscope électronique de l'ultrastructure du centriole chez les vertébrés. *Z. Zellforsch. mikrosk. Anat.*, **45,** 378–398.

HOLTER, H. 1961. Pinocytosis. In *Biological structure and function.* Vol. 1. T. W. Goodwin and O. Lindberg (eds.). Academic Press, New York. 157–168.

KANASEKI, T. and K. KADOTA. 1969. The 'vesicle in a basket'. A morphological study of the coated vesicle isolated from the nerve endings of the guinea pig brain, with special reference to the mechanism of membrane movements. *J. Cell Biol.*, **42,** 202–220.

KARNOVSKY, M. J. and S. M. SHEA. 1970. Transcapillary transport by pinocytosis. *Microvasc. Res.*, **2,** 353–360.

KIDWAI, A. M., M. A. RADCLIFFE and E. E. DANIEL. 1971. Studies on smooth muscle plasma membrane. I. Isolation and characterization of plasma membrane from rat myometrium. *Biochim. biophys. Acta.*, **233,** 538–549.

KONO, T., F. KAKUMA, M. HOMMA and S. FUKUDA. 1964. The electron-microscopic structure and chemical composition of the isolated sarcolemma of the rat skeletal muscle cell. *Biochem. biophys. Acta.*, **88,** 155–176.

LAGUENS, R. 1964. Ciliated smooth muscle cells in the uterus of the rat. *Experientia*, **20,** 322–323.

LANDIS, E. M. and J. R. PAPPENHEIMER. 1963. Exchange of substance through the capillary walls. In *Handbook of Physiology*, Section 2, *Circulation*, Vol. 2. W. F. Hamilton (ed.). American Physiological Society, Washington. 961–1034.

LING, G. N. 1966. Cell membrane and cell permeability. *Ann. N.Y. Acad. Sci.*, **137,** 837–859.

LOW, F. N. 1967. Developing boundary (basement) membranes in the chick embryo. *Anat. Rec.*, **159,** 231–238.

MAURO, A. and W. R. ADAMS. 1961. The structure of the sarcolemma of the frog skeletal muscle fiber. *J. biophys. biochem. Cytol.*, **10,** Suppl., 177–185.

MAYERSON, H. S., C. G. WOLFRAM, H. H. SHIRLEY, JR. and K. WASSERMAN. 1960. Regional differences in capillary permeability. *Am. J. Physiol.*, **198,** 155–160.

MOVAT, H. Z. and N. V. P. FERNANDO. 1962. The fine structure of connective tissue. I. The fibroblast. *Exp. Mol. Pathol.*, **1,** 509–534.

MYERS, D. B., T. C. HIGHTON and D. G. RAYNS. 1973. Ruthenium red-positive filaments interconnecting collagen fibrils. *J. Ultrastruct. Res.*, **42,** 87–92.

PALADE, G. E. and R. R. BRUNS. 1968. Structural modifications of plasmalemmal vesicles. *J. Cell Biol.*, **37,** 633–649.

PAPPENHEIMER, J. R. 1953. Passage of molecules through capillary walls. *Physiol. Rev.*, **33,** 387–423.

PAPPENHEIMER, J. R., E. M. RENKIN and L. M. BORRERO. 1951. Filtration, diffusion and molecular sieving through peripheral capillary membranes. A contribution to the pore theory of capillary permeability. *Am. J. Physiol.*, **167,** 13–46.

PIERCE, G. B. 1966. The development of basement membranes of the mouse embryo. *Devl Biol.*, **13,** 231–249.

PINTO DA SILVA, P. and D. BRANTON. 1970. Membrane splitting in freeze-etching. Covalently bound ferritin as a membrane marker. *J. Cell Biol.*, **45,** 598–605.

POOLE, J. C. F., S. B. CROMWELL and E. D. BENDITT. 1971. Behaviour of smooth muscle cells and formation of extracellular structures in the reaction of arterial walls to injury. *Am. J. Path.*, **62,** 391–413.

PROSSER, C. L., G. BURNSTOCK and J. KAHN. 1960. Conduction in smooth muscle; comparative structural properties. *Am. J. Physiol.*, **199,** 545–552.

RAPOPORT, S. I. 1972. Mechanical properties of the sarcolemma and myoplasm in frog muscle as a function of sarcomere length. *J. gen. Physiol.*, **59,** 559–585.

RASH, J. E., J. W. SHAY and J. J. BIESELE. 1969. Cilia in cardiac differentiation. *J. Ultrastruct. Res.*, **29,** 470–484.

RAYNS, D. G., F. O. SIMPSON and W. S. BERTAUD. 1968. Surface features of striated muscle. II. Guinea-pig skeletal muscle. *J. Cell Sci.*, **3,** 475–482.

REED, R., T. W. HOUSTON and P. M. TODD. 1966. Structure and function of the sarcolemma of skeletal muscle. *Nature, Lond.*, **211,** 534–536.

RENKIN, E. M. 1964. Transport of large molecules across capillary walls. *Physiologist, Wash.*, **7,** 13–28.

SANTOS-BUCH, C. A. 1966. Extrusion of ATPase activity from pinocytotic vesicles of abutting endothelium and smooth muscle to the internal elastic membrane of the major arterial circle of the iris of rabbits. *Nature, Lond.*, **211,** 600–602.

SATIR, P. 1965. Studies on cilia. II. Examination of the distal region of the ciliary shaft and the role of the filaments in motility. *J. Cell Biol.*, **26,** 805–834.

SCHRODT, G. R. and S. M. WALKER. 1966. Ultrastructure of membranes in denervation atrophy. *Am. J. Path.*, **49,** 33–51.

SCOTT, R. E., L. T. FURCHT and R. E. BARNETT. 1974. Modulation of membrane structure and control of proliferation in normal and transformed cells. *Am. J. Path.*, **74,** 63a–64a.

SHEA, S. M. and M. J. KARNOVSKY. 1966. Brownian motion: a theoretical explanation for the movement of vesicles across the endothelium. *Nature, Lond.*, **212,** 353–355.

SHEA, S. M., M. J. KARNOVSKY and W. H. BOSSERT. 1969. Vesicular transport across endothelium: simulation of a diffusion model. *J. Theor. Biol.*, **24,** 30–42.

SMITH, D. S. and H. C. ALDRICH. 1971. Membrane systems of freeze-etched striated muscle. *Tissue & Cell*, **3,** 261–281.

SOROKIN, S. 1962. Centrioles and the formation of rudimentary cilia by fibroblasts and smooth muscle cells. *J. Cell Biol.*, **15,** 363–377.

VERGARA, J., W. LONGLEY and J. D. ROBERTSON. 1969. A hexagonal arrangement of subunits in membrane of mouse urinary bladder. *J. molec. Biol.*, **46,** 593–596.

VRACKO, R. and E. P. BENDITT. 1970. Capillary basal lamina thickening. Its relationship to endothelial cell death and replacement. *J. Cell Biol.*, **47,** 281–285.

VRACKO, R. and E. P. BENDITT. 1972. Basal lamina: the scaffold for orderly cell replacement. Observations on regeneration of injured skeletal muscle fibers and capillaries. *J. Cell Biol.*, **55,** 406–419.

WARNER, F. D. and P. SATIR. 1973. The substructure of ciliary microtubules. *J. Cell Sci.*, **12,** 313–326.

WHEATLEY, D. N. 1971. Cilia in cell-cultured fibroblasts. III. Relationship between mitotic activity and cilium frequency in mouse 3T6 fibroblasts. *J. Anat.*, **110,** 367–382.

YAMAMOTO, T. 1963. On the thickness of the unit membrane. *J. Cell Biol.*, **17,** 413–422.

ZACKS, S. I., M. F. SHEFF and A. SAITO. 1973. Structure and staining characteristics of myofiber external lamina. *J. Histochem. Cytochem.*, **21,** 703–714.

5 Muscle Attachment Sites

By far the most common attachment site for skeletal muscle is the tendon; other attachment sites include aponeurosis, periosteum, dermis and almost any kind of dense connective tissue structure within the body.

The muscle tendon junction of striated muscle is characterized by a number of deep indentations of the sarcolemma between the myofibrils. The sarcolemma is covered externally by a basal lamina approximately 30 nm thick. Collagen fibrils approach the sarcolemma and attach to the outer aspect of the basal lamina, many extending deeply into the clefts and invaginations to do so. Microfilaments, 10–20 nm diameter, attach to the sarcolemma and run across the basal lamina into a glycoprotein cementing substance between the collagen fibres of the tendon. Thus the function of the microfilaments is apparently to transmit force from actin filaments (which insert on the inner surface of the sarcolemma), to the collagen fibres of the tendon.

It has been suggested that in skeletal muscle several fibres interdigitate within the length of the muscle between the tendons of origin and insertion. However, the majority of fibres extend the whole length of the muscle, sometimes being up to 34 cm in length. Smooth muscle cells are rarely longer than 0·5 mm and several cells interdigitate with each other in the walls of visceral organs. A similar method of anchorage of one cell to another via connective tissue elements may occur in these situations since the tips of cells are again surrounded by a thick basal lamina with associated microfilaments.

In visceral organs, the attachment sites for muscle, whether striated (as in arthropods) or smooth muscle (as in vertebrates), are not tendons, although these structures do have some features in common with them.

Plate 101

In the striated muscle–tendon junction, thin actin filaments emerge from the myofibrils (containing both thick and thin myofilaments) into the finger-like projections at the end of the muscle fibre. These terminate in an electron-dense material along the sarcolemma. Collagen fibrils (C) approach the sarcolemma and attach to the outer aspect of the basal lamina (Bm), many extending deeply into the clefts to do so. Microfilaments (double headed arrow) extend from the sarcolemma to a cementing substance amongst the collagen fibres.

Muscle–tendon junction in vertebrate striated muscle: guinea-pig diaphragm. Longitudinal section. Glutaraldehyde fixation. ×63 000.

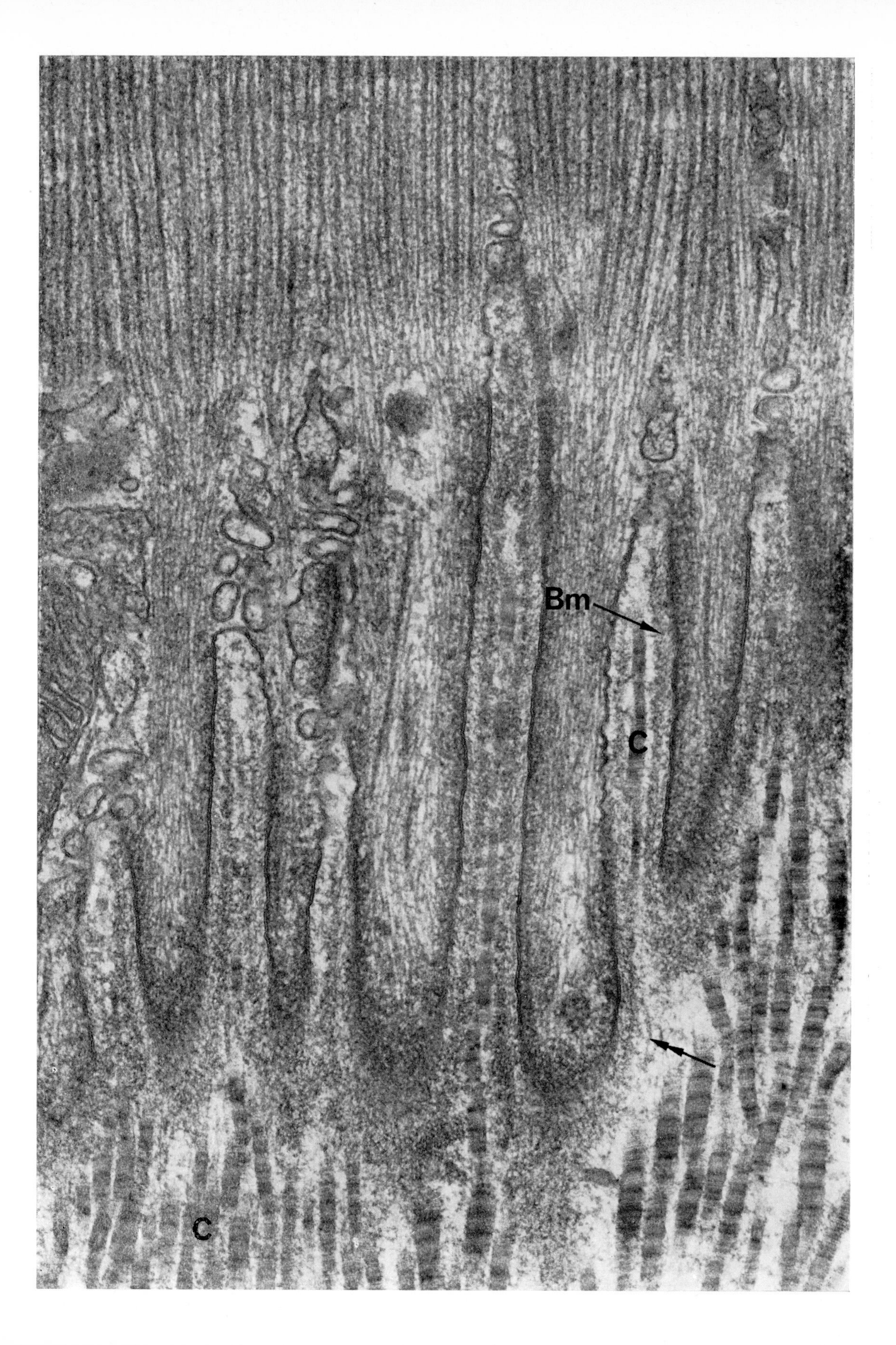
Bm
C
C

Plate 102

What appear to be finger-like projections in longitudinal section at the muscle–tendon junction are in reality clefts or infoldings of the sarcolemma. Both thick and thin myofilaments extend between the invaginations (In) formed by these infoldings. However, only thin filaments are seen within the electron dense material lining the sarcolemma. Note that myofilament bundles are not all aligned in the same direction. The sarcolemma is surrounded by a basal lamina about 40 nm thick and by collagen fibrils.

Muscle–tendon junction in vertebrate striated muscle: rat sternothyroid muscle. Transverse section. Glutaraldehyde fixation. ×37 000.

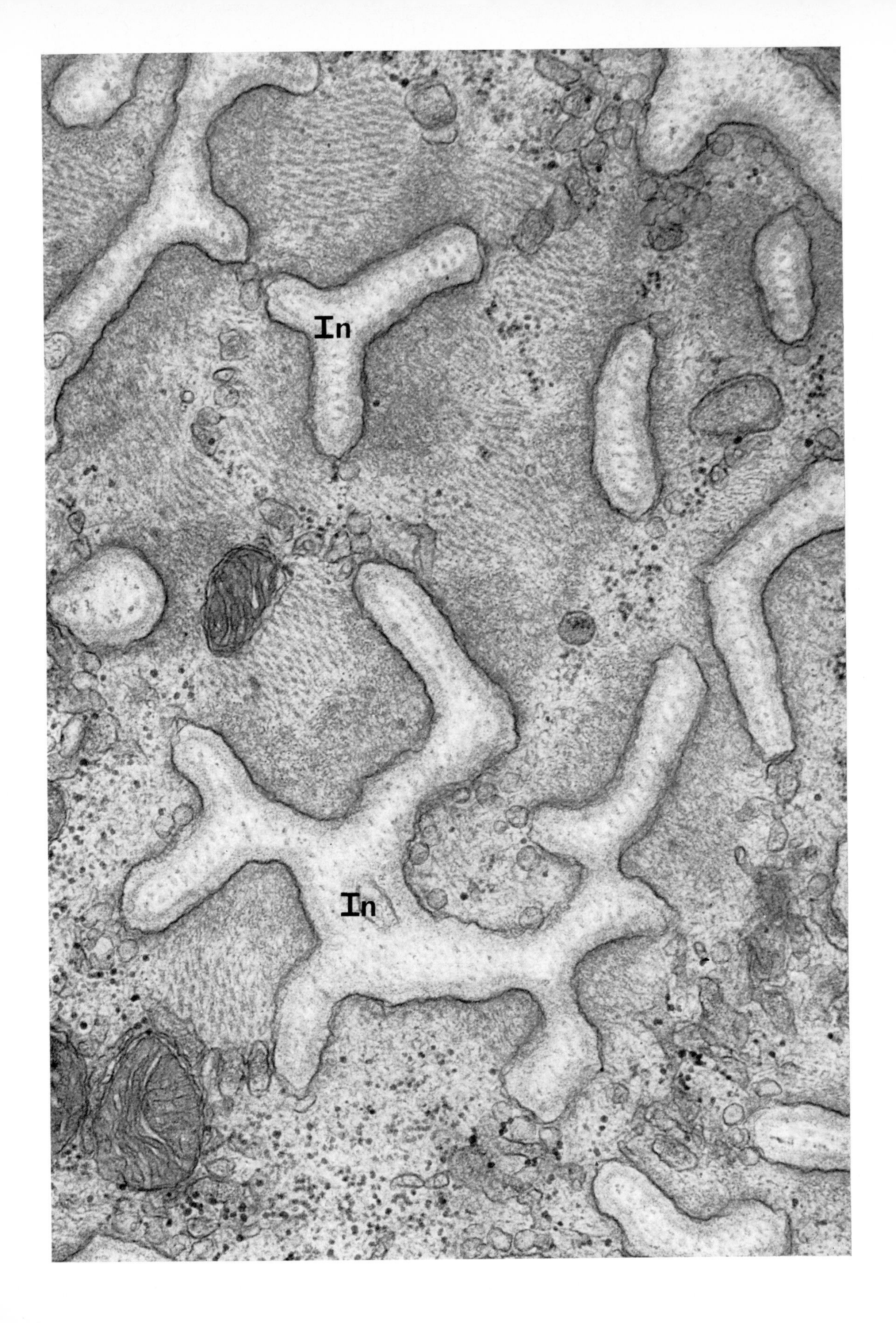
In
In

Plate 103

The gut muscle in millipedes is striated (see Plate 58); muscle fibres attach to a part of the gut tube and pass spirally down where they attach to another part of the tube. Both thick and thin myofilaments extend into the finger-like projections at the muscle junction. The sarcolemma is invested extracellularly by a thick basal lamina and intracellularly by an electron dense material. Myofilaments appear to attach to the sarcolemma via the electron-dense material in a manner comparable to that seen at the vertebrate striated muscle–tendon junction (see Plate 101). Collagen fibrils (C) extend between the projections. Between the muscle and the gut epithelium (Ep) is a thick (about 200 nm), compact basal lamina (Bm), and this appears to extend to envelop the whole muscle in a foliated form (fb). The gut epithelial cells appear to be attached to this basal lamina by semi-desmosomes and the foliated basal lamina surrounding the muscle is continuous with it. Mu, muscle fibre.

Muscle junction in an invertebrate visceral striated muscle: millipede gut. Transverse section. Glutaraldehyde fixation. ×13 400.

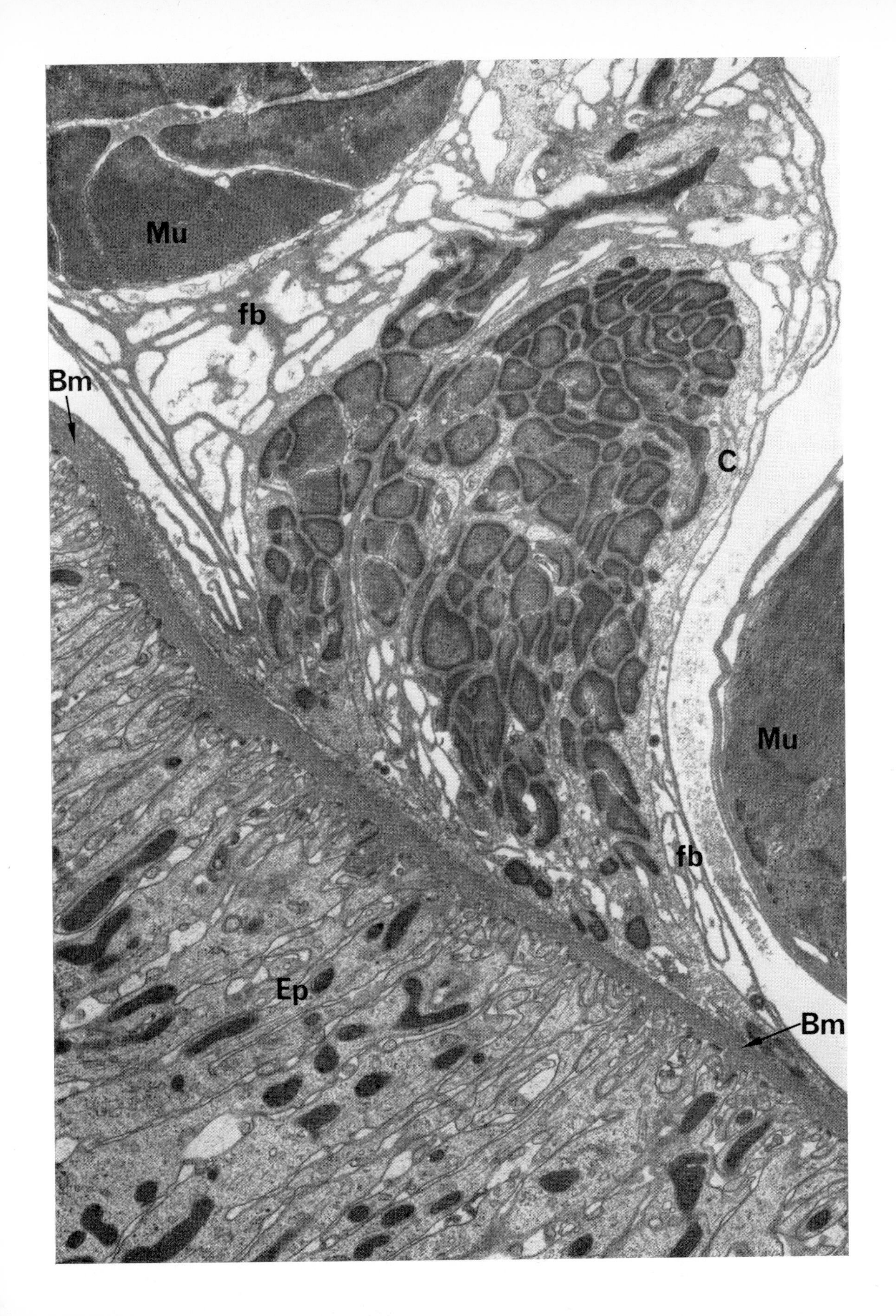
Mu
fb
Bm
C
Mu
fb
Ep
Bm

Plate 104

When a striated muscle fibre terminates within the length of the whole muscle, i.e. somewhere between its origin and insertion, the muscle fibre tapers and sometimes bifurcates. The fibre tips appear to attach in shallow grooves on neighbouring muscle fibres. Here, the muscle tips are surrounded by a thick, compact basal lamina which is continuous with that of the neighbouring fibres. Collagen fibrils and microfilaments intermingle with the basal lamina. The tips of the muscle fibres are less than 1 μm in diameter, and contain thick and thin filaments. The sarcolemma is lined internally by dense filamentous material.

Termination of vertebrate striated muscle fibres: finch rectus intermedius femoris. Transverse section. Glutaraldehyde fixation. $\times$51 000.

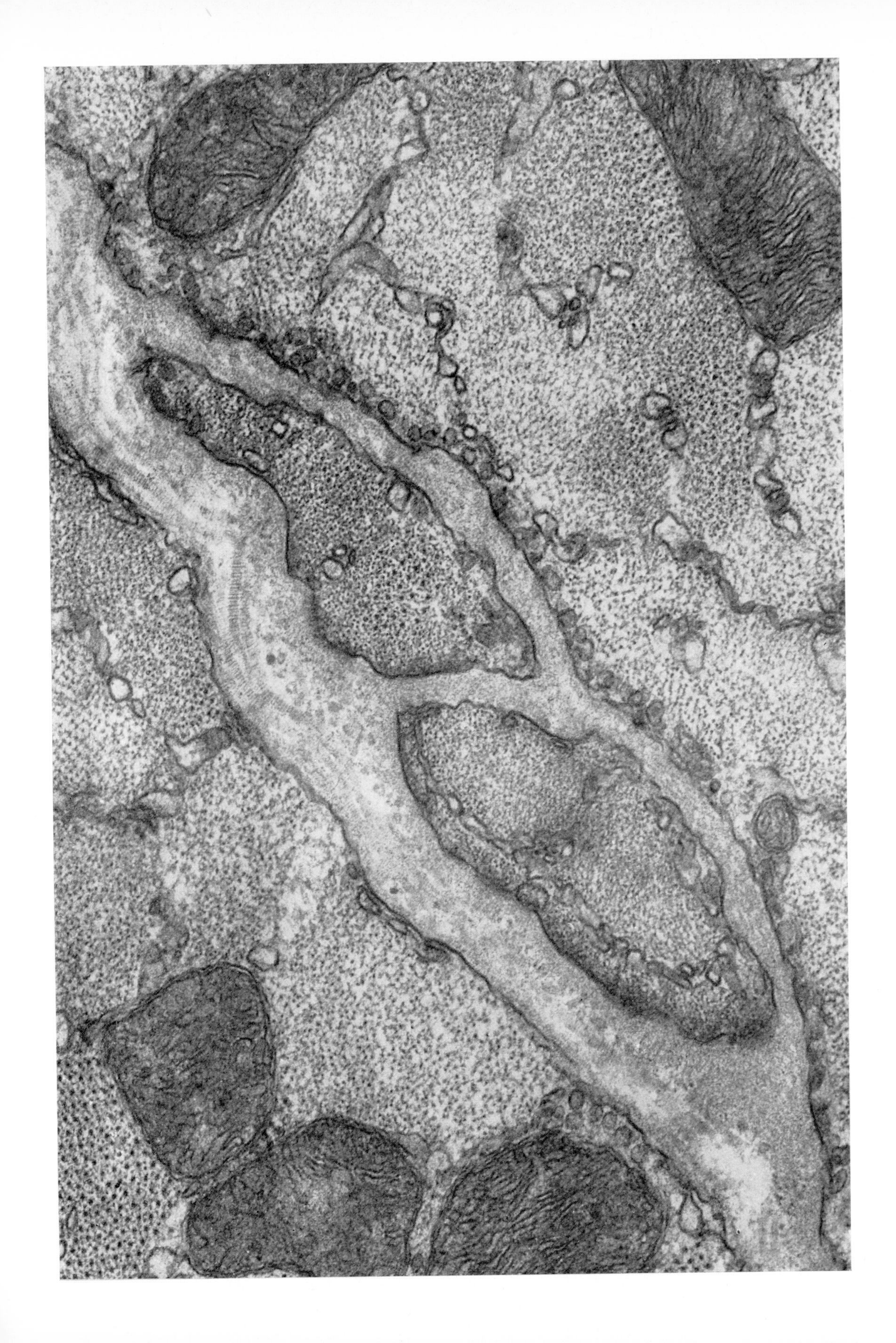

Plate 105

The tip of the smooth muscle illustrated contains myofilaments and is surrounded by a relatively thick basal lamina. As in skeletal muscle–tendon junctions, electron dense filamentous material (apparently equivalent to the dense areas in other regions of the smooth muscle cell) is continuous along the inside of the sarcolemma (see Plate 102). Muscle cells contain closely packed myofilaments of two kinds, thick and thin. But in the small processes, only thin filaments can be seen. The tips of smooth muscle cells often have many processes which interdigitate with each other as shown.

Termination of vertebrate smooth muscle fibres: mouse vas deferens. Transverse section. Glutaraldehyde fixation. ×11 800.

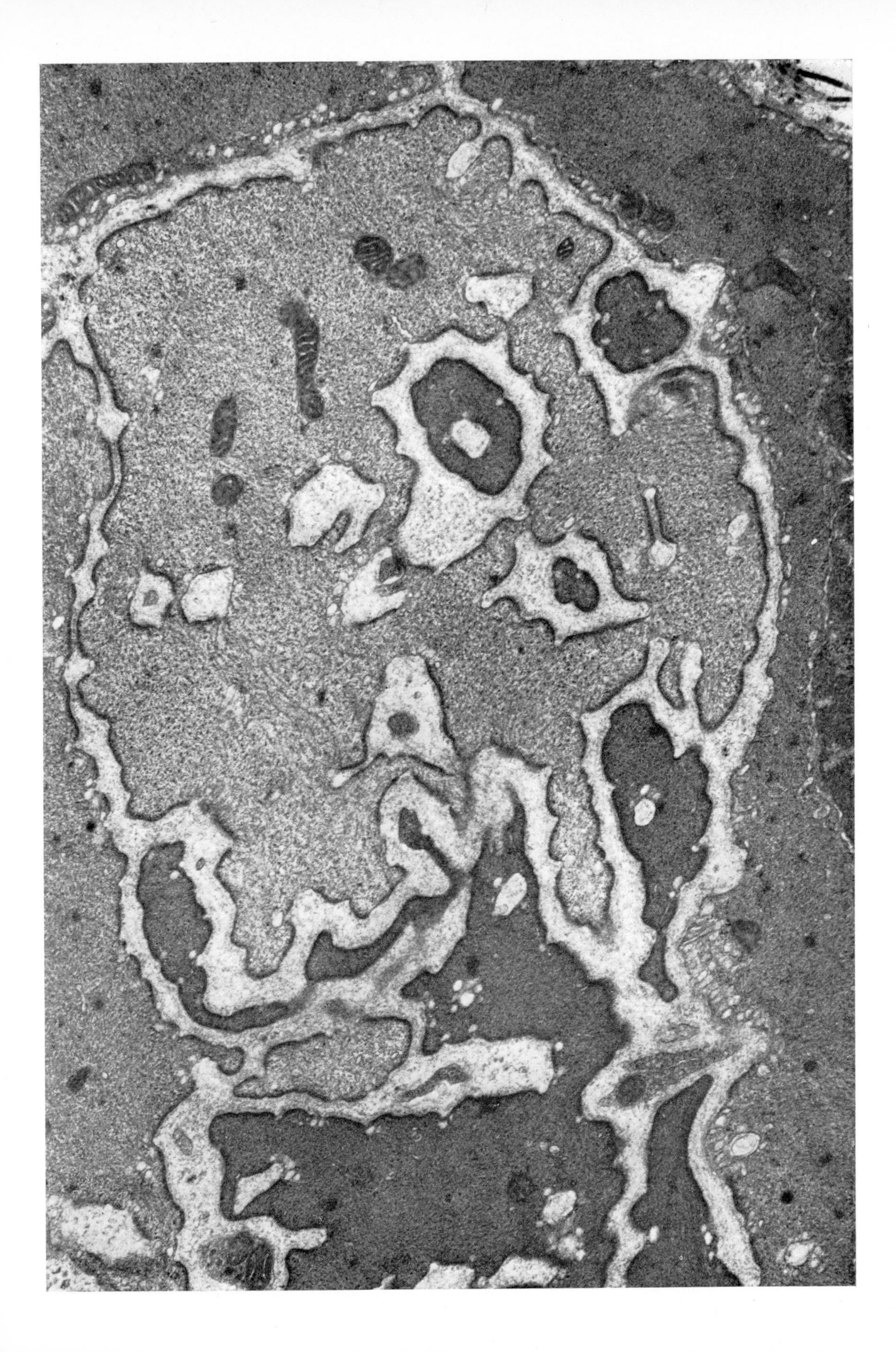

Plate 106

The opposing tips of two smooth muscle cells have long finger-like projections which interdigitate with each other, with close apposition of membranes in some places. Myofilaments extend into the projections, which are surrounded by basal lamina material. Dense areas extend over most of the terminal plasma membranes and few plasmalemmal vesicles or cell organelles are present in these regions.

Terminations of vertebrate smooth muscle cells: guinea-pig ureter. Longitudinal section. OsO_4–glutaraldehyde–OsO_4 fixation. ×86 000.

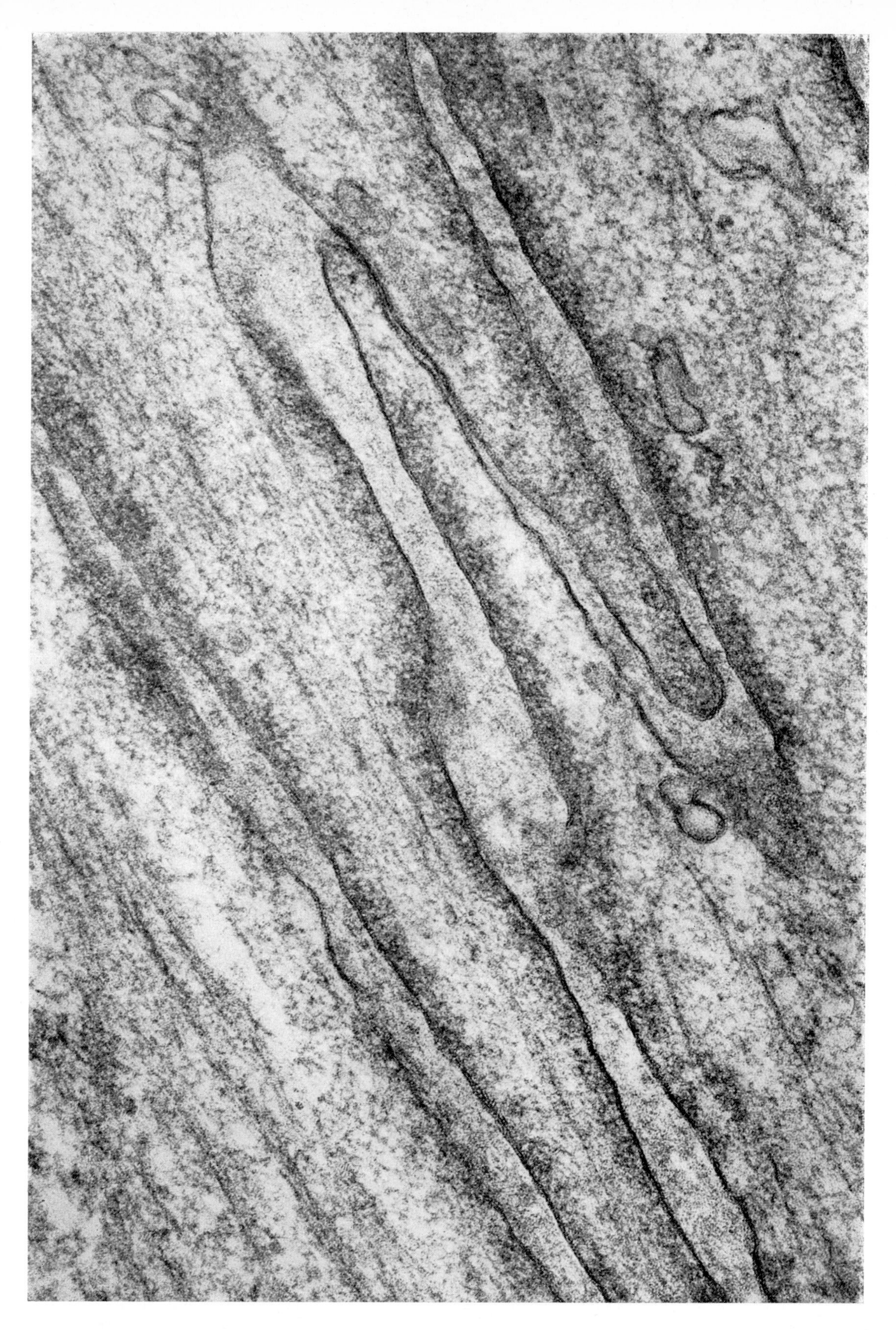

M I—L

Selected articles

BOULIGAND, Y. 1962. Les ultrastructures de muscle strié et de ses attaches au squelette chez les Cyclops (Crustacés copépodes). *J. Microsc. (Fr.)*, **1,** 377–394.

CAVENEY, S. 1969. Muscle attachment related to cuticle architecture in Apterygota. *J. Cell Sci.*, **4,** 541–560.

COUTEAUX, R. 1958. Sur le mode de terminaison des myofibrilles et leurs connexions avec la membrane sarcoplasmique au niveau de la jonction musculo-tendineuse. *C.r. hebd. Seanc. Acad. Sci., Paris*, **246,** 307–309.

COUTEAUX, R. 1959. Observations sur l'ultrastructure de la jonction musculo-tendineuse. *C.r. hebd. Seanc. Acad. Sci., Paris*, **249,** 964–966.

DORN, A. 1965. Licht- und submikroskopische Untersuchungen zum Bau der bindegewebigen Elemente im Skeletmuskel unter besonderer Berücksichtigung der Muskelfaser Schnen-Verbindung. *Wiss. Z. d. Ernst-Moritz-Arndt-Univ. Greifswald, Math. -naturwiss. Reihe.*, **14,** 1–12.

GELBER, D., D. H. MOORE and H. RUSKA. 1960. Observations of the myo-tendon junction in mammalian skeletal muscle. *Z. Zellforsch. mikrosk. Anat.*, **52,** 396–400.

GREENLEE, T. K. JR. and R. RUSSELL. 1967. The development of the rat flexor digital tendon, a fine structural study. *J. Ultrastruct. Res.*, **18,** 354–376.

GRUNER, J.-E. 1961. La structure fine du fuseau neuromusculaire humain. *Revue neurol.*, **104,** 490–507.

HANAK, H. and P. BOCK. 1971. Die Feinstruktur der Muskel-Schnenverbindung von Skelett- und Herzmuskel. *J. Ultrastruct. Res.*, **36,** 68–85.

ISHIKAWA, H. 1965. The fine structure of myo-tendon junction in some mammalian skeletal muscles. *Arch. histol. jap.*, **25,** 275–296.

KORNELIUSSEN, H. 1973. Ultrastructure of myotendinous junctions in *Myxine* and rat. *Z. Anat. EntwGesch.*, **142,** 91–101.

LAI-FOOK, J. 1967. The structure of developing muscle insertions in insects. *J. Morph.*, **123,** 503–527.

LUFT, J. H. 1966. Ruthenium red staining of the striated muscle cell membrane and the myotendinal junction, *Electron microscopy 1966*. Vol. 2. *Biology*. Sixth International Congress for Electron Microscopy. R. Uyeda (ed.). Maruzen, Tokyo. 65–66.

MACKAY, D., T. J. HARBOP and A. R. MUIR. 1969. Fine structure of the muscle tendon junction in the rat. *Acta. anat.*, **73,** 588–604.

MAIR, W. G. P. and F. M. S. TOMÉ. 1972. The ultrastructure of the adult and developing human myotendinousjunction. *Acta neuropath.*, **21,** 239–252.

MATTER, A. and W. G. FORSSMANN. 1967. Muskelsehnenverbindungen. *Verh. anat. Ges., Jena*, **62,** 73–81.

MUIR, A. R. 1961. Observations on the attachment of myofibrils to the sarcolemma at the muscle–tendon junction. In *Electron Microscopy in Anatomy*. J. Boyd, F. R. Johnson and J. D. Lever (eds.). Edward Arnold, London. 267–277.

REISSIG, D. and K. SCHIPPEL. 1967. Elektronenmikroskopische Befunde am Muskel-Sehnenübergang im Zwerchfell von Ratte und Kaninchen. *Z. mikrosk.-anat. Forsch.*, **76,** 1–11.

SANGER, J. W. and F. V. McCANN. 1968. Ultrastructure of moth alary muscles and their attachment to the heart wall. *J. Insect Physiol.*, **14,** 1539–1544.

SATO, Y. and T. YAMAMOTO. 1960. Electron microscopy studies on the muscle tendon attachment in the rat. *Nikon Univ. J. Med.*, **2,** 429–440.

SCHIPPEL, K. and D. REISSIG. 1968. Zur Feinstruktur des Muskel-Sehnenüberganges. *Z. mikrosk.-anat. Forsch.*, **78,** 235–255.

SCHIPPEL, K. and D. REISSIG. 1969. Zur Feinstruktur des Rückenflossenmuskels der kleinen Schlangennadel (*Nerophis ophidion*) unter besonderer Berücksichtígung des Muskel-Sehnenüberganges. *Z. mikrosk.-anat. Forsch.*, **81,** 304–312.

SCHWARZACHER, H. G. 1960*a*. Untersuchungen über die Skeletmuskel-Sehnenverbindung. I. Elektronenmikroskopische und lichtmikroskopische Untersuchungen über den Feinbau der Muskelfaser-Sehnenverbindung. *Acta anat.*, **40,** 59–86.

SCHWARZACHER, H. G. 1960*b*. Untersuchungen über die Skeletmuskel-Sehnenverbindung.

III. Die Form der Muskelfaserenden. *Acta anat.*, **43,** 144–157.

SHAW, K. 1974. The fine structure of muscle cells and their attachments in the tardigrade *Macrobiotus hufelandi*. *Tissue & Cell*, **6,** 431–446.

SMITH, D. S., U. JÄRLFORS and F. E. RUSSELL. 1969. The fine structure of the muscle attachments in a spider (*Latrodectus mactans* Fabr.). *Tissue & Cell*, **1,** 673–687.

6 Cell to Cell Relationships

There are several types of structural specializations of opposing plasma membranes at the contact area of cells, in a wide variety of tissues. These various forms of cell to cell relationships serve at least two vital roles, namely mechanical attachment or adhesion and intercellular communication.

A Vertebrate striated muscle

The only close junctions between neighbouring fibres found in vertebrate striated muscle are those in the developing and adult heart and in developing skeletal muscle. Cardiac muscle consists of separate mononuclear muscle cells joined by distinct surface specializations, the *intercalated discs*, although in former times cardiac muscle was thought to be a syncitium. Intercalated discs contain three types of junctional specialization, termed: the *desmosome* (or *macula adhaerens*); the *fascia adhaerens*; and the *fascia occludens* (or *nexus* or *gap junction*).

Desmosomes play an important role in cell-to-cell adhesion. In the cytoplasm adjacent to the membrane at these sites, tonofilaments, 7–10 nm in diameter, insert into a layer of very condensed filamentous material. The intercellular space in desmosomes contains organized material (see Plate 109). Desmosomes are also present in large numbers in stratified squamous epithelia, tissue that is subjected to great mechanical stress. Many tonofilaments insert into these junctions and it has been suggested that they have a cytoskeletal role. Thin filaments do not appear to insert into desmosomes.

The *fascia adhaerens* differs from the macula adhaerens, because in the cytoplasm adjacent to the membrane, there is a loose accumulation of filamentous material termed the *filamentous mat* into which the thin actin filaments of the muscle insert.

The *nexus* or *gap junctions* in heart muscle appear to have two roles, namely cell-to-cell adhesion, and communication between cells. This communication can be expressed in two ways: (1) by providing low resistance pathways for electrotonic coupling and (2) by allowing the passage of small molecules across the junction.

The only type of junction seen between developing skeletal muscle fibres are small gap junctions, where there are focal areas of close apposition of the outer leaflets of adjacent plasma membranes. From the time the fertilized egg undergoes its first cleavage to yield two cells, intercellular contacts serve at least two vital roles: adhesion and intercellular communication. Gap junctions appear between both embryonic muscle cells and between cells aggregating in tissue culture. Junctions, which extend over greater areas, develop at a later stage.

Plate 107

The intercalated disc usually runs transversely across the myofibrils at the level of Z-discs, but at different levels in adjacent myofibrils; this gives the intercalated disc a step-like appearance. Details of the structure of the intercalated disc in the region indicated by the rectangle is illustrated at high magnification in Plate 108.

Intercalated discs between vertebrate cardiac muscle cells: guinea-pig ventricle. Lower power longitudinal section. Glutaraldehyde fixation. ×24 600.

Plate 108

The intercalated disc illustrated here (and defined in Plate 107) consists of three components, the *desmosome* (*macula adhaerens*) (D), the *fascia adhaerens* (Fa), and the *nexus* or *gap junction* (G). The desmosome is easily recognized by an accumulation of electron dense material alongside the junction and by the strictly parallel confronting membranes (see Plate 109). The *fascia adhaerens* is similar in appearance to the intermediate junction of epithelial junctional complexes. The myofilaments appear to attach to an accumulation of filamentous material, the filamentous mat. The termination of these myofilaments is comparable to that seen at the muscle-tendon junction of skeletal muscle (see Plate 101). The gap junction appears as a pentalaminal membrane complex in low power (see Plate 110 for details of structure). No myofilaments are seen in association with either the desmosome or the gap junction.

Intercalated disc of vertebrate cardiac muscle: guinea-pig ventricle. Longitudinal section. Glutaraldehyde fixation. ×76 000.

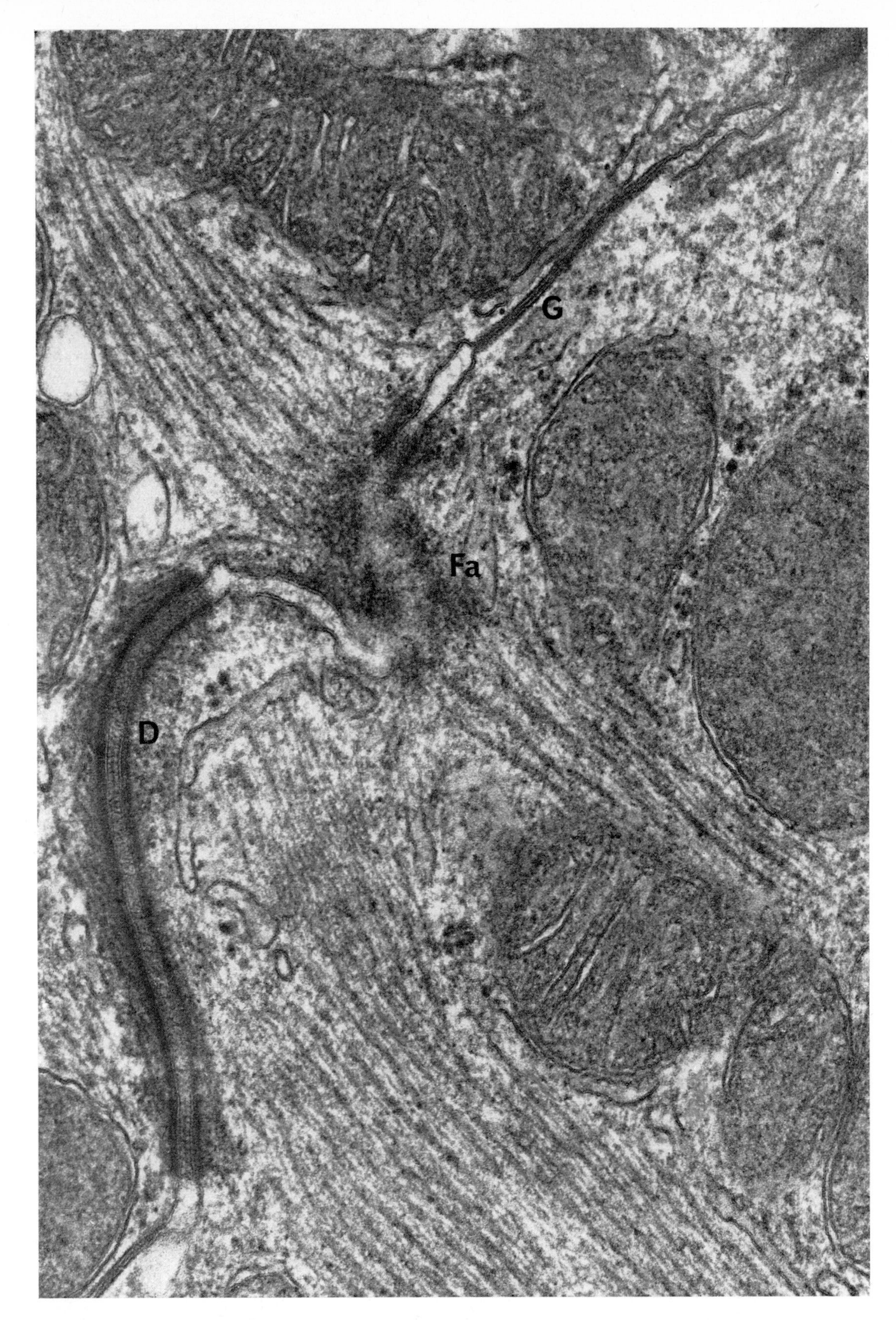
G
Fa
D

Plate 109

At high magnification desmosomes can be seen to consist of two parallel plasma membranes, separated by a constant interspace 30 nm wide, with a dense fibrillar plaque in the subjacent cytoplasm. The interspace is continuous with the extracellular space and contains a condensation of proteinaceous material which often forms a dense stratum parallel to the membranes.

Staining with compounds such as ruthenium red and lanthanum hydroxide, which are extracellular markers, has demonstrated interconnecting strands between the electron dense stratum and the adjacent membranes. Tonofilaments can be seen within and adjacent to the fibrillar plaque along the plasma membranes of the desmosome. The desmosome is the major site of adhesion between adjacent muscle cells.

Desmosome in vertebrate cardiac muscle: guinea-pig ventricle. Longitudinal section. Glutaraldehyde fixation. ×337 000.

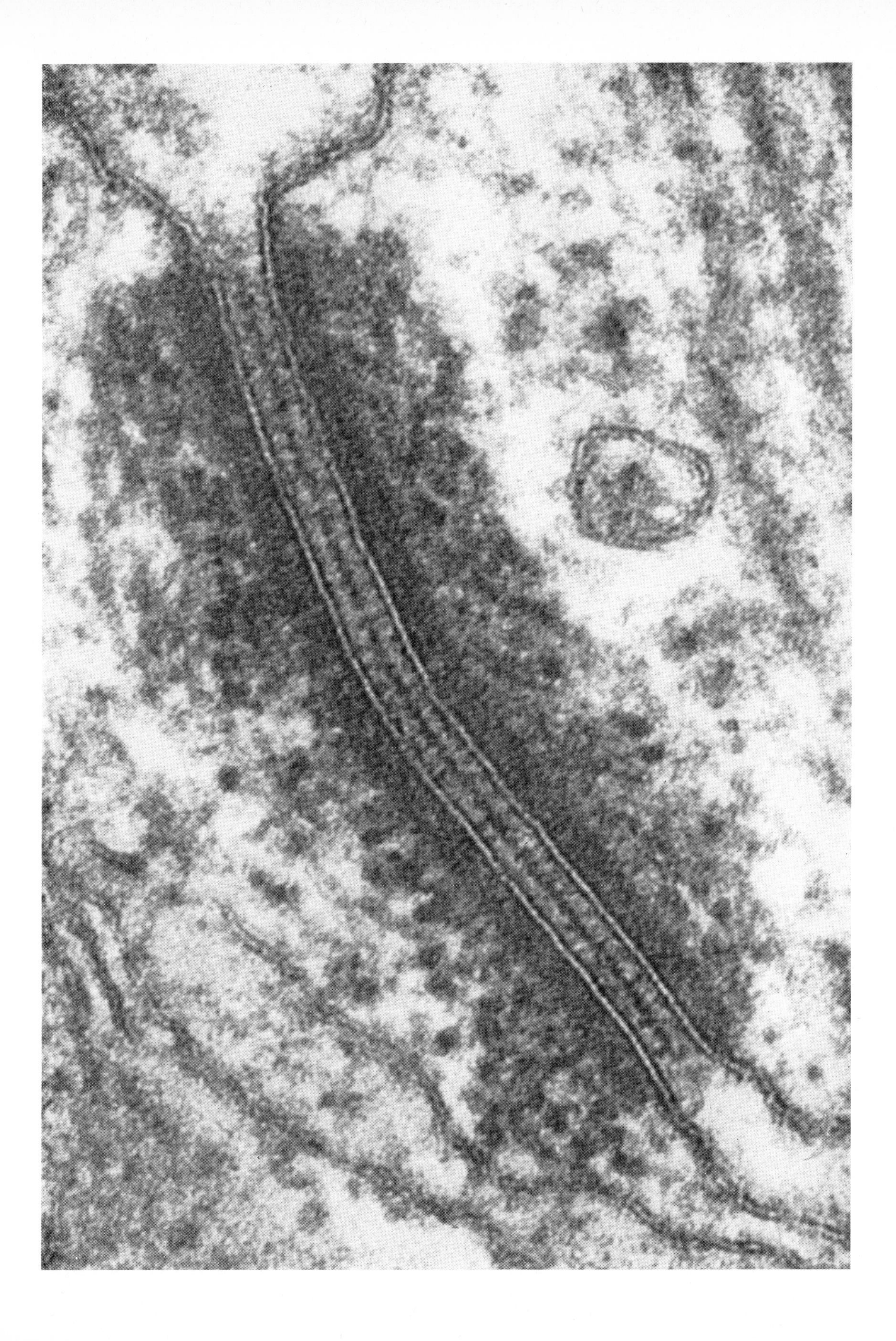

Plate 110

The high power electron micrograph of the gap junction or nexus illustrated, shows that it is formed by two plasma membranes organized in a seven-layered complex, with the two tri-laminar membranes separated by 2–3 nm.

The gap junctions form low resistance path-ways which allow rapid spread of excitation. This enables the heart to perform as a functional syncytium. Gap junctions are also frequently found in smooth muscle (see Chapter 6B).

Gap junction in vertebrate cardiac muscle: guinea-pig ventricle. Glutaraldehyde fixation. ×314 000.

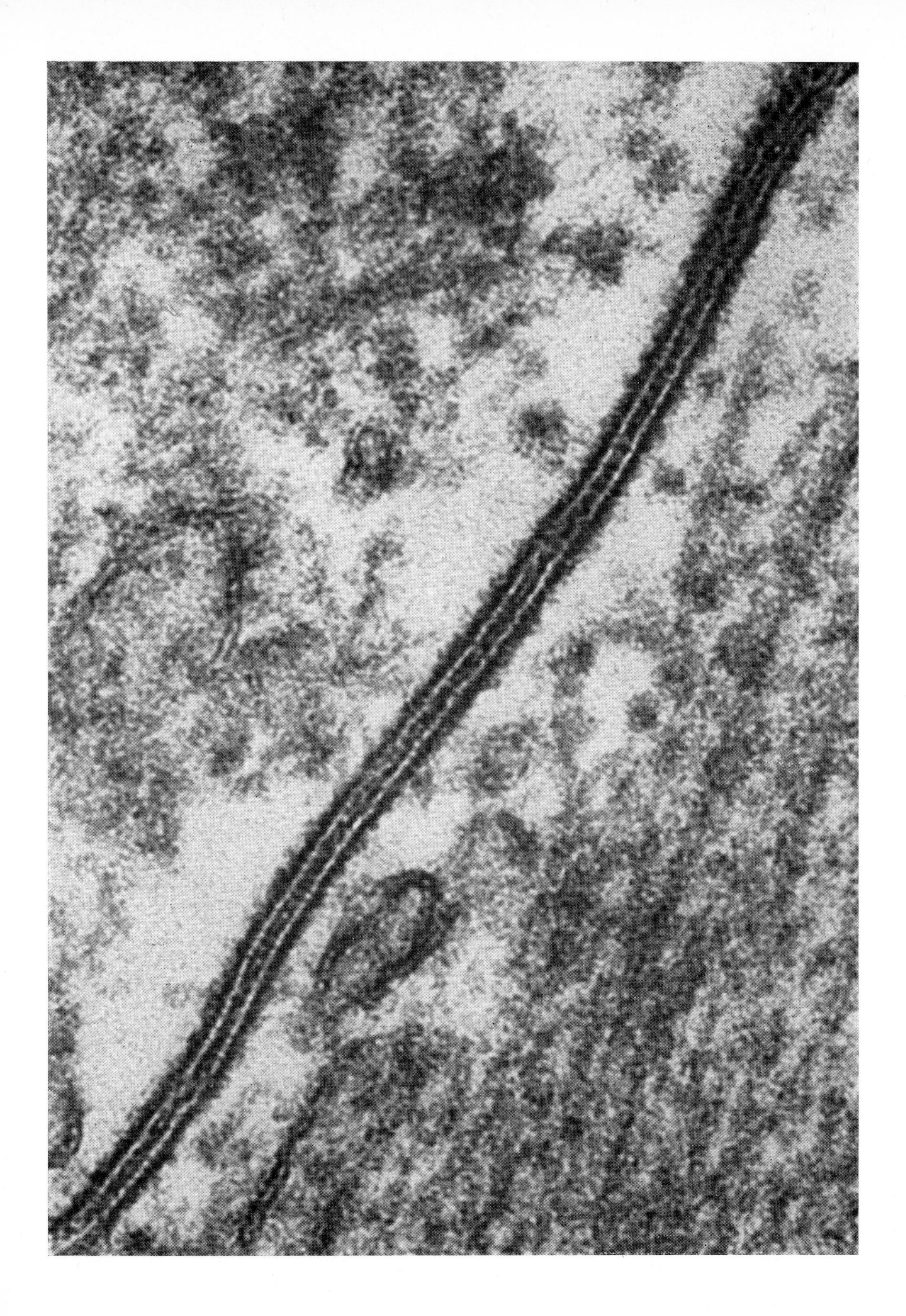

Plate 111

The subsarcolemmal filamentous mat of the *fascia adhaerens* has staining characteristics similar to that of the Z-disc, and occasionally the two are continuous. This has been noted in a number of animals, for example (as illustrated) in adult cat atrium, in foetal human cardiac muscle and in reptilian cardiac muscle. Continuity between Z-discs and desmosomes was also reported in a number of earlier studies, but this has not been confirmed with improved fixation methods.

Fascia adhaerens in vertebrate cardiac muscle: dog ventricle. Longitudinal section. Glutaraldehyde fixation. ×40 000. (Courtesy of N. C. R. Merrillees, Department of Anatomy, University of Melbourne.)

Plate 112

Junctions of the type illustrated are sometimes found in developing skeletal muscle, where the fibres are separated by a narrow gap of less than 20 nm without an interposed basal lamina. These junctions are smaller than the gap junctions seen in adult smooth muscle and are thought to have a three fold function, being concerned with: (1) alignment of cells during development; (2) electrotonic coupling of cells; and (3) allowing the intercellular passage of molecules involved in growth and differentiation.

Junction between developing vertebrate skeletal muscle fibres: 18-day foetal rat sternothyroid muscle. Transverse section. Glutaraldehyde fixation. ×137 000.

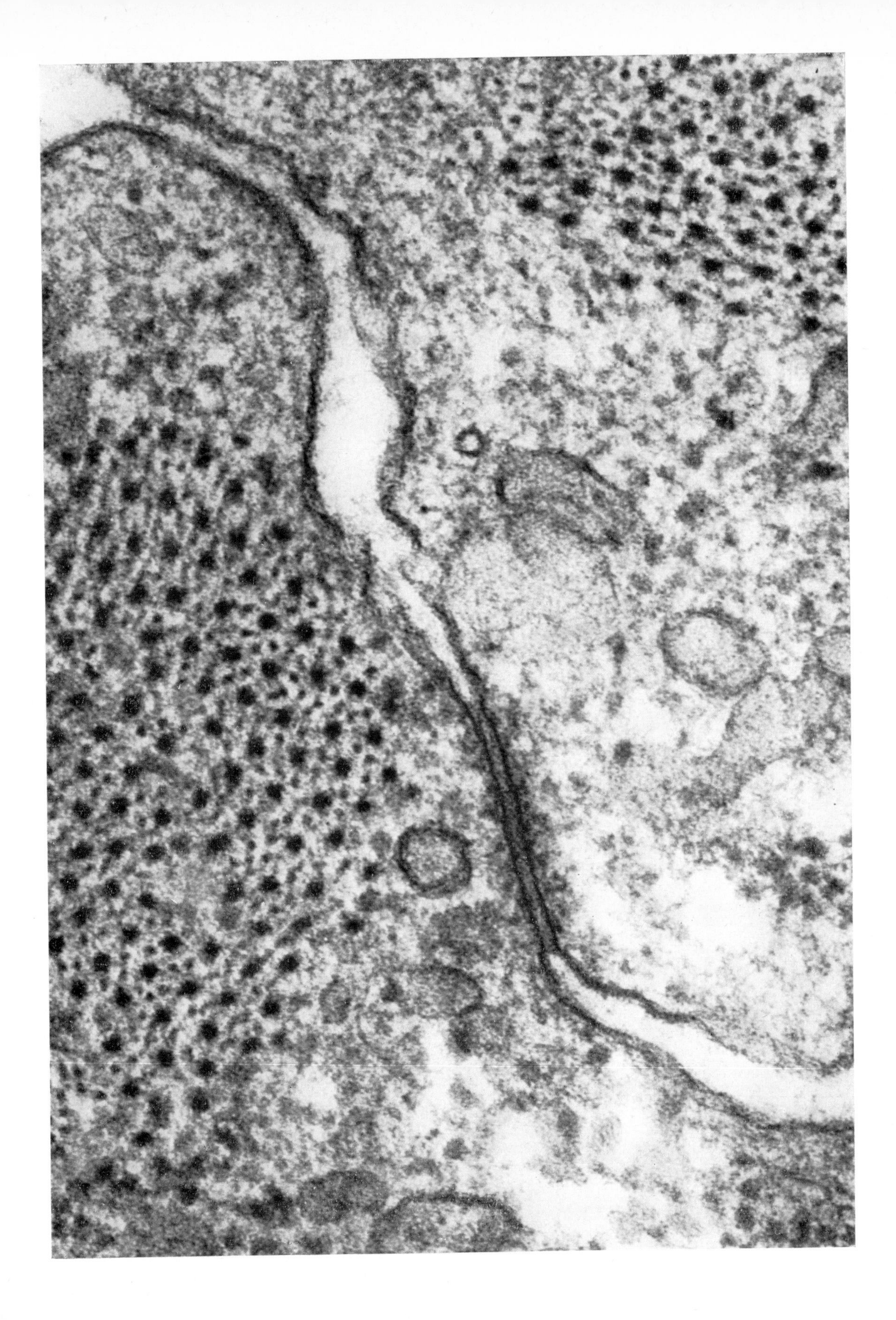

Selected reviews

BENNET, M. V. L. 1973. Function of electrotonic junctions in embryonic and adult tissues. *Fedn Proc.*, **32,** 65–75.

BURCH, G. E. and R. S. SOHAL. 1969. Morphologic and pathologic aspects of intercalated disc of the heart. *Am. Heart J.*, **78,** 358–368.

DE MAAN, R. L. and M. G. SACHS. 1972. Cell coupling in developing systems: The heart–cell paradigm. In *Current Topics in Developmental Biology*. Vol. 7. A. A. Moscona and A. Monroy (eds.). Academic Press, New York. 193–228.

FURSHPAN, E. J. and D. D. POTTER. 1968. Low-resistance junctions between cells in embryos and tissue culture. In *Current Topics in Developmental Biology*. Vol. 3. A. A. Moscona and A. Monroy (eds.). Academic Press, New York. 95–127.

LOEWENSTEIN, W. R. 1973. Membrane junctions in growth and differentiation. *Fedn Proc.*, **32,** 60–64.

McNUTT, N. S. 1970. Ultrastructure of intercellular junctions in adult and developing cardiac muscle. *Am. J. Cardiol.*, **25,** 169–183.

McNUTT, N. S. and R. S. WEINSTEIN. 1973. Membrane ultrastructure at mammalian intercellular junctions. In *Progress in Biophysics and Molecular Biology*. Vol. 26. J. A. V. Butler and D. Noble (eds.). Pergamon Press, Oxford. 45–101.

NIAS, A. H. W. and M. FOX. 1971. Synchronization of mammalian cells with respect to the mitotic cycle. *Cell & Tiss. Kinet.*, **4,** 375–398.

SOMMER, J. R. and E. A. JOHNSON. 1970. Comparative ultrastructure of cardiac cell membrane specialization. A review. *Am. J. Cardiol.*, **25,** 184–194.

Selected articles

ARLUK, D. J. and J. A. G. RHODIN. 1974. The ultrastructure of calf heart conducting fibers with special reference to nexuses and their distribution. *J. Ultrastruct. Res.*, **49,** 11–23.

ARMSTRONG, P. B. 1970. A fine structural study of adhesive cell junctions in heterotypic cell aggregates. *J. Cell Biol.*, **47,** 197–210.

BARR, L., M. M. DEWEY and W. BERGER. 1965. Propagation of action potentials and the structure of the nexus in cardiac muscle. *J. gen. Physiol.*, **48,** 797–823.

BENEDETTI, E. L. and P. EMMELOT. 1968. Hexagonal array of subunits in tight junctions separated from isolated rat liver plasma membranes. *J. Cell Biol.*, **38,** 15–24.

BENNETT, M. V. L. and J. P. TRINKAUS. 1970. Electrical coupling between embryonic cells by way of extracellular space and specialized junctions. *J. Cell Biol.*, **44,** 592–610.

BERRILL, N. J. and H. SHELDON. 1964. The fine structure of the connections between muscle cells in ascidian tadpole larva. *J. Cell Biol.*, **23,** 664–668.

BORYSENKO, J. Z. and J.-P. REVEL. 1973. Experimental manipulation of desmosome structure. *Am. J. Anat.*, **137,** 403–422.

BREEMAN, V. L. VAN. 1953. Intercalated discs in heart muscle studied with the electron microscope. *Anat. Rec.*, **117,** 49–63.

BULLIVANT, S. and W. R. LOEWENSTEIN. 1968. Structure of coupled and uncoupled cell junctions. *J. Cell Biol.*, **37,** 621–632.

BURCH, G. E. and R. S. SOHAL. 1969. Morphologic and pathologic aspects of intercalated disc of the heart. *Am. Heart J.*, **78,** 358–368.

CHALLICE, C. E. and G. A. EDWARDS. 1960. The intercalated disc of the goldfish heart. *Experientia*, **16,** 70–72.

CHUAQUI, B. J. 1971. Über die zwischenzelligen Verbindungen im Sinus- und A-V-Knotengewebe beim Menschen. *Virchows Arch. Abt. A Path. Anat.*, **354,** 24–34.

COBB, J. L. S. 1974. Gap junctions in the heart of teleost fish. *Cell & Tissue Res.*, **154,** 131–134.

DE BEYER, J. M., J. C. H. DE MAN and J.-P. PERSIJN. 1962. ATPase activity on the intercalated disc and C_2 bands of mouse heart muscle. *J. Cell Biol.*, **13,** 452–456.

DEVIS, R. and D. W. JAMES. 1964. Close association between adult guinea-pig fibroblasts in tissue culture, studied with the electron microscope. *J. Anat.*, **98,** 63–68.

FARQUHAR, M. G. and G. E. PALADE, 1965. Cell junctions in amphibian tissue. *J. Cell Biol.*, **26,** 263–292.

FRIEND, D. S. and N. B. GILULA. 1972. Variations in tight and gap junctions in mammalian tissues. *J. Cell Biol.*, **53,** 758–776.

GILULA, N. B. 1973. Development of cell junctions. *Am. Zool.*, **13,** 1109–1117.

GOSHIMA, K. 1970. Formation of nexuses and electrotonic transmission between myocardial and FL cells in monolayer culture. *Expl Cell Res.*, **63,** 124–130.

GOULD, R. P., A. DAY and L. WOLPERT. 1972. Mesenchymal condensation and cell contact in early morphogenesis of the chick limb. *Expl Cell Res.*, **72,** 325–336.

GRIMLEY, P. M. and G. A. EDWARDS. 1960. The ultrastructure of cardiac desmosomes in the toad and their relationship to the intercalated disc. *J. biophys. biochem. Cytol.*, **8,** 305–318.

HAMA, K. 1960. The fine structure of the desmosomes in frog mesothelium. *J. biophys. biochem. Cytol.*, **7,** 575–578.

HEAYSMAN, J. E. M. and S. M. PEGRUM. 1973. Early contacts between fibroblasts. An ultrastructural study. *Expl Cell Res.*, **78,** 71–78.

ITO, S. and W. R. LOEWENSTEIN. 1969. Ionic communication between early embryonic cells. *Devl Biol.*, **19,** 228–243.

KARRER, H. E. 1960. The striated musculature of blood vessels. II. Cell interconnections and cell surface. *J. biophys. biochem. Cytol.*, **8,** 135–150.

KAWAMURA, K. and T. N. JAMES. 1971. Comparative ultrastructure of cellular junctions in working myocardium and the conduction system under normal and pathologic conditions. *J. Mol. & Cell. Cardiol.*, **3,** 31–60.

KAWAMURA, K. and T. KONISHI. 1967. Ultrastructure of the cell junction of heart muscle with special reference to its functional significance in excitation contraction and to the concept of 'disease of the intercalated disc'. *Jap. Circul. J.*, **31,** 1533–1543.

KEETER, J. S. and G. D. PAPPAS. 1973. Gap junctions in embryonic skeletal muscle. *Anat. Rec.*, **175,** 355.

LIPTON, B. H. and I. R. KONIGSBERG. 1972. A fine-structural analysis of the fusion of myogenic cells. *J. Cell Biol.*, **53,** 348–364.

LOEWENSTEIN, W. R. and Y. KANNO. 1967. Intercellular communication and tissue growth. I. Cancerous growth. *J. Cell Biol.*, **33,** 225–234.

LOEWENSTEIN, W. R. and R. D. AENN. 1967. Intercellular communication and tissue growth. II. Tissue regeneration. *J. Cell Biol.*, **33,** 235–254.

LORBER, V. and D. G. RAYNS. 1972. Cellular junctions in the tunicate heart. *J. Cell Sci.*, **10,** 211–228.

MARON, B. J. and V. J. FERRANS. 1973. Significance of multiple interelated discs in hypertrophied human myocardium. *Am. J. Pathol.*, **73,** 81–96.

MARTINEZ-PALOMO, A. and R. MENDEZ. 1971. Presence of gap junctions between cardiac cells in the heart of nonmammalian species. *J. Ultrastruct. Res.*, **37,** 592–600.

MATTER, A. 1973. A morphometric study on the nexus of rat cardiac muscle. *J. Cell Biol.*, **56,** 690–696.

McNUTT, N. S. 1970. Ultrastructure of intercellular junctions in adult and developing cardiac muscle. *Am. J. Cardiol.*, **25,** 169–183.

McNUTT, N. S. and R. S. WEINSTEIN. 1970. The ultrastructure of the nexus. A correlated thin-section and freeze-cleave study. *J. Cell Biol.*, **47,** 666–688.

MERK, F. B. and N. S. McNUTT. 1972. Nexus junctions between dividing and interphase granulosa cells of the rat ovary. *J. Cell Biol.*, **55,** 511–515.

MILLONIG, G. and G. GIUDICE. 1967. Electron microscopic study of the reaggregation of cells dissociated from sea urchin embryos. *Devl. Biol.*, **15,** 91–101.

MUIR, A. R. 1957. An electron microscope study of the embryology of the intercalated disc in the heart of the rabbit. *J. biophys. biochem. Cytol.*, **3,** 193–202.

OVERTON, J. 1973. Experimental manipulation of desmosome formation. *J. Cell Biol.*, **56,** 636–646.

PAGE, E. and L. P. McCALLISTER. 1973. Studies on the intercalated disk of rat left ventricular myocardial cells. *J. Ultrastruct. Res.*, **43,** 388–411.

PINTO DA SILVA, P. and N. B. GILULA. 1972. Gap junctions in normal and transformed fibroblasts in culture. *Expl. Cell Res.*, **71,** 393–401.

PUCCI-MINAFRA, I. and G. ORTOLANI. 1968. Differentiation and tissue interaction during muscle development of ascidian tadpoles. An electron microscope study. *Devl Biol.*, **17,** 692–712.

RAYNS, D. G., F. O. SIMPSON and J. M. LEDINGHAM. 1969. Ultrastructure of desmosomes in mammalian intercalated disc; appearances after lanthanum treatment. *J. Cell Biol.*, **42,** 322–325.

REVEL, J.-P. and M. J. KARNOVSKY. 1967. Hexagonal array of subunits in intercellular junctions of the mouse heart and liver. *J. Cell Biol.*, **33,** C7–C12.

REVEL, J.-P., A. G. YEE and A. J. HUDSPETH. 1971. Gap junctions between electronically coupled cells in tissue culture and in brown fat. *Proc. natn. Acad. Sci. U.S.A.*, **68,** 2924-2927.

REVEL, J.-P., P. YIP and L. L. CHANG. 1973. Cell junctions in the early chick embryo — A freeze etch study. *Devl Biol.*, **35,** 302–317.

ROBERTSON, J. D. 1963. The occurrence of a subunit pattern in the unit membranes of club endings in Mauthner cell synapses in goldfish brains. *J. Cell Biol.*, **19,** 201–221.

SHERIDAN, J. D. 1966. Electrophysiological study of special connections between cells in the early chick embryo. *J. Cell Biol.*, **31**, C1–C5.

SHERIDAN, J. D. 1968. Electrophysiological evidence for low-resistance intercellular junctions in the early chick embryo. *J. Cell Biol.*, **37,** 650–659.

SHERIDAN, J. D. 1971. Dye movement and low-resistance junctions between reaggregated embryonic cells. *Devl Biol.*, **26,** 627–636.

SHIENVOL, D. F. L. and D. E. KELLY. 1974. Desmosome structure revealed by freeze-fracture and tannic acid staining. *J. Cell Biol.*, **63,** 313a.

SHIMADA, Y. 1971. Electron microscope observations on the fusion of chick myoblasts *in vitro*. *J. Cell Biol.*, **48,** 128–142.

SJÖSTRAND, F. S. and E. ANDERSSON-CEDERGREN. 1960. Intercalated discs of heart muscle. In *The Structure and Function of Muscle.* Vol. 1. G. H. Bourne (ed.). Academic Press, New York. 421–445.

SJÖSTRAND, F. S., E. ANDERSSON-CEDERGREN and M. M. DEWEY. 1958. The ultrastructure of the intercalated discs of frog, mouse and guinea-pig cardiac muscle. *J. Ultrastruct. Res.*, **1,** 271–287.

SOHAL, R. S. and G. E. BURCH. 1969. Effects of alcohol ingestion on the intercalated disc in the mouse heart. *Experientia*, **25,** 279–280.

SPERELAKIS, N., R. RUBIO and J. REDICK. 1970. Sharp discontinuity in sarcomere lengths across intercalated discs of fibrillating cat hearts. *J. Ultrastruct. Res.*, **30,** 503–532.

SPIRA, A. W. 1971. The nexus in the intercalated disc of the canine heart: quantitative data for an estimation of its resistance. *J. Ultrastruct. Res.*, **34,** 409–425.

STAEHELIN, L. A. 1972. Three types of gap junction interconnecting intestinal epithelial cells visualized by freeze-etching. *Proc. natn. Acad. Sci. U.S.A.*, **69,** 1318–1321.

STEERE, R. L. and J. R. SOMMER. 1972. Stereo ultrastructure of nexus faces exposed by freeze-fracturing. *J. Microsc.* (*Fr.*), **15,** 205–218.

TAMARIN, A. and L. M. SREEBNY. 1963. An analysis of desmosome shape, size, and orientation by the use of histometric and densitometric methods with electron microscopy. *J. Cell Biol.*, **18,** 125–134.

THAEMERT, J. C. 1969. Fine structure of neuro-muscular relationships in mouse heart. *Anat. Rec.*, **163,** 575–586.

TRAUTWEIN, W. 1973. Membrane currents in cardiac muscle fibers. *Physiol. Rev.*, **53,** 793–835.

TRELSTAD, R. L., E. D. HAY and J.-P. REVEL. 1967. Cell contact during early morphogenesis in the chick embryo. *Devl Biol.*, **16,** 78–106.

VAN BREEMAN, V. L. 1953. Intercalated discs in heart muscle studied with the electron microscope. *Anat. Rec.*, **117,** 49–63.

WADE, J. B. and M. J. KARNOVSKY. 1974. The structure of the zonula occludens. A single fibril model based on freeze-fracture. *J. Cell Biol.*, **60,** 168–180.

WEIDMANN, S. 1969. Electrical coupling between myocardial cells. In *Process in Brain Research.* Vol. 31. *Mechanisms of Synaptic Transmission.* K. Akert and P. G. Waser (eds.). Elsevier, Amsterdam. 275–281.

ZACCHEI, A. M. and S. CARAVITA. 1972. Observations on the ultrastructure of chick-embryo cardiac myoblasts re-aggregated in long-term cultures. *J. Embryol. exp. Morph.*, **28,** 571–589.

ZIMNY, M. L., M. SHERMAN and C. C. ROMANO. 1968. Ultrastructural modifications of the intercalated disc during hypothermia in the rat and the ground squirrel. *Cryobiology*, **4,** 317–328.

B Vertebrate smooth muscle

The major junctional structure seen between vertebrate smooth muscle cells is the *nexus* or *gap junction*. For a number of years controversy existed as to the actual form of this junction but this has now been resolved by freeze-etch studies and the use of tracer substances such as lanthanum hydroxide.

The overall thickness of the apposed membranes in the region of the gap junction is about 15 nm, and the gap between is approximately 2–4 nm. The gap is not uniform but is interrupted by a quasi-hexagonal lattice of units which bridge it at a periodicity of about 10 nm. This structure is comparable to that described for cardiac muscle (see Chapter 6A). Gap junctions have also been observed at electrical synapses between neurones.

Direct evidence of the function of these gap junctions for electrotonic coupling has been shown by microelectrode experiments with cultured smooth muscle cells. However, their role in other processes has not as yet been established. The passage of dyes such as fluorescein and neutral red across gap junctions of electrically coupled cultured cells is well documented. One would expect similar transjunctional fluxes to occur in smooth muscle. Details of the number and arrangement of gap junctions in smooth muscle effector bundles in different organs and their relation to density of innervation have not yet been determined.

The 'tight junction' is another type of close apposition between cells, where there appears to be complete fusion of the outer leaflets of apposing plasma membranes. Tight junctions were reported between smooth muscle cells in earlier literature, but more recent high resolution studies, including the use of lanthanum and freeze-etch studies suggest that this is not the case. While they do not appear in smooth muscle, they are present in epithelial cells, where they prevent leakage of substances across the epithelium through the extracellular space. Thus, tight junctions are often called occluding junctions, since they are impermeable to tracer substances and usually form a complete band around the cell.

Plate 113

Gap junctions are often present when a protrusion of one smooth muscle cell comes into close contact with another. Gap junctions in smooth muscle sometimes extend for several microns.

Gap junction between vertebrate smooth muscle cells: ureter of sheep. OsO_4–glutaraldehyde–OsO_4 fixation. ×160 000. (Reproduced from Uehara, Y. and G. Burnstock, 1970, *J. Cell Biol.*, **44,** 215.)

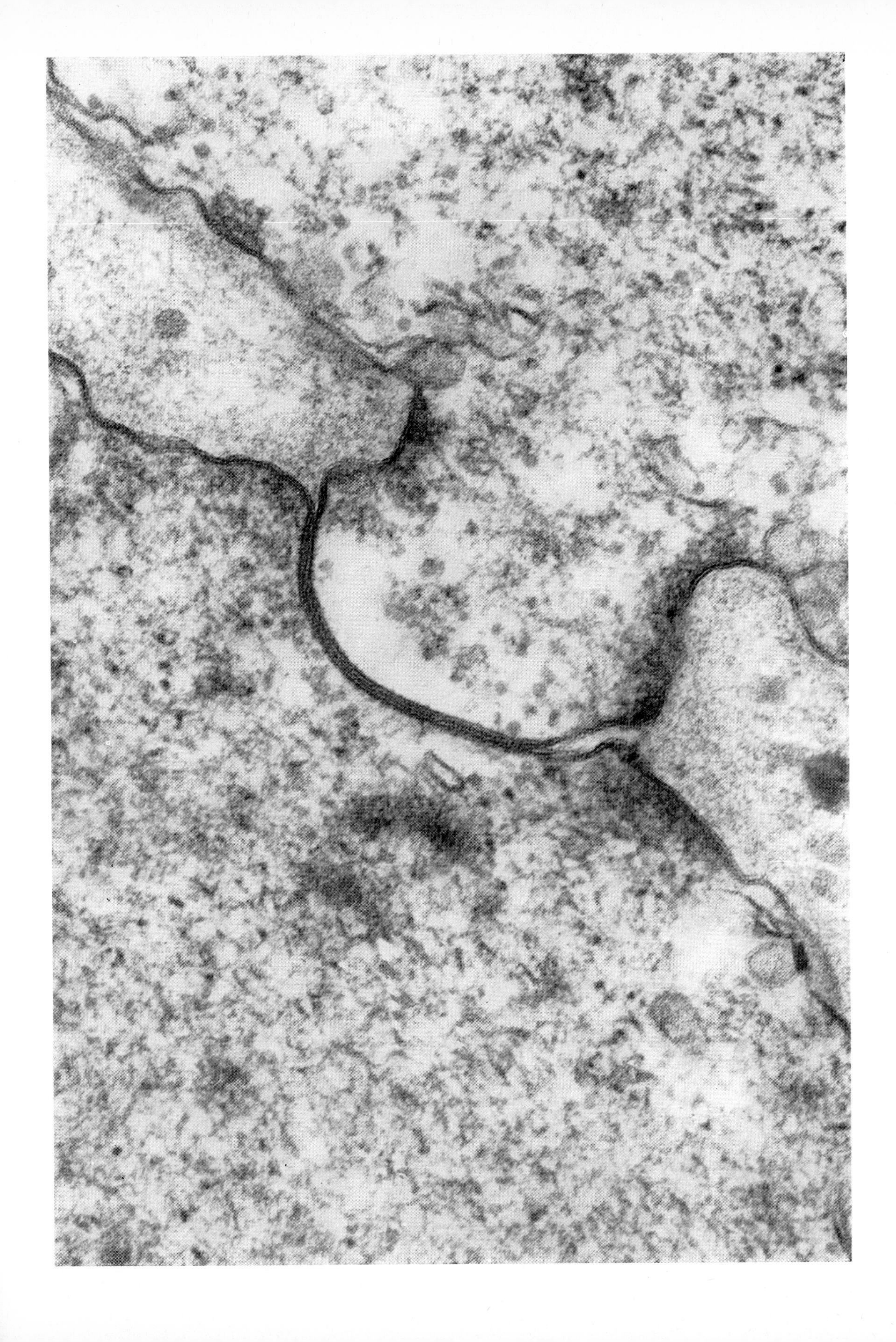

Plate 114

The gap junction consists of seven layers and is 18 ± 1 nm thick. The outer leaflets of the plasma membrane are separated from each other by a gap of 2–3 nm except in regions where the leaflets appear to be fused (arrows). These form extracellular channels which are the basis of the hexagonal lattice observed in freeze-etch and lanthanum preparations.

Gap junction between cultured vertebrate smooth muscle cells: 16-day chicken gizzard 4 days in culture. Glutaraldehyde fixation. × 1 000 000. (Reproduced from Campbell, G. R., Y. Uehara, G. Mark and G. Burnstock, 1971, *J. Cell Biol.*, **49,** 21.)

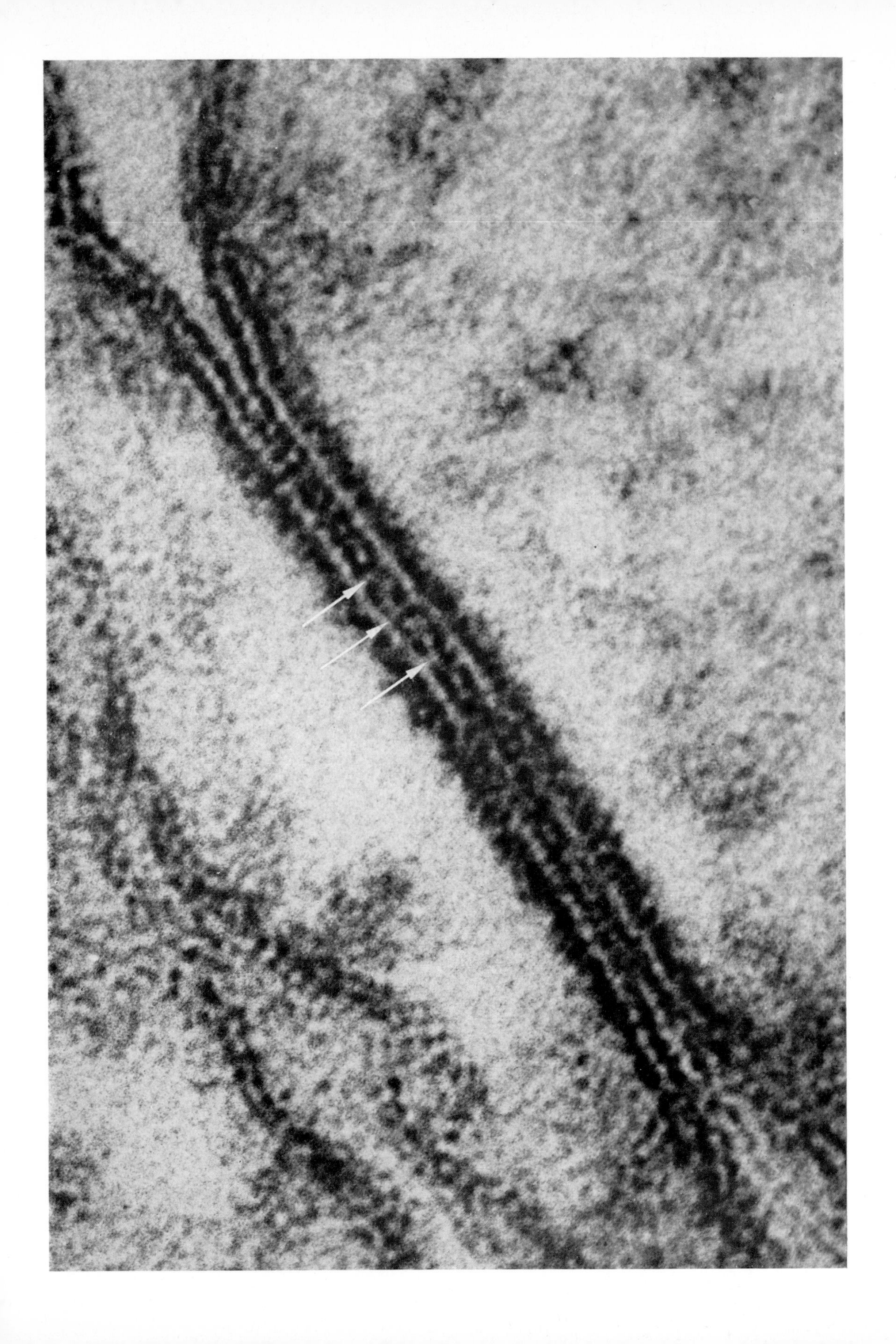

Plate 115

Few desmosomes have been observed between adult smooth muscle cells, although some, in modified form, appear during development. In the accompanying plate, the junction appears in the form of two 'dense areas' separated by a gap of 40 nm and bisected by a 20 nm thick line of electron-dense material.

Desmosome-like junction between vertebrate smooth muscle cells: guinea-pig taenia coli. Glutaraldehyde fixation. ×157 000.

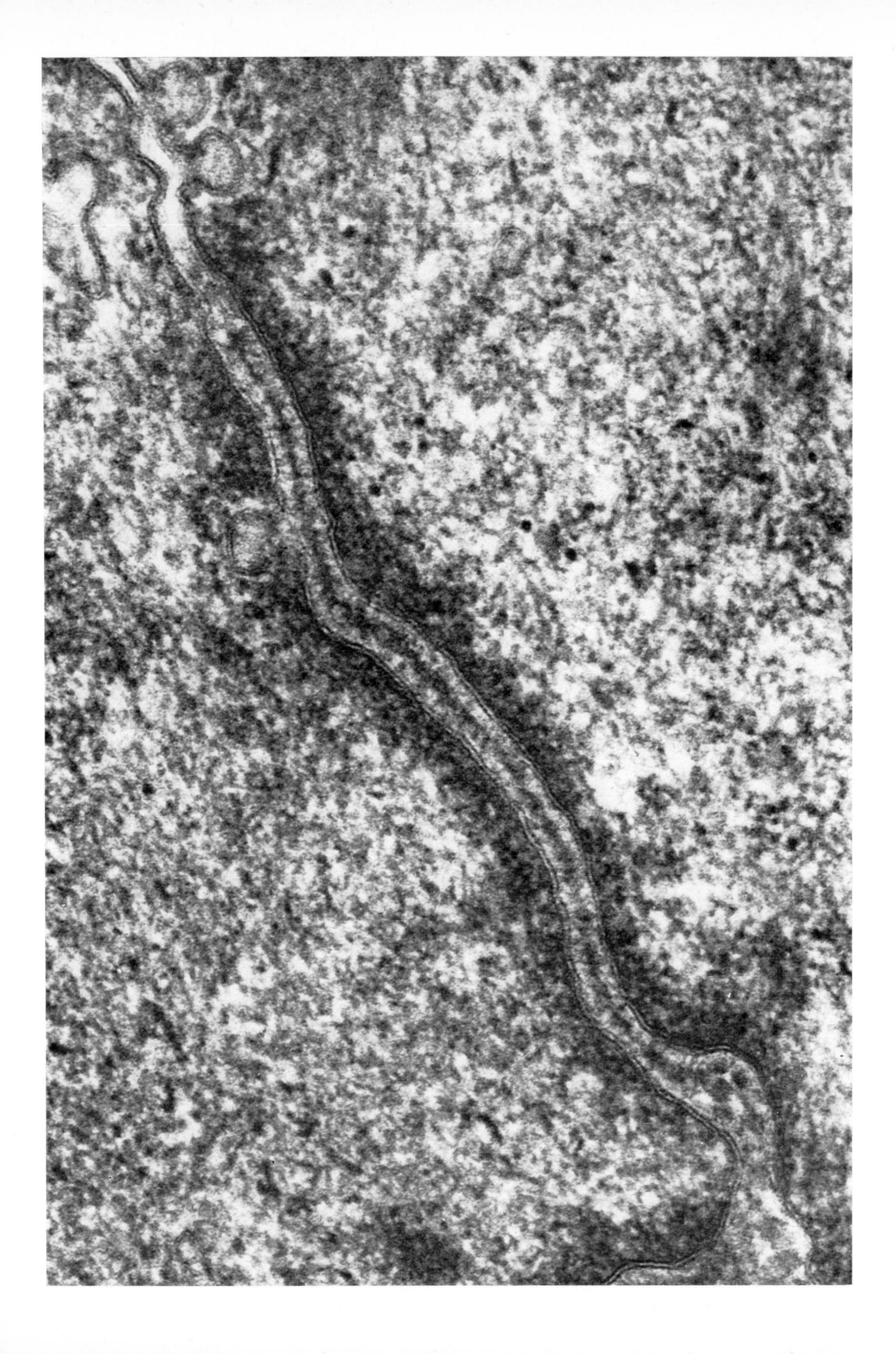

Selected articles

BARR, L., W. BERGER and M. M. DEWEY. 1968. Electrical transmission at the nexus between smooth muscle cells. *J. gen. Physiol.*, **51,** 347–368.

COBB, J. L. S. and T. BENNETT. 1969*a*. A study of intercellular relationships in developing and mature visceral smooth muscle. *Z. Zellforsch. mikrosk. Anat.*, **100,** 516–526.

COBB, J. L. S. and T. BENNETT. 1969*b*. A study of nexuses in visceral smooth muscle. *J. Cell Biol.*, **41,** 287–298.

DEWEY, M. M. 1965. The anatomical basis of propagation in smooth muscle. *Gastroenterology*, **49,** 395–402.

DEWEY, M. M. and L. BARR. 1962. Intercellular connection between smooth muscle cells: the nexus. *Science, N.Y.*, **137,** 670–671.

DEWEY, M. M. and L. BARR. 1964. A study of the structure and distribution of the nexus. *J. Cell Biol.*, **23,** 553–585.

EVANS, D. H. L. and E. M. EVANS. 1964. The membrane relationships of smooth muscles: an electron microscope study. *J. Anat.*, **98,** 37–46.

GABELLA, G. 1972. Intercellular junctions between circular and longitudinal intestinal muscle layers. *Z. Zellforsch. mikrosk. Anat.*, **125,** 191–199.

HARMAN, J. W., M. T. O'HEGARTY and C. K. BYRNES. 1962. Ultrastructure of human smooth muscle. I. Studies of cell surface and connections in normal and achalasia esophageal smooth muscle. *Exp. mol. Pathol.*, **1,** 204–228.

HENDERSON, R. M., G. DUCHON and E. E. DANIEL. 1971. Cell contacts in duodenal smooth muscle layers. *Am. J. Physiol.*, **221,** 564–574.

IWAYAMA, T. 1971. Nexuses between areas of the surface membrane of the same arterial smooth muscle cell. *J. Cell Biol.*, **49,** 521–524.

KELLY, R. E. 1973. Intercalated disc-like structures in transitional smooth muscle. *Anat. Rec.*, **175,** 356.

LANE, B. P. and J. A. G. RHODIN. 1964. Cellular interrelationships and electrical activity in two types of smooth muscle. *J. Ultrastruct. Res.*, **10,** 470–488.

NAGASAWA, J. and T. SUZUKI. 1967. Electron microscopic study on the cellular interrelationships in the smooth muscle. *Tohoku J. exp. Med.*, **91,** 299–313.

OOSAKI, T. and S. ISHII. 1964. Junctional structure of smooth muscle cells. The ultrastructure of the regions of junction between smooth muscle cells in the rat small intestine. *J. Ultrastruct. Res.*, **10,** 567–577.

PACE, J. L. 1968. The interconnexions of the muscle layers of the human colon. *J. Anat.*, **103,** 289–296.

ROGERS, D. 1972. Cell contacts and smooth muscle bundle formation in tissue transplants into the anterior eye chamber. *Z. Zellforsch. mikrosk. Anat.*, **133,** 21–33.

THAEMERT, J. C. 1959. Intercellular bridges as protoplasmic anastomoses between smooth muscle cells. *J. biophys. biochem. Cytol.*, **6,** 67–70.

UEHARA, Y. and G. BURNSTOCK. 1970. Demonstration of 'gap junctions' between smooth muscle cells. *J. Cell Biol.*, **44,** 215–217.

C Invertebrate muscle

Junctions of a similar nature to those found in vertebrate muscle are present in invertebrates. For example, intercalated discs are present in the neurogenic hearts of lobster, shrimp, arachnids, and cockroach as well as in the myogenic hearts of moth and snail. However, the gap junction of the intercalated disc of the arachnid, *Limulus* is absent.

Some morphological differences between 'gap junctions' have also been noted. For example those seen in *Hydra* resemble the gap junction seen in adult vertebrates, but have an increased gap of 3–4 nm and larger (8.5 nm) subunits of the hexagonal lattice.

Plate 116

The desmosome illustrated has a similar orm to that described in vertebrate cardiac muscle, with electron dense material along the inner leaflet of the two opposing membranes (see Plate 109). A number of filaments, 6–8 nm in diameter, appear to be associated with the dense material. The gap between the two cells is approximately 25 nm and is almost completely filled with electron dense material.

Desmosome in an invertebrate visceral obliquely striated muscle: earthworm gut. Glutaraldehyde fixation. × 222 000.

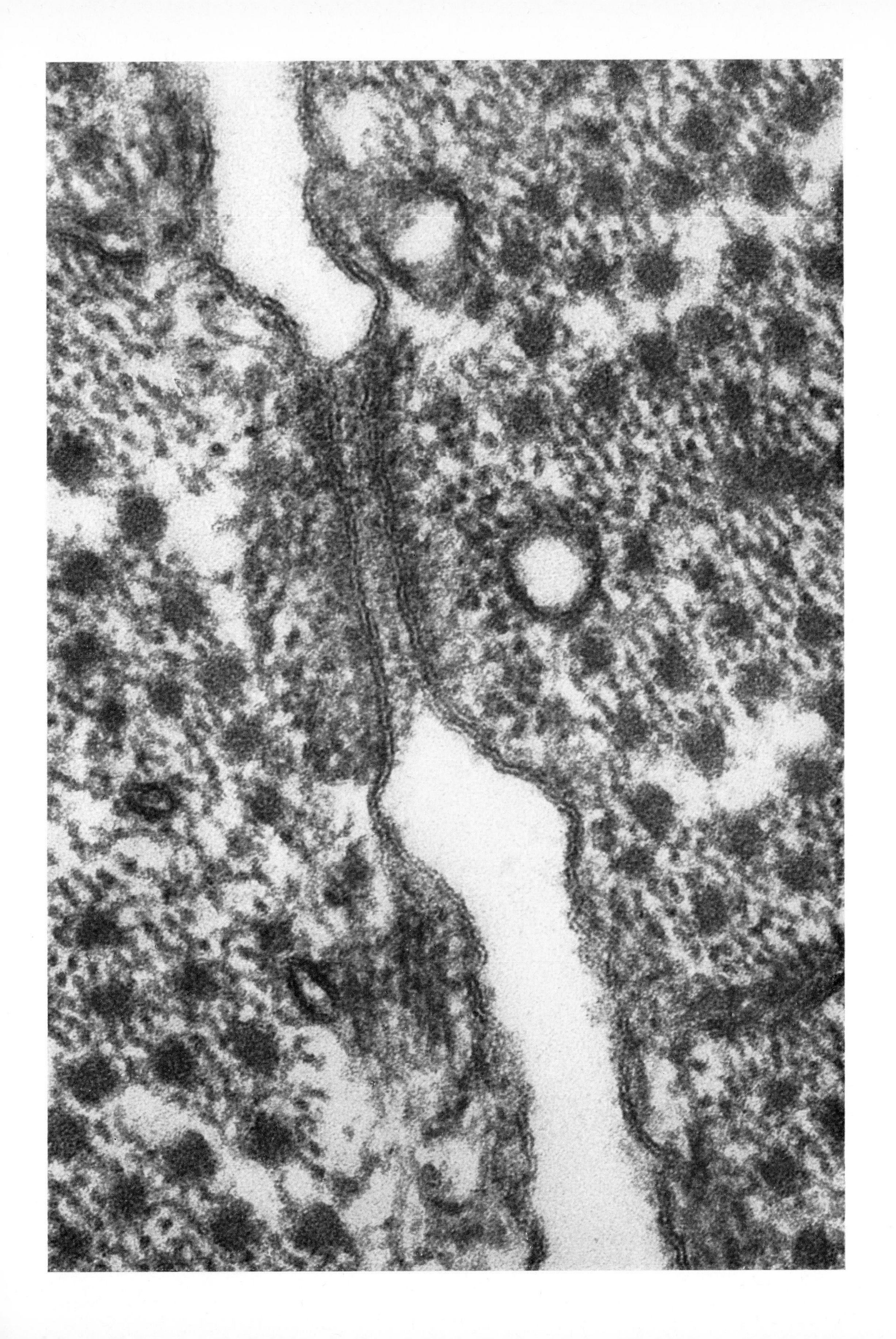

Plate 117

The junction illustrated has features characteristic of desmosomes seen in vertebrate cells, such as electron dense material along the cell membrane, and a fairly constant distance between the cells over the extent of the junction. While there appears to be no indication of an intermediate electron dense line between the two cells, a cementing substance may be present which is not preserved with the fixation procedure used.

Desmosome-like junction between invertebrate muscle cells: starfish tube foot. Glutaraldehyde fixation. × 123 000

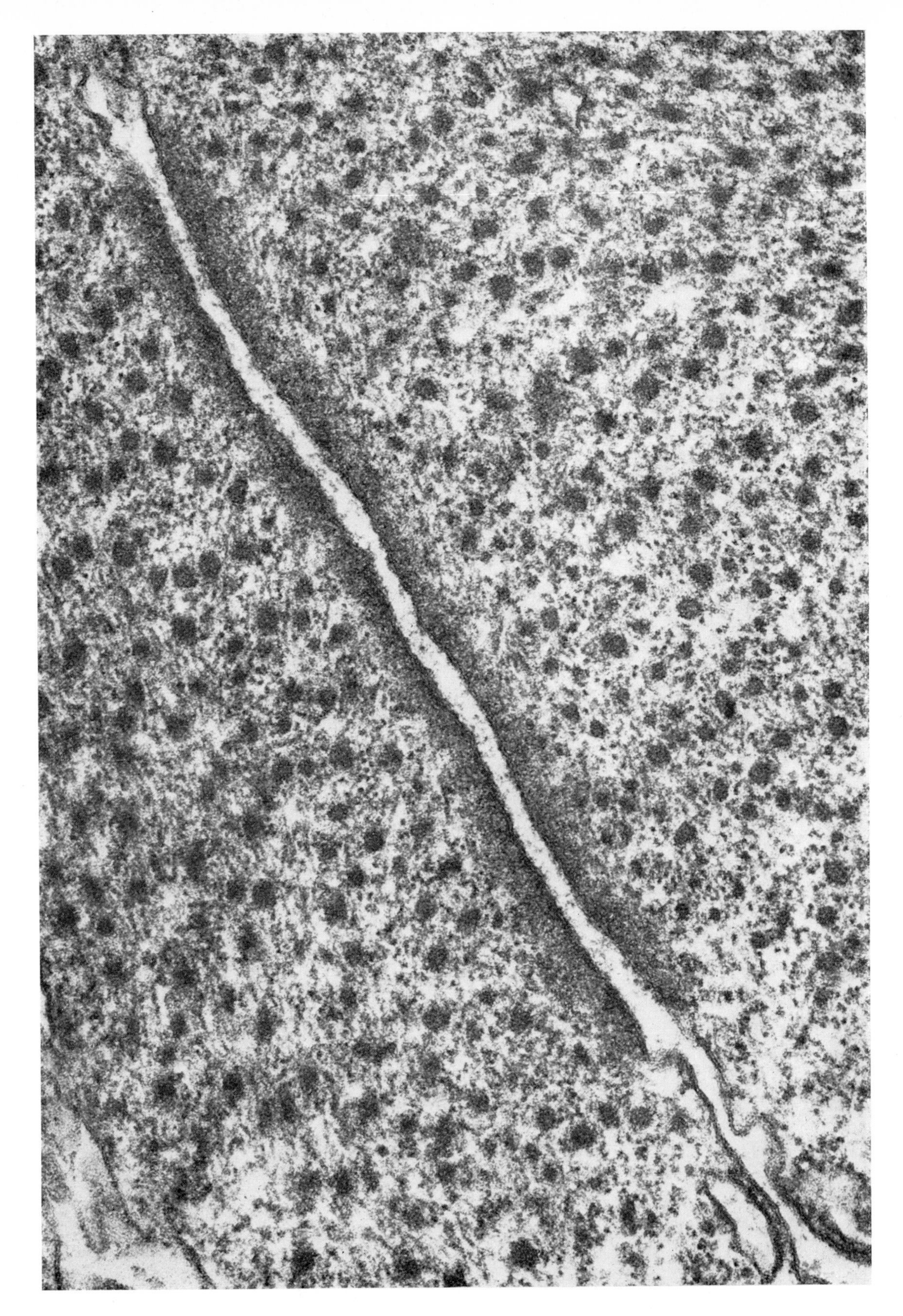

M I—M

Selected articles

ASHHURST, D. E. 1970. An insect desmosome. *J. Cell Biol.*, **46,** 421–425.

FLOWER, N. E. 1971. Septate and gap junctions between the epithelial cells of an invertebrate, the mollusc *Cominella maculosa*. *J. Ultrastruct. Res.*, **37,** 259–268.

GILULA, N. B. and P. SATIR. 1971. Septate and gap junctions in molluscan gill epithelium. *J. Cell Biol.*, **51,** 869–872.

HAND, A. R. and S. GOBEL. 1972. The structural organization of the septate and gap junctions of *Hydra*. *J. Cell Biol.*, **52,** 397–408.

HUDSPETH, A. J. and J.-P. REVEL. 1971. Coexistence of gap and septate junctions in an invertebrate epithelium. *J. Cell Biol.*, **50,** 92–101.

JOHNSON, R. G., W. S. HERMAN and D. M. PREUS. 1973. Homocellular and heterocellular gap junctions in *Limulus*: a thin-section and freeze-fracture study. *J. Ultrastruct. Res.*, **43,** 298–312.

LASANSKY, A. 1967. Cell junctions in ommatidia of *Limulus*. *J. Cell Biol.*, **33,** 365–384.

McKENNA, O. C. and J. ROSENBLUTH. 1973. Myoneural and intermuscular junctions in a molluscan smooth-muscle. *J. Ultrastruct. Res.*, **42,** 434–450.

TWAROG, B. M., M. M. DEWEY and T. HIDAKA. 1973. The structure of *Mytilus* smooth muscle and the electrical constants of the resting muscle. *J. gen. Physiol.*, **61,** 207–221.

7 Innervation

A Nerve fibres

Nerve fibres are the extended processes of nerve cells or neurones. Most nerves consist of a bundle of hundreds of these fibres. In a typical motor neurone, one process of the cell body, the *axon*, which carries impulses to the effector is much longer than the remaining processes, known as *dendrites*; in sensory neurones a single dendrite (or dendron) is often longer than the axon. The region of the cell body from which the axon arises is called the *axon hillock*. The axon carries messages to muscle effector organs, while the dendrites carry messages from the axons of other nerve fibres.

This chapter is concerned largely with the ultrastructure of neuromuscular junctions where messages are transmitted from the axon terminals to muscle cells. However, a brief account of nerve fibre structure and function is included in this section. Axons of the peripheral nervous system are typically surrounded by a Schwann cell sheath. In the *myelinated* (or medullated) nerve fibres of vertebrates, the Schwann cells are specialized to form a thick sheath of myelin lamellae, which acts as an insulating layer. Each Schwann cell forms a single myelin segment and the zone between adjacent segments is known as the *node of Ranvier*. Nodes are regions of low insulating resistance and are involved in the specialized saltatory conduction that operates in vertebrate myelinated nerves to facilitate fast propagation of impulses and the distance between them is approximately proportional to the diameter of the fibre. In the *non-myelinated* nerves of invertebrates and vertebrates (particularly in the autonomic nervous system), the Schwann sheath is very thin and sometimes only partially envelops the axon.

Impulses are conducted along axons in an all-or-none fashion at velocities of from 0.5–2 m s^{-1} in small diameter C fibres (autonomic and some sensory), 3–14 m s^{-1} in B fibres (mainly visceral sensory) and from 15–100 m s^{-1} in large diameter A fibres (motor and some sensory). Essentially the nerve fibre is a polarized cable-like structure, organized such that changes in electrical potential are transmitted by local current flow to adjacent regions. According to the ionic hypothesis, impulses are conducted by a mechanism involving the distribution of charged ions, particularly Na^+, K^+ and Cl^-, between the axoplasm and the extracellular fluid, and also by the special properties of the excitable membrane which determine the passage of these ions across the membrane. In the resting state, the inside of the nerve fibre has a resting potential of about 100 mV negative relative to the outside, due largely to the distribution of potassium ions. During the passage of an impulse, this potential is briefly reversed to form the action potential, as the result of a sudden increase in the conductivity of the membrane to sodium ions. This sets up a disequilibrium of charge across adjacent regions of the nerve membrane, which leads to passive electrotonic depolarization of the membrane and initiation of an action potential further down the nerve. In this way the action potential is self-propagating and all-or-none conduction occurs.

It is interesting that an understanding of the mechanism of impulse conduction down nerve fibres was developed mainly from work on the squid giant axon, a fibre about a half a millimetre in diameter, far larger than any nerve fibres known in vertebrates. The process of spreading activation is made much more efficient in vertebrate myelinated nerve by the insulating sheath, which increases efficiency about 10 times. Furthermore, since the ionic exchange is restricted to the narrow nodal areas between the myelinated segments, and the internodal areas have such a low capacity, a small proportion of the ionic exchange occurs relative to non-myelinated axons of similar size; this again represents a gain in efficiency.

Axoplasm contains mainly *neurotubules*, *neurofilaments*, mitochondria and vesicles of various sizes. There is evidence for both anterograde (towards axon terminal) and retrograde (towards cell body) translocation of material along axons. Particulate material, including vesicles and associated enzymes, flow to the axon terminals at a relatively fast rate of about 10 mm h^{-1}, while axonal proteins flow at a slower rate of about 0.5 mm h^{-1}.

Plate 118

Each neurone cell body or *soma* consists of a *nucleus* and the surrounding cytoplasm, often called the *perikaryon*. The nucleus is large and generally spherical to oval in shape, with a prominent nucleolus. In the cytoplasm or perikaryon are Golgi complexes, granular vesicles, mitochondria, Nissl bodies or rough endoplasmic reticulum, free ribosomes, neurotubules, neurofilaments, lysosomes, lipofuscin granules, and multivesicular bodies.

In many parts of the autonomic nervous system, a satellite or mantle cell usually invests each ganglion cell. The nucleus of the satellite cell is small with a relatively large nucleolus. The cytoplasm contains mitochondria, rough endoplasmic reticulum, a large number of free ribosomes, Golgi complexes, filaments and dense bodies.

Autonomic neurone: rat superior cervical ganglion. Longitudinal section. OsO_4–glutaraldehyde–OsO_4 fixation. ×9700. (Courtesy of J. Heath, B. Evans, B. Gannon, G. Burnstock and V. James, 1972, *Virch. Arch. Abt. B. Zellpath.*, **11,** 182.)

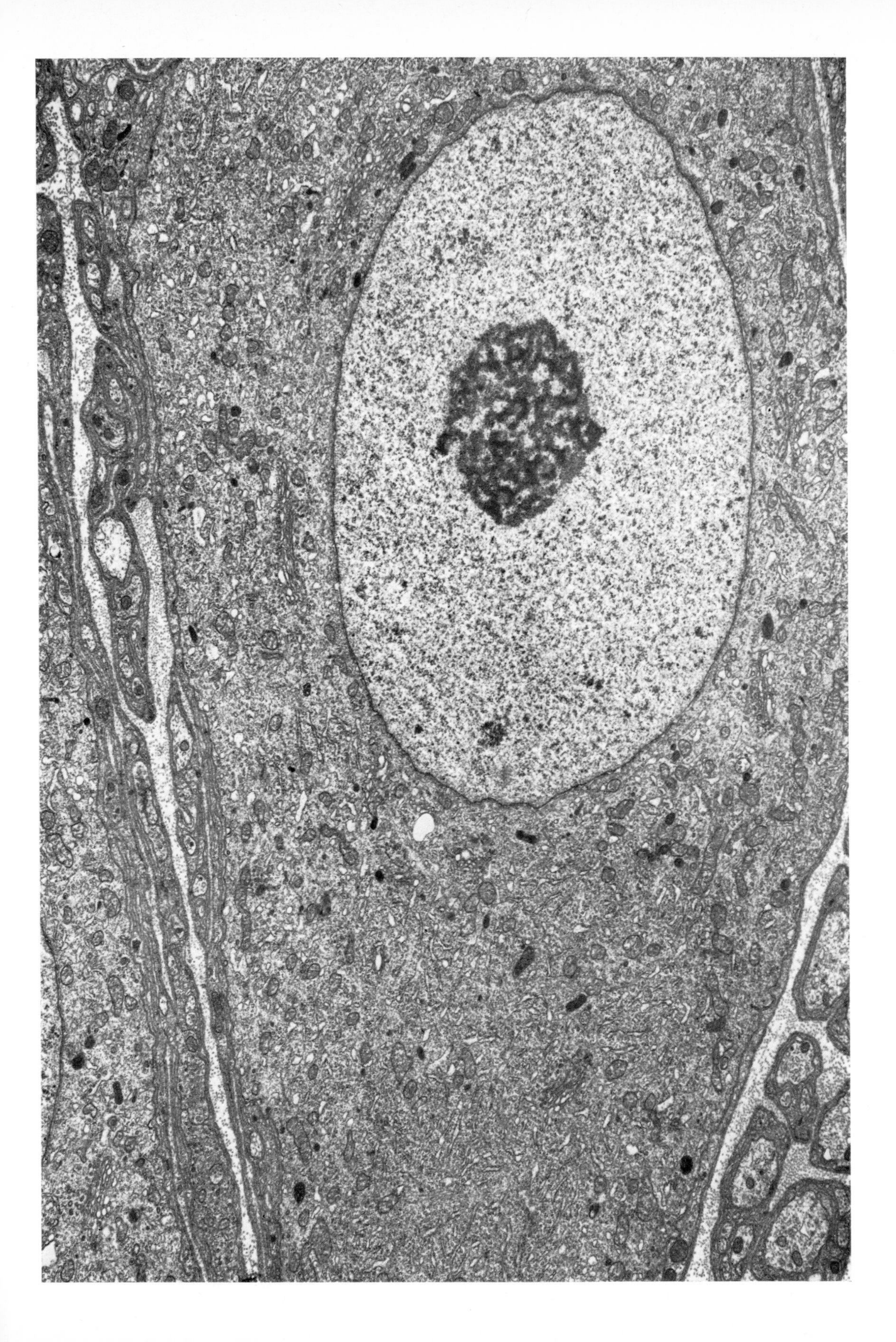

Plate 119

Nissl bodies are a major cytoplasmic component of the perikaryon of neurones. When stained with basic aniline dyes such as toluidine blue, thionine, or crystal violet, Nissl bodies appear as coarse granules throughout the perikaryon, except in the axon hillock region. They are present in dendrites, but not axons.

With the electron microscope, the Nissl bodies are seen to consist of aggregations of rough endoplasmic reticulum in ordered parallel array. Clusters or rosettes of free ribosomes are present between the arrays of rough endoplasmic reticulum. Nissl bodies are sites of protein synthesis.

Nissl body in neurone: intramural autonomic neurone in finch ureter. Glutaraldehyde fixation. ×123 000.

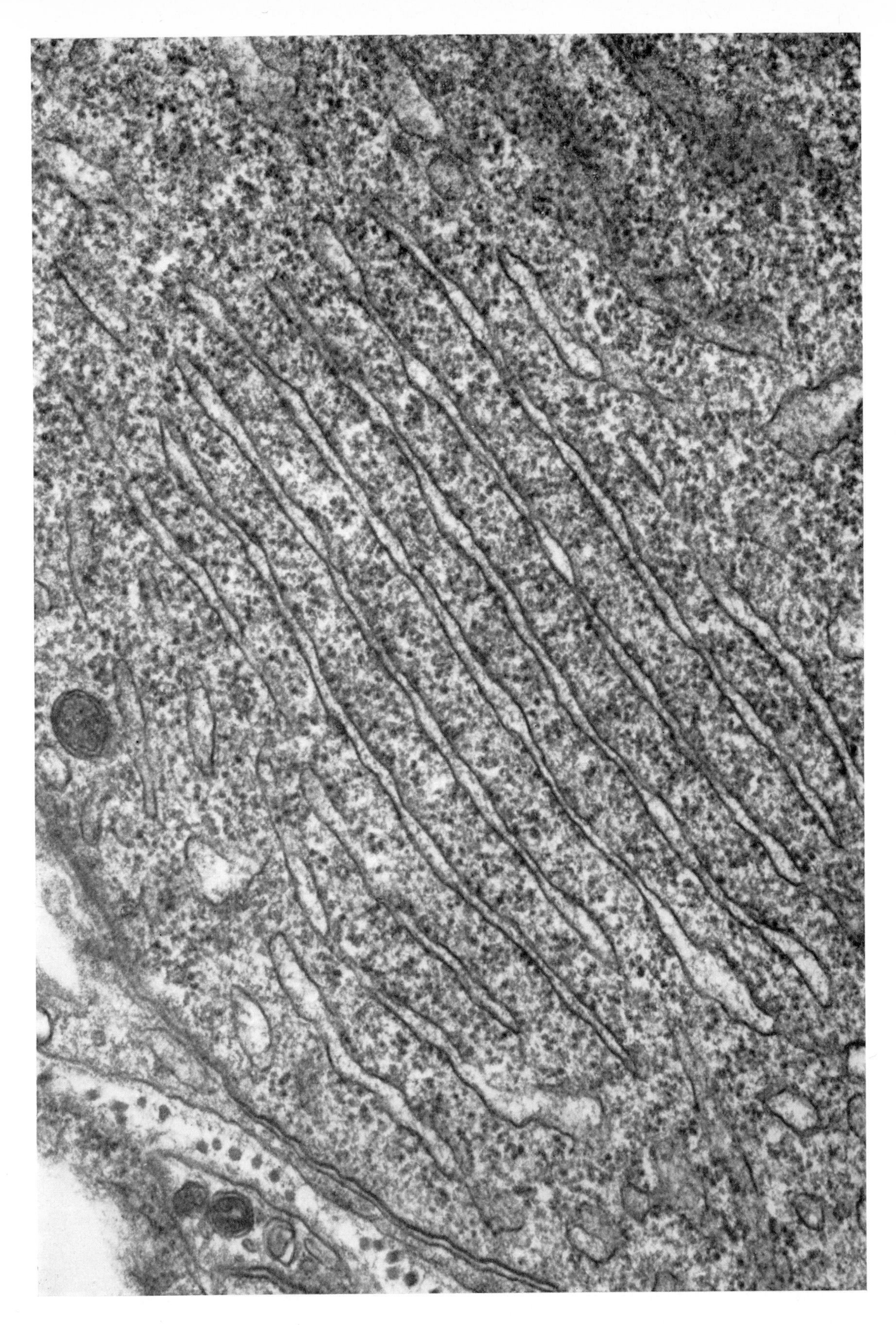

Plate 120

Processes of postganglionic nerve cell bodies in autonomic ganglia are usually non-myelinated and consist of both dendrites and axons. Preganglionic fibres in ganglia are often myelinated. Axons (Ax) are in close association with Schwann cells (Sw). The axons contain mitochondria, neurotubules and neurofilaments, a small amount of smooth endoplasmic reticulum, and a few large and small vesicles.

Autonomic nerve processes within ganglia: rat superior cervical ganglion. OsO_4–glutaraldehyde–OsO_4 fixation. ×10 800.

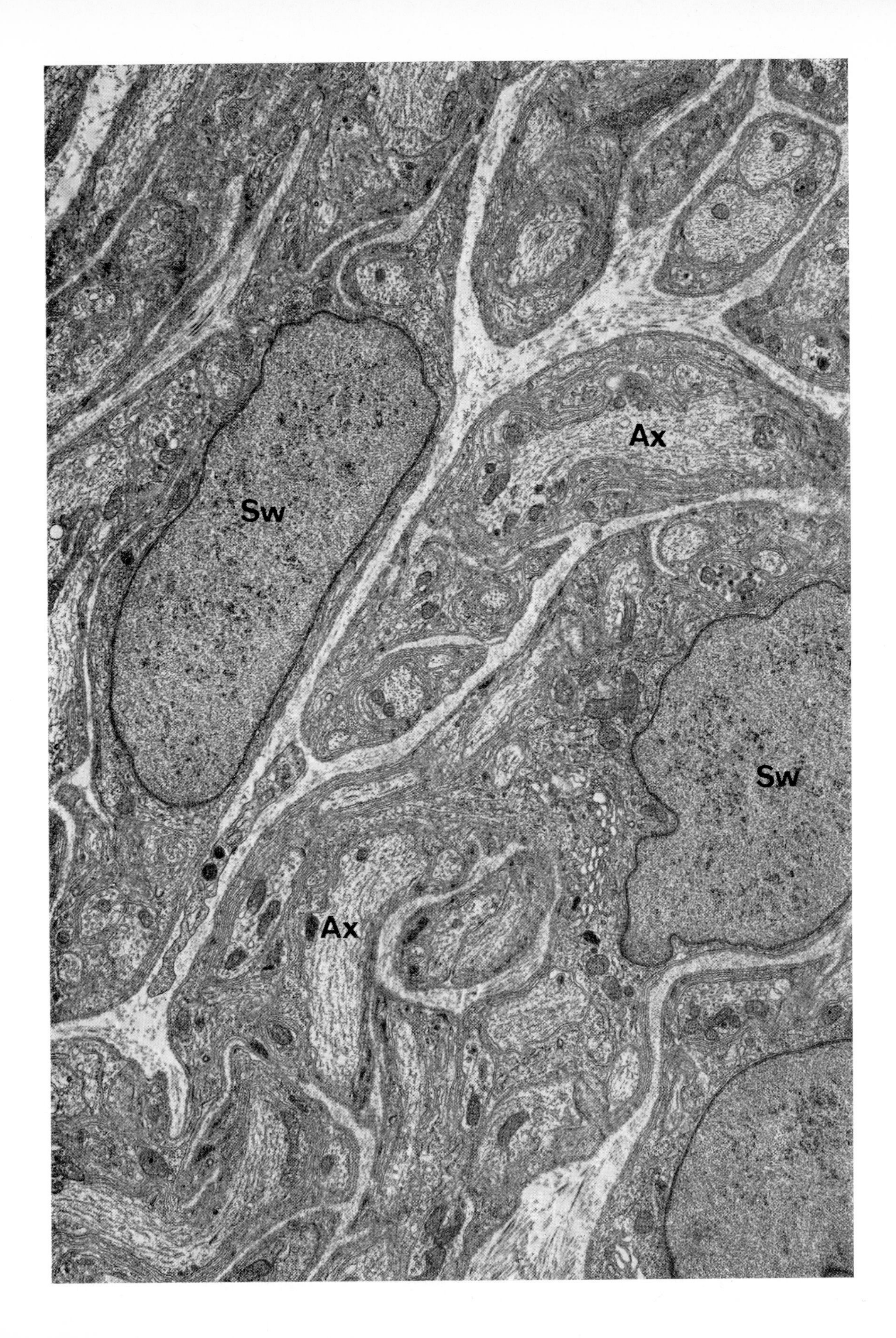

Ax
Sw
Sw
Ax

Plate 121

Motor nerve fibres supplying skeletal muscles are myelinated. The myelin sheath appears as a series of light and dark lines in a repeating unit about 12 nm wide completely surrounding the axon, which contains neurofilaments and neurotubules (see also Plate 125). The spiral of lamellae commences on the inside of the sheath at the *internal mesaxon* (Im) and terminates on the outside of the sheath at the *external mesaxon* (Om). The dark line of the repeating unit is about 3 nm wide and is formed through the apposition of the inner surface (i.e. the cytoplasmic side) of the *Schwann cell* (Sw) membrane. Midway between each of the dark lines is a less dense intraperiod line which represents the union of the outer surface of the Schwann cell membrane.

Myelinated nerve: nerve trunk supplying rat rectus femoris muscle. Transverse section. OsO_4–glutaraldehyde –OsO_4 fixation. ×50 000.

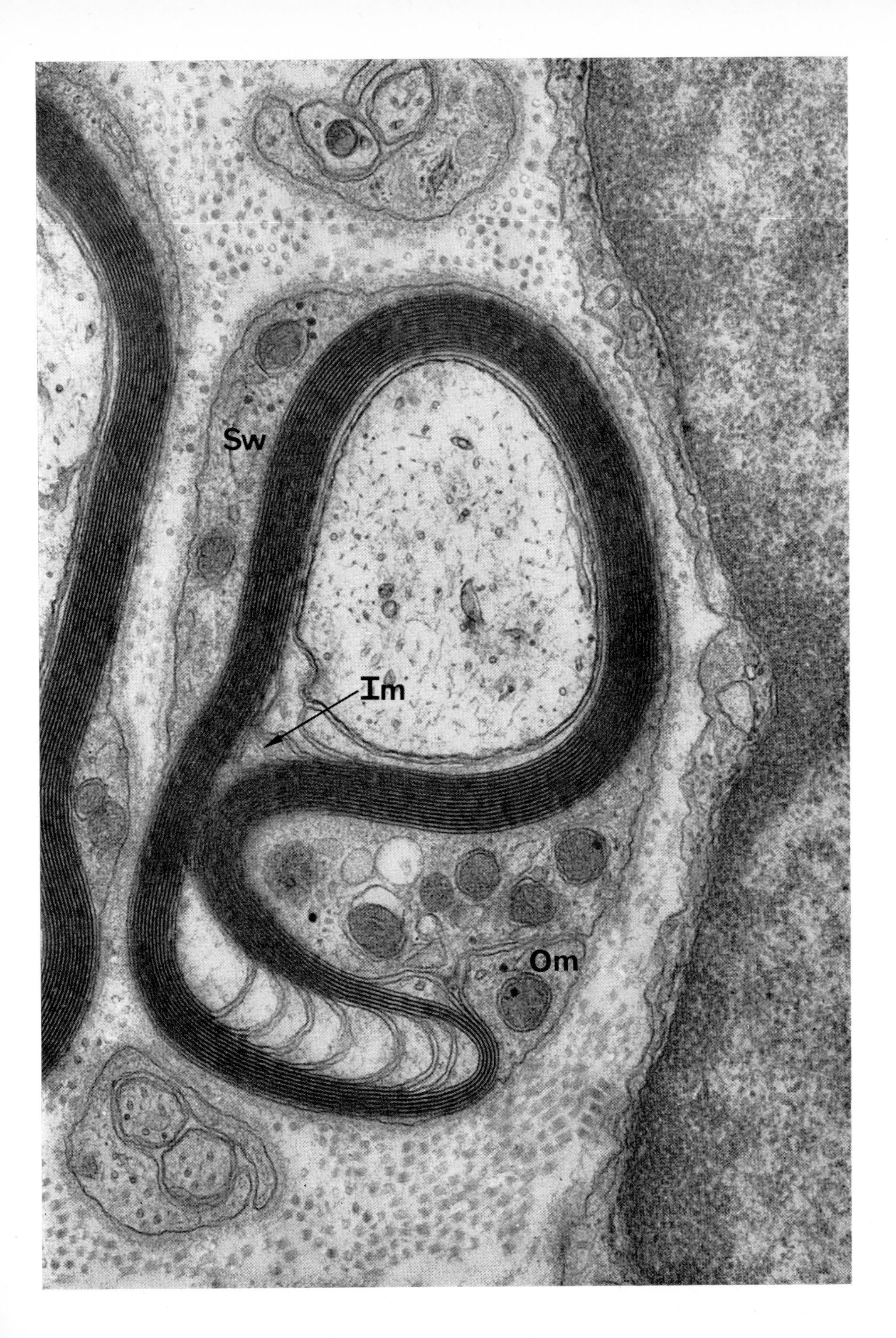
Sw
Im
Om

Plate 122

At the region of the node of Ranvier, the myelin sheath is interrupted. This marks the extent of successive Schwann cells along the nerve fibre. In longitudinal section, it can be seen that myelin peels off successively on both sides of the node, forming a series of loops containing Schwann cytoplasm. Although not enclosed by a myelin sheath, the axon remains surrounded by finger-like processes of the Schwann cells on either side of the node. In transverse sections through the node, the axon is enclosed by a complex arrangement of Schwann cell processes. Intercellular spaces can be traced from the axon surface to the tissue space containing collagen fibrils. The basal lamina of the Schwann cells forms the external investment of the nodes.

Node of Ranvier in myelinated nerve: nerve trunks supplying rat rectus femoris muscle.
(*a*) Longitudinal section. ×26 700.
(*b*) Transverse section. ×29 000.
OsO_4–glutaraldehyde–OsO_4 fixation.

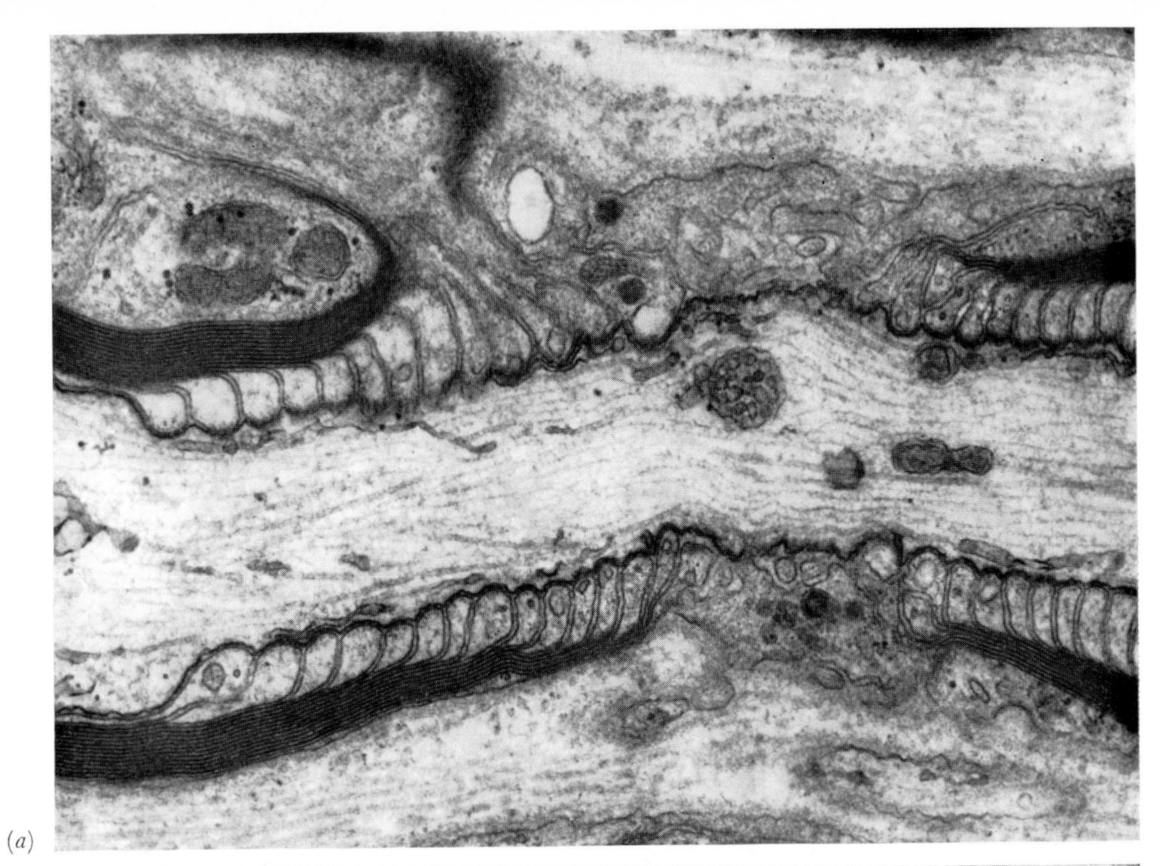

(*a*)

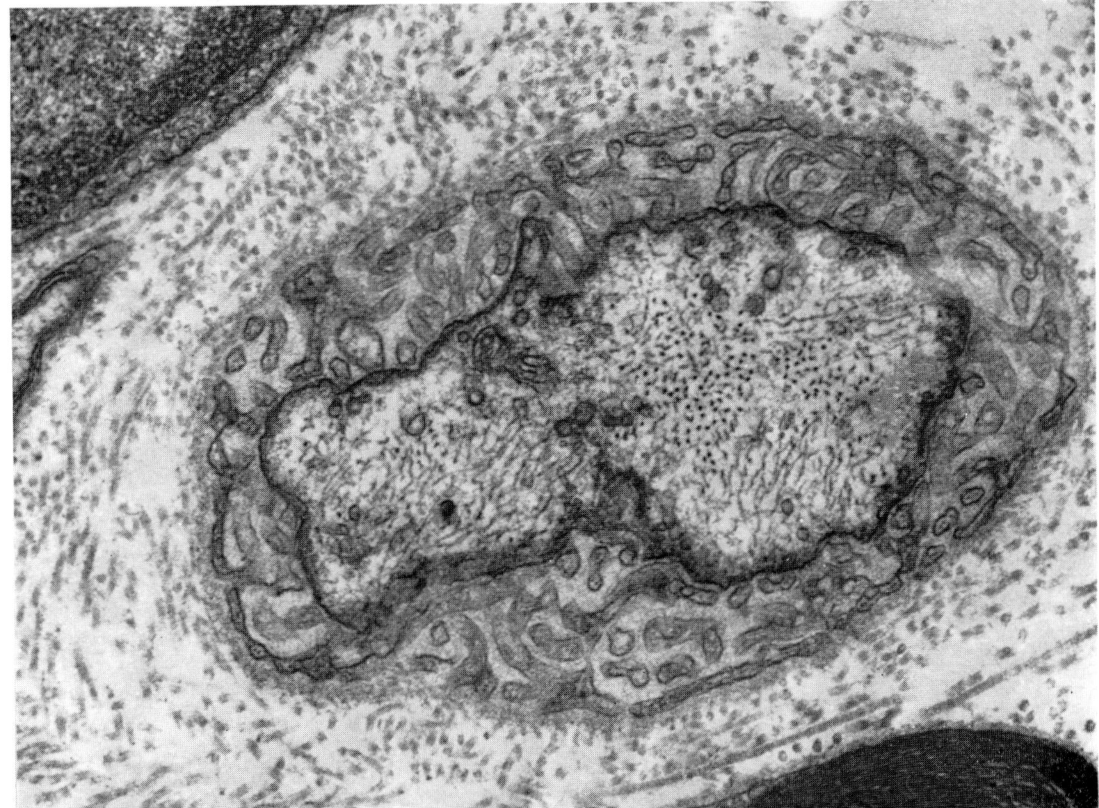

(*b*)

Plate 123

The myelin in the region where the myelin sheath terminates, near to the motor end plate, peels off forming a series of pockets containing Schwann cell cytoplasm, comparable to those seen at the nodes of Ranvier.

Termination of myelin sheath near motor end plate: rat anterior tibialis muscle. Longitudinal section. Glutaraldehyde fixation. ×17 200.

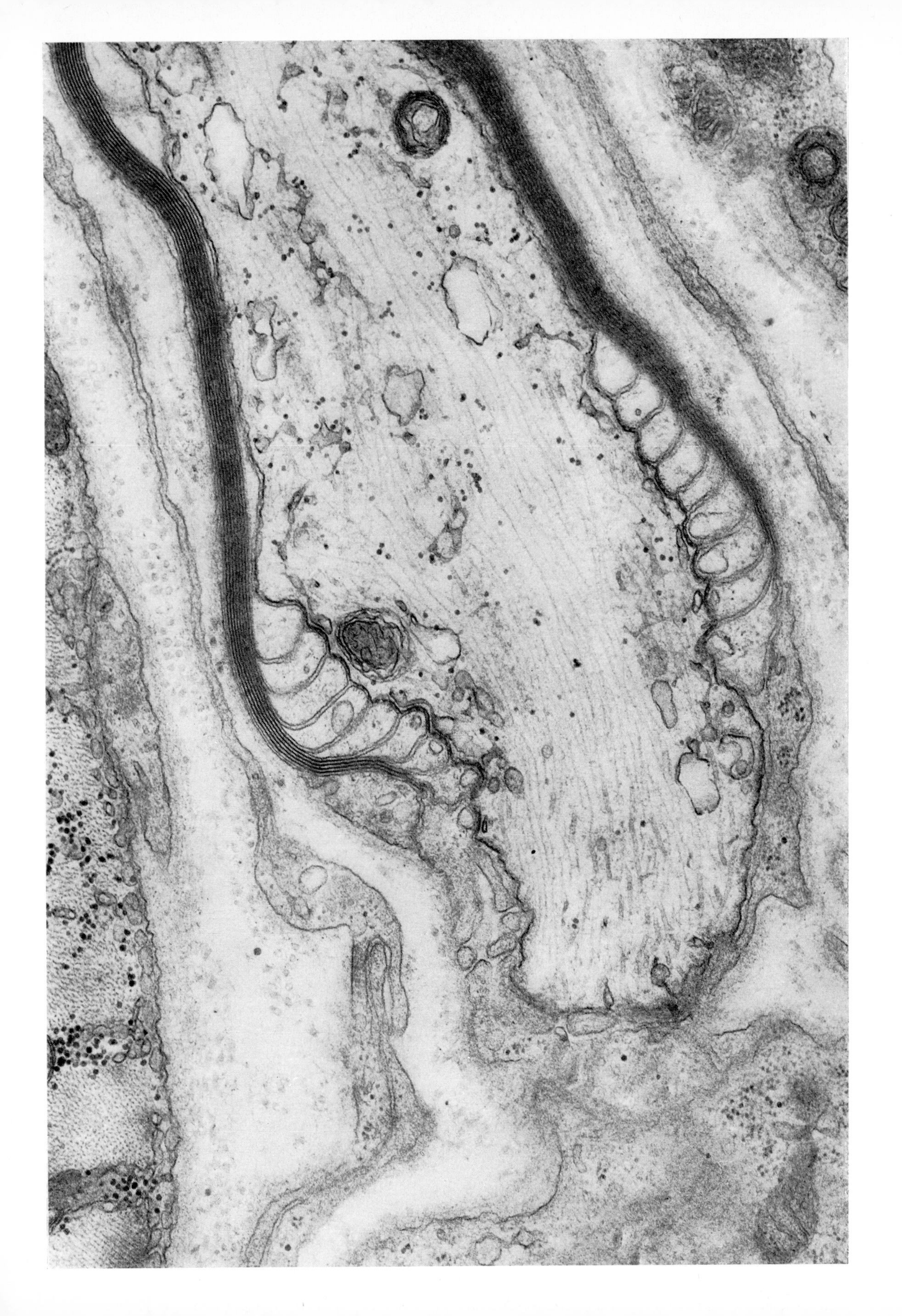

Plate 124

In nonmyelinated nerves, Schwann cells do not form a myelin sheath but surround the axons by their processes. The number of axons per Schwann cell varies considerably (from 1 to more than 40) in different nerve trunks. In the micrograph illustrated, Schwann cell processes (Sw) appear to pass randomly between the axons and have a flatter profile.

Nonmyelinated nerve fibres: mouse vas deferens. Transverse section. Glutaraldehyde fixation. ×52 000.

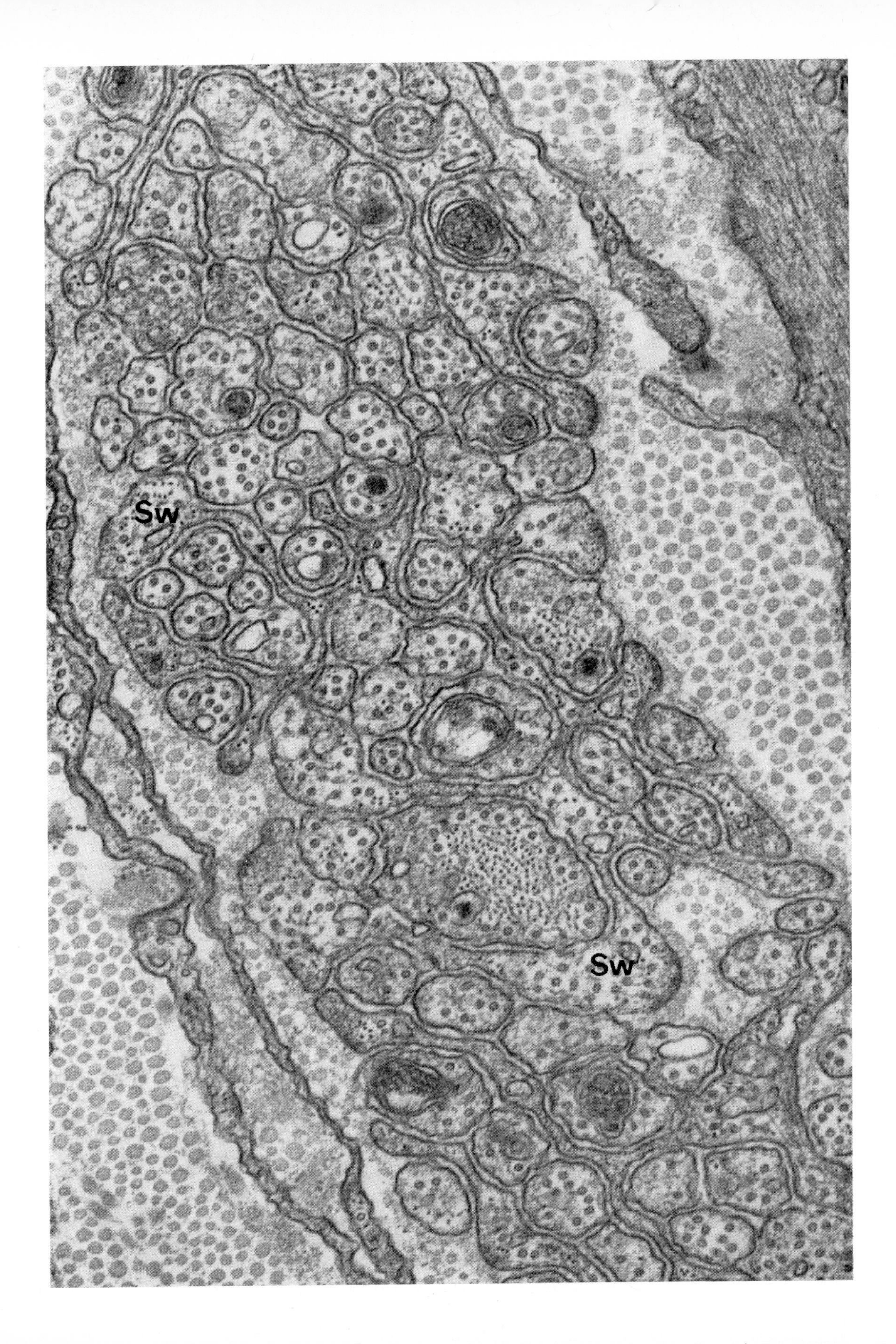
Sw
Sw

Plate 125

In the electronmicrograph illustrated, each axon (Ax) is surrounded by and separated from its neighbours by a Schwann cell sheath (Sw). Axons contain mitochondria, neurotubules (single headed arrow), neurofilaments (double headed arrow), large granular vesicles, and small granular vesicles. The neurotubules (which are comparable to microtubules found in other cell types) are approximately 25 nm in diameter with a 10 nm thick wall and are up to 8 μm long. They consist of a filamentous substructure, the wall being composed of thirteen protofilaments. The main protein of the neurotubules is *tubulin*. Neurofilaments are circular in profile and about 10 nm in diameter. They are helical structures comprising four subfilaments each 3 nm in diameter around an electron-opaque core. The subfilaments are composed of 3 nm globules or subunits possibly of the protein *filarin*.

A number of functions have been suggested for neurotubules and neurofilaments, including mechanical support, axoplasmic flow, nerve movement and transmitter release.

Nonmyelinated nerve fibres: guinea-pig vas deferens. Transverse section. Glutaraldehyde fixation. $\times$110 000.

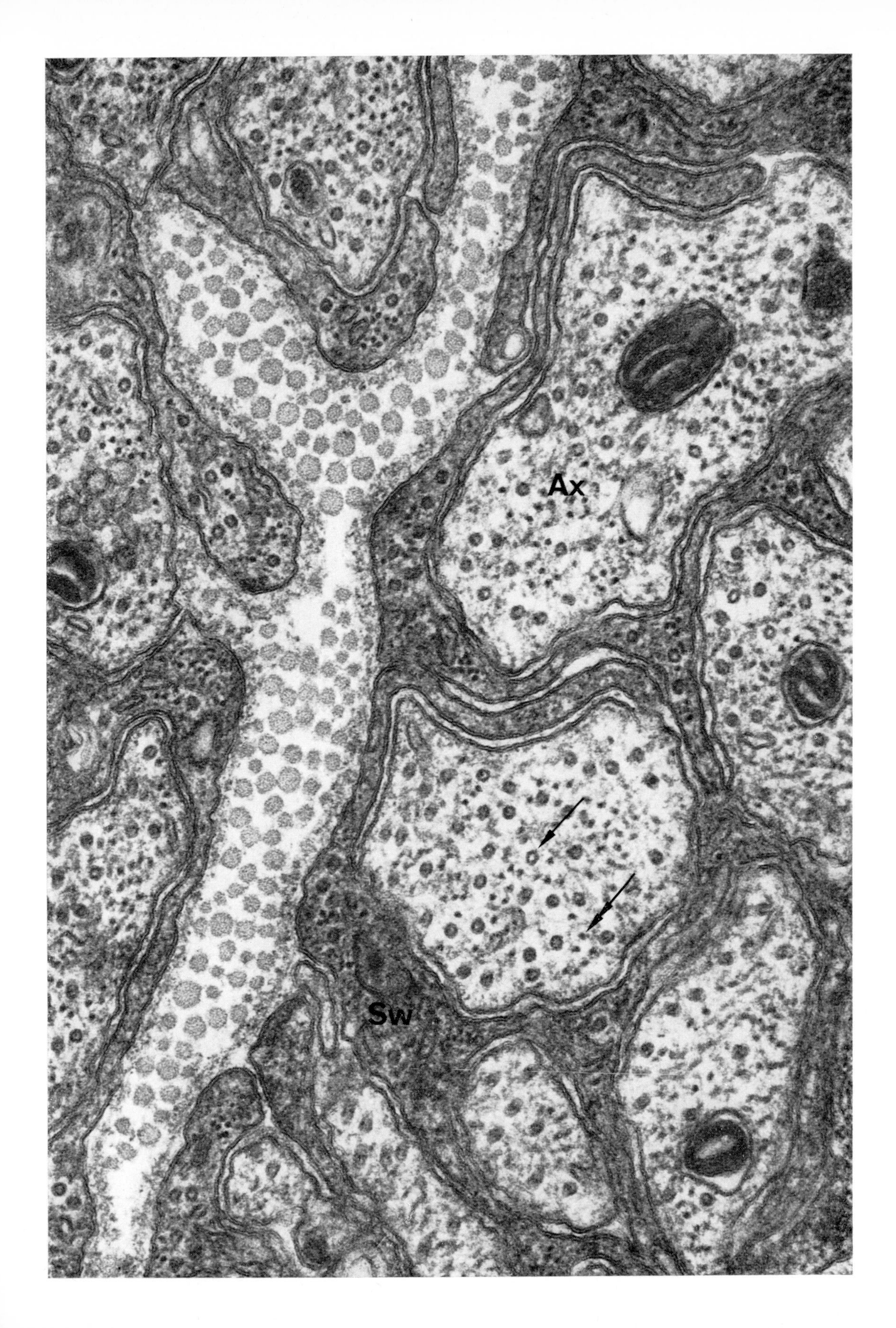
Ax
Sw

Plate 126

The degree of association of Schwann cell investment with axons varies considerably in different nerves and between different animals. The axons in large nerve bundles are usually almost completely invested with Schwann cells. However, small bundles of nonmyelinated fibres and terminal axons in effector organs are often free of Schwann cell investment (see Chapter 7D and Plate 141). In some structures, such as the avian ureter (finch), small axon bundles appear to have no accompanying Schwann cell processes.

Nerve fibres without Schwann investment: finch ureter. Transverse section. Glutaraldehyde fixation. ×121 000.

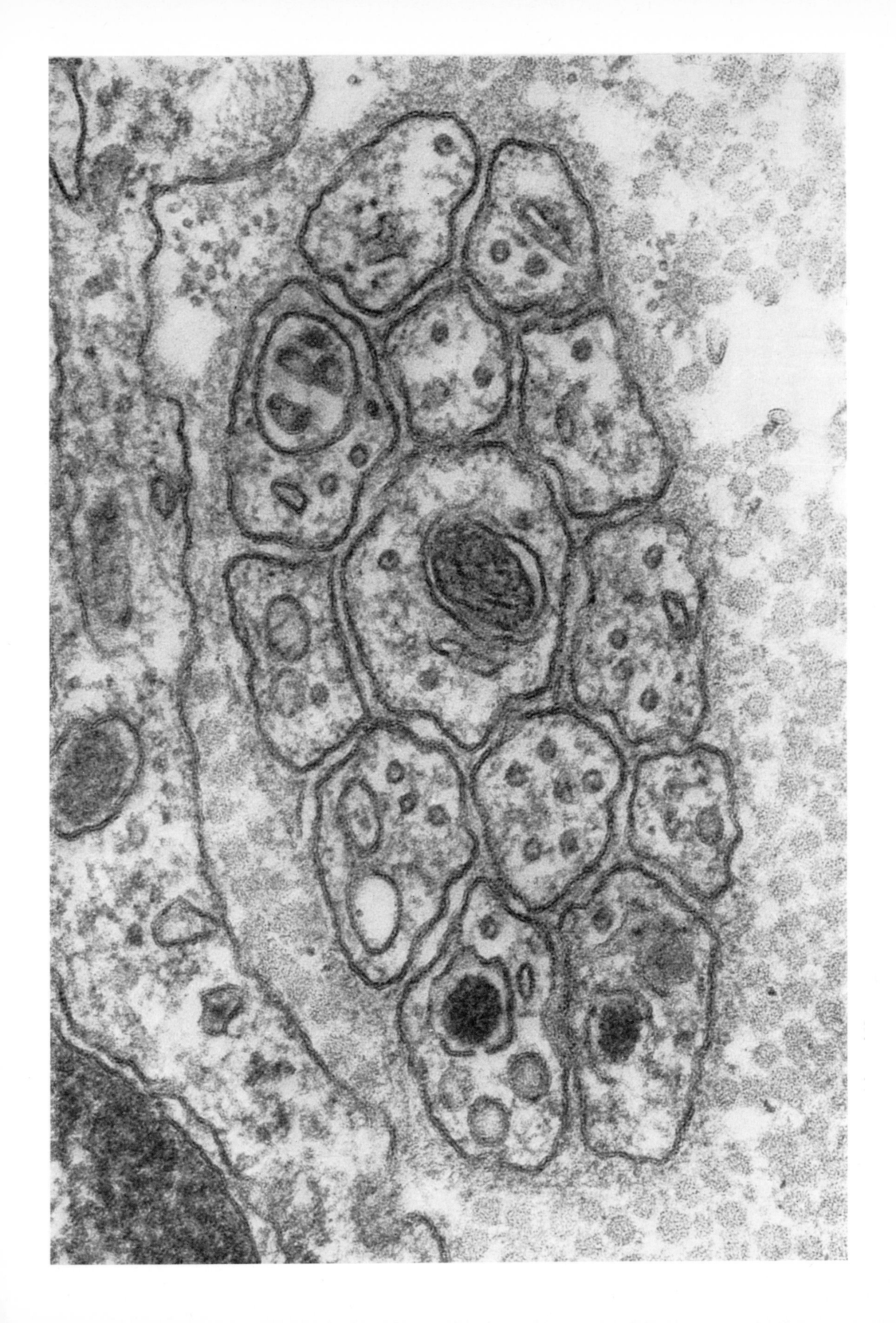

Plate 127

In the early stages of development, myelinated nerves consist of a bundle of naked axons enclosed by a common Schwann cell sheath. The Schwann cell is relatively large at this stage and contains mitochondria, rough endoplasmic reticulum and free ribosomes. Later in development, Schwann cell processes gradually extend to separate axons into smaller bundles and eventually delineate single axons in adults.

The accompanying micrograph shows a nerve bundle in an early stage of development. The mesaxon is formed by the Schwann cell which wraps itself around the axon. After a few turns of the mesaxon, the Schwann cell membrane layers come together to form myelin.

Developing nerve fibres: 16-day foetal rat sternothyroid muscle. Transverse section. Glutaraldehyde fixation. ×67 000. (Reproduced from Uehara Y., 1973, *Z. Zellforsch. mikrosk. Anat.*, **136,** 513.)

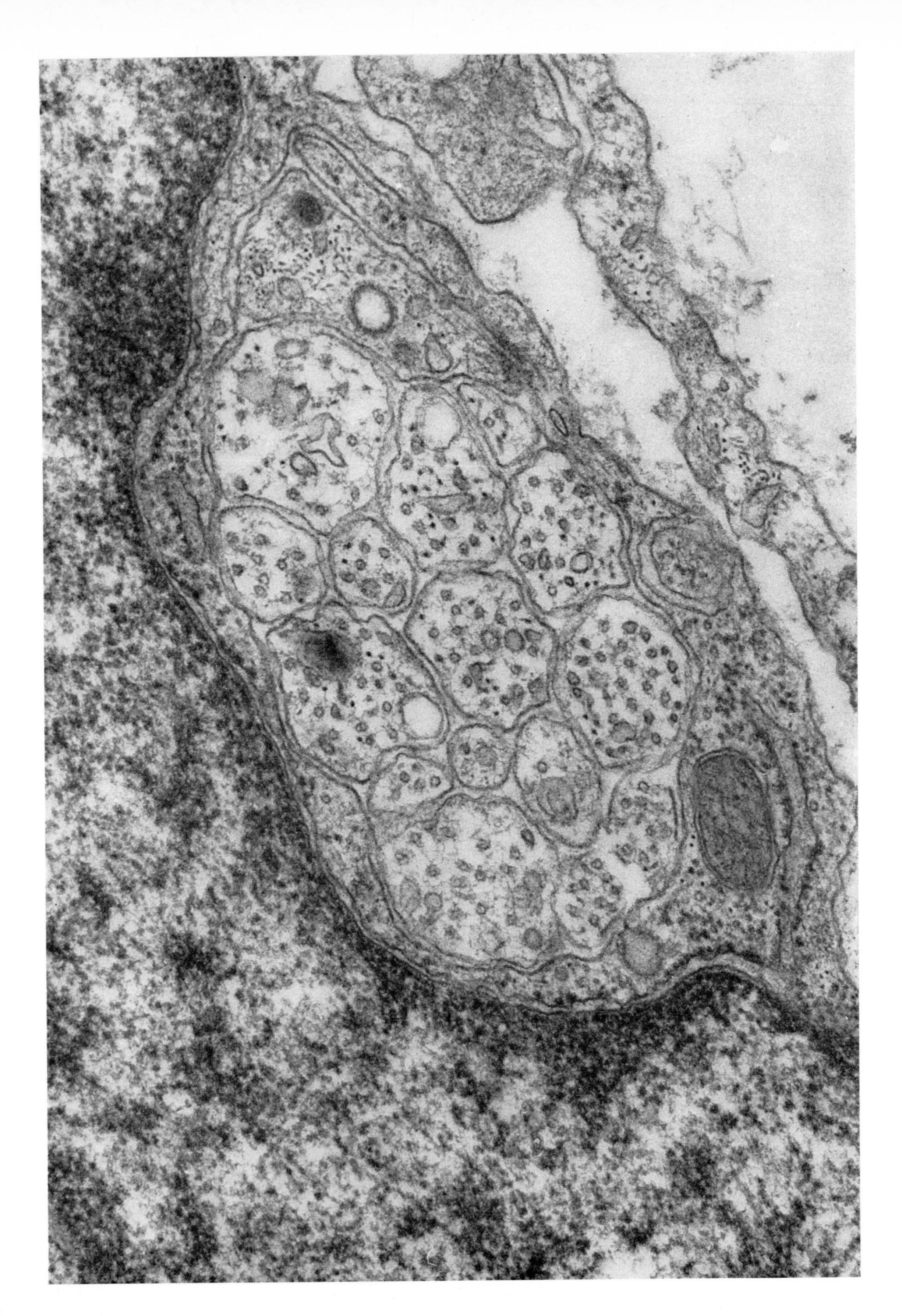

Plate 128

One of the characteristic features of autonomic nerve fibres is the presence of varicosities, i.e. the nerve fibre consists of a series of dilatations connected by thinner portions (see Chapter 7D). Within the effector organ, some of the varicosities are partially devoid of their Schwann cell sheath in the regions where they approach close to muscle fibres. In the accompanying electronmicrograph, a longitudinal section through a single axon in the outgrowth from rat sympathetic chain in tissue culture is illustrated. The varicosities shown in higher magnification on the right hand side contain various cytoplasmic organelles including mitochondria, agranular vesicles of various sizes and small and large granular vesicles. Intervaricosities contain many neurotubules and neurofilaments. This cultured axon has no associated Schwann cell.

Varicose terminal autonomic axon: rat sympathetic nerve, 21 days in culture. Longitudinal section. Glutaraldehyde fixation. ×23 000; ×56 000. (Reproduced from Chamley J. H., G. E. Mark, G. R. Campbell and G. Burnstock, 1972, *Z. Zellforsch. mikrosk. Anat.*, **135**, 287.)

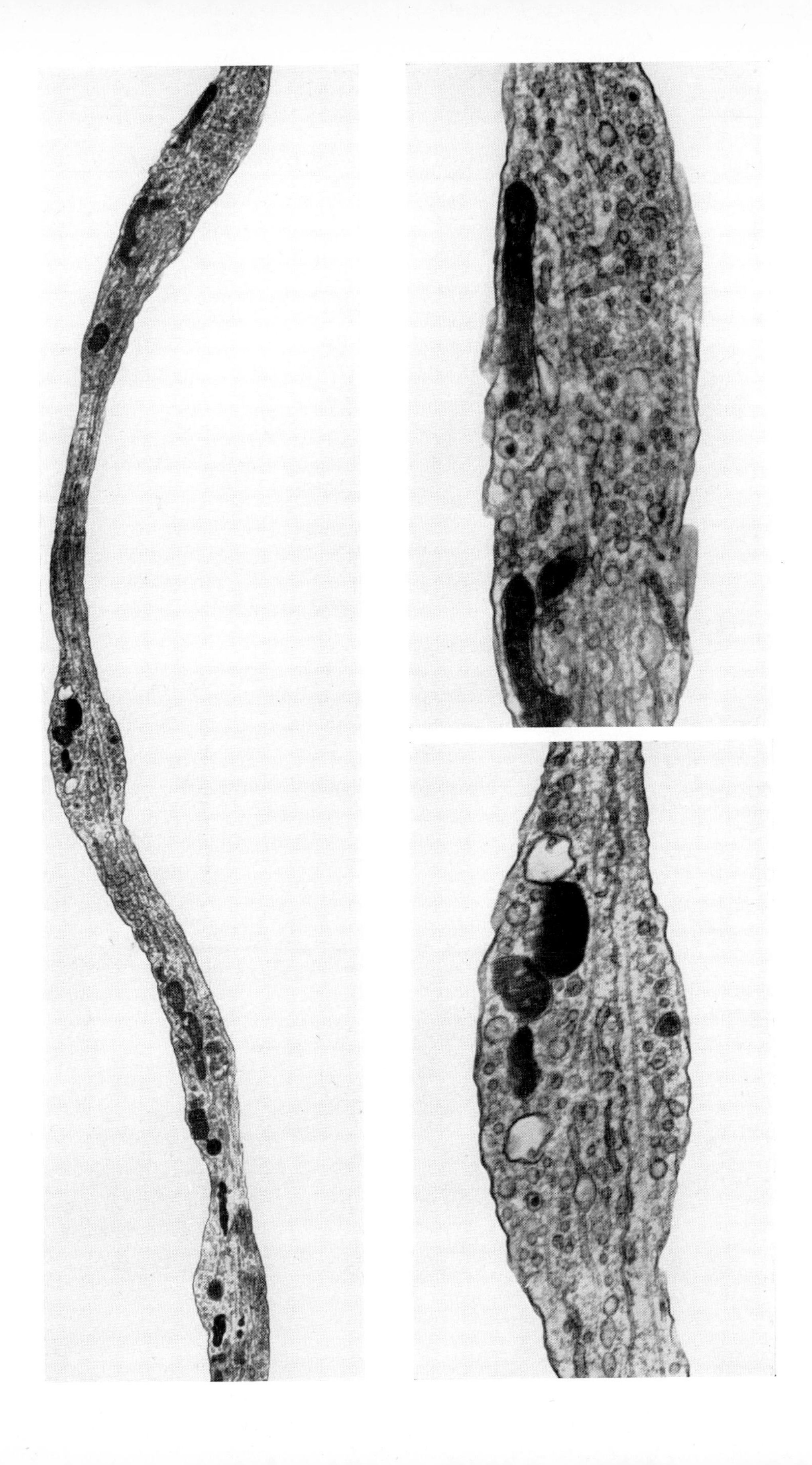

Selected reviews

ADAMS, C. W. M. and A. N. DAVISON. 1965. The Myelin Sheath. In *Neurohistochemistry*. C. W. M. Adams (ed.). Elsevier, Amsterdam. 332–400.

BABEL, J., A. BISCHOFF and H. SPOENDLIN. 1970. *Ultrastructure of the Peripheral Nervous System and Sense Organs. Atlas of Normal and Pathological Anatomy*. C. V. Mosby, St. Louis, Missouri.

BAILEY, T. D. and D. E. SMITH (eds.). 1968. *The Central Nervous System*. Williams and Wilkins, Baltimore.

BOTÁR, J. 1966. *The Autonomic Nervous System. An Introduction to its Physiological and Pathological Histology*. Akadémiai Kiado, Budapest.

BOURNE, G. H. (ed.). 1968–1972. *The Structure and Function of Nervous Tissue*. Vols. 1 to 6. Academic Press, New York.

BULLOCK, T. H. and G. A. HORRIDGE. 1965. *Structure and Function in the Nervous Systems of Invertebrates*. Vols 1, 2. W. H. Freeman, San Francisco.

BURNSTOCK, G. 1972. Purinergic Nerves. *Pharmacol. Revs.*, **24,** 509–581.

BURNSTOCK, G. and T. IWAYAMA. 1972. Fine structural identification of autonomic nerves and their relation to smooth muscle. *Progress in Brain Research*, **34,** 389–404.

ECCLES, J. C. 1957. *The Physiology of Nerve Cells*. Oxford University Press, London.

ECCLES, J. C. 1964. *The Physiology of Synapses*. Springer, Berlin.

GEFFEN, L. B. and B. G. LIVETT. 1971. Synaptic vesicles in sympathetic neurons. *Physiol. Rev.*, **51,** 98–157.

GRAFSTEIN, B. 1969. Axonal transport: communication between soma and synapse. In *Advances in Biochemical Psychopharmacology*. Vol. 1. E. Costa and P. Greengard (eds.). Raven Press, New York. 11–25.

GRAY, E. G. 1964. Tissue of the central nervous system. In *Electron Microscopic Anatomy*. S. M. Kurt (ed.). Academic Press, New York. 369–417.

GRAY, E. G. 1970. The fine structure of nerve. *Comp. Biochem. Physiol.*, **36,** 419–448.

GRAY, E. G. and R. W. GUILLERY. 1966. Synaptic morphology in the normal and degenerating nervous system. *Int. Rev. Cytol.*, **19,** 111–182.

GUTH, L. 1968. 'Trophic' influences of nerve on muscle. *Physiol. Rev.*, **48,** 645–681.

HODGKIN, A. L. 1964. *The Conduction of the Nerve Impulse*. C. C. Thomas, Springfield, Illinois.

JOHNSTON, P. V. and B. I. ROOTS. 1972. *Nerve Membranes. A study of the biological and chemical aspects of neuronglia relationships*. International Series of Monographs in Pure and Applied Biology, Zoology Division. Vol. 36. Pergamon Press, Oxford.

LASEK, R. J. 1970. Protein transport in neurons. *Int. Rev. Neurobiol.*, **13,** 289–321.

LIEBERMAN, A. R. 1971. The axon reaction: A review of the principal features of perikaryal responses to axon injury. *Int. Rev. Neurobiol.*, **14,** 49–124.

MINCKLER, J. and K. T. NEUBERGER (eds.). 1969. *Neuropathology*. Vol. 1. McGraw-Hill, New York.

PALAY, S. L. 1956. Structure and function in the neuron. In *Progress in Neurobiology*. I. Neurochemistry. S. R. Korey and J. I. Nurnberger (eds.). Hoeber-Harper, New York. 64–82.

PEASE, D. C. (ed.) 1971. Cellular Aspects of Neural Growth and Differentiation. *ULCA Forum in Medical Sciences, No. 14*. University of California Press, Berkeley.

PETERS, A., S. L. PALAY and H. DE F. WEBSTER. 1970. *The Fine Structure of the Nervous System. The Cells and their Processes*. Harper and Row, New York.

PICK, J. 1970. *The Autonomic Nervous System*. J. B. Lippincott, Philadelphia.

RICHTER, D. (ed.). 1957. *Metabolism of the Nervous System*. Pergamon Press, Oxford.

SCHARRAR, E. and B. SCHARRER. 1963. *Neuroendocrinology*. Columbia University Press, New York.

SINGER, M. and J. P. SCHADÉ (eds.). 1964. *Mechanisms of Neural Regeneration. Progress in Brain Research, Vol. 13*. Elsevier, Amsterdam.

TASAKI, I. 1968. *Nerve Excitation. A Macromolecular Approach*. C. C. Thomas, Springfield, Illinois.

TAXI, J. and C. SOTELO. 1972. Le problème de la migration des catécholamines dans les neurones sympathiques. *Rev. Neurol.*, **127,** 23–36.

WOLSTENHOLME, F. E. W. and M. O'CONNOR (eds.). 1968. *Growth of the Nervous System.* Little and Brown, Boston.
WUERKER, R. B. and J. B. KIRKPATRICK. 1972. Neuronal microtubules, neurofilaments and microfilaments. *Int. Rev. Cytol.* **33,** 45–75.

B Vertebrate skeletal muscle

Three distinct types of skeletal muscle fibres are found in many mammals, namely, fast twitch fibres (α white), intermediate fibres (α red), and slow twitch fibres (β red) (see Chapter 2B). These can be distinguished by differences in fibre diameter, mitochondrial content, colour, glycogen, and lipid content (see Plate 85), width of Z-disc (see Fig. 13), form of sarcoplasmic reticulum (see Chapter 2E) and structural differences at the motor end plate as well as by physiological characteristics. Most mammalian muscles are composed of more than one of the three fibre types. In the motor endings on the red (slow) fibre, the post synaptic junctional folds are poorly developed, sparse and irregular in arrangement; these endings are distributed along the length of the muscle fibre. In the white (fast twitch) fibre the junctional folds are well developed and far more numerous than those of the red fibre. The motor ending on the intermediate fibre contains the most widely spaced and deepest junctional folds. The slow tonic fibres identified in amphibian muscle appears to be absent in the limbs of mammals. Their extraocular muscles, however, contain both slow tonic and fast twitch fibres. Nerve endings on slow tonic and twitch muscle fibres are called '*en grappe*' and '*en plaque*' motor nerve endings respectively. These terms are based on their appearance in light microscopy following silver staining.

The specialized region at the end of the motor nerve where it makes contact with twitch skeletal muscle fibres is called the *motor end plate*; this is usually found at the middle of the muscle fibre. Impulses are transmitted from the motor nerves to the muscle fibre at this site initiating contraction. Agranular (synaptic) vesicles present at the motor end plate are the sites of storage of the transmitter substance *acetylcholine* (ACh).

A feature of the motor end plate is the thickening of the post synaptic membrane and it is here that ACh alters the conductivity of the sarcolemma to Na^+ and K^+, leading to depolarization. ACh is spontaneously released as discrete units or quanta from the motor nerve terminals. These quanta produce small depolarizations or *miniature end plate potentials* which do not reach the threshold level for initiation of action potentials. The effect of a nerve impulse is to cause the simultaneous release of a large number of these quanta of ACh which result in *end plate potentials*; this leads to the initiation of an action potential and contraction.

After ACh has depolarized the muscle cell membrane, it is quickly broken down to choline and acetate by the enzyme *acetylcholinesterase.* The choline is taken up by the nerve ending and resynthesized into ACh for further use. In the synthesis of ACh in nerve terminals, acetyl-CoA is first formed from ATP and CoA (*coenzyme A*) via the enzyme *acetokinase.* Acetyl-CoA is then combined with choline to form ACh, via the enzyme *choline acetylase.*

The morphological basis of the quantal behaviour of ACh, has for many years been the subject of debate. The most attractive suggestion was that ACh was stored in the synaptic vesicles, but supporting evidence, until recently, was inconclusive. When venom from the black widow spider is applied to the neuromuscular junction, not only is there an increase in the frequency of miniature end plate potentials, but there is a reduction in the number of synaptic vesicles within the nerve ending. Fusion of vesicles with the presynaptic membrane is a regular occurrence during this process. After some time miniature end plate potentials cease, and synaptic vesicles are absent, although apart from this, the motor end plate looks relatively normal.

Denervation of skeletal muscle causes a number of gross changes such as paralysis, change of colour, loss of weight, reduction of muscle fibre diameter, and alterations of muscle enzyme activities. Ultrastructurally, two major phases of atrophy have been observed following denervation. The first involves a degenerative autolytic process. Z-disc material is the first to be altered, this is followed by disorganization of the myofilaments resulting in large areas of the cell containing only ground substance, glycogen and some mitochondria. The second stage of atrophy appears to involve the detachment of filaments from the periphery of the myofibril and their subsequent breakdown. Most of the effects can be reversed by reinnervating the skeletal muscle with any motor nerve (orginal or foreign) provided denervation atrophy has not proceeded too far.

The response of mammalian muscle to *tenotomy* (section of the tendon) appears in many instances to be similar to the primary changes seen in denervation, with alteration of the Z-disc and disorganization of the myofilaments.

Plate 129

The motor axon usually loses its myelin sheath just before termination (see Plate 123). It is then associated solely with Schwann cells (Sw) which form the *teloglia*. These are usually limited to the side of the axon (Ax) away from the muscle. At the surface of the muscle fibre (Mu), the terminal branches occupy cavities, called *synaptic gutters* or *primary synaptic clefts*. From the synaptic gutter radiate a number of *subneural folds* (Sf) or *secondary synaptic clefts* which are formed not only by the sarcolemma but also by the basal lamina which accompanies the sarcolemma in its invagination (and is joined by the basal lamina of the axon). End plates occur singly, or in small numbers, usually about midway along the length of each muscle fibre.

'En plaque' motor end plate in a mammalian skeletal fast twitch muscle fibre: rat rectus femoris. Transverse section. Glutaraldehyde fixation. ×44 000.

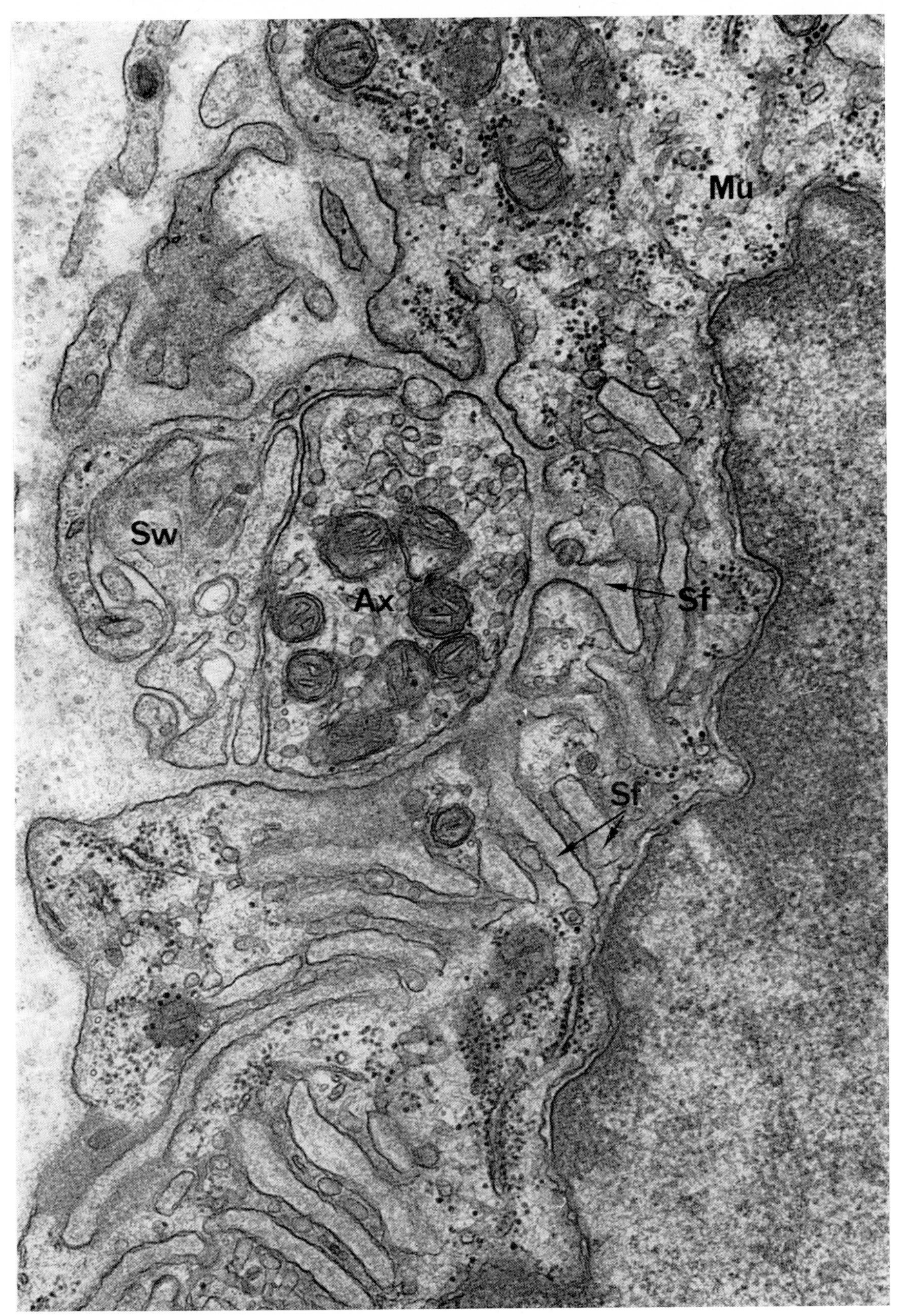
Mu
Sw
Ax
Sf
Sf

Plate 130

In the high magnification micrograph illustrated, synaptic vesicles (Sv), 40–60 nm in diameter, are distributed throughout the axon terminal. Some glycogen granules are intermixed with these vesicles. The axon is separated from the sarcolemma by a synaptic cleft of about 50 nm. The basal lamina of the axon and muscle are fused to form an intermediate dense line in the middle of the cleft. The dense line continues into the subneural folds which radiate from the cleft. The region of the muscle opposing the nerve terminal is rich in cytoplasmic organelles such as mitochondria, rough endoplasmic reticulum, free ribosomes and microtubules.

'En plaque' motor end plate in a mammalian skeletal fast twitch muscle fibre: rat rectus femoris. Transverse section. Glutaraldehyde fixation. ×76 000.

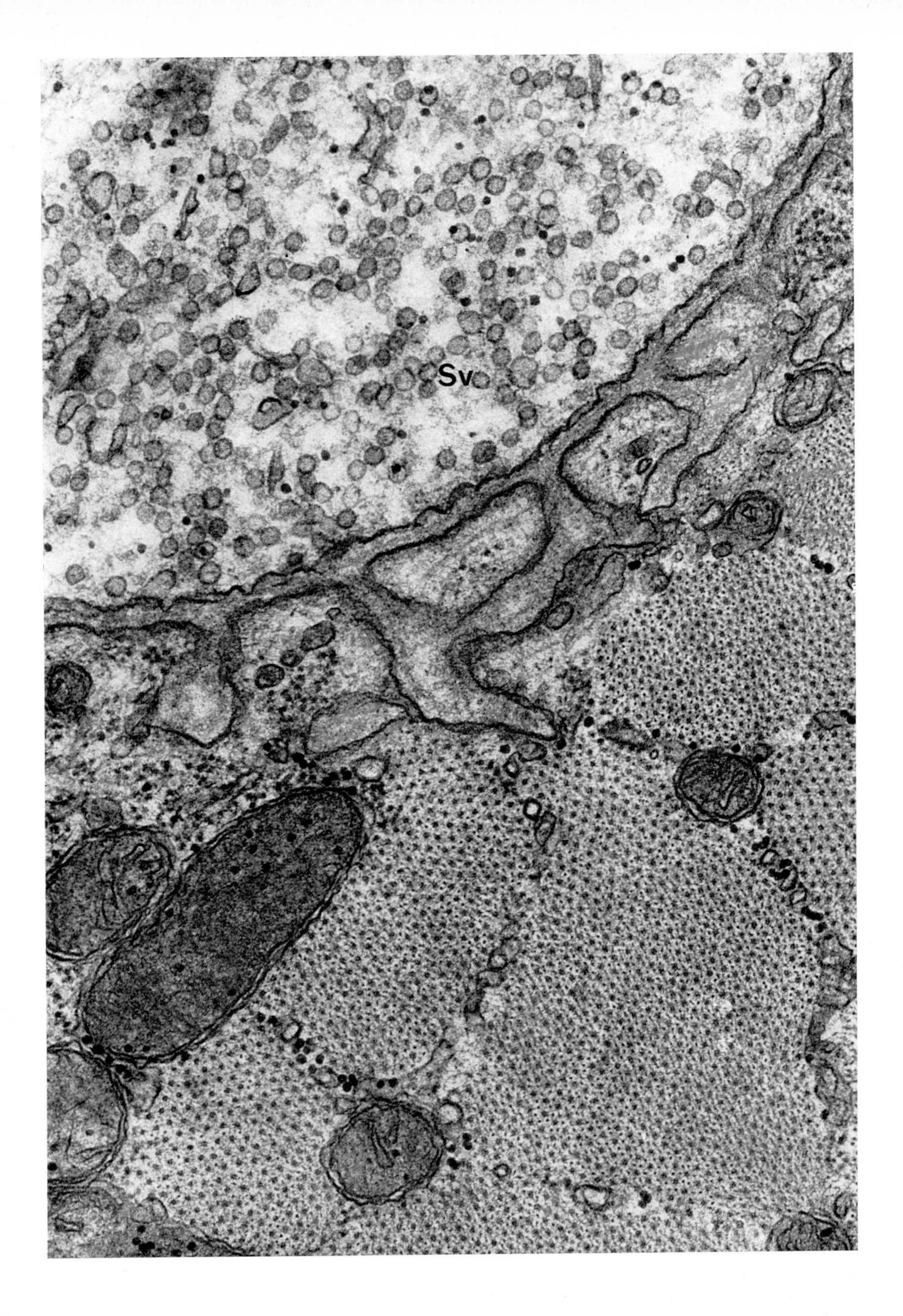
Sv

Plate 131

Acetylcholinesterase localization within the synaptic gutter and subneural folds of the motor end plate is illustrated. The thiolacetic acid–lead nitrate method has been employed and is used as an example of the application of histochemistry in electronmicroscopy. Various inhibitors can be used to distinguish acetylcholinesterase from non-specific cholinesterases. Other histochemical methods, as well as biochemical and auto-radiographic techniques have also shown that a high concentration of acetylcholinesterase is located on the postsynaptic membrane, in the synaptic gutter and in the subneural folds.

Acetylcholinesterase localization at an 'en plaque' motor end plate in a mammalian fast twitch muscle fibre: rat rectus femoris. Transverse section. Glutaraldehyde fixation. ×75 000.

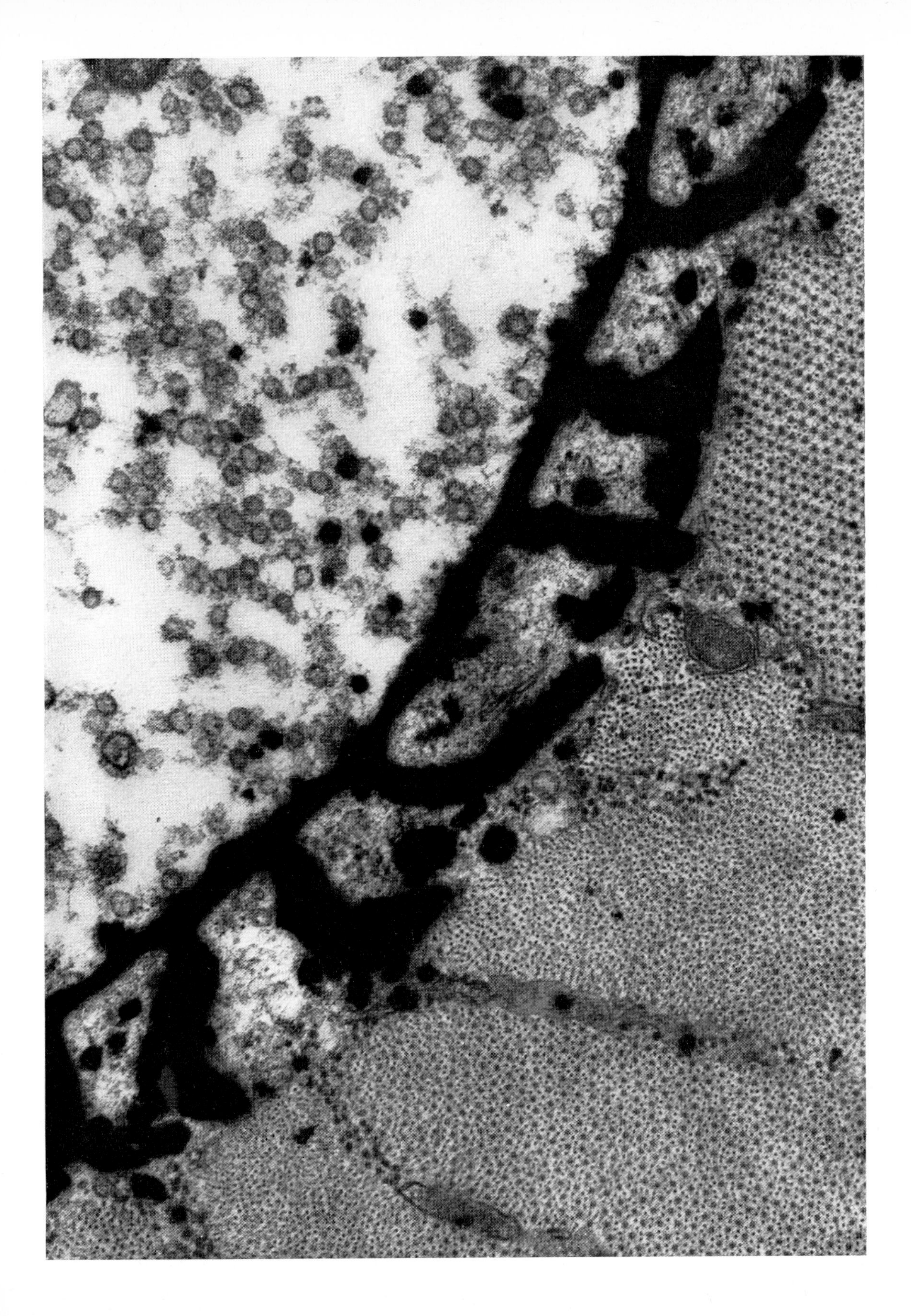

Plate 132

In contrast to the discrete 'en plaque' endings in fast twitch muscle fibres, the endings in slow tonic fibres are diffusely distributed along the length of the fibre ('multiple' innervation) and are called 'en grappe' endings. Myelinated nerves lose their myelin sheath to produce bundles of unmyelinated axons. These bundles then give rise to the terminations which are scattered along the length of the muscle fibre. The size of each 'en grappe' ending is smaller and the structure simpler than the 'en plaque' endings. The terminal axons at 'en grappe' endings are located in shallow grooves in the muscle fibres and they lack subsynaptic folds. Few cellular organelles are present in the muscle cytoplasm facing the nerve endings. However, the axonal content appears similar to that of the 'en plaque' ending. The non-synaptic surface is covered by Schwann cells (teloglia). Presynaptic and postsynaptic membranes are separated by a gap of approximately 70 nm containing a basal lamina. 'En grappe' endings have been reported in mammalian ocular muscle.

'En grappe' motor ending in a reptilian slow tonic skeletal muscle fibre: lizard ilio-tibialis. Transverse section. Glutaraldehyde fixation. ×23 700.

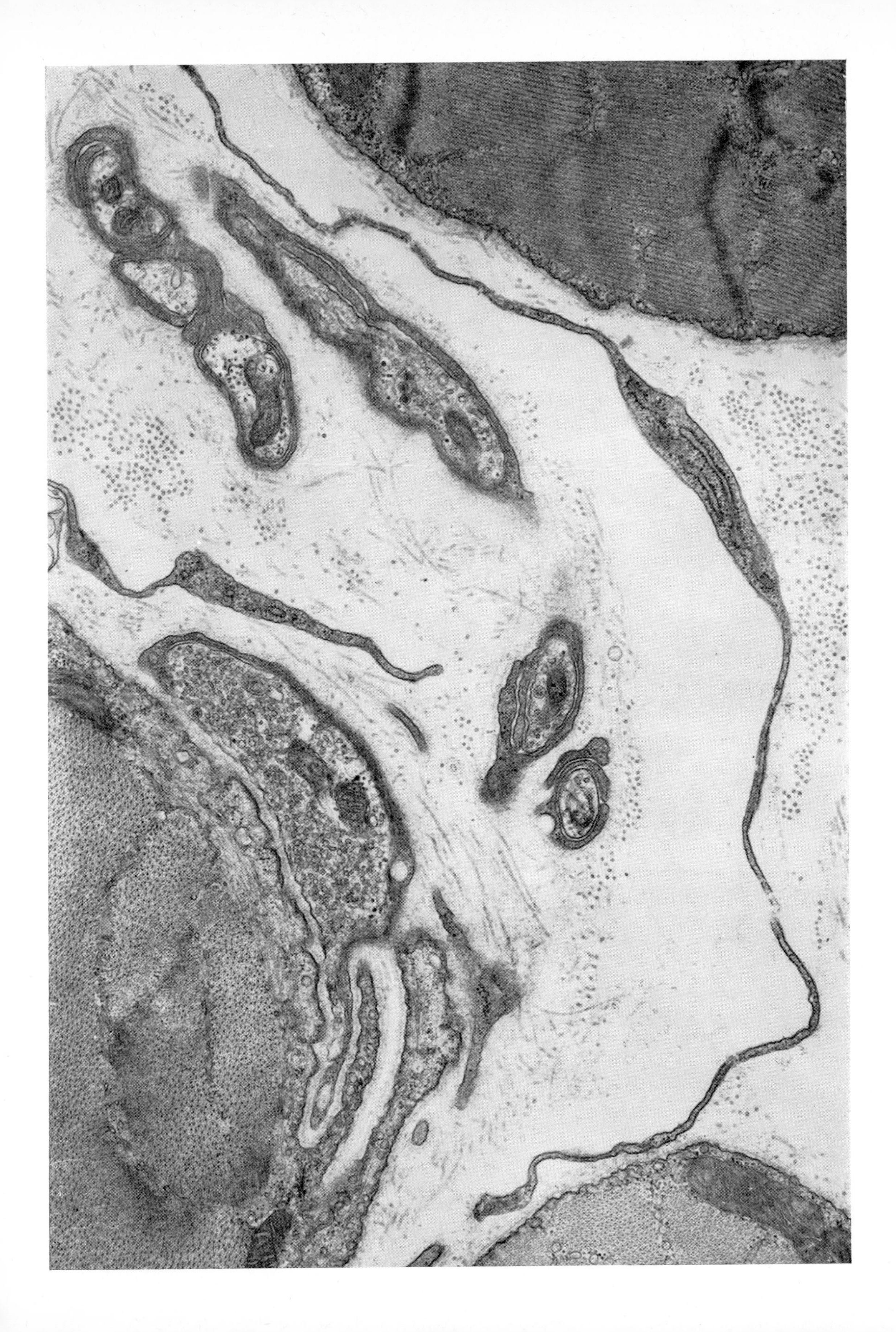

Plate 133

In the electron micrograph illustrated, the outer side of the axon terminal is ensheathed by the teloglia. The terminal axon contains numerous agranular vesicles, about 50 nm in diameter. The presynaptic membrane is separated from the postsynaptic membrane by a gap of 70–100 nm, except that at one point a pseudopod-like evagination of the nerve (arrow) projects into the muscle. The membranes of the evagination and the muscle cell are separated by a gap of about 20 nm which contains no basal lamina. A few large agranular vesicles of about 100 nm diameter are present in the evagination. This type of evagination has also been observed in the extraocular muscles of many mammals.

'En grappe' end plate in avian skeletal muscle: finch rectus femoris. Transverse section. Glutaraldehyde fixation. ×38 200.

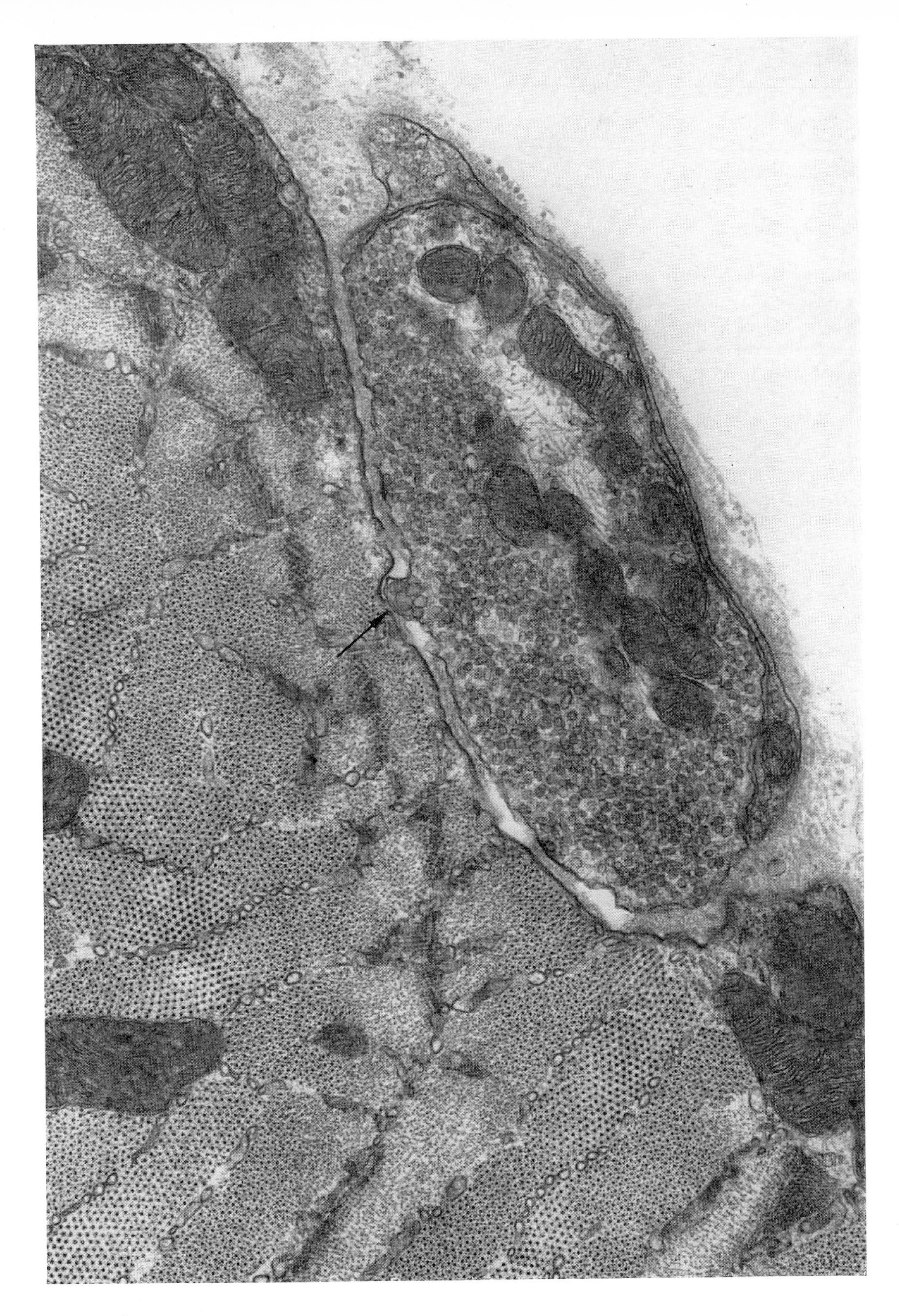

Plate 134

In some segmentally arranged muscles of the lower vertebrates, the motor nerve endings are confined to the muscle–tendon junction; this has been termed myoseptal innervation. Myoseptal junctions are comparable to 'en grappe' endings in their structural organization. The two axons (Ax) seen here are ensheathed by the Schwann cell (teloglia) (Sw), and contain small agranular vesicles 50 nm in diameter and a large granular vesicle, 100 nm in diameter. The presynaptic membrane is separated from the postsynaptic membrane by a synaptic gap of about 70 nm, containing basal lamina. Note the electron dense material on the presynaptic membrane (arrow), a feature characteristic of many neuromuscular junctions (see Plates 140 and 147). It has been suggested that these are sites where synaptic vesicles fuse with the axon membrane during the process of exocytosis.

Myoseptal neuromuscular junction at a muscle–tendon junction in amphibian skeletal muscle: tail muscle of axolotl. Transverse section. Glutaraldehyde fixation. ×55 000.

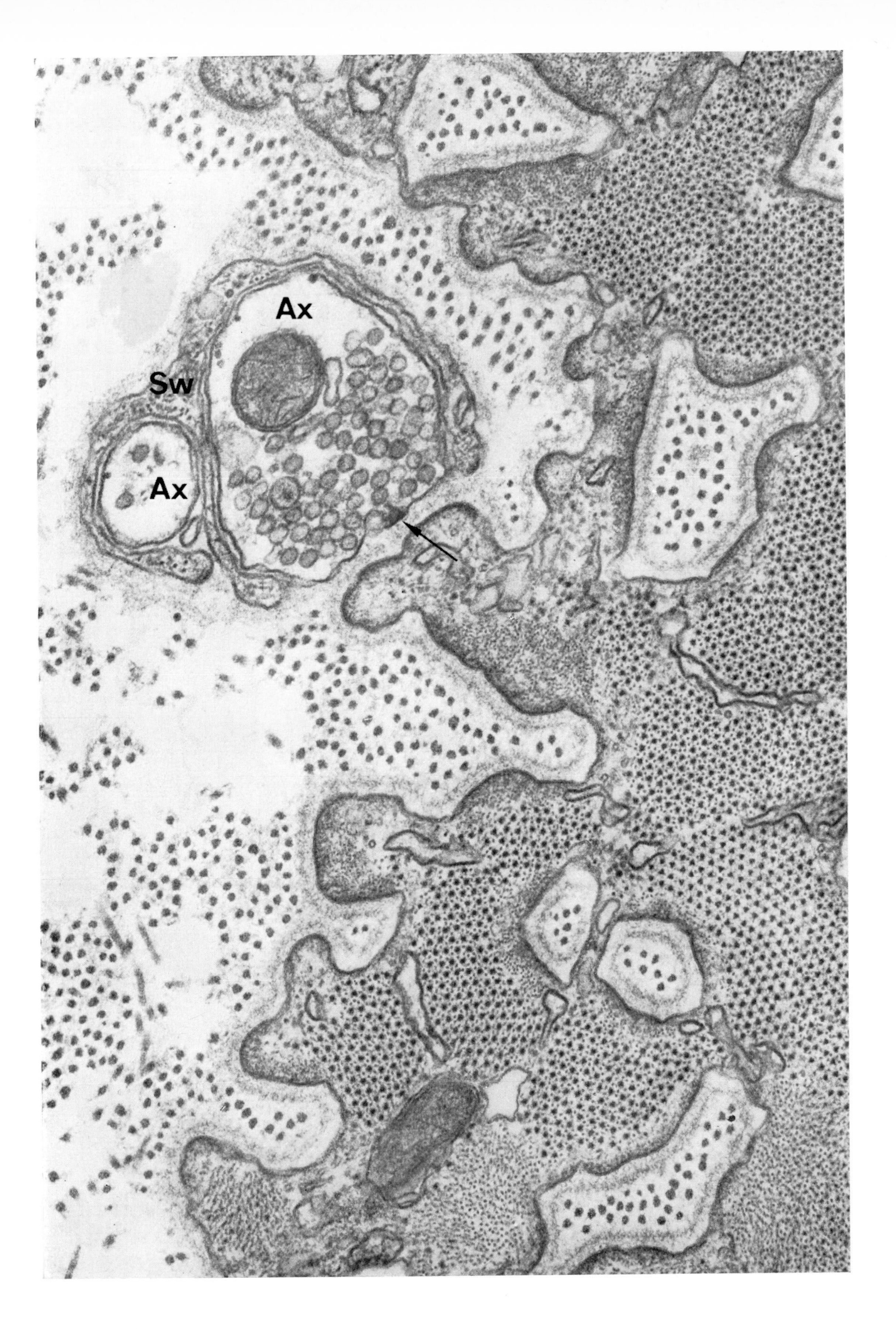
Ax
Sw
Ax

Plate 135

At the site of initial contact during the development of the neuromuscular junction, no specialization occurs. After contact, the density of both the pre- and postsynaptic membranes increase sharply. At this stage the nerve ending is located in the middle of the fibre and takes on the appearance of a typical 'en grappe' ending. At a later stage, subneural folds develop to produce the 'en plaque' configuration.

The accompanying micrograph shows an early stage in the development of the motor end plate in a 17-day-old foetal rat. The terminal axons are small in size containing few synaptic vesicles and other organelles. The Schwann cell associated with the axon is relatively large containing rough endoplasmic reticulum and free ribosomes. The axon and muscle are separated by a gap of about 70 nm in which the basal lamina forms an intermediate dense line. In the underlying muscle cell, a number of mitochondria and free ribosomes are present. Note the invaginations of sarcolemma containing basal lamina, this suggests the initial formation of subsynaptic folds.

Developing motor end plate in mammalian skeletal muscle: sternothyroid muscle of 17-day foetal rat. Glutaraldehyde fixation. ×66 000.

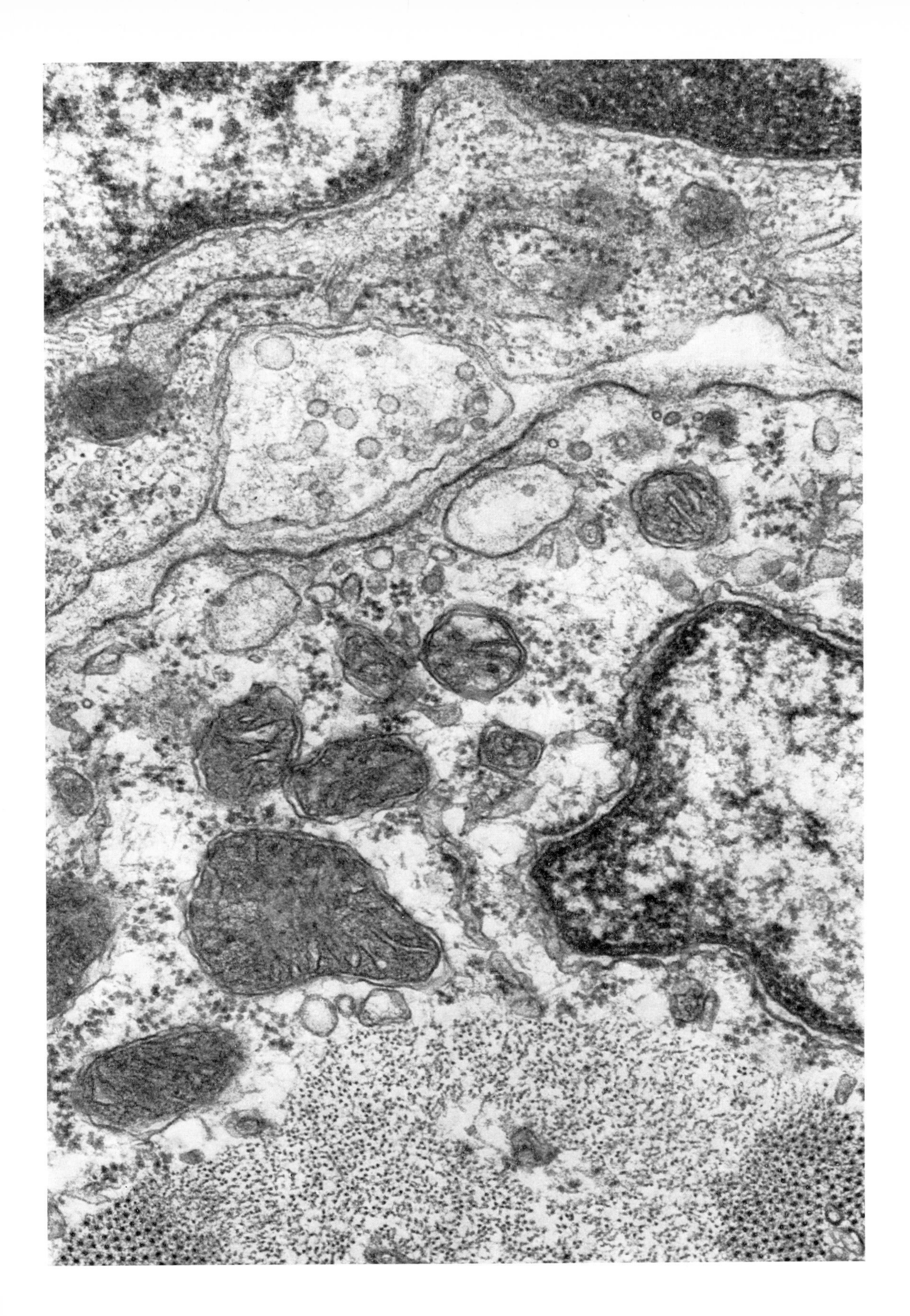

Selected reviews

COUTEAUX, R. 1972. Structure and cytochemical characteristics of the neuromuscular junction. In *Neuromuscular Blocking and Stimulating Agents. International Encyclopedia of Pharmacology and Therapeutics. Section 14*. Vol. 1. J. Cheymol (ed.). Pergamon Press, Oxford. 7–56.

DE CASTILLO, J. and B. KATZ. 1956. Biophysical aspects of neuromuscular transmission. *Prog. Biophys. biophys. Chem.*, **6,** 121–170.

DE ROBERTIS, E. 1964. *Histophysiology of Synapses and Neurosecretion.* Pergamon Press, Oxford.

FRIEDENBERG, R. M. and A. M. SELIGMAN. 1972. Acetylcholinesterase at the myoneural junction: Cytochemical ultrastructure and some biochemical considerations. *J. Histochem. Cytochem.*, **20,** 771–792.

GUTMAN, E. (ed.). 1962. *The Denervated Muscle.* Czech. Acad. Sci., Prague.

HUBBARD, J. I. 1970. Mechanism of transmitter release. *Prog. Biophys. & Mol. Biol.*, **21,** 33–124.

HUBBARD, J. I. 1973. Microphysiology of vertebrate neuromuscular transmission. *Physiol. Rev.*, **53.** 674–723.

HUBBARD, J. I., R. LLINÁS and D. M. J. QUASTEL. 1969. *Electrophysiological Analyses of Synaptic Transmission.* Edward Arnold, London.

KATZ, B. 1962. The transmission of impulses from nerve to muscle and the subcellular unit of synaptic action. *Proc. Roy. Soc. Ser. B*, **155,** 455–477.

KATZ, B. 1969. *The Release of Neural Transmitter Substances.* Liverpool University Press, Liverpool.

McLENNAN, H. 1970. *Synaptic Transmission.* 2nd edition. W. B. Saunders, Philadelphia.

MARK, R. F. 1969. Matching muscles and motorneurones. A review of some experiments on motor nerve regeneration. *Brain Res.*, **14,** 245–254.

MOMMAERTS, W. F. H. M. 1970. The role of the innervation of the functional differentiation of muscle. In *The Physiology and Biochemistry of Muscle as a Food.* Vol. 2. E. J. Briskey, R. G. Cassens and B. B. Marsh (eds.). University of Wisconsin Press, Madison, Wisconsin. 53–86.

SHIMADA, Y. and D. A. FISCHMAN. 1973. Morphological and physiological evidence for the development of functional neuromuscular junctions *in vitro. Devl. Biol.*, **31,** 200–225.

Selected articles

ANDRES, K. H. and M. VON DÜRING. 1966. Mikropinozytose in motorischen Endplatten. *Naturwissenschaften*, **53,** 615.

ATWOOD, H. L., F. LANG and W. A. MORIN. 1972. Synaptic vesicles. Selective depletion in crayfish excitatory and inhibitory axons. *Science, N.Y.*, **176,** 1353.

BARKER, D. 1968. L'innervation motrice du muscle strié des vertébrés. *Actual. Neurophysiol.*, **8,** 23–71.

BARRNETT, R. J. 1962. The fine structural localization of acetylcholinesterase at the myoneural junction. *J. Cell Biol.*, **12,** 247–262.

BARRNETT, R. J. 1966. Ultrastructural histochemistry of normal neuromuscular junctions. *Ann. N.Y. Acad. Sci.*, **135,** 27–34.

BAUMGARTEN, H. G. 1965. Über die Muskulatur und die Nerven in der Darmwand der Schleie (*Tinca Vulgaris* Cuv.) *Z. Zellforsch. mikrosk. Anat.*, **68,** 116–137.

BENNETT, M. R., E. M. McLACHLAN and R. S. TAYLOR. 1973. The Formation of synapses in mammalian striated-muscle reinnervated with autonomic preganglionic nerves. *J. Physiol., Lond.*, **233,** 501–517.

BERGMAN, R. A. 1967. Motor nerve endings of twitch muscle fibers in *Hippocampus hudsonius. J. Cell Biol.*, **32,** 751–756.

BERGMAN, R. A. and A. K. AFIFI. 1969. The structure of the rabbit soleus muscle and the structural alterations resulting from tenotomy. *Johns Hopkins Med. J.*, **124,** 119–131.

BIRKS, R. I. 1966. The fine structure of motor nerve endings at frog myoneural junctions. *Ann. N.Y. Acad. Sci.*, **135,** 8.

BIRKS, R., H. E. HUXLEY and B. KATZ. 1960. The fine structure of the neuromuscular junction of the frog. *J. Physiol., Lond.*, **150,** 134–144.

BIRKS, R., B. KATZ and R. MILEDI. 1960. Physiological and structural changes at the amphibian myoneural junction, in the course of nerve degeneration. *J. Physiol., Lond.*, **150,** 145–168.

BITTNER, G. D. and D. KENNEDY. 1970. Quantitative aspects of transmitter release. *J. Cell Biol.*, **47,** 585.

BONE, Q. 1972. The dogfish neuromuscular junction: dual innervation of vertebrate striated muscle fibres? *J. Cell Sci.*, **10,** 657–666.

BORNSTEIN, M. B., H. IWANAMI, G. M. LEHRER and L. BREITBART. 1968. Observations on the appearance of neuromuscular relationships in cultured mouse tissues. *Z. Zellforsch. mikrosk. Anat.*, **92,** 197–206.

BRYANT, S. V., D. FYFE and M. SINGER. 1971. The effects of denervation on the ultrastructure of young limb regenerates in the newt, *Triturus. Devl Biol.*, **24,** 577–595.

BRZIN, M. and Z. MAJCEN–TKAČEV. 1963. Cholinesterase in denervated end plates and muscle fibers. *J. Cell Biol.*, **19,** 349–358.

CALAPSO, DI P. and G. VERMIGLIO. 1970. Istochimica delle ossido-reduttasi e reperti ultrastrutturali nella miopatia sperimentale da tenotomia. *Acta histochem.*, **38,** 31–44.

CECCARELLI, B., W. P. HURLBOT and A. MAURO. 1972. Depletion of vesicles from frog neuromuscular junctions by prolonged tetanic stimulation. *J. Cell Biol.*, **54,** 30–38.

CECCARELLI, B., W. P. HURLBUT and A. MAURO. 1973. Turnover of transmitter and synaptic vesicles at the frog neuromuscular junction. *J. Cell Biol.*, **57,** 499–524.

CLARK, A. W., W. P. HURLBUT and A. MAURO. 1972. Changes in the fine structure of the neuromuscular junction of the frog caused by black widow spider venom. *J. Cell Biol.*, **52,** 1–14.

CSILLIK, B. and E. KNYIHÁR. 1968. On the effect of motor-nerve degeneration on the fine-structural localization of esterases in the mammalian motor end-plate. *J. Cell Sci.*, **3,** 529–538.

COUTEAUX, R. and M. PÉCOT-DECHAVASSINE. 1970. Vésicules synaptiques et poches au niveau des 'zones actives' de la jonction neuromusculaire. *C.r. hebd. Sean. Acad. Sci. Ser. D. Paris*, **271,** 2346–2349.

DAVIS, R. and G. B. KOELLE. 1967. Electron microscopic localization of acetylcholinesterase and nonspecific cholinesterase at the neuromuscular junction by the gold-thiocholine and gold-thiolacetic acid methods. *J. Cell Biol.*, **34,** 157–172.

DEL CASTILLO, J. and B. KATZ. 1954. Statistical factors involved in neuromuscular facilitation and depression. *J. Physiol., Lond.*, **124,** 574.

DEL CASTILLO, J. and B. KATZ. 1956. Biochemical aspects of neuro-muscular transmission. *Progr. Biophys. biophys. Chem.*, **6,** 121.

DINIZ, C. R., A. F. PIMENTA, J. COURINHO NETTO, S. POMPOLO, M. V. GOMEZ and G. M. BÖHM. 1974. Effect of scorpion venom from *Tityus serrulatus* (Tityustoxin) on the acetylcholine release and fine structure of the nerve terminals. *Experientia*, **30,** 1304–1305.

DUCHEN, L. W. 1971. An electron microscopic comparison of motor end-plates of slow and fast skeletal muscle fibres of the mouse. *J. Neurol. Sci.*, **14,** 37–46.

DUCHEN, L. W. 1973*a*. The effects of tetanus toxin on the motor end-plates of the mouse. An electron microscopic study. *J. Neurol. Sci.*, **19,** 153–167.

DUCHEN, L. W. 1973*b*. The local effects of tetanus toxin on the electron microscopic structure of skeletal muscle fibres of the mouse. *J. Neurol. Sci.*, **19,** 169–177.

DÜRING, M. VON. 1967. Über die Feinstruktur der motorischen Endplatte von höheren Wirbeltieren. *Z. Zellforsch. mikrosk. Anat.*, **81,** 74–90.

FIDZIAŃSKA, A. 1971. Electron microscopic study of the development of human foetal muscle, motor end-plate and nerve. Preliminary report. *Acta Neuropathol.*, **17,** 234–247.

FOROGLOU, C. and G. WINCKLER. 1973. Ultrastructure du fuseau neuro-musculaire chez l'homme. Comparaison avec le rat. *Z. Anat. Entw Gesch.*, **140,** 19–37.

GAUTHIER, G. F. and R. A. DUNN. 1973. Ultrastructural and cytochemical features of mammalian skeletal muscle fibres following denervation. *J. Cell Sci.*, **12,** 525–547.

GOODWIN, B. C. and I. W. SIZER. 1965. Effects

of spinal cord and substrate on acetylcholinesterase in chick embryonic skeletal muscle. *Devl Biol.*, **11,** 136–154.

GONZENBACH, H. R. and P. G. WASER. 1973. Electron microscopic studies of degeneration and regeneration of rat neuromuscular junctions. *Brain Res.*, **63,** 167–174.

GREEN, K. 1966. Electron microscopic observations on the relationship between synthesis of synaptic vesicles and acetylcholine. *Anat. Rec.*, **154,** 351.

HESS, A. 1960. The structure of extrafusal muscle fibers in the frog and their innervation studied by the cholinesterase technique. *Am. J. Anat.*, **107,** 129–151.

HESS, A. 1962. Further morphological observations of 'en plaque' and 'en grappe' nerve endings on mammalian extrafusal muscle fibers with the cholinesterase technique. *Rev. can. Biol.*, **21,** 241–248.

HESS, A. 1963. Two kinds of extrafusal muscle fibers and their nerve endings in the garter snake. *Am. J. Anat.*, **113,** 347–364.

HESS, A. 1965. The sarcoplasmic reticulum, the T system, and the motor terminals of slow and twitch muscle fibers in the garter snake. *J. Cell Biol.*, **26,** 467–476.

HEUSER, J. E., B. KATZ and R. MILEDI. 1971. Structural and functional changes of frog neuromuscular junctions in high calcium solutions. *Proc. R. Soc. Ser. B*, **178,** 407–415.

HEUSER, J. E. and R. MILEDI. 1971. Effect of lanthanum ions on function and structure of frog neuromuscular junctions. *Proc. R. Soc. Ser. B.*, **179,** 247–260.

HEUSER, J. E. and T. S. REESE. 1972. Stimulation induced uptake and release of peroxidase from synaptic vesicles in frog neuromuscular junctions. *Anat. Rec.*, **172,** 329–330.

HEUSER, J. E. and T. S. REESE. 1973. Evidence for recycling of synaptic vesicle membrane during transmitter release at the frog neuromuscular junction. *J. Cell Biol.*, **57,** 315–344.

HIKIDA, R. S. and W. J. BOCK. 1970. The structure of pigeon muscle and its changes due to tenotomy. *J. exp. Zool.*, **175,** 343–356.

HIKIDA, R. S. and W. J. BOCK. 1971. Innervation of the avian tonus larissimus dorsi anterior muscle. *Am. J. Anat.*, **130,** 269–280.

HIKIDA, R. S. and W. J. BOCK. 1972. Effect of denervation on pigeon slow skeletal muscle. *Z. Zellforsch. mikrosk. Anat.*, **128,** 1–18.

HIRANO, H. 1967. Ultrastructural study on the morphogenesis of the neuromuscular junction in the skeletal muscle of the chick. *Z. Zellforsch. mikrosk. Anat.*, **79,** 198–208.

HSU, L. and T. L. LENTZ. 1972. Effect of colchicine on the fine structure of the neuromuscular junction. *Z. Zellforsch. mikrosk. Anat.*, **135,** 439–448.

IP, M. C. 1974. Some morphological features of the myoneural junctions in certain normal muscles of the rat. *Anat. Rec.*, **180,** 605–616.

JAMES, D. W. and R. L. TRESMAN. 1969. An electron-microscopic study of the de novo formation of neuromuscular junctions in tissue culture. *Z. Zellforsch. mikrosk. Anat.*, **100,** 126–140.

JONES, S. F. and S. KWANBUNBUMPEN. 1970. The effects of nerve stimulation and hemicholinium on synaptic vesicles at the mammalian neuromuscular junction. *J. Physiol., Lond.*, **207,** 31–50.

KATZ, B. 1962. The transmission of impulses from nerve to muscle, and the subcellular unit of synaptic action. *Proc. R. Soc. Ser. B*, **155,** 455–477.

KATZ, B. and R. MILEDI. 1965. Propagation of electric activity in motor nerve terminals. *Proc. R. Soc. Ser. B*, **161,** 453–482.

KELLY, A. M. and S. I. ZACKS. 1969. The fine structure of motor end-plate morphogenesis. *J. Cell Biol.*, **42,** 154–169.

KLINKERFUSS, G. H. and M. J. HAUGH. 1970. Disuse atrophy of muscle; histochemistry and electron microscopy. *Archs Neurol. Chicago*, **22,** 309–320.

KORNELIUSSEN, H. 1972. Ultrastructure of normal and stimulated motor end plates, with comments on the origin and fate of synaptic vesicles. *Z. Zellforsch. mikrosk. Anat.*, **130,** 28.

KORNELIUSSEN, H. and O. WAERHAUG. 1973. Three morphological types of motor nerve terminals in the rat diaphragm, and their possible innervation of different muscle fiber types. *Z. Anat. Entw Gesch.*, **140,** 73–84.

KUCHNOW, K. P. and R. MARTIN. 1970. Fine structure of elasmobranch iris muscle and associated nervous structures. *Expl Eye Res.*, **10,** 345–351.

LENTZ, T. L. 1969. Development of the neuromuscular junction. I. Cytological and cytochemical studies on the neuromuscular junction of differentiating muscle in the regenerating limb of the newt *Triturus*. *J. Cell Biol.*, **42,** 431–443.

LENTZ, T. L. 1970. Development of the neuromuscular junction. II. Cytological and cytochemical studies on the neuromuscular junction of dedifferentiating muscle in the regenerating limb of the newt *Triturus*. *J. Cell Biol.*, **47,** 423–436.

LENTZ, T. L. 1972. Development of the neuromuscular junction. III. Degeneration of motor end plates after denervation and maintenance *in vitro* by nerve explants. *J. Cell Biol.*, **55,** 93–103.

LEWIS, D. M. 1973. Effect of denervation on the differentiation of twitch muscles in the kitten hind limb. *Nature, New Biology*, **241,** 285–286.

LEWIS, P. R. and C. C. D. SHUTE. 1966. The distribution of cholinesterase in cholinergic neurons demonstrated with the electron microscope. *J. Cell Sci.*, **1,** 381–390.

LÜLLMAN-RAUCH, R. 1971. The regeneration of neuromuscular junctions during spontaneous re-innervation of the rat diaphragm. *Z. Zellforsch. mikrosk. Anat.*, **121,** 593–603.

McMAHAN, V. J., N. C. SPITZER and K. PEPER. 1972. Visual identification of nerve terminals in living isolated skeletal muscle. *Proc. R. Soc. Ser. B*, **181,** 421–430.

MANOLOV, S. 1974. Initial changes in the neuromuscular synapses of denervated rat diaphragm. *Brain Res.*, **65,** 303–316.

MAYR, R. 1968. Zur Charakteristik vegetativ innervierter quergestreifter Muskulatur. Die Ultrastruktur der quergestreiften Muskulatur des Schleiendarms. *Anat. Ges.*, **62,** 25–37.

MILEDI, R. and L. T. POTTER. 1971. Acetylcholine receptors in muscle fibers. *Nature, Lond.*, **233,** 599.

MILEDI, R. and C. R. SLATER. 1968. Electrophysiology and electron-microscopy of rat neuromuscular junctions after nerve degeneration. *Proc. R. Soc. Ser. B*, **169,** 289–306.

MILEDI, R. and C. R. SLATER. 1969. Electron-microscopic structure of denervated skeletal muscle. *Proc. R. Soc. Ser. B*, **174,** 253–269.

MILEDI, R. and E. STEFANI. 1969. Non-selective re-innervation of slow and fast muscle fibres in the rat. *Nature, Lond.*, **222,** 569–571.

MILEDI, R. and R. THIES. 1971. Tetanic and post-tetanic rise in frequency of miniature end plate potentials in low-calcium solutions. *J. Physiol., Lond.*, **212,** 245.

MURATA, F. and T. OGATA. 1969. The ultrastructure of neuromuscular junctions of human red, white and intermediate striated muscle fibers. *Tohuku J. exp. Med.*, **99,** 289–301.

MUSCATELLO, U., A. MARGRETH and M. ALOISI. 1965. On the differential response of sarcoplasm and myoplasm to denervation in frog muscle. *J. Cell Biol.*, **27,** 1–24.

NAGASAWA, J., W. W. DOUGLAS and R. A. SCHULZ. 1970. Ultrastructural evidence of secretion by exocytosis and of 'synaptic vesicle' formation in posterior pituitary glands. *Nature, Lond.*, **227,** 407.

NAGASAWA, J., W. W. DOUGLAS and R. A. SCHULZ. 1971. Micropinocytotic origin of coated and smooth microvesicles ('synaptic vesicles') in neurosecretory terminals of posterior pituitary glands demonstrated by incorporation of horseradish peroxidase. *Nature, Lond.*, **232,** 341.

NAKAI, J. 1969. The development of neuromuscular junctions in cultures of chick embryo tissues. *J. exp. Zool.*, **170,** 85–106.

NAKAJIMA, Y. 1969. Fine structure of red and white muscle fibers and their neuromuscular junctions in the snake fish (*Ophiocephalus argus*). *Tissue & Cell*, **1,** 229–246.

OGATA, T., T. HONDO and T. SEITO. 1967. An electron microscopic study on differences in the fine structures of motor endplate in red, white and intermediate muscle fibers of rat intercostal muscle. A preliminary study. *Acta med. Okayama.*, **21,** 327–338.

PACHTER, B. R., J. DAVIDOWITZ and G. M. BREININ. 1973. Morphological changes associated with the myoneural junction in extraocular muscle of the dystrophic mouse. *Acta Neuropathol.*, **24,** 214-221.

PADYKULA, H. A. and G. F. GAUTHIER. 1970. The ultrastructure of the neuromuscular junctions of mammalian red, white and intermediate skeletal muscle fibers. *J. Cell Biol.*, **46,** 27–41.

PAPPAS, G. D., E. R. PETERSON, E. B. MASUROVSKY and S. M. CRAIN. 1971. Electron microscopy of the *in vitro* development of mammalian motor end plates. *Ann. N.Y. Acad. Sci.*, **183,** 33–45.

PAPPAS, G. D. and D. P. PURPURA. (eds.) 1972. *Structure and function of synapses.* Raven Press, New York.

PELLEGRINO, C. and C. FRANZINI. 1963. An electron microscope study of denervation atrophy in red and white skeletal muscle fibers. *J. Cell Biol.*, **17,** 327–349.

PERRI, V., O. SACCHI, E. RAVIOLA and G. RAVIOLA. 1972. Evaluation of the number and distribution of synaptic vesicles at cholinergic nerve-endings after sustained stimulation. *Brain Res.*, **39,** 526.

PETERS, A. and B. MACKAY. 1961. The structure and innervation of the myotomes of the lamprey. *J. Anat.*, **95,** 575–585.

PFENNINGER, K., K. AKERT, H. MOOR and C. SANDRI. 1972. The fine structure of freeze-fractured presynaptic membranes. *J. Neurocytol.*, **1,** 129–149.

POTTER, L. T. 1970. Synthesis, storage, and release of 14C acetylcholine in isolated rat diaphragm muscles. *J. Physiol., Lond.*, **206,** 145.

RASH, J. E. and M. H. ELLISMAN. 1974. Studies of excitable membranes. I Macromolecular specializations of the neuromuscular junction and the nonjunctional sarcolemma. *J. Cell Biol.*, **63,** 567–586.

REGER, J. F. 1961. The fine structure of neuromuscular junctions and the sarcoplasmic reticulum of extrinsic eye muscles of *Fundulus heteroclitus*. *J. biophys. biochem. Cytol.*, **10,** 111–112.

RESNICK, J. S., W. KING ENGEL and P. G. NELSON. 1968. Changes in the Z disc of skeletal muscle induced by tenotomy. *Neurology, Minneap.*, **18,** 737–740.

ROBERTSON, J. D. 1960. Electron microscopy of the motor end plate and the neuromuscular spindle. *Am. J. phys. Med.*, **39,** 1–43.

RODRIGUEZ DE LORES ARNAIZ, G. and E. DE ROBERTIS. 1972. Properties of the isolated nerve endings. In *Current Topics in Membranes and Transport.* Vol. 3. F. Bonner and A. Kleinzeller (eds.). Academic Press, New York. 237–272.

SAITO, A. and S. I. ZACKS. 1969*a*. Fine structure of neuromuscular junctions after nerve section and implantation of nerve in denervated muscle. *Exp. Mol. Pathol.*, **10,** 256–273.

SAITO, A. and S. I. ZACKS. 1969*b*. Ultrastructure of Schwann and perineural sheaths in the mouse neuromuscular junction. *Anat. Rec.*, **164,** 379–390.

SALPETER, M. M. 1967. Electron microscope radioautography as a quantitative tool in enzyme cytochemistry. The distribution of acetylcholinesterase at motor end plates of a vertebrate twitch muscle. *J. Cell Biol.*, **32,** 379–390.

SAMARASINGHE, D. D. 1972. Some observations on the innervation of the striated muscle in the mouse oesophagus—an electron microscope study. *J. Anat.*, **112,** 173–184.

SANTA, T., A. G. ENGEL and E. G. LAMBERT. 1972*a*. Histometric study of neuromuscular junction ultrastructure. I. Myasthenia gravis. *Neurology, Minneap.*, **22,** 71–82.

SANTA, T., A. G. ENGEL and E. G. LAMBERT. 1972*b*. Histometric study of neuromuscular junction ultrastructure. II. Myasthenic syndrome. *Neurology, Minneap.*, **22,** 370–376.

SCHICK, G. and F. JERUSALEM. 1973. Ultrastrukturelle Befunde in der frühen Regenerationsphase des denervierten Rattenmuskels. *Beitr. path. Biol.*, **148,** 127–140.

SHIMADA, Y. and D. A. FISCHMAN. 1973. Morphological and physiological evidence for development of functional neuromuscular junctions *in vitro*. *Devl Biol.*, **31,** 200–225.

SHIMADA, Y., D. A. FISCHMAN and A. A. MOSCONA. 1969. The development of nerve-muscle junctions in monolayer cultures of embryonic spinal cord and skeletal muscle cells. *J. Cell Biol.*, **43,** 382–387.

SONG, S. K. 1968. Electron microscopic study of terminal nerves, motor end-plates and sarcoplasmic structures in denervated skeletal muscle. *J. Neuropath. exp. Neurol.*, **27,** 108–109.

TANNENBAUM, A. S. and J. ROSENBLUTH. 1972. Myoneural junctions in larval Ascidian tail. *Experientia*, **28,** 1210–1212.
TENNYSON, V. M., M. BRZIN and P. SLOTWINER. 1971. The appearance of acetylcholinesterase in the myotome of the embryonic rabbit. An electron microscope cytochemical and biochemical study. *J. Cell Biol.*, **51,** 703–721.
TERÄVÄINEN, H. 1968*a*. Development of the myoneural junction in the rat. *Z. Zellforsch. mikrosk. Anat.*, **87,** 249–265.
TERÄVÄINEN, H. 1968*b*. Electron microscopic and histochemical observations on different types of nerve endings in the extraocular muscles of the rat. *Z. Zellforsch. mikrosk. Anat.*, **90,** 372–388.
TERÄVÄINEN, H. 1969. Axonal protrusions in the small multiple endings in the extraocular muscles of the rat *Z. Zellforsch mikrosk. Anat.*, **96,** 206–211.
TOMANEK, R. J. and R. R. COOPER. 1972. Ultrastructural changes in tenotomized fast- and slow-twitch muscle fibers. *J. Anat.*, **113,** 409–424.
TUFFERY, A. R. 1971. Growth and degeneration of motor end-plates in normal cat hind limb muscles. *J. Anat.*, **110,** 221–248.
ZACKS, S. I. and J. M. BLUMBERG. 1961. Observations on the fine structure and cytochemistry of mouse and human intercostal neuromuscular junctions. *J. biophys. biochem. Cytol.*, **10,** 517–528.
ZELENÁ, J. and I. JIRMANOVÁ. 1973. Ultrastructure of chicken slow muscle after nerve crossunion. *Expl Neurol.*, **38,** 272–285.
ZENKER, W. and E. KRAMMER. 1967. Studies on the fine structure and innervation of the internal eye muscles of chickens. *Z. Zellforsch. mikrosk. Anat.*, **83,** 147–168.

C Vertebrate cardiac muscle

The heart is innervated by two major components of the autonomic nervous system (see also Chapter 7D): (1) the *vagus* (Xth cranial nerve). This parasympathetic nerve contains both sensory and motor components. Motor neurones to the mammalian heart primarily innervate both the *sino-atrial* (S-A) and the *atrio-ventricular* (A-V) nodes. Their transmitter is *acetylcholine*, which slows the heart beat and diminishes the vigour of contraction resulting in a lowering of cardiac output. (2) The *cardiac* or accelerator nerves are sympathetic in origin. They are composed of postganglionic fibres arising from the first five thoracic segments of the sympathetic chain or from the superior, middle, or inferior cervical ganglia. The cardiac nerves innervate the S-A and A-V nodes, and also the myocardium of the atria and ventricles. The transmitter released from these nerves (*noradrenaline*) increases the speed and force of contraction of the heart, resulting in an increase in cardiac output. The normal sequence of electrical activity in the heart is from the S-A node or *pacemaker*, where the impulse originates through the atrial muscle to the A-V node. The impulse then passes to the *atrioventricular bundle* (bundle of His) for rapid conduction into the branches distributed to the ventricles. The S-A node is located beneath the epicardium at the junction of the superior vena cava and the right atrium. The A-V node is found beneath the endocardium in the lower part of the interatrial septum close to the opening of the coronary sinus. The bundle of His originates from the A-V node and passes into the interventricular septum to be distributed to the ventricles.

Both the S-A and A-V nodes are densely innervated, with both adrenergic and cholinergic nerves in close contact with muscle cells. Sometimes the nerve terminals are present in tunnels within the nodal cells or in grooves on their surface. Intramural ganglion cells are also found in close contact with the S-A and A-V nodes in some animals.

The specialized muscle cells of the nodal tissue are generally smaller than ordinary cardiac muscle cells. These slender cells are irregular in shape and are arranged in a complex network with frequent interdigitation. Nodal cells contact each other by numerous desmosomes and rare intercalated discs that contain short 'gap junctions'. In contrast, specialized cells of the bundle of His (*Purkinje fibres*) are much larger than ordinary muscle cells, and are relatively sparse in myofibrils. Their sarcoplasm contains large amounts of glycogen and numerous mitochondria. The transverse tubular system (T-system) appears to be absent from these cells. Few typical intercalated discs are found between Purkinje fibres, desmosomes are infrequent and many nexuses are apparent.

Generally the density of innervation of the vertebrate heart is much higher in the atria than in the ventricles. The atrium and ventricle of a fish, the atria (usually) and ventricle of an amphibian, and the atria and partially or completely subdivided ventricle of a reptile, appear to have a predominance of cholinergic nerve terminals. On the other hand, the atria of birds and mammals and the ventricles of vertebrate classes higher than amphibia are supplied by both cholinergic and adrenergic nerves. Many sensory and motor nerves supply the coronary vascular tree, particularly the 'intimal cushion' of branching sites and the precapillary sphincters.

Chromaffin or small intensely fluorescent cells (SIF cells) have also been reported in the hearts of the turtle and the lamprey as well as in human foetal heart. Their role in cardiac regulation is not yet understood.

Plate 136

The two types of nerve endings found in vertebrate cardiac muscle, adrenergic and cholinergic, contain different kinds of synaptic vesicles. The adrenergic nerve endings contain predominantly 'small granular vesicles', 40–60 nm in diameter, with an electron dense central core while cholinergic endings contain predominantly 'small agranular vesicles', 40–60 nm in diameter, identical to those seen in the motor endings of skeletal muscles.

The varicosities of terminal axons in cardiac muscle at their closest apposition are separated from the fibres by a narrow gap of less than 20 nm without interposed basal lamina.

After the administration of 5-hydroxydopamine, a substance used to enhance the electron dense core in the small granulated vesicles (see also Chapter 7D), adrenergic nerves are clearly distinguished from cholinergic nerves. Adrenergic nerve endings containing a number of small granular vesicles with enhanced dense cores are illustrated in (*a*) while cholinergic endings containing predominantly agranular vesicles and several large granulated vesicles 100 nm are illustrated in both (*a*) and (*b*). Cholinergic nerves are unaffected by the drug.

Nerve terminals in mammalian heart: mouse atrium. Glutaraldehyde fixation. Tissue pretreated with 5-hydroxydopamine (200 mg kg^{-1}) for identification of adrenergic nerves.

(*a*) adrenergic and cholinergic nerves. ×44 000.
(*b*) cholinergic nerve. ×35 000.
(Courtesy of A. Yamauchi, Department of Anatomy, Iwate Medical University, Morioku, Japan.)

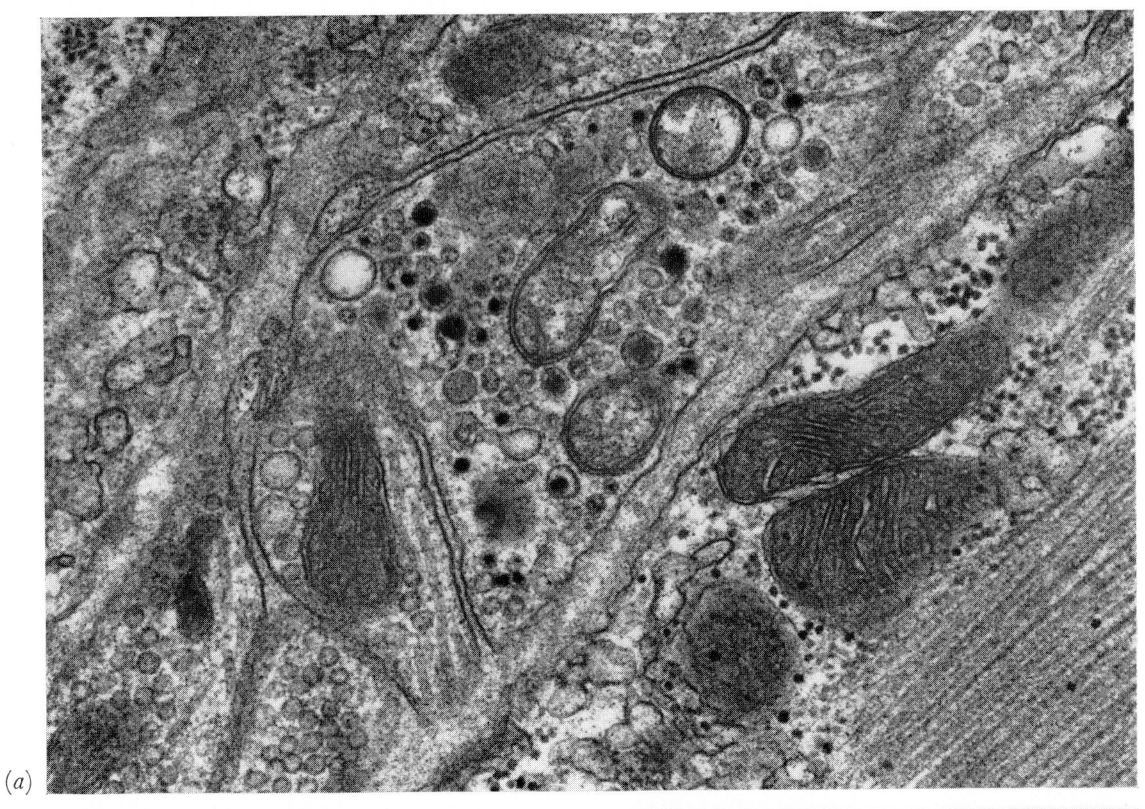
(a)

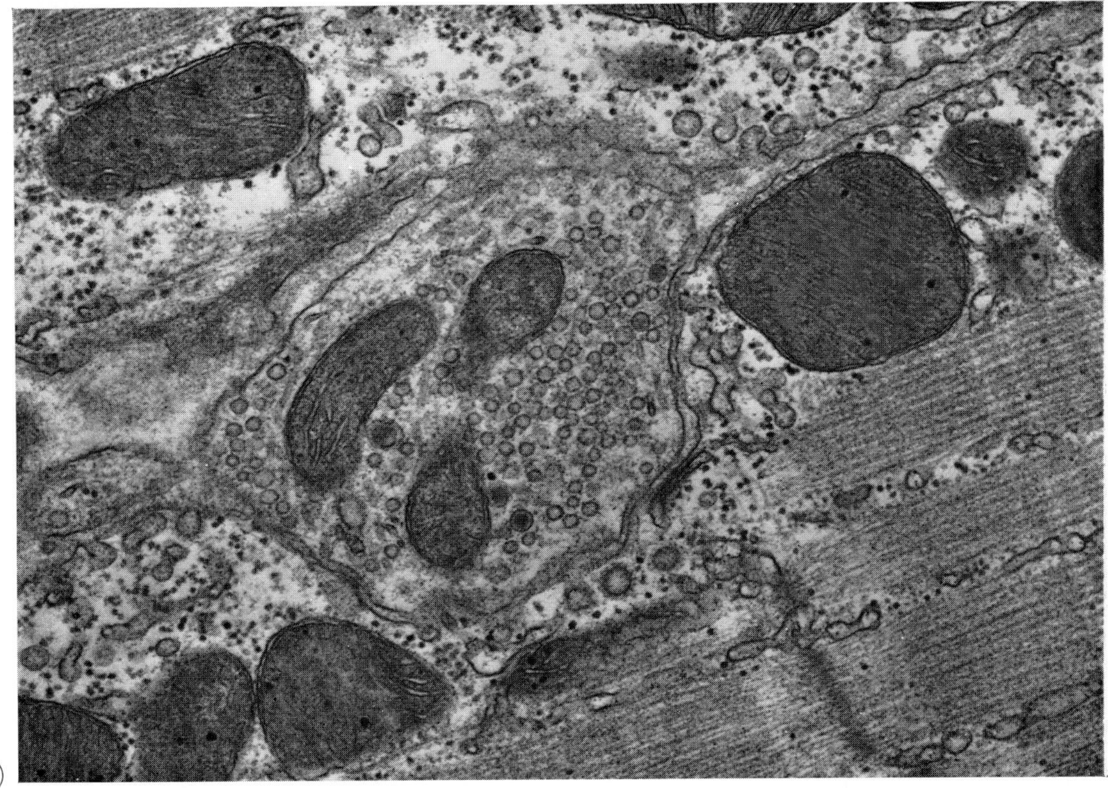
(b)

Plate 137

An autonomic nerve and associated Schwann cell processes between two muscle cells is illustrated. Nerves within the echidna heart are similar to those seen within the reptile heart. Intraneuronal vesicles are from 80 –100 nm in diameter with an electron opaque core. Not all vesicles are round, some being dumb-bell shaped. The nature of the transmitter is unknown. Similar axon profiles have been observed in smooth muscle tissues in the echidna.

Autonomic nerve in the heart of a monotreme: atrium of echidna. Longitudinal section. Glutaraldehyde fixation. × 16 000. (Courtesy of M. Canny, Department of Zoology, University of Melbourne.)

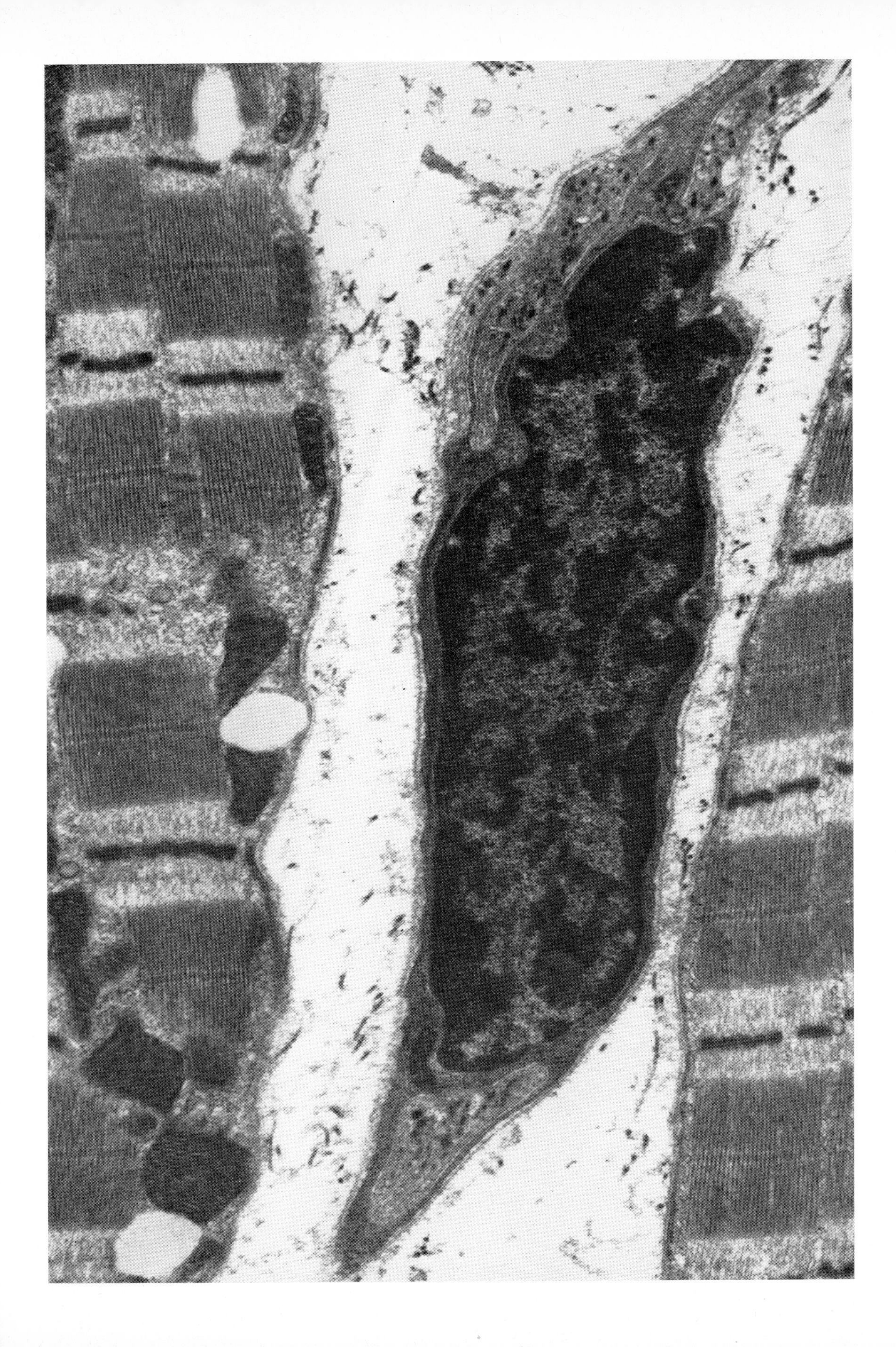

Selected reviews

ABRAHAM, A. 1972. *Microscopic Innervation of the Heart and Blood Vessels in Vertebrates Including Man.* Pergamon Press, Oxford.

CHALLICE, C. E. and G. A. EDWARDS. 1961. The micromorphology of the developing ventricular muscle. In *The Specialized Tissues of the Heart.* A. P. de Caravalho, W. C. de Mello and B. F. Hoffman (eds.). Elsevier, Amsterdam. 44–75.

HIGGINS, C. B., S. F. VATNER and E. BRAUNWALD. 1973. Parasympathetic control of the heart. *Pharmac. Rev.*, **25,** 119–155.

KAWAMURA, K., H. MITSUI, K. HAYASHI, Y. NOHARA and M. TAKAYASU. 1970. The ultrastructure of the AV node in mammalian hearts. In *Cardiology—Current Topics and Progress.* M. Eliakim and H. N. Neufeld (eds.). Academic Press, New York. 269–273.

MAEKAWA, M., Y. NOHARA, K. KAWAMURA and K. HAYASHI. 1967. Electron microscopy of the conduction system in mammalian hearts. In *Electrophysiology and Ultrastructure of the Heart.* T. Sano, V. Mizuhira and K. Matsuda (eds.). Bunkodo, Tokyo. 41–54.

MULLINS, L. J. (ed.). 1972. Neural regulation of the cardiovascular system. Physiology Society Symposium. *Fedn Proc.*, **31,** 1197–1252.

SOBEL, B. E. and S. E. MAYER. 1973. Cyclic adenosine monophosphate and cardiac contractility. *Circulation Res.*, **32,** 407–414.

YAMAUCHI, A. 1969. Innervation of the vertebrate heart as studied with the electron microscope. *Arch. histol. jap.*, **31,** 83–117.

Selected articles

ANDERSON, R. H. 1972*a*. The disposition, morphology and innervation of cardiac specialized tissue in the guinea-pig. *J. Anat.*, **111,** 453–468.

ANDERSON, R. H. 1972*b*. The disposition and innervation of atrioventricular ring specialized tissue in rats and rabbits. *J. Anat.*, **113,** 197–212.

BENCOSME, S. A., A. TRILLO, J. ALANIS and D. BENITEZ. 1969. Correlative ultrastructural and electrophysiological study of the Purkinje system of the heart. *J. Electrocardiol.*, **2,** 27–38.

BERINGER, T. and R. HADEK. 1973. Ultrastructure of sinus venosus innervation in *Petromyzon marinus. J. Ultrastruct. Res.*, **42,** 312–323.

BISHOP, S. P. and C. R. COLE. 1967. Morphology of the specialized conducting tissue in the atria of the equine heart. *Anat. Rec.*, **158,** 401–416.

CAESAR, R., G. A. EDWARDS and H. RUSKA. 1958. Electron microscopy of the impulse conducting system of the sheep heart. *Z. Zellforsch. mikrosk. Anat.*, **48,** 698–719.

CHALLICE, C. E. 1966. Studies on the microstructure of the heart. I. The sino-atrial node and sino-atrial ring bundle. *Jl R. microsc. Soc.*, **85,** 1–21.

CHIBA, T. and A. YAMAUCHI. 1970. On the fine structure of the nerve terminals in the human myocardium. *Z. Zellforsch. microsk. Anat.*, **108,** 324–338.

CHIBA, T. and A. YAMAUCHI. 1973. Fluorescence and electron microscopy of the monoamine containing cells in the turtle heart. *Z. Zellforsch. mikrosk. Anat.*, **140,** 25–37.

CHUAQUI, J. B. 1972. Über die Ausbreitungsbündel des Sinusknotens: Eine kritische Analyse der wichtigsten Arbeiten. *Virchows Arch. Abt. A Path. Anat.*, **355,** 179–208.

DAVIES, F. and E. T. B. FRANCIS. 1946. The conducting system of the vertebrate heart. *Biol. Rev.*, **21,** 173–188.

DE ALMEIDA, D. F. 1961. Histological aspects of the atrioventricular node of the rabbit heart. In *The Specialized Tissues of the Heart.* A. P. de Carvahlo, W. C. de Mello, B. F. Hoffman (eds.). Elsevier, Amsterdam. 134–142.

DE FELICE, L. J. and C. E. CHALLICE. 1969. Anatomical and ultrastructural study of the electrophysiological atrioventricular node of the rabbit. *Circulation Res.*, **24,** 457–474.

DOWD, D. A. 1969. The coronary vessels and conducting system in the heart of monotremes. *Acta anat.*, **74,** 547–573.

ELLISON, J. P. 1971. Cholinesterase-positive and catecholamine-containing nerves in the guinea pig pericardium. *Am. J. Anat.*, **131,** 121–132.

ELLISON, J. P. 1974. The adrenergic cardiac nerves of the cat. *Am. J. Anat.*, **139,** 209–226.

ELLISON, J. P. and R. G. HIBBS. 1974. Catecholamine-containing cells of the guinea pig heart: An ultrastructural study. *J. Mol. & Cell Cardiol.*, **6,** 17–26.

FENOGLIO, J. J. JR., T. D. PHAM, A. L. WITT, A. L. BASSETT and B. M. WAGNER. 1972. Canine mitral complex: Ultrastructure and electromechanical properties. *Circulation Res.*, **31,** 417–430.

FRIEDMAN, W. F., P. E. POOL, D. JACOBOWITZ, S. C. SEAGREN and E. BRAUNWALD. 1968. Sympathetic innervation of the developing rabbit heart. Biochemical and histochemical comparisons of fetal, neonatal and adult myocardium. *Circulation Res.*, **23,** 25–32.

GRILLO, M. A. 1970. Extracellular synaptic vesicles in the mouse heart. *J. Cell Biol.*, **47,** 547–554.

HADEK, R. and P. J. TALSO. 1967. A study of nonmyelinated nerves in the rat and rabbit heart. *J. Ultrastruct. Res.*, **17,** 257–265.

HAYASHI, K. 1962. An electron microscopy study on the conduction system of the cow heart. *Jap. Circ. J.*, **26,** 765–842.

HAYASHI, S. 1971. Electron microscopy of the heart conduction system of the dog. *Arch. histol. jap.*, **33,** 67–86.

HERNDON, R. M. 1963. The fine structure of the Purkinje cell. *J. Cell Biol.*, **18,** 167–180.

HIRAKOW, R. 1966. Fine structure of Purkinje fibers in chick heart. *Arch. histol. jap.*, **27,** 485–499.

HIRANO, H. and K. OGAWA. 1967. Ultrastructural localization of cholinesterase activity in nerve endings in the guinea pig heart. *J. Electron Microsc.*, **16,** 313–321.

HIRSCH, E. F., M. JELLINEK and T. COOPER. 1964. Innervation of the systemic heart of the California hagfish. *Circulation Res.*, **14,** 212–217.

HOAR, R. M. and J. L. HALL. 1970. The early pattern of cardiac innervation in the fetal guinea pig. *Am. J. Anat.*, **128,** 499–508.

JAMES, T. N. 1964. Anatomy of the A-V node of the dog. *Anat. Rec.*, **148,** 15–28.

JAMES, T. N. 1965. Anatomy of the sinus node A-V node and os cordis of the beef heart. *Anat. Rec.*, **153,** 361–373.

JAMES, T. N. 1967. Anatomy of the cardiac conduction system in the rabbit. *Circulation Res.*, **20,** 638–648.

JAMES, T. N. 1970. Cardiac conduction system: Fetal and postnatal development. *Am. J. Cardiol.*, **25,** 213–226.

JAMES, T. N. and L. SHERF. 1968. Ultrastructure of the human atrioventricular node. *Circulation*, **37,** 1049–1070.

JAMES, T. N. and L. SHERF. 1971*a*. Specialized tissues and preferential conduction in the atria of the heart. *Am. J. Cardiol.*, **28,** 414–427.

JAMES, T. N. and L. SHERF. 1971*b*. Fine structure of the His bundle. *Circulation*, **44,** 9–28.

JAMES, T. N., L. SHERF, G. FINE and A. R. MORALES. 1966. Comparative ultrastructure of the sinus node in man and dog. *Circulation*, **34,** 139–162.

JENSEN, D. 1961. Cardioregulation in an aneural heart. *Comp. Biochem. Physiol.*, **2,** 181–201.

KARNOVSKY, M. J. 1964. The localization of cholinesterase activity in rat cardiac muscle by electron microscopy. *J. Cell Biol.*, **23,** 217–232.

KATZ, B. and R. MILEDI. 1973. The effect of atropine on acetylcholine action at the neuromuscular junction. *Proc. R. Soc. Ser. B*, **184,** 221–226.

KAWAMURA, K. 1961*a*. Electron miscroscope studies on the cardiac conduction system of the dog. I. The Purkinje fibres. *Jap. Circul. J.*, **25,** 594–616.

KAWAMURA, K. 1961*b*. Electron microscope studies on the cardiac conduction system of the dog. II. The sinoatrial and atrioventricular nodes. *Jap. Circul. J.*, **25,** 973–1013.

KAWAMURA, K. and K. HAYASHI. 1966. Electron microscope study of the cardiac conducting system. *Jap. Circul. J.*, **30,** 149–151.

KIM, S. and N. BABA. 1971. Atrioventricular node and Purkinje fibers of the guinea pig heart. *Am. J. Anat.*, **132,** 339–354.

LEV, M. and H. C. THAEMERT. 1973. The conduction system of the mouse heart. *Acta Anat.*, **85,** 342–352.

McKIBBEN, J. S. and R. GETTY. 1968*a*. A comparative morphologic study of the cardiac innervation in domestic animals. I. The canine. *Am. J. Anat.*, **122,** 533–544.

McKIBBEN, J. S. and R. GETTY. 1968*b*. A comparative morphologic study of the

cardiac innervation in domestic animals. II. The feline. *Am. J. Anat.*, **122,** 545–554.
McKIBBEN, J. S. and R. GETTY. 1969. A study of the cardiac innervation in domestic animals: cattle. *Anat. Rec.*, **165,** 141–152.
MAEKAWA, M., K. KAWAMURA, H. TORII and K. HAYASHI. 1964. Ultrastructure of the cardiac conduction system in mammals including man. *Proc. 3rd. Asian-Pacific Congr. Cardiol.*, 1703–1707.
MARTINEZ-PALOMO, A., J. ALANIS and D. BENITEZ. 1970. Transitional cardiac cells of the conductive system of the dog heart. Distinguishing morphological and electrophysiological features. *J. Cell Biol.*, **47,** 1–17.
MILLER, M. R. and M. KASAHARA. 1964. Studies on the nerve endings in the heart. *Am. J. Anat.*, **115,** 217–234.
MUIR, A. R. 1957. Observations on the fine structure of the Purkinje fibers in the ventricles of the sheep's heart. *J. Anat.*, **91,** 251–258.
NILSSON, E. and B. SPORRONG. 1970. Electron microscopic investigation of adrenergic and non-adrenergic axons in the rabbit SA-node. *Z. Zellforsch. mikrosk. Anat.*, **111,** 404–412.
NOVI, A. M. 1968. An electron microscopic study of the innervation of papillary muscles in the rat. *Anat. Rec.*, **160,** 123–142.
PAGE, E. 1967. Tubular systems in Purkinje cells of the cat heart. *J. Ultrastruct. Res.*, **17,** 72–83.
RHODIN, J. A. G., P. DEL MISSIER and L. C. REID. 1961. The structure of the specialized impulse-conducting system of the steer heart. *Circulation*, **24,** 349–367.
SCOTT, T. M. 1971. The ultrastructure of normal and Purkinje cells of the fowl heart. *J. Anat.*, **110,** 259–274.
SMITH, R. B. 1971. Intrinsic innervation of the atrioventricular and semilunar valves in various mammals. *J. Anat.*, **108,** 115–122.
SOMMER, J. R. and E. A. JOHNSON. 1968*a*. Cardiac muscle. A comparative study of Purkinje fibers and ventricular fibers. *J. Cell Biol.*, **36,** 497–526.
SOMMER, J. R. and E. A. JOHNSON. 1968*b*. Purkinje fibers of the heart examined with the peroxidase reaction. *J. Cell Biol.*, **37,** 570–574.
SULKIN, N. M. and D. F. SULKIN. 1965. An electron microscopic study of the effects of chronic hypoxia on cardiac muscle, hepatic, and autonomic ganglion cells. *Lab. Invest.*, **14,** 1523–1546.
SULLIVAN, J. M. and C. A. RICHINS. 1973. Adrenergic innervation of the left atrium and ventricle of the guinea pig heart. *Anat. Rec.*, **175,** 453.
THAEMERT, J. C. 1966. Ultrastructure of cardiac muscle and nerve continuities. *J. Cell Biol.*, **29,** 156–162.
THAEMERT, J. C. 1969. Fine structure of neuromuscular relationships in mouse heart. *Anat. Rec.*, **163,** 575–586.
THAEMERT, J. C. 1970. Atrioventricular node innervation in ultrastructural three dimensions. *Am. J. Anat.*, **128,** 239–263.
THAEMERT, J. C. 1973. Fine structure of the atrioventricular node as viewed in serial sections. *Am. J. Anat.*, **136,** 43–66.
THAEMERT, J. C. and S. S. EMMETT. 1968. The ultrastructure of neuromuscular relationships within the atrioventricular node of the heart. *Anat. Rec.*, **160,** 518.
THORNELL, L. E. 1973. Evidence of an imbalance in synthesis and degradation of myofibrillar proteins in rabbit Purkinje fibres. An electron microscopic study. *J. Ultrastruct. Res.*, **44,** 85–95.
TORII, H. 1962. Electron microscope observations of the S-A and A-V nodes and Purkinje fibers of the rabbit. *Jap. Circul. J.*, **26,** 206–211.
TRANUM-JENSEN, J. and F. BOJSEN-MØLLER. 1973. The ultrastructure of the sinoatrial ring bundle and of the caudal extension of the sinus node in the right atrium of the rabbit heart. *Z. Zellforsch. mikrosk. Anat.*, **138,** 97–112.
TRAUTWEIN, W. and K. UCHIZONO. 1963. Electron microscopic and electrophysiologic study of the pacemaker in the sino-atrial node of the rabbit heart. *Z. Zellforsch. mikrosk. Anat.*, **61,** 96–109.
TRUEX, R. C. 1961. Comparative anatomy and functional considerations of the cardiac conduction system. In *The Specialized Tissues of the Heart.* A. P. de Carvalho, W. C. de Mello and B. F. Hoffman (eds.). Elsevier, Amsterdam. 22–43.

TRUEX, R. C. and M. Q. SMYTHE. 1965. Comparative morphology of the cardiac conduction tissue in animals. *Ann. N.Y. Acad. Sci.*, **127,** 19–33.

TRUEX, R. C. and M. Q. SMYTHE. 1967. Reconstruction of the human atrio-ventricular node. *Anat. Rec.*, **158,** 11–20.

TRUEX, R. C., M. Q. SMYTHE and M. J. TAYLOR. 1967. Reconstruction of the human sinoatrial node. *Anat. Rec.*, **159,** 371–378.

UNGE, G., E. MANDACHE and A. LJUNGQVI. 1973. Sympathetic myocardial innervation in various forms of experimental cardiac hypertrophy—histochemical and ultra-structural study. *Acta path.*, **81,** 366–375.

VIRÁGH, SZ. and A. PORTE. 1961. Elements nerveux intracardiaques et innervation du myocarde. *Z. Zellforsch. mikrosk. Anat.*, **55,** 282–296.

YAMAUCHI, A. 1965. Electron microscopic observations on the development of S-A and A-V nodal tissues in the human embryonic heart. *Z. Anat. Entw Gesch.*, **124,** 562–587.

YAMAUCHI, A. and G. BURNSTOCK. 1968. An electron microscopic study on the inner-vation of the trout heart. *J. comp. Neurol.*, **132,** 567–588.

YAMAUCHI, A. and T. CHIBA. 1973. Adrenergic and cholinergic innervation of the turtle heart ventricle. *Z. Zellforsch. mikrosk. Anat.*, **143,** 485–493.

YAMAUCHI, A., Y. FUJIMAKI and R. YOKOTA. 1973. Fine structural studies of the sino-auricular nodal tissue in the heart of a teleost fish, Misgurnus, with particular reference to the cardiac internuncial cell. *Am. J. Anat.*, **138,** 407–430.

D Vertebrate smooth muscle

In contrast to the motor end plate in fast-twitch skeletal muscle, where there is a discrete junction between a single nerve fibre and a single muscle cell, the autonomic neuromuscular junction consists of a bundle of muscle cells in electrical continuity with each other, and varicose nerves releasing transmitter 'en passage' over considerable lengths of their terminal regions.

There is now clear evidence that a bundle of cells electrically coupled to each other rather than a single cell represents the smooth muscle effector. Sites of electrotonic coupling are represented morphologically by areas of close apposition of the plasma membranes of adjacent cells called 'nexuses'. High resolution electron-micrographs show that the membranes in these areas form 'gap junctions' (see Chapter 6B).

In the vicinity of effector muscle bundles, an autonomic axon becomes varicose and branches from many terminal axons combine to form the 'autonomic ground plexus'. The varicose nature of terminal axons can be demonstrated by fluorescence histochemistry (for adrenergic nerves), by scanning electronmicroscopy and by transmission electronmicroscopy (see Chapter 7A and Plate 128). A serial electronmicroscope study of the vas deferens has shown that varicosities vary in diameter from 1–2 μm, while intervaricosities vary from 0.1–0.5 μm, and that the last few varicosities of a fibre become completely free of their Schwann cell invest-ment. Varicosities are packed with mito-chondria and vesicles of various kinds, while intervaricosities contain predominantly neuro-tubules and neurofilaments. There are about 250–300 varicosities per millimeter in most adrenergic nerves. Indirect estimates suggest that terminal varicose axons can extend for up to 10–20 cm in some situations. There is physio-logical, histochemical and ultrastructural evi-dence for 'en passage' release of transmitter from varicosities.

Considerable variation in the relationship of individual nerve varicosities with smooth muscle cells in different organs is apparent. Nerve–muscle separations in the regions of closest apposition in the vas deferens, nictitating membrane and sphincter pupillae are in the range 15–30 nm. From an analysis of serial electronmicroscope sections combined with an electrophysiological study of the neural environ-ment of single muscle cells in the vas deferens, it has been concluded that transmitter released from varicosities further than about 100 nm do not have a significant effect on muscle cells. Nerve profiles in the vas deferens occasionally penetrate and probably terminate deep inside smooth muscle cells, sometimes even forming close relations with nuclear membranes. In contrast, the closest apposition between adrenergic nerves and smooth muscle cells in most blood vessels, where the nerves are confined to the adventitial–medial border and rarely penetrate the smooth muscle coat, is about 50–80 nm and the maximum effective neuromuscular cleft proposed is about 1000 nm. The closest approach of autonomic nerves to smooth muscle observed in the longitudinal coat in the intestine is about 100 nm. However, nerve and muscle separation of 15–30 nm has been described in the circular coat, including 'multiaxonal' junctions where groups of up to seven profiles lie in close apposition to single cells.

Interruption of the basal lamina of smooth muscle occurs in areas of close (10–30 nm) neuromuscular apposition. In addition, various postjunctional features have been described, although these appear to be inconsistent structures not present at all junctions. Postjunctional structures of three main kinds have been described, namely aggregations of plasmalemmal vesicles, areas of increased density of the postjunctional membrane and subsurface cisternae (see Plate 144).

Microelectrode and sucrose-gap studies of the responses of smooth muscle cells to stimulation of autonomic nerves, have provided a useful approach to studies of the nature of the autonomic neuromuscular junction. Excitatory junction potentials (EJP's) have been recorded in smooth muscle cells of a variety of tissues including vas deferens, bladder, dog retractor penis, seminal vesicles, gut and various small- and medium-sized arteries. When the depolarization, attained during a single EJP or train of EJP's which exhibit facilitation, reaches a critical level, an action potential is initiated and contraction occurs. EJP's recorded in arterial muscle are smaller than those recorded from the vas deferens and this is probably due to the difference in minimum width of the junctional cleft in the two tissues. Inhibitory junction potentials (IJP's) which lead to relaxation have also been recorded in smooth muscle cells of the alimentary tract. In the absence of nerve stimulation, a random discharge of spontaneous EJP's occurs, which probably represents the spontaneous release of packets of transmitter from the nerve terminals. There is post-tetanic potentiation of spontaneous EJP's following nerve stimulation. These results suggest that the mechanism of autonomic transmission is essentially similar to that known for the skeletal neuromuscular junction. However there are some differences, including: the long latency and time course of the junction potentials; the overall reduction in amplitude of EJP's in all cells rather than complete loss in localized areas following reduction of the number of nerve fibres stimulated; the lack of effect of depolarizing or hyperpolarizing currents on the amplitude of junction potentials in the majority of cells. These differences can be explained largely in terms of electrotonic coupling of activity between neighbouring cells and 'en passage' release of transmitter from extensive terminal varicosities; there is also a slower time course of postjunctional receptor activation.

On the basis of the histochemical, electron-microscopic and electrophysiological data briefly mentioned earlier, the following generalized model of the autonomic neuromuscular junction has been proposed (see Fig. 20). The essential features of the model are that: (1) the effector is the muscle bundle rather than the single cell; individual cells within muscle effector bundles are connected by low resistance pathways represented by nexuses, which allow electrotonic spread of activity; (2) transmitter is released 'en passage' from large numbers of terminal varicosities; (3) some proportion of the muscle cells within an effector bundle are '*directly-innervated*', i.e. they are directly affected by transmitter released from the nerve; (4) the cells adjoining 'directly-innervated cells' are coupled electrotonically to them so that excitatory junction potentials (EJP's) can be recorded; these cells have been termed '*coupled cells*'; (5) when the muscle cells in an area of an effector bundle become depolarized in this way, an all-or-none action potential is initiated which propagates through the tissue. Thus, in some tissues, many cells, termed '*indirectly coupled cells*', are neither directly innervated nor coupled yet are activated upon stimulation of the nerves supplying the organ. It seems unlikely that the three cell types described in this model are different in structure and properties. On the contrary, these cells may play the role of a 'directly innervated', 'coupled' or 'indirectly coupled' cell at different times during the normal physiological pattern of nervous control of the organ.

While this model serves as a useful general definition of the autonomic neuromuscular junction, there is considerable variation in the density and pattern of innervation of smooth muscle in different organs, so the model needs to be modified to suit the more extreme situations. For example, all the muscle cells of the mouse and rat vas deferens are 'directly-innervated' with at least one and probably up to six close neuromuscular junctions, although even in these tissues some electrotonic coupling occurs. In other organs such as the urinary bladder, nictitating membrane, guinea-pig vas deferens and dog retractor penis, about $\frac{1}{3}$ to $\frac{2}{3}$ of the muscle cells are 'directly innervated'. Finally in such organs as the uterus, ureter and many arteries only a small proportion of muscle cells are directly innervated, so that a large number of cells are 'indirectly coupled' and are activated via a well developed interfibre nexus system. In some large arteries it would appear that most of the muscle cells are activated by neurohormones reaching them from the circulation, rather than from the adventitial nerve plexus; many muscle cells in these vessels are not electrically coupled.

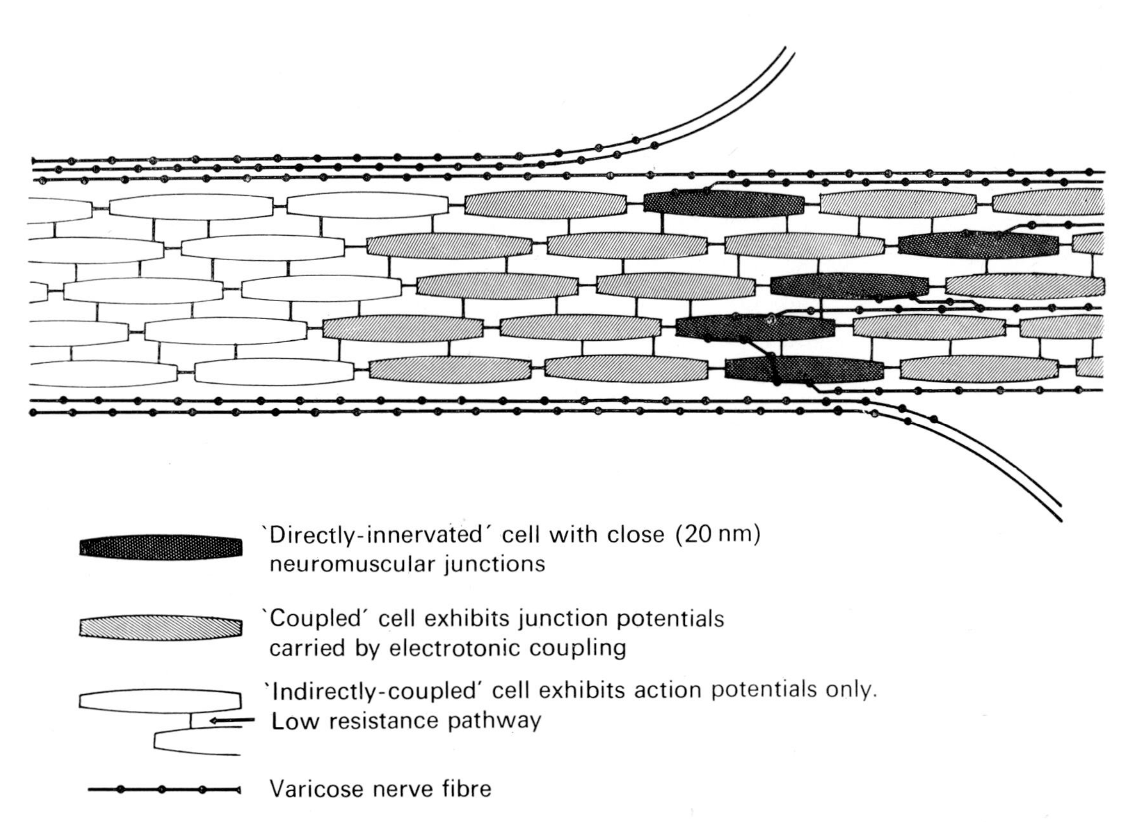

Fig. 20 Schematic representation of autonomic innervation of smooth muscle. (From Burnstock, G. and T. Iwayama, 1971, *Prog. Brain Res.*, **34,** 389.)

While the autonomic nervous system is considered classically to consist of two components, cholinergic and adrenergic nerves, a third component has been discovered which is neither adrenergic nor cholinergic. In view of the evidence that these nerves release a purine nucleotide, probably ATP, they have been termed 'purinergic'.

Current views regarding the synthesis, storage, release and metabolism of acetylcholine (ACh) in cholinergic nerves are summarized in Fig. 21. Synthesis of the ACh by choline acetyltransferase occurs both in the neuron body and in the peripheral terminal axon. The ACh is stored in electron-transparent 'agranular vesicles', 30–60 nm in diameter, and released into the junctional cleft. Inactivation of ACh following its interaction with the postjunctional receptors is due in the main to local hydrolysis by postjunctionally situated acetylcholinesterase (AChE), although a small fraction of ACh may diffuse away from the junctional cleft to be hydrolysed by cholinesterases elsewhere in the effector tissue or in the circulation. Re-uptake of ACh itself into the nerve terminals does not occur. However, choline produced by ACh hydrolysis is actively resorbed, and may be important in maintaining continued transmitter synthesis. It must be emphasized that, although there are now ample grounds for concluding that cholinergic axons contain predominantly agranular vesicles, there is no proof that all axons with this characteristic are cholinergic. In contrast with the capacity of adrenergic vesicles to concentrate electron-opaque noradrenaline (NA) analogues, no specific technique so far exists by which the ACh content of the vesicles can be characterized in a tissue section. Postganglionic cholinergic autonomic axons can be distinguished by the relatively high AChE-reactivity of their axolemma, although adrenergic nerves in some species also show AChE activity. Cholinergic excitation of smooth muscle is associated with increases in conductance of Na^{+}, K^{+} and perhaps Ca^{2+} ions. In cardiac muscle, cholinergic inhibition is

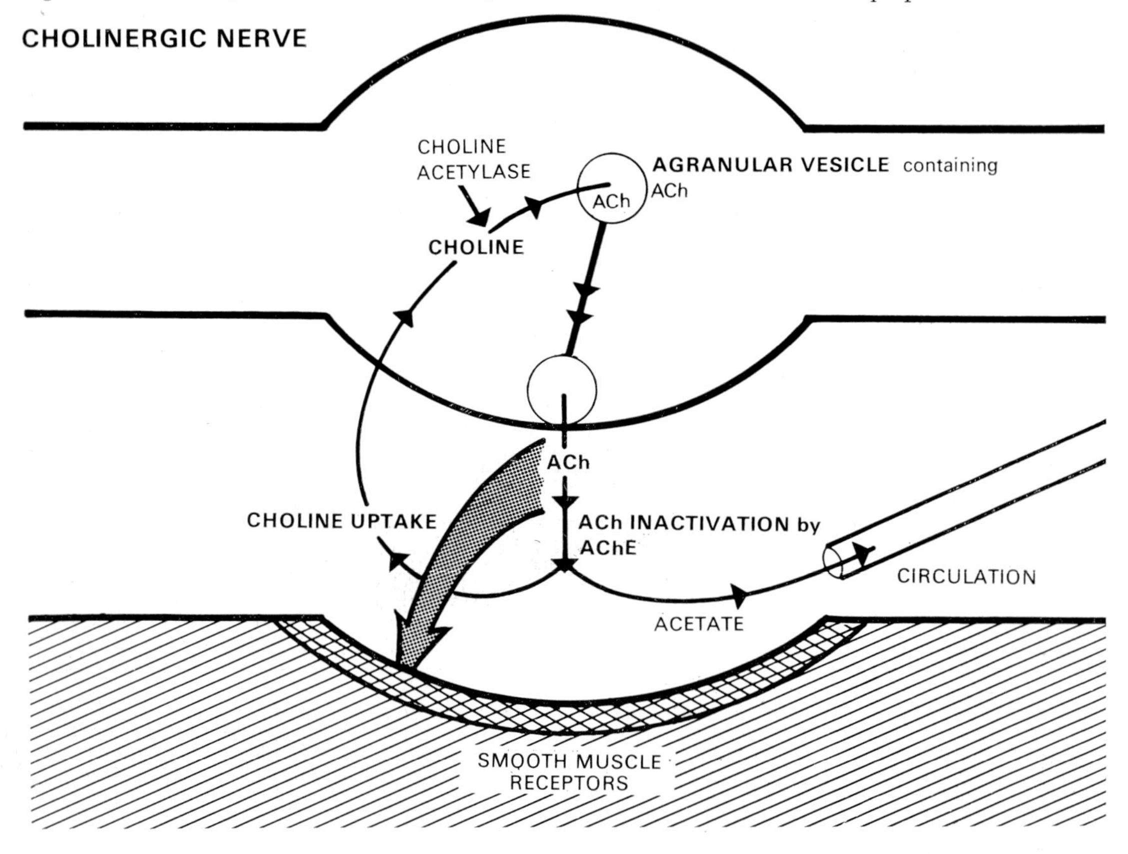

Fig. 21 Schematic representation of synthesis, storage, release and inactivation of autonomic neurotransmitters at cholinergic neuro-muscular junctions. (From Burnstock, G., 1972, *Pharmac. Rev.*, **24,** 536.)

associated with an increase in K^+ conductance.

Current views concerning the process of synthesis, storage, release and inactivation of noradrenaline (NA) at the adrenergic neuro-muscular junction are summarized in Fig. 22. All the enzymes involved in the synthesis and breakdown of NA (tyrosine hydroxylase, DOPA-decarboxylase, dopamine-β-hydroxylase, monoamine oxidase (MAO) and probably some catechol-O-methyl transferase (COMT) are present throughout the adrenergic neurone. Tyrosine hydroxylase forms the rate limiting step in NA synthesis, and control is mediated by feedback inhibition of its activity by an extravesicular pool of NA which rapidly equilibrates with vesicular stores. NA is stored mainly in small granular vesicles (30–60 nm) together with chromogranin and dopamine-β-hydroxylase. During transmission NA, together with these proteins, is released into the junctional cleft, probably by a process of exocytosis. Following its action on the post-synaptic muscle membrane, NA is inactivated largely by reuptake into the nerves where it is either reincorporated into vesicular stores or degraded by MAO. Some NA is taken up by smooth muscle cells and inactivated by intra-cellular MAO or COMT, while any NA that leaks away into the circulation is inactivated by the same enzymes largely in the liver or kidney.

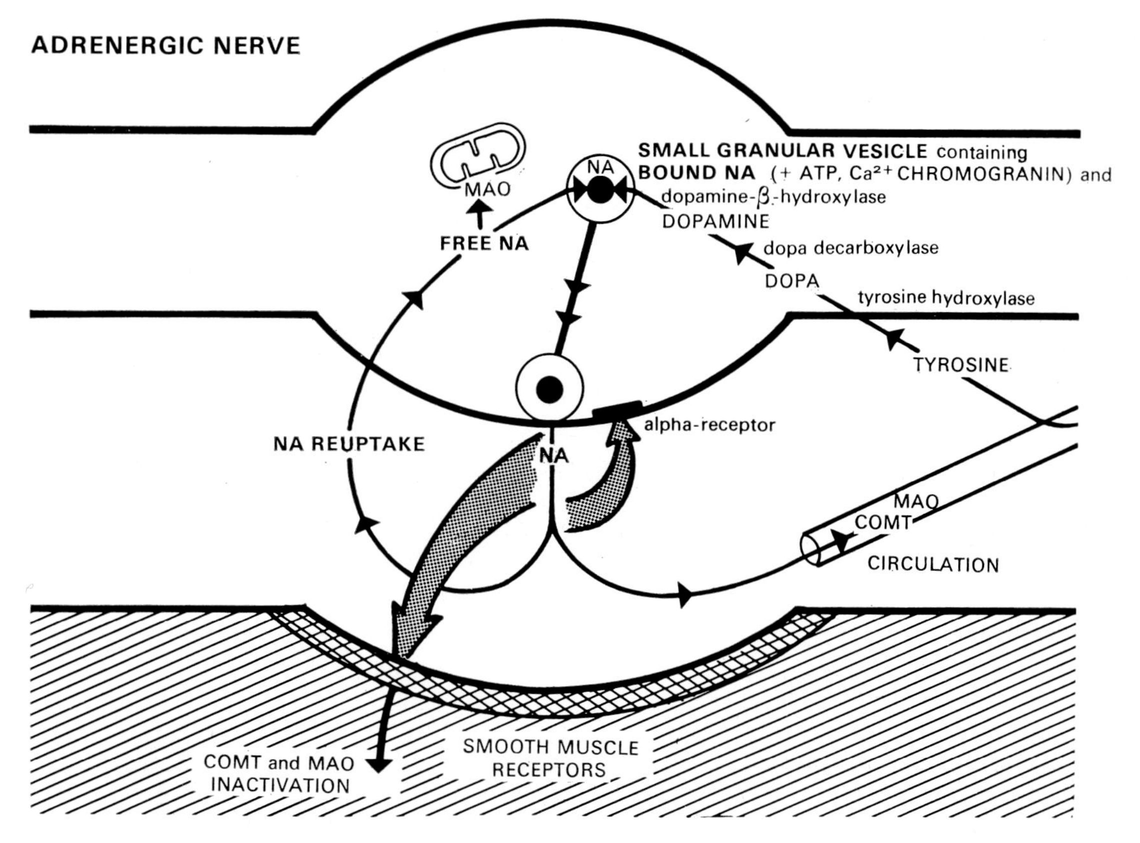

Fig. 22 Schematic representation of synthesis, storage, release and inactivation of autonomic neurotransmitters at adrenergic neuro-muscular junctions. (From Burnstock, G., 1972, *Pharmac. Rev.*, **24,** 537.)

The hypothesis that intra-axonal ACh might play a part in the release of NA from post-ganglionic adrenergic nerve fibres was first proposed by Burn and Rand (1959) and has been the subject of considerable controversy since this time. The possibility has also been considered that release of ACh from cholinergic terminals, shown to be in close relation with the terminal varicosities of adrenergic nerves, could lead to the release of NA.

A tentative model of synthesis, storage, release and inactivation of ATP at non-adrenergic, non-cholinergic ('purinergic') neuromuscular junctions has been proposed and is summarized in Fig. 23. By analogy with cholinergic and adrenergic transmission systems, it seems likely that the ATP is contained in 'large opaque vesicles' (100–200 nm), which differ from the 'large granular vesicles' (80–120 nm) found in small numbers in adrenergic and cholinergic nerves. After activating the postjunctional muscle membrane, the transmitter is rapidly broken down by Mg-activated ATPase and 5′-nucleotidase to adenosine. Adenosine is taken up by the nerve terminals, resynthesized to ATP and may be incorporated into physiological stores for reuse. Any adenosine which is not taken up by the nerves is broken down by adenosine deaminase to inosine which is pharmacologically inactive, cannot be taken up by the nerve and is carried away in the circulation. 'Purinergic' neurones are present throughout the gastrointestinal tract of all vertebrate groups and also appear to supply the lung and possibly the bladder, trachea and parts of the eye, brain and cardiovascular system. 'Purinergic' nerves rather than adrenergic nerves provide the main antagonistic inhibitory system to cholinergic excitatory nerves during propulsion of material through the gut. For example, there is strong evidence that they are concerned in the mechanism of reflex relaxation of the oesophago-gastric junction and of 'receptive relaxation' of the stomach. They are responsible for the phase of 'descending inhibition' in peristalsis, which is unaffected by sympathetic denervation. 'Purinergic' nerves have also been implicated in the mechanism of 'reflex relaxation' of the anal sphincter.

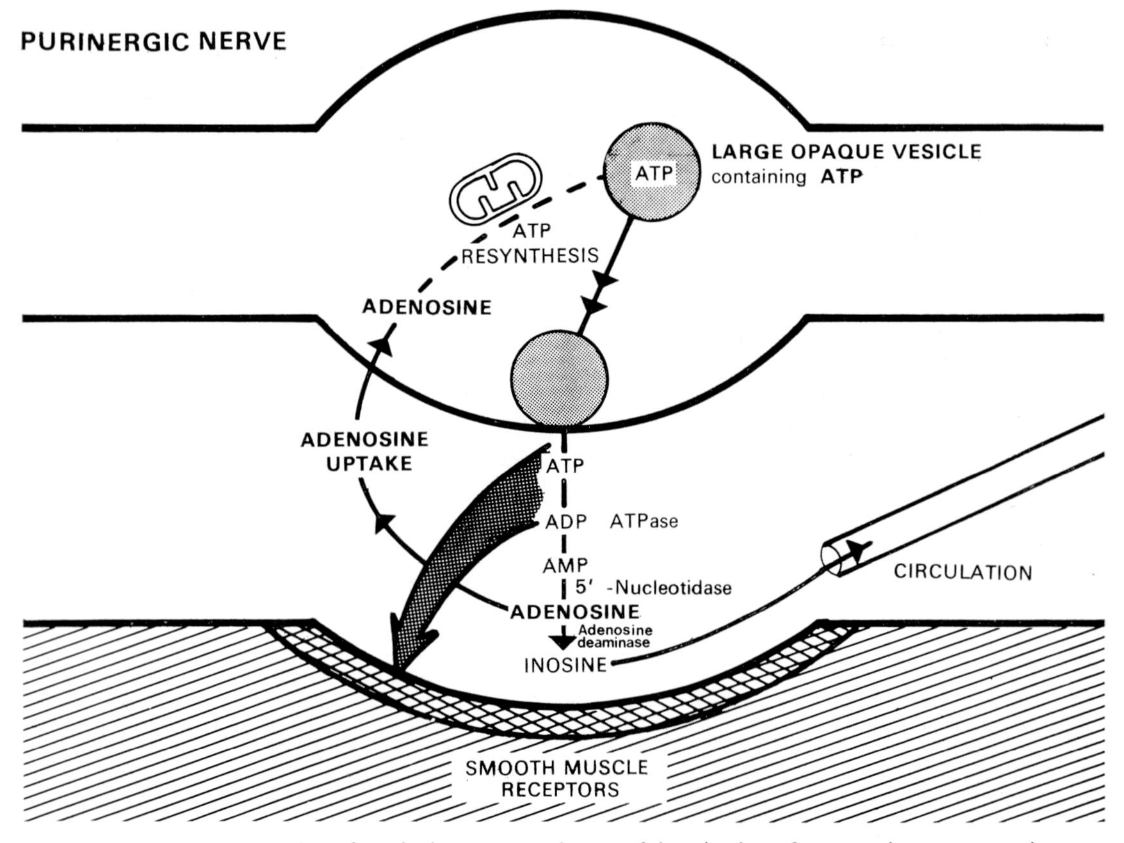

Fig. 23 Schematic representation of synthesis, storage, release and inactivation of autonomic neurotransmitters at purinergic neuro-muscular junctions. (From Burnstock, G., 1972, *Pharmac. Rev.*, **24,** 537.)

Plate 138

The terminal varicosities of autonomic nerves run roughly parallel to the long axis of the muscle cells. In heavily innervated tissue such as the rat vas deferens, illustrated here, a number of nerve profiles can be seen in relation to smooth muscle cells. A bundle of axons partially enveloped by Schwann cell and a single axon, without Schwann cell investment are present.

Autonomic nerves in mammalian smooth muscle: rat vas deferens. Transverse section. OsO_4–glutaraldehyde–OsO_4 fixation. ×26 800. (Courtesy of J. Heath, Department of Zoology, University of Melbourne.)

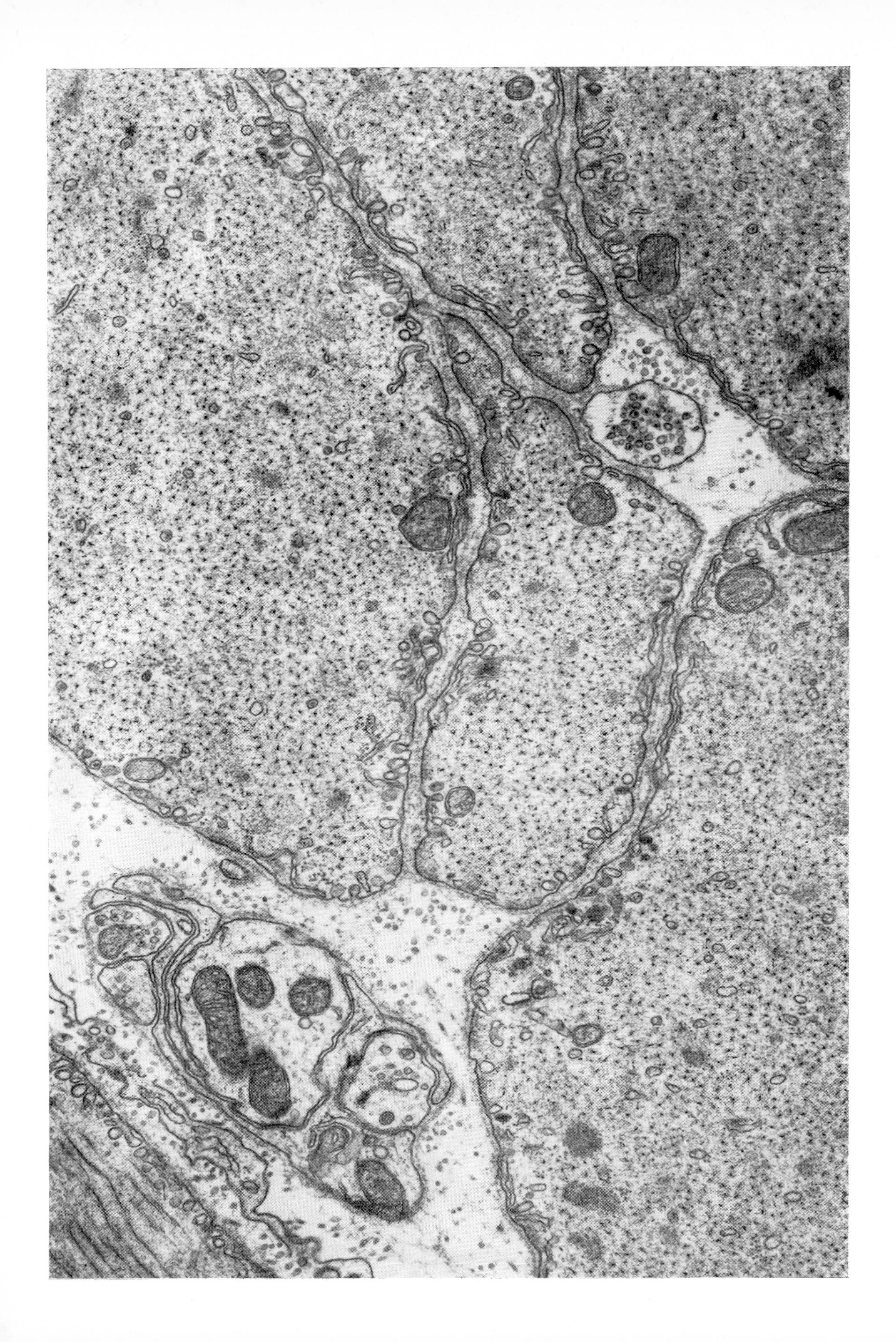

Plate 139

Two axon varicosities are illustrated which are partly enclosed by Schwann cell sheath. The side of the varicosities facing the muscle is free of Schwann cell investment. There appears to be no specialized neuromuscular junction at this level where the separation of nerve and muscle membrane is greater than 50 nm and contains basal lamina. The axons contain mitochondria, neurotubules and neurofilaments, and small agranular vesicles.

Terminal varicosities of autonomic nerves in mammalian smooth muscle: guinea-pig iris. Transverse section. OsO_4–glutaraldehyde–OsO_4 fixation. ×137 000. (Reproduced from Y. Uehara and G. Burnstock, 1972, *J. Cell Biol.*, **53,** 849.)

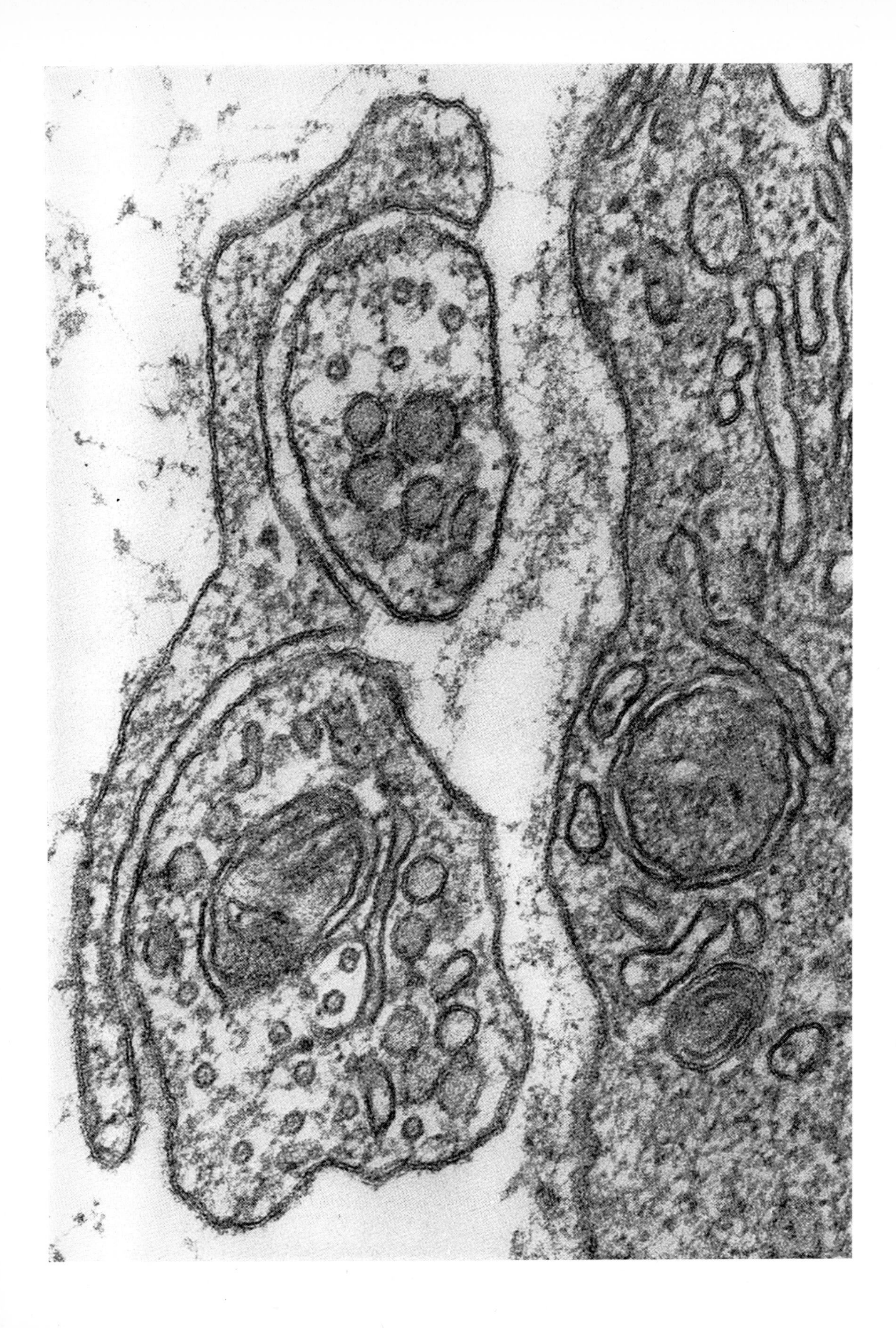

Plate 140

Adrenergic nerves are characterized by a predominance of small granular vesicles (40–60 nm) which are storage sites for noradrenaline. A few large granular vesicles (80–120 nm) are usually present, which also contain noradrenaline. The small agranular vesicles found in adrenergic nerves are 'empty' small granular vesicles, since their percentage relative to granular vesicles is reduced following 'loading' of the nerves with noradrenaline.

Inconsistency in preservation with a variety of fixatives has led to the supposition that the transmitter is bound to a protein and the appearance of the granule depends upon the ability of the fixative to preserve the protein. Potassium permanganate appears to be the only consistent fixation method for small granular vesicles, and incubation in Kreb's solution before fixation also results in good preservation of the granulation of adrenergic storage vesicles.

Adrenergic nerve varicosity in mammalian smooth muscle: sheep ureter. Transverse section. Glutaraldehyde fixation. ×32 000.

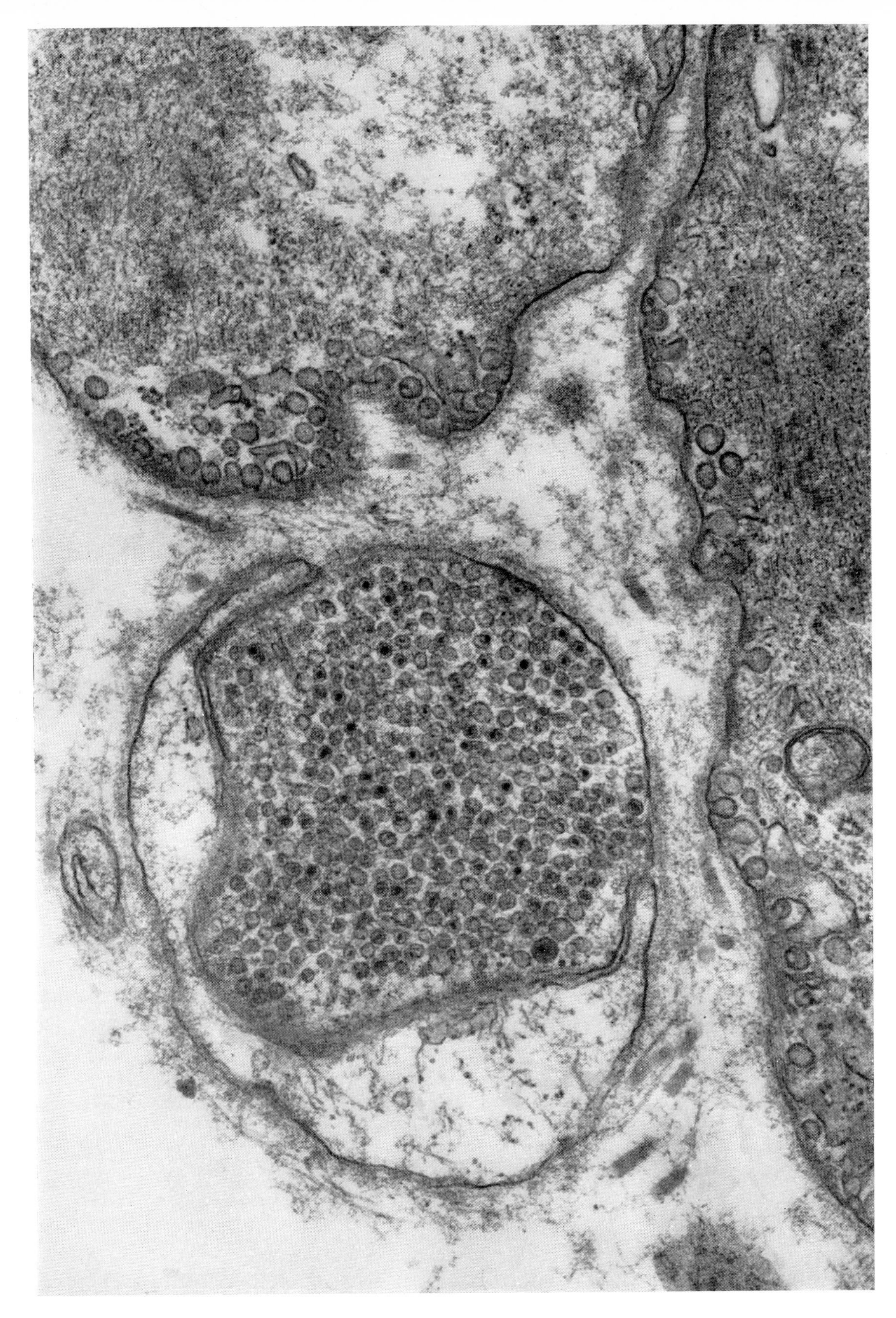

Plate 141

Both 5-hydroxydopamine (5-OHDA) and 6-hydroxydopamine (6-OHDA) displace noradrenaline from intraaxonal vesicular stores. Both large and small vesicles after the administration of these drugs show great enhancement of their granular cores within the first 1/2 to 1 hour following treatment, which can therefore be used as convenient 'markers' for adrenergic nerves. 6-OHDA, but not 5-OHDA, eventually produces degeneration of the nerve terminals in a manner similar to that of surgical denervation.

Adrenergic varicosity in mammalian smooth muscle: mouse vas deferens. Transverse section. Preincubation in 6-hydroxydopamine (250 mg Kg^{-1}) prior to OsO_4–glutaraldehyde–OsO_4 fixation. ×112 000. (Reproduced from Furness, J., G. R. Campbell, S. Gillard, T. Malmfors J. L. S. Cobb and G. Burnstock, 1970, *J. Pharmac. exp. Ther.*, **174,** 111.)

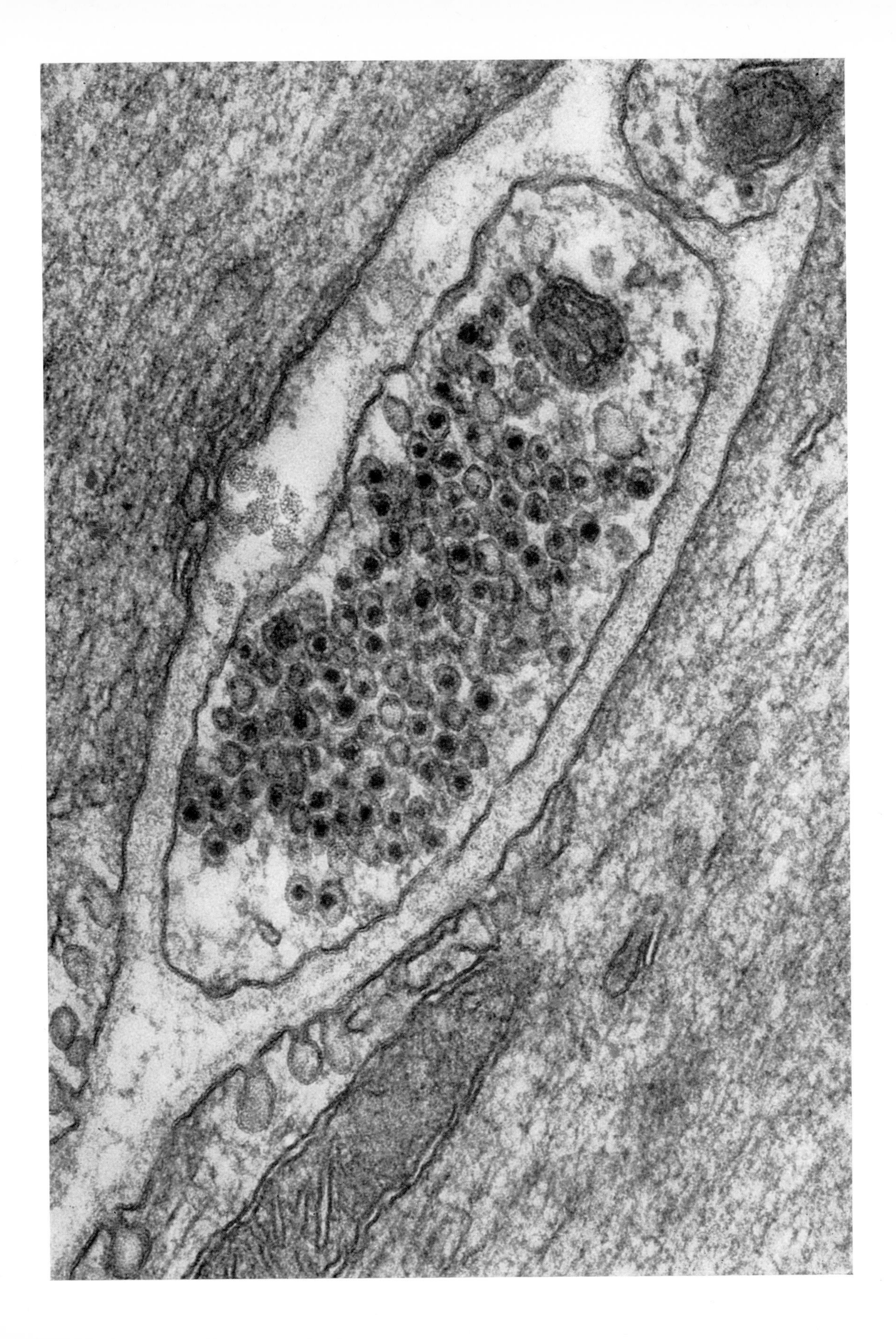

Plate 142

The axon varicosity illustrated shows a predominance of 'large opaque vesicles' (100–200 nm). These vesicles differ from the 'large granular vesicles', which are found in small numbers in both adrenergic and cholinergic nerves, in that they are usually larger and have a less prominent halo between the granular matrix and the vesicle membrane. Such profiles fulfil the ultrastructural criteria for non-adrenergic, non-cholinergic ('purinergic') nerves that are present in the gastrointestinal tract and lung (see page 408). This preparation was fixed 54 hours after injection of the animal with 6-hydroxydopamine (which destroys adrenergic nerve terminals) and with 5,6-dihydroxytryptamine (which destroys mono-aminergic nerve terminals including those containing 5-hydroxytryptamine). Note the accompanying profiles through intervaricose regions of terminal nerve fibres.

Non-adrenergic, non-cholinergic nerve varicosity in mammalian intestinal smooth muscle: guinea-pig taenia coli. Glutaraldehyde fixation. ×60 000. (Courtesy of R. D. Cook, Department of Zoology, University of Melbourne.)

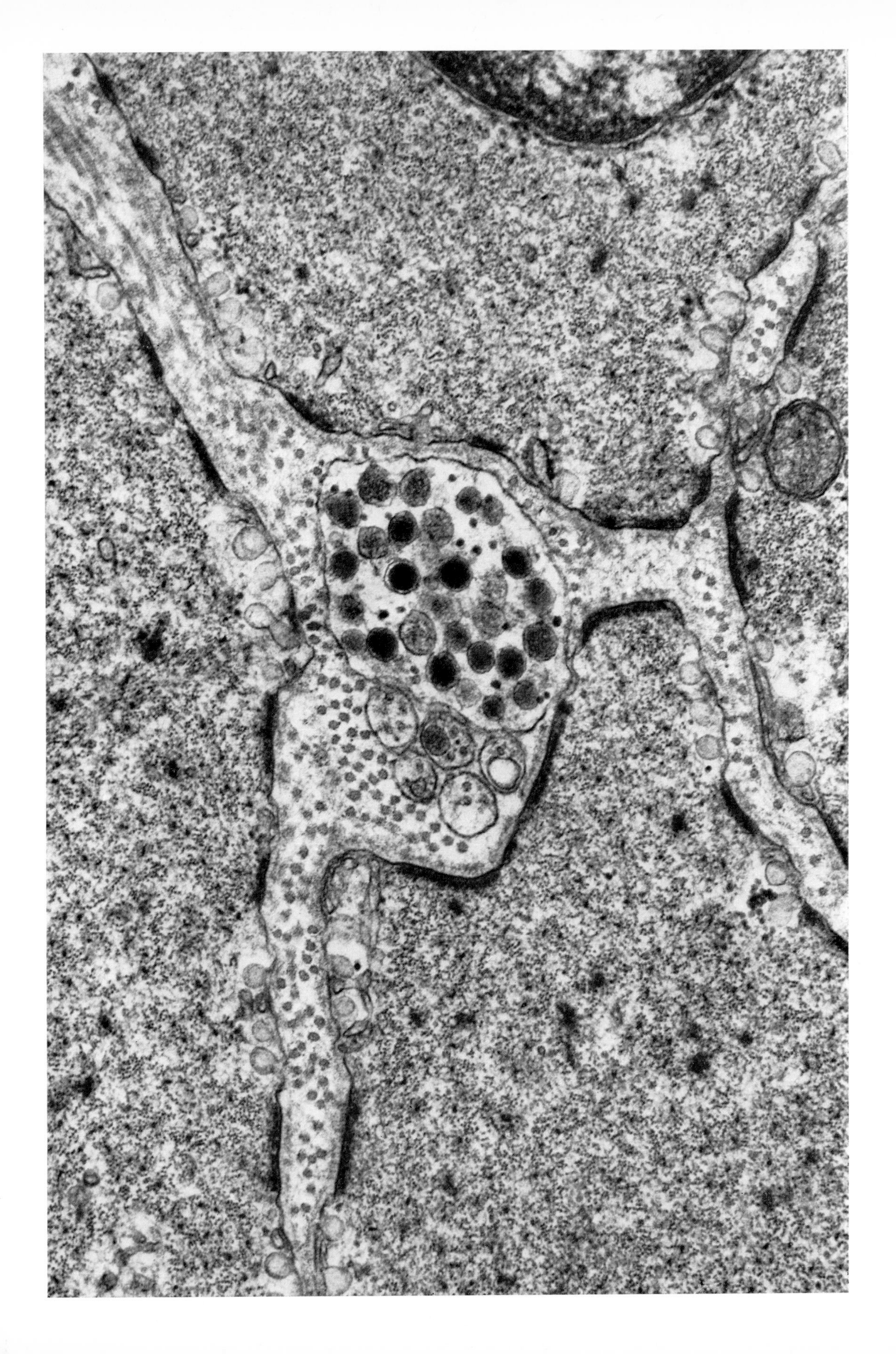

Plate 143

Axon profiles either in grooves or penetrating deep inside smooth muscle cells have been observed in the vas deferens of the rat, mouse and guinea-pig, where they are separated from the surrounding muscle cells by a narrow regular gap of about 20 nm. Occasionally they have even been observed embedded among the perinuclear organelles or even in close apposition to the nuclear membrane; the significance of the latter observation is not known.

Terminal autonomic nerve penetrating 'inside' a smooth muscle cell: rat vas deferens. Glutaraldehyde fixation. ×49 000. (Courtesy of J. Heath, Department of Zoology, University of Melbourne.)

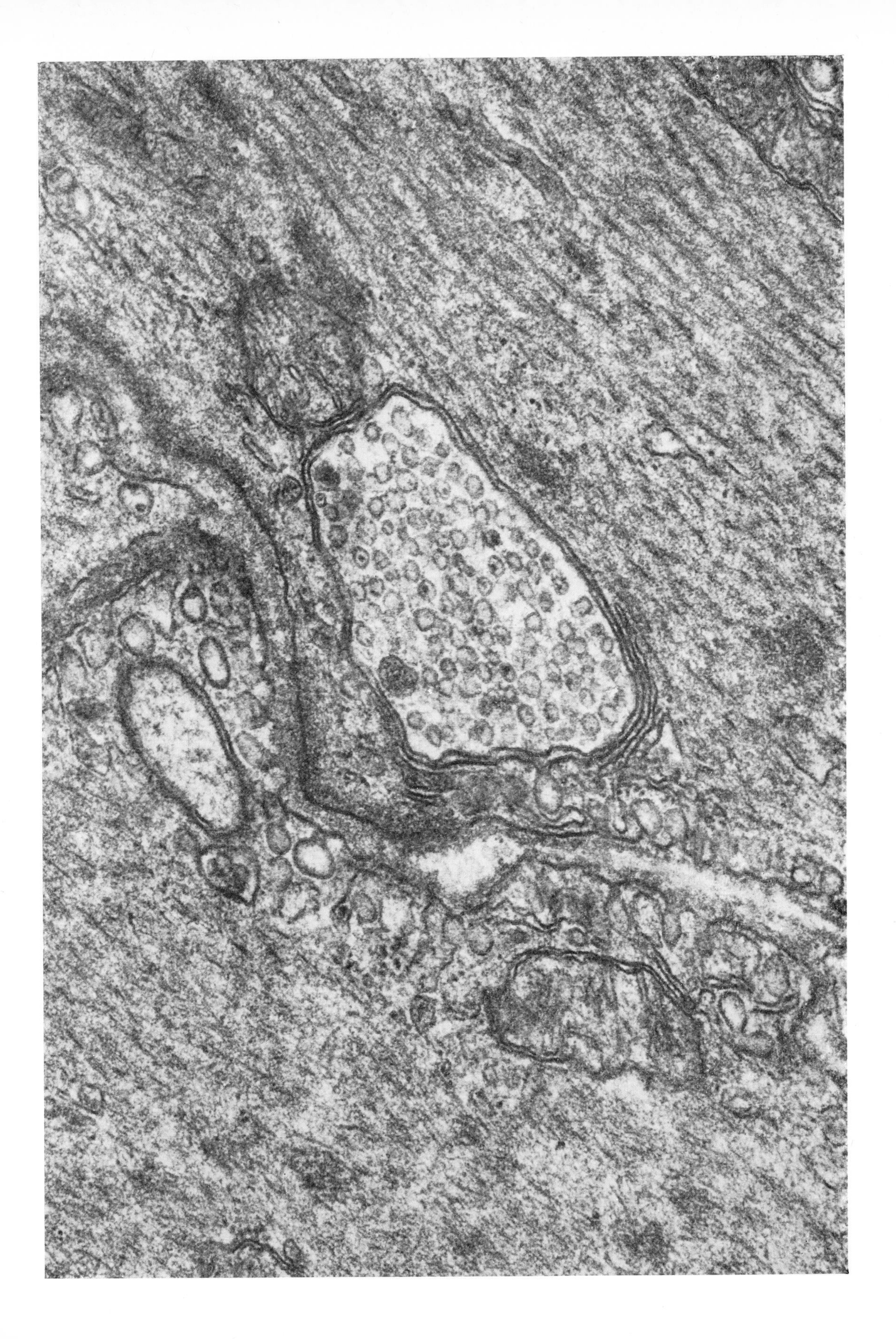

Plate 144

At close (<20 nm) neuromuscular junctions in some smooth muscles such as vas deferens and iris, subsurface cisternae have been observed beneath the plasma membrane of the muscle cell in the area adjacent to the naked axon.

A characteristic feature of the subsurface cisternae in the guinea-pig iris muscle is the occurrence of a continuous electron-opaque intermediate line interposed between the muscle membrane and the distal membrane of the cisternae, which may be involved in the transmission process.

Post-junctional specialization in a mammalian smooth muscle: guinea-pig iris. OsO_4–glutaraldehyde–OsO_4 fixation. ×162 000. (Reproduced from Y. Uehara and G. Burnstock, 1972, *J. Cell Biol.*, **53,** 849.)

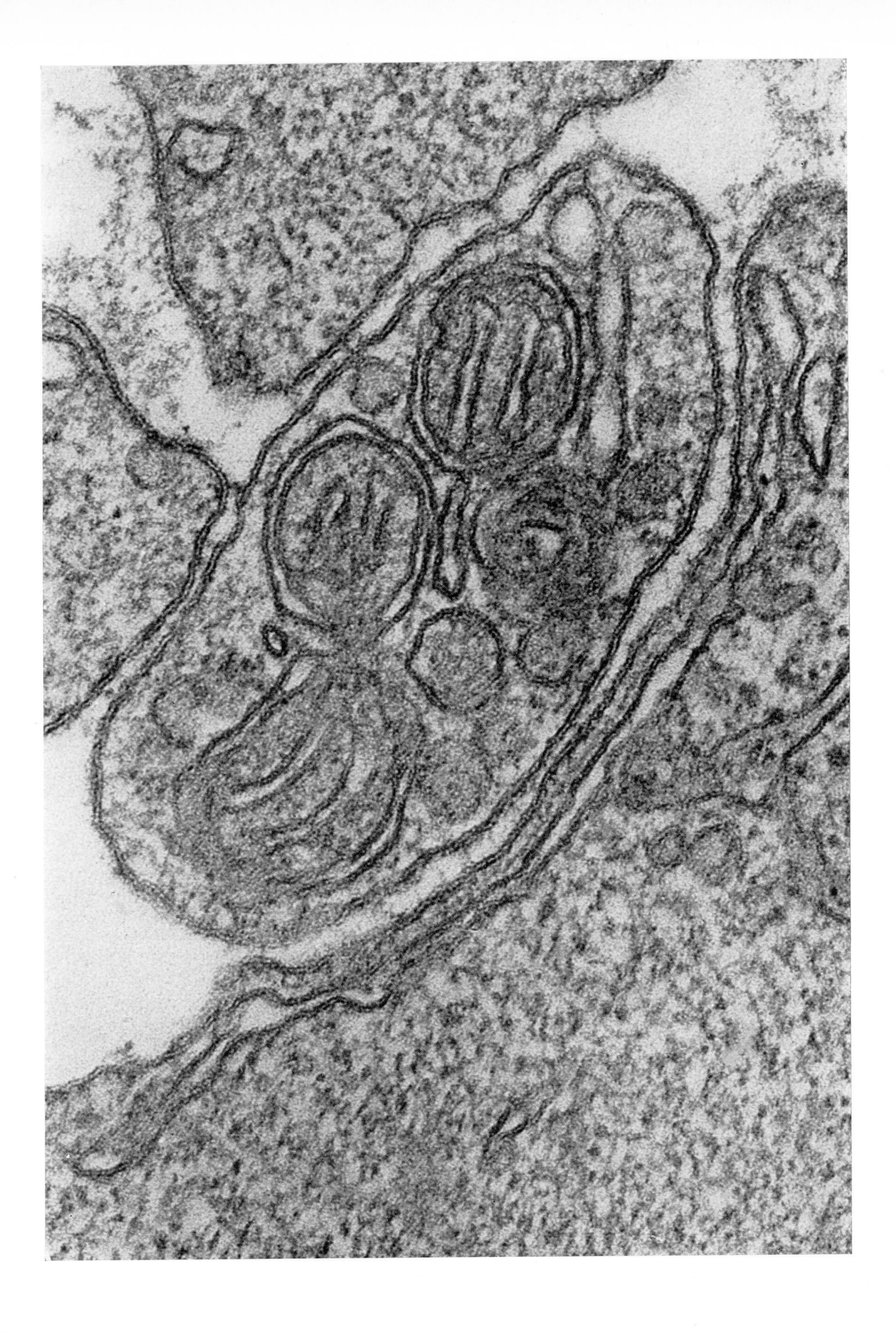

Selected reviews

Symposium on Dynamic Aspects of the Synapse. 1973. *Brain Res.* **62,** 299–606.

BENNETT, M. R. 1973. *Autonomic Neurones in Smooth Muscle.* 20th Monograph of the Physiological Society. Cambridge University Press, London.

BLASCHKO, H. and E. MUSCHOLL (eds.). 1972. *Catecholamines. Handbook of Experimental Pharmacology No. 33.* Springer-Verlag, Berlin.

BLOOM, F. E. 1970. The fine structural localization of biogenic monoamines in nervous tissue. *Int. Rev. Neurobiol.*, **13,** 27–66.

BURNSTOCK, G. 1969. Evolution of the autonomic innervation of visceral and cardiovascular systems in vertebrates. *Pharmac. Rev.*, **21,** 247–324.

BURNSTOCK, G. 1970. Structure of smooth muscle and its innervation. In *Smooth Muscle.* E. Bülbring, A. Brading, A. Jones and T. Tomita (eds.). Edward Arnold, London. 1–69.

BURNSTOCK, G. 1972. Purinergic nerves. *Pharmac. Rev.*, **24,** 509–581.

BURNSTOCK, G. 1975. Ultrastructure of autonomic nerves and neuroeffector junctions; analysis of drug action. In *Methods in Pharmacology.* Vol. 3. *Smooth Muscle.* E. E. Daniel and D. M. Paton (eds.). Appleton-Century Crofts, Edmonton. 113–137.

BURNSTOCK, G. and C. BELL. 1974. Peripheral autonomic transmission. In *The Peripheral Nervous System.* J. I. Hubbard (ed.). Plenum Press, New York. 277–327.

BURNSTOCK, G. and M. E. HOLMAN. 1963. Smooth muscle: autonomic nerve transmission. *A. Rev. Physiol.*, **25,** 61–90.

BURNSTOCK, G., M. E. HOLMAN and C. L. PROSSER. 1963. Electrophysiology of smooth muscle. *Physiol. Rev.*, **43,** 482–527.

COTTEN, M. DE V. (ed.). 1972. New York Heart Association Symposium on: Regulation of catecholamine metabolism in the sympathetic nervous system. *Pharmac. Rev.*, **24,** 163–430.

EICHNA, L. W. (ed.). 1962. Proceedings of a symposium on vascular smooth muscle. *Physiol. Rev.*, **42,** Suppl. 5, 1–365.

EMMELIN, N. and U. TRENDELENBURG. 1972. Degeneration activity after parasympathetic or sympathetic denervation. *Ergebn. Physiol.*, **66,** 147–211.

GRIGOR'EVA, T. A. 1962. *The Innervation of Blood Vessels.* Pergamon Press, New York.

GRILLO, M. A. 1966. Electronmicroscopy of sympathetic tissues. *Pharmac. Rev.*, **18,** 387–399.

IVERSEN, L. L. (ed.). 1973. Catecholamines. *Br. med. Bull.*, **29,** 91–178.

NICKERSON, M. 1973. Adrenergic receptors. *Circulation Res.*, **32,** Suppl. I, I-53–60.

SCHÜMANN, H. J. and G. KRONEBERG (eds). 1970. *New Aspects of Storage and Release Mechanisms of Catecholamines. Bayer-Symposium II.* Springer-Verlag, New York.

SMITH, A. D. 1972. Subcellular localization of noradrenaline in sympathetic neurons. *Pharmac. Rev.*, **24,** 435–458.

STEINER, G. and E. SCHÖNBAUM (eds.). 1972. *Immuno-sympathectomy.* Elsevier, Amsterdam.

TRIGGLE, D. J. 1971. *Neurotransmitter-Receptor Interactions.* Academic Press, London.

ZAIMIS, E. and J. KNIGHT (eds.). 1972. *Nerve Growth Factor and its Antiserums. A Symposium.* Athlone, London.

Selected articles

APPENZELLER, O. 1964. Electron microscopic study of the innervation of the auricular artery in the rat. *J. Anat.*, **98,** 87–91.

ARMALY, M. F. 1968. Degeneration of ciliary muscle and iris sphincter following resection of the ciliary ganglion. *Trans. Am. Ophthal. Soc.*, **66,** 475–502.

AUNG-KHIN, M. 1973. The innervation of the ureter. *Invest. Urol.*, **10,** 370–378.

AUSTIN, L., I. W. CHUBB and B. G. LIVETT. 1967. The subcellular localization of catecholamines in nerve terminals in smooth muscle tissue. *Neurochem.*, **14,** 473–478.

AUSTIN, J., W. ROBERTS, M. NEVILLE and D. ARMSTRONG. 1971. The role of the sympathetic nervous system in lipid deposition. I. Increased lipid deposits in the iris of the sympathectomized eye in rabbits fed an atherogenic diet. *Stroke (J. Cereb. Circ.)*, **2,** 23–24.

BAUMGARTEN, H. G., H. BRAAK and H. WARTENBERG. 1969. Demonstration of dense core vesicles by means of pyrogallol derivatives in noradrenaline containing neurones from the organon vasculosum hypothalami of *Lacerta*. *Z. Zellforsch. mikrosk. Anat.*, **95,** 396–404.

BELL, C. 1969. Fine structural localisation of acetylcholinesterase at a cholinergic vasodilator nerve–arterial smooth muscle synapse. *Circulation Res.*, **24,** 61–70.

BENNETT, M. R. and N. C. R. MERRILLEES. 1966. An analysis of the transmission of excitation from autonomic nerves to smooth muscle. *J. Physiol., Lond.*, **185,** 520–535.

BENNETT, M. R. and D. C. ROGERS. 1967. A study of the innervation of the taenia coli. *J. Cell Biol.*, **33,** 573–596.

BENNETT, T. and J. L. S. COBB. 1969*a*. Studies on the avian gizzard: morphology and innervation of the smooth muscle. *Z. Zellforsch. mikrosk. Anat.*, **96,** 173–185.

BENNETT, T. and J. L. S. COBB. 1969*b*. Studies on the avian gizzard: Auerbach's plexus. *Z. Zellforsch. mikrosk. Anat.*, **99,** 109–120.

BENNETT, T. and J. L. S. COBB. 1969*c*. Studies on the avian gizzard: The development of the gizzard and its innervation. *Z. Zellforsch. mikrosk. Anat.*, **98,** 599–621.

BEVAN, J. A. 1968. Fine structure study of the terminal effector plexus, neuromuscular and intermuscular relationships in the muscle of the vas deferens. *J. Physiol., Lond.*, **206,** 645–661.

BIRMINGHAM, A. T. 1970. Sympathetic denervation of the smooth muscle of the vas deferens. *J. Physiol., Lond.*, **206,** 645–661.

BLOOM, F. E. and R. J. BARRNETT. 1966. Fine structural localization of noradrenaline in vesicles of autonomic nerve endings. *Nature, Lond.*, **210,** 599–601.

BLÜMCKE, S. and H. J. DENGLER. 1970. Noradrenalin content and ultrastructure of adrenergic nerves of rabbit iris after sympathectomy and hypoxia. *Virchows Arch. Abt. B. Zellpath.*, **6,** 281–293.

BONDAREFF, W. and B. BORDON. 1966. Submicroscopic localisation of norepinephrine in sympathetic nerves of rat pineal. *J. Pharmac. exp. Ther.*, **153,** 42–47.

BRETTSCHNEIDER, H. 1962. Elektronenmikroskopische Untersuchungen über die Innervation der glatten Muskulatur des Darmes. *Z. mikrosk.-anat. Forsch.* **68,** 333–360.

BUDD, G. C. and M. M. SALPETER. 1969. The distribution of labelled norepinephrine within sympathetic nerve terminals studied with electron microscope radioautography. *J. Cell Biol.*, **41,** 21–32.

BURN, J. H. and RAND, M. J. 1959. Sympathetic postganglionic mechanism. *Nature, Lond.*, **184,** 163–165.

BURNSTOCK, G. 1971. Neural nomenclature. *Nature, Lond.*, **229,** 282–283.

BURNSTOCK, G. 1972. Ultrastructural identification of purinergic nerves. In *Histochemistry and Cytochemistry*. T. Takeuchi, K. Ogawa and S. Fujita (eds.). Nakanishi, Kyoto. 53–54.

BURNSTOCK, G. 1973. The autonomic neuroeffector system. *Proc. Austr. Physiol. Pharmacol. Soc.*, **4,** 6–22.

BURNSTOCK, G., B. GANNON and T. IWAYAMA. 1970. Sympathetic innervation of vascular smooth muscle in normal and hypertensive animals. In *Symposium on Hypertensive Mechanisms. Circulation Res.*, **27,** Suppl. II, II-5–24.

BURNSTOCK, G. and M. E. HOLMAN. 1963. Smooth muscle: autonomic nerve transmission. *A. Rev. Physiol.*, **25,** 61–90.

BURNSTOCK, G. and M. E. HOLMAN. 1966. Effect of drugs on smooth muscle. *A. Rev. Pharmacol.*, **6,** 129–156.

BURNSTOCK, G. and M. E. HOLMAN. 1966. Junction potentials at adrenergic synapses. *Pharmac. Rev.*, **18,** 481–493.

BURNSTOCK, G., M. E. HOLMAN and N. C. R. MERRILLEES. 1963. Correlation of fine structure and physiology of the innervation of smooth muscle in the guinea pig vas deferens. *J. Cell Biol.*, **19,** 629–550.

BURNSTOCK, G. and T. IWAYAMA. 1971. Fine structural identification of autonomic nerves and their relation to smooth muscle. In *Histochemistry of nervous transmission*. O. Eränko (ed.). *Progress in Brain Research*, **34,** 389–404.

BURNSTOCK, G. and N. C. R. MERRILLEES. 1964. Structural and experimental studies on autonomic nerve endings in smooth muscle.

In *Pharmacology of Smooth Muscle. Proc. 2nd Int. Pharmac. Meeting, Prague.* Vol. 6. E. Bülbring (ed.). Macmillan, New York. 1–17.

BURNSTOCK, G. and P. M. ROBINSON. 1967. Localization of catecholamines and acetylcholinesterase in autonomic nerves. *Circulation Res.*, **21,** Suppl. III, III-43–55.

CAESAR, R., G. A. EDWARDS and H. RUSKA. 1957. Architecture and nerve supply of mammalian smooth muscle tissue. *J. biophys. biochem. Cytol.*, **3,** 867–878.

CAMPBELL, G. 1970. Autonomic nervous system. In *Fish Physiology*. Vol. 4. 2nd edition. W. S. Hoar and D. J. Randall (eds.). Academic Press, New York. 109–132.

CHAMLEY, J. H., G. R. CAMPBELL and G. BURNSTOCK. 1973. An analysis of the interactions between sympathetic nerve fibres and smooth muscle cells in tissue culture. *Devl Biol.*, **33,** 344–361.

COOK, R. D. and A. S. KING. 1970. Observations on the ultrastructure of the smooth muscle and its innervation in the avian lung. *J. Anat.*, **106,** 273–284.

COUTURIER-TURPIN, M.-H. 1968. Données recentes sur l'ultrastructure et l'innervation du muscle lisse gastro-intestinal. *Presse Med.*, **76,** 319–321.

DAHL, E. 1973. The innervation of the cerebral arteries. *J. Anat.*, **115,** 53–63.

DAHL, E. and E. NELSON. 1964. Electron microscopic observations on human intracranial arteries. II. Innervation. *Archs Neurol., Chicago*, **10,** 158–164.

DEVINE, C. E. and F. O. SIMPSON. 1967. The fine structure of vascular sympathetic neuromuscular contacts in the rat. *Am. J. Anat.*, **121,** 153–174.

DEVINE, C. E., F. O. SIMPSON and W. S. BERTAUD. 1971. Freeze-etch studies on the innervation of mesenteric arteries and vas deferens. *J. Cell Sci.*, **9,** 411–426.

DIXON, J. S. and J. A. GOSLING. 1971. Histochemical and electron microscopic observations on the innervation of the upper segment of the mammalian ureter. *J. Anat.*, **110,** 57–66.

DIXON, J. S. and J. A. GOSLING. 1972. The distribution of autonomic nerves in the musculature of the rat vas deferens. A light and electron microscope investigation. *J. comp. Neurol.*, **146,** 175–187.

DIXON, J. S. and J. A. GOSLING. 1973. The fine structure of pacemaker cells in the pig renal calices. *Anat. Rec.*, **175,** 139–154.

ESTERHUIZEN, A. C., T. L. B. SPRIGGS and J. D. LEVER. 1968. Axon beadings in autonomic cholinergic nerves. *J. Cell Biol.*, **38,** 454–457.

FARRELL, K. E. 1968. Fine structure of nerve fibres in smooth muscle of the vas deferens in normal and reserpinized rats. *Nature, Lond.*, **217,** 279–281.

FURNESS, J. B., G. R. CAMPBELL, S. M. GILLARD, T. MALMFORS, J. L. S. COBB and G. BURNSTOCK. 1970. Cellular studies of the sympathetic denervation produced by 6-hydroxydopamine in the vas deferens. *J. Pharmac. exp. Ther.*, **174,** 111–122.

FURNESS, J. B. and T. IWAYAMA. 1971. Terminal axons ensheathed in smooth muscle cells of the vas deferens. *Z. Zellforsch. mikrosk. Anat.*, **113,** 259–270.

FURNESS, J. B. and T. IWAYAMA. 1972. The arrangement and identification of axons innervating the vas deferens of the guinea-pig. *J. Anat.*, **113,** 179–196.

GABELLA, G. 1970. Electron microscopic observation on the innervation of the intestinal inner muscle layer. *Experentia*, **26,** 44–46.

GABELLA, G. 1972. Innervation of intestinal muscular coat. *J. Neurocytol.*, **1,** 341–362.

GELTZER, A. I. 1969. Autonomic innervation of the cat iris. An electron microscopic study. *Archs Opthal., N.Y.*, **81,** 70–83.

GOSLING, J. A. and J. S. DIXON. 1969. The fine structure of the vasa recta and associated nerves in the rabbit kidney. *Anat. Rec.*, **165,** 503–514.

GOSLING, J. A. and J. S. DIXON. 1971. Morphologic evidence that the renal calyx and pelvis control uteric activity in the rabbit. *Am. J. Anat.*, **130,** 393–408.

GOSLING, J. A. and J. S. DIXON. 1972*a*. Structural evidence in support of an urinary tract pacemaker. *Br. J. Urol.*, **44,** 550–560.

GOSLING, J. A. and J. S. DIXON. 1972*b*. The effect of 6-hydroxydopamine on nerves in the rat upper urinary tract. *J. Cell Sci.*, **10,** 192–210.

GOSLING, J. A. and J. S. DIXON. 1972*c*. Differences in the manner of autonomic innervation of the muscle layers of the guinea-pig ductus deferens. *J. Anat.*, **112,** 81–91.

GRILLO, M. A. and S. L. PALAY. 1962. Granule-containing vesicles in the autonomic nervous system. In *Proc. 5th Int. Congr. Electron Microscopy*. Vol. 2. S. S. Breese (ed.). Academic Press, New York. U1.

HIRANO, S. 1969. Electron microscopic study on the innervation of the ciliary muscle: comparison of nerve endings in the iris muscle and the ciliary muscle. *Acta Soc. ophthal. jap.*, **73,** 695–709.

HÖKFELT, T. 1966. Electron microscopic observations on nerve terminals in the intrinsic muscles of the albino rat iris. *Acta physiol. scand.*, **67,** 255–256.

HÖKFELT, T. 1967. Ultrastructural studies on adrenergic nerve terminals in the albino rat iris after pharmacological and experimental treatment. *Acta physiol. scand.*, **69,** 125–126.

HÖKFELT, T. 1969. Distribution of noradrenaline storing particles in peripheral adrenergic neurons as revealed by electron microscopy. *Acta physiol. scand.*, **76,** 427–440.

HÖKFELT, T. and O. NILSSON. 1965. Electron microscopy of the adrenergic and cholinergic innervation of the iris muscle. *J. Ultrastruct. Res.*, **12,** 237.

HUNG, K.-S. and C. G. LOOSLI. 1974. Ultrastructure and innervation of pulmonary veins of the mouse. *Anat. Rec.*, **178,** 380.

IMAIZUMI, M. and K. HAMA. 1969. An electron microscopic study of the interstitial cell of the gizzard in the love-bird (*Uroloncha domestica*). *Z. Zellforsch. mikrosk. Anat.*, **97,** 351–357.

IVENS, C., D. R. MOTTRAM, J. D. LEVER, R. PRESLEY and G. HOWELLS. 1973. Studies on the acetylcholinesterase (Ache)-positive and -negative autonomic axons supplying smooth muscle in the normal and 6-hydroxydopamine (6-OHDA) treated rat iris. *Z. Zellforsch. mikrosk. Anat.*, **138,** 211–222.

IWAYAMA, T. and J. B. FURNESS. 1971. Enhancement of the granulation of adrenergic storage vesicles in drug-free solution. *J. Cell Biol.*, **48,** 699–703.

IWAYAMA, T., J. B. FURNESS and G. BURNSTOCK. 1970. Dual adrenergic and cholinergic innervation of the cerebral arteries of the rat. An ultrastructural study. *Circulation Res.*, **26,** 635–646.

KAPELLER, K. and D. MAYOR. 1969*a*. An electron microscope study of the early changes proximal to a constriction in sympathetic nerves. *Proc. R. Soc. Ser. B*, **172,** 39–51.

KAPELLER, K. and D. MAYOR. 1969*b*. An electron microscope study of the early changes distal to a constriction in sympathetic nerves. *Proc. R. Soc. Ser. B*, **172,** 53–63.

KRAPP, J. 1962. Elektronenmikroskopische Untersuchungen über die Innervation von Iris und Corpus ciliare der Hauskatze unter besonderer Berücksichtigung der Muskulatur. *Z. mikrosk.-anat. Forsch.*, **68,** 418–447.

KUSKIYA, I. 1968. An electron microscope study of the muscular coats in the ampulla of the rabbit oviduct, with special reference to the neuromuscular relationship. *J. Electron microsc.*, **17,** 127–138.

LEVER, J. D., J. D. P. GRAHAM, G. IRVINE and W. J. CHICK. 1965. The vesiculated axons in relation to arteriolar smooth muscle in the pancreas. A fine structural and quantitative study. *J. Anat.*, **99,** 299–313.

LEVER, J. D., T. L. B. SPRIGGS and J. D. P. GRAHAM. 1967. Paravascular nervous distribution in the pancreas. *J. Anat.*, **101,** 189–190.

LEVER, J. D., T. L. B. SPRIGGS and J. D. P. GRAHAM. 1968. A formol-fluorescence, fine-structural and autoradiographic study of the adrenergic innervation of the vascular tree in the intact and sympathectomized pancreas of the cat. *J. Anat.*, **103,** 15–34.

LOREZ, H. P., H. KUHN and J. P. TRANZER. 1973. The adrenergic innervation of the renal artery and vein of the rat. A fluorescence histochemical and electron microscopical study. *Z. Zellforsch. mikrosk. Anat.*, **138,** 261–272.

MALMFORS, T., J. B. FURNESS, G. R. CAMPBELL and G. BURNSTOCK. 1971. Re-innervation of smooth muscle of the vas deferens transplanted into the anterior chamber of the eye. *J. Neurobiol.*, **2,** 193–207.

MALMFORS, T. and H. THOENEN (eds.). 1971.

6-hydroxydopamine and Catecholamine Neurons. North Holland, Amsterdam.

MALOR, R., C. J. GRIFFIN and S. TAYLOR. 1973. Innervation of the blood vessels in guinea-pig atria. *Cardiovasc. Res.*, **7,** 95–104.

MARK, G., J. CHAMLEY and G. BURNSTOCK. 1973. Interactions between autonomic nerves and smooth and cardiac muscle cells in tissue culture. *Devl Biol.*, **32,** 194–200.

MERRILLEES, N. C. R. 1968. The nervous environment of individual smooth muscle cells of the guinea pig vas deferens. *J. Cell Biol.*, **37,** 794–817.

MERRILLEES, N. C. R., G. BURNSTOCK and M. E. HOLMAN. 1963. Correlation of fine structure and physiology of the innervation of smooth muscle in the guinea-pig vas deferens. *J. Cell Biol.*, **19,** 529–550.

MOFFAT, D. B. 1967. The fine structure of the blood vessels of the renal medulla with particular reference to the control of the medullary circulation. *J. Ultrastruct. Res.*, **19,** 532–545.

NAGASAWA, J. and S. MITO. 1967. Electronmicroscopic observations on the innervation of the smooth muscle. *Tohoku J. exp. Med.*, **91,** 277–293.

NELSON, E. and M. RENNELS. 1970. Innervation of intracranial arteries. *Brain*, **93,** 475–490.

NILSON, K. C., CH. OWMAN and B. SPORRONG. 1971. Ultrastructure of the autonomic innervation apparatus in the main pial arteries of rats and cats. *Brain Res.*, **27,** 26–32.

NISHIDA, S. and M. SEARS. 1969*a*. Fine structural innervation of the dilator muscle of the iris of the albina guinea pig studied with permanganate fixation. *Exp. Eye Res.*, **8,** 292–296.

NISHIDA, S. and M. SEARS. 1969*b*. Dual innervation of the iris sphincter muscle of the albino guinea pig. *Exp. Eye res.*, **8,** 467–469.

NOTLEY, R. G. 1969. The innervation of the upper ureter in man and in the rat: an ultrastructural study. *J. Anat.*, **105,** 393–402.

OCHI, J., M. KONISHI, H. YOSHIKAWA and Y. SANO. 1968. Fluorescence and electron microscopic evidence for the dual innervation of the iris sphincter muscle of the rabbit. *Z. Zellforsch. mikrosk. Anat.*, **91,** 90–95.

ORFANOS, C. 1966. Electron microscope investigation of the smooth muscle fibers in the skin and their innervation. *Dermatologica*, **132,** 445–459.

O'SHEA, J. D. 1970. An electron microscope study of smooth muscle, and its innervation, in the ovary of the rat. *J. Anat.*, **106,** 196.

PELLEGRINO DE IRALDI, A. and A. M. SUBURO. 1972. Morphological evidence of a connection between the core of granulated vesicles and their membrane. *Neurobiol.*, **2,** 8–11.

RICHARDSON, K. C. 1958. Electronmicroscope observations on Auerbach's plexus in the rabbit with special reference to the problem of smooth muscle innervation. *Am. J. Anat.*, **103,** 99–135.

RICHARDSON, K. C. 1960. Studies on the structure of autonomic nerves in the small intestine, correlating the silver-impregnated image in the light microscopy with the permanganate-fixed ultrastructure in electronmicroscopy. *J. Anat.*, **94,** 457–472.

RICHARDSON, K. C. 1962. The fine structure of autonomic nerve endings in smooth muscle of the rat vas deferens. *J. Anat.*, **96,** 427–442.

RICHARDSON, K. C. 1964. The fine structure of the albino rabbit iris with special reference to the identification of adrenergic and cholinergic nerves and nerve endings in its intrinsic muscles. *Am. J. Anat.*, **114,** 173–205.

RICHARDSON, K. C. 1966. Electron microscope identification of autonomic nerve endings. *Nature, Lond.*, **210,** 756.

ROBINSON, P. M. 1965. Fine structure of the autonomic innervation of the smooth muscle of the toad lung. *J. Anat.*, **99,** 948–949.

ROBINSON, P. M. 1969. A cholinergic component in the innervation of the longitudinal smooth muscle of the guinea-pig vas deferens. The fine structural localization of acetylcholinesterase. *J. Cell Biol.*, **41,** 462–476.

ROBINSON, P. M., J. R. McLEAN and G. BURNSTOCK. 1971. Ultrastructural identification of non-adrenergic inhibitory nerve fibers. *J. Pharmac. exp. Ther.*, **179,** 149–160.

ROGERS, D. C. and G. BURNSTOCK. 1966*a*. The

interstitial cell and its place in the concept of the autonomic ground plexus. *J. comp. Neurol.*, **126,** 255–284.

ROGERS, D. C. and G. BURNSTOCK. 1966*b*. Multi-axonal autonomic junctions in intestinal smooth muscle of the toad (*Bufo marinus*). *J. Comp. Neurol.*, **126,** 625–652.

ROSENBLUTH, J. 1962. Subsurface cisterns and their relationship to the neuronal plasma membrane. *J. Cell Biol.*, **13,** 405–421.

ROSTGAARD, J. and R. J. BARRNETT. 1964. Fine structure localisation of nucleoside phosphatases in relation to smooth muscle cells and unmyelinated nerves in the small intestine of the rat. *J. Ultrastruct. Res.*, **11,** 193–207.

ROTH, C. D. and K. C. RICHARDSON. 1969. Electron microscopical studies on axonal degeneration in the rat iris following ganglionectomy. *Am. J. Anat.*, **124,** 341–360.

SAMARASINGHE, D. D. 1965. The innervation of the cerebral arteries in the rat: an electronmicroscope study. *J. Anat.*, **99,** 815–828.

SATO, S. 1966. An electron microscopic study on the innervation of the intracranial artery of the rat. *Am J. Anat.*, **118,** 873–890.

SHAKHLAMOV, V. A. 1971. Role of the pericytes in the innervation of blood capillaries. *Bull. exp. Biol. Med.*, **71,** 452–455.

SILVA, D. G. 1967. The ultrastructure of the myometrium of the rat with special reference to the innervation. *Anat. Rec.*, **158,** 21–34.

SILVA, D. G. and M. IKEDA. 1971. Ultrastructural and acetylcholinesterase studies on the innervation of the ductus arteriosus, pulmonary trunk and aorta of the fetal lamb. *J. Ultrastruct. Res.*, **23,** 358–374.

SIMPSON, F. O. and C. E. DEVINE. 1966. The fine structure of autonomic neuromuscular contacts in arterioles of sheep renal cortex. *J. Anat.*, **100,** 127–137.

SUWA, K. 1962. An electronmicroscope study on the aortic media in human with special reference to the innervation of the tunica media. *Acta med. Okayama.*, **16,** Suppl., 1–13.

THAEMERT, J. C. 1963. The ultrastructure and disposition of vesiculated nerve processes in smooth muscle. *J. Cell Biol.*, **16,** 361–377.

THAEMERT, J. C. 1966. Ultrastructural inter-relationships of nerve processes and smooth muscle cells in three dimensions. *J. Cell Biol.*, **28,** 37–49.

UEHARA, Y. and G. BURNSTOCK. 1972. Postsynaptic specialization of smooth muscle at close neuromuscular junctions in the guinea pig sphincter pupillae. *J. Cell Biol.*, **53,** 849–853.

VERITY, M. A. and J. A. BEVAN. 1968. Fine structural study of the terminal effector plexus, neuromuscular and intermuscular relationships in the pulmonary artery. *J. Anat.*, **103,** 49–63.

WATANABE, H. 1969. Electron microscopic observations on the innervation of smooth muscle in the guinea pig vas deferens. *Acta anat. nippon.*, **44,** 189–202.

WEIN, A. J., J. V. LEONI, J. G. GREGORY, H. W. SCHOENBERG and D. JACOBOWITZ. 1972. The effect of 6-hydroxydopamine on canine ureteral contractility: Further evidence in favor of a non-neurogenic theory of ureteral function. *J. Urol.*, **108,** 402–405.

WOLFE, D. E., L. T. POTTER, K. C. RICHARDSON and J. AXELROD. 1962. Localizing tritiated norepinephrine in sympathetic axons by electron microscope autoradiography. *Science, N.Y.*, **138,** 440–442.

YAMADA, H. and S. MIYAKE. 1960. Elektronenmikroskopische Untersuchungen an Nervenfasern in menschlichen Schweissdrüsen. *Z. Zellforsch. mikrosk. Anat.*, **52,** 129–139.

YAMAMOTO, T. 1960. Electron microscope investigation on the relationship between the smooth muscle cell of the proc. vermiformis and the autonomic peripheral nerves. *Acta neuroveg.*, **21,** 406–425.

YAMAUCHI, A. 1964. Electron microscopic studies on the autonomic neuro-muscular junction in the taenia coli of the guinea-pig. *Acta anat. nippon.*, **39,** 22–38.

YAMAUCHI, A. and G. BURNSTOCK. 1967. Nerve–myoepithelium and nerve–glandular epithelium contacts in the lacrimal gland of the sheep. *J. Cell Biol.*, **34,** 917–920.

YAMAUCHI, A. and G. BURNSTOCK. 1969. Post-natal development of the innervation of the mouse vas deferens. A fine structural study. *J. Anat.*, **104,** 17–32.

YEGHIAYAN, E., J. M. ROJO-ORTEGA and J. GENEST. 1972. Parathyroid vessel innervation: an ultrastructural study. *J. Anat.*, **112,** 137–142.

E Invertebrate muscle

Enormous diversification exists not only in the types of muscle found in invertebrates but in their mode of activation by nerves. However, there appear to be two features common to both vertebrate and invertebrate nerve–muscle junctions. One is the close association of the nerve terminal with the muscle cell and the second is the presence of synaptic vesicles which are the sites of storage of the chemical transmitter.

The chemical transmitters vary considerably but acetylcholine (Ach) has been reported to excite various muscles in nematodes, annelids and molluscs. Glutamate excites muscles of crustaceans and insects, while γ-aminobutyric acid (GABA) inhibits muscles of nematodes, annelids, crustaceans and insects. 5-hydroxytryptamine (5-HT) and dopamine (DA) appear to be neurotransmitters to some molluscan muscles. These chemical transmitters are released from the nerve terminals and depolarize the muscle membrane, as in vertebrate muscle, by altering the conductivity to certain ions, although the precise ions involved are not always the same as in vertebrates.

Arthropod skeletal muscle possesses many neuromuscular junctions per fibre ('multiterminal' innervation), as is the case with slow tonic vertebrate muscles, and excitatory and inhibitory types of axon may supply the same fibre ('polyneuronal' innervation). It has been suggested that axons in which the synaptic vesicles are predominantly round and approximately 50 nm in diameter are excitatory, while those with vesicles which are less regular, slightly smaller and often flattened are inhibitory. The leg muscles of some insects and crustaceans are innervated by from one to four excitatory neurones and by from one to five inhibitory neurones. Both types of neurone branch extensively and form multiple synaptic contacts with the muscle fibres as well as with each other. The force and speed of muscle fibre contraction is the result of the convergent and antagonistic effects of these inputs.

In the earthworm, two types of neuromuscular junctions are present. One contains a predominance of clear vesicles (Type I) resembling cholinergic profiles of vertebrate muscle, and the other contains large dense-cored vesicles (Type II). Earthworm muscle cells exhibit both excitatory and inhibitory junction potentials and it has been suggested that Type I endings represent cholinergic excitatory junctions and Type II endings represent GABA inhibitory junctions.

The anterior byssus retractor muscle (ABRM) of *Mytilus* receives a dual innervation, one producing the sustained contraction of *catch* state, the other producing relaxation. ACh produces contraction while 5-HT is responsible for relaxation. Combined ultrastructural and fluorescence histochemical studies have demonstrated the existence of two or possibly three types of nerve ending in the ABRM separated from the muscle by a gap of 15–20 nm. These profiles contain various types and proportions of agranular and granular vesicles and are thought to represent cholinergic, 5-hydroxytryptaminergic and possibly dopaminergic nerve endings.

Neuromuscular junctions in many coelenterates resemble the 'en passage' varicose junctions described in vertebrate smooth muscle with junctional clefts of about 20 nm (see Chapter 7D). Furthermore, at scyphozoan neuromuscular junctions, there are subsurface cisternae of smooth endoplasmic reticulum which are separated from the epitheliomuscular cell membrane by a 10–30 nm wide cytoplasmic gap. Both agranular and granular vesicles (70–150 nm in diameter) have been identified in nerve endings on muscle. The neurotransmitters have not yet been identified, although some data indicates the presence of ACh, catecholamines and 5-HT.

Combined ultrastructural, physiological studies of the heart of the horseshoe crab *Limulus* suggest that most myocardial cells have one or more neuromuscular junctions. *Limulus* heart, like the hearts of most arthropods (insects, crustaceans, arachnids), are *neurogenic*. That is, the heart beats with its own inherent rhythm which is modified in rate and amplitude by direct nervous control. L-glutamic acid has been shown to mimic the action of the nerves on the heart of some species.

Plate 145

Two types of axon supply earthworm obliquely striated muscle. Type I axons (Ax) illustrated in somatic muscle in (*a*) resembles cholinergic nerve terminals and contains a number of agranular vesicles, approximately 50 nm in diameter and a number of larger granular vesicles approximately 150 nm in diameter. The axon is separated from the postsynaptic membrane by a gap 80–150 nm wide containing basal lamina. This postsynaptic membrane shows unusual specializations which are illustrated in (*b*). The inner leaflet of the postsynaptic membrane is covered by electron dense material. A number of fine obliquely orientated filaments are inserted onto the outer leaflet of the membrane of the muscle cell (Mu). The axon (Ax) contains agranular vesicles (Sv). The second type of axon (Type II) is described in Plate 146.

Neuromuscular junction in an annelid somatic obliquely striated muscle: earthworm body wall. Glutaraldehyde fixation.

(*a*) ×97 000.
(*b*) ×134 000.

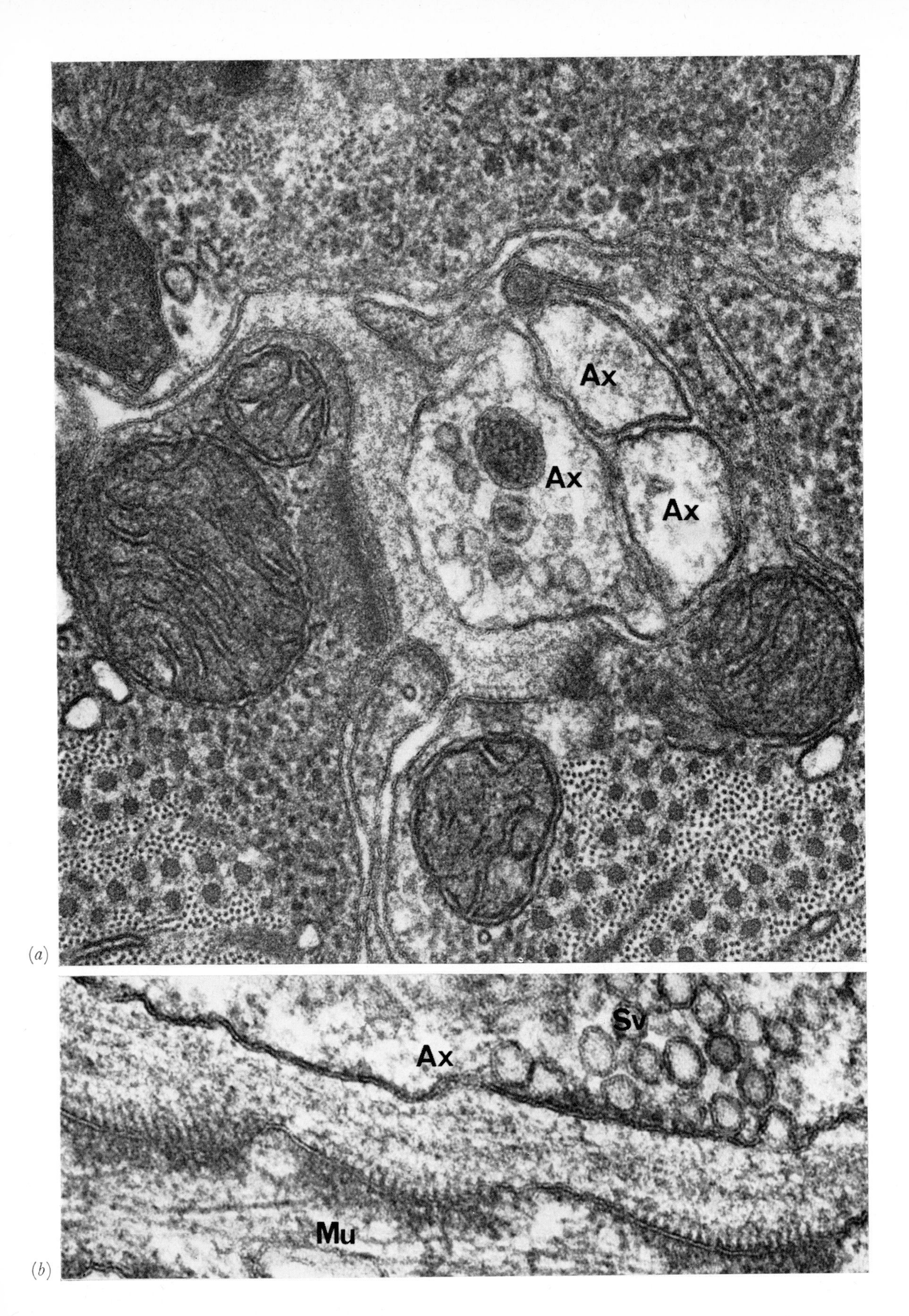
Ax
Ax
Ax
(a)
Sv
Ax
Mu
(b)

Plate 146

The second type of junction (Type II) found in visceral and vascular muscle in the earthworm (Type I is illustrated in Plate 145) resembles adrenergic nerve terminals of the vertebrate autonomic nervous system. These axons (Ax) usually contain a predominance of dense cored vesicles about 100 nm in diameter although some can be up to 400 nm in diameter. The gap between the axons and the postsynaptic membrane is much narrower than at the myoneural junction illustrated in Plate 145 and is usually less than 20 nm wide. No specialization of the post synaptic membrane is present.

Neuromuscular junction in an annelid visceral obliquely striated muscle: earthworm intestine. Glutaraldehyde fixation. ×144 000.

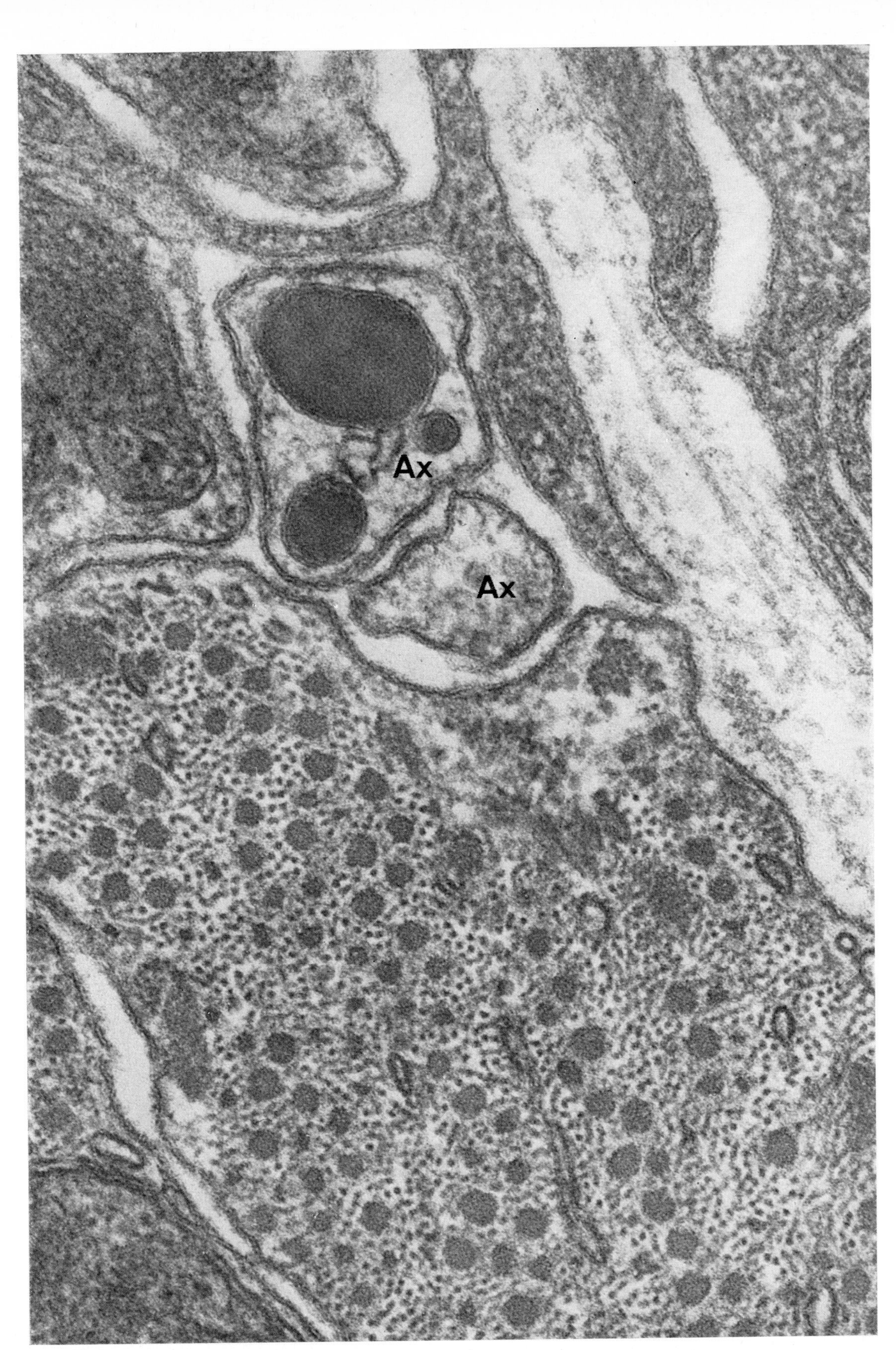
Ax
Ax

Plate 147

The micrograph shows another example of an invertebrate neuromuscular junction. The axon illustrated resembles cholinergic nerve terminals in the vertebrate autonomic nervous system. It contains predominantly small agranular vesicles, 40–60 nm in diameter, and some large granular vesicles about 100 nm in diameter.

The arrow indicates a pre-synaptic accumulation of electron dense material, a feature of the terminal region of many different types of nerve throughout the animal kingdom (see for example Plate 134). The nerve is in close contact (<20 nm) with a thin process of the muscle cell, a feature also occasionally found at myoneural junctions in earthworm somatic muscle.

Neuromuscular junction in an arthropod muscle: millipede intestine. Longitudinal section. Glutaraldehyde fixation. ×82 000.

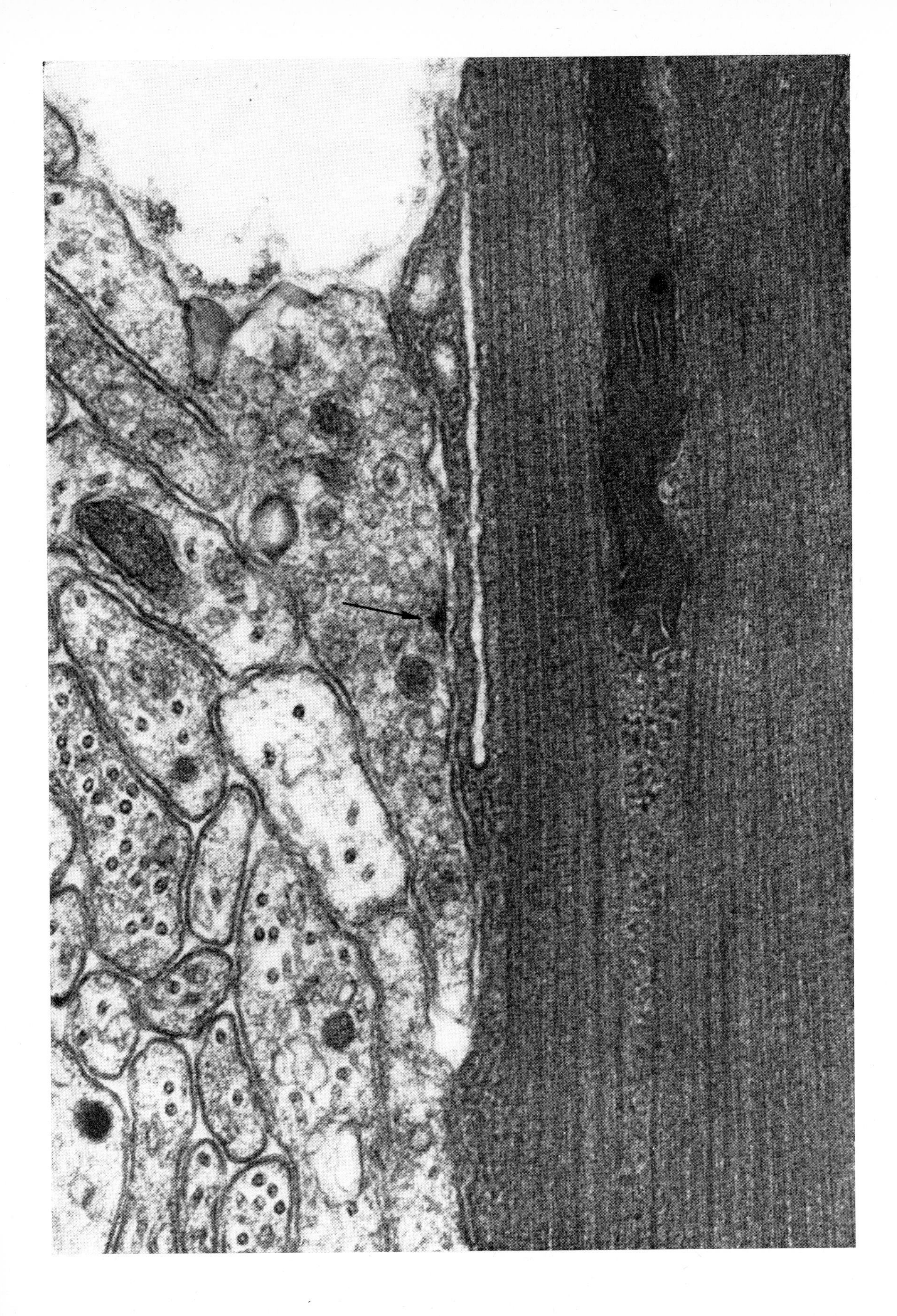

Plate 148

A nerve profile is illustrated in close association (<20 nm) with muscle cells of the starfish tube foot. The vesicles in this profile are from 200 to 400 nm in diameter with a central dense granular core surrounded by a halo approximately 10 nm wide. Similar profiles have been noted in muscles of annelids, molluscs, and amphibians, where they may be neurosecretory. No postsynaptic specialization is apparent.

Neuromuscular junction in an echinoderm muscle: starfish tube foot. Glutaraldehyde fixation. ×59 400.

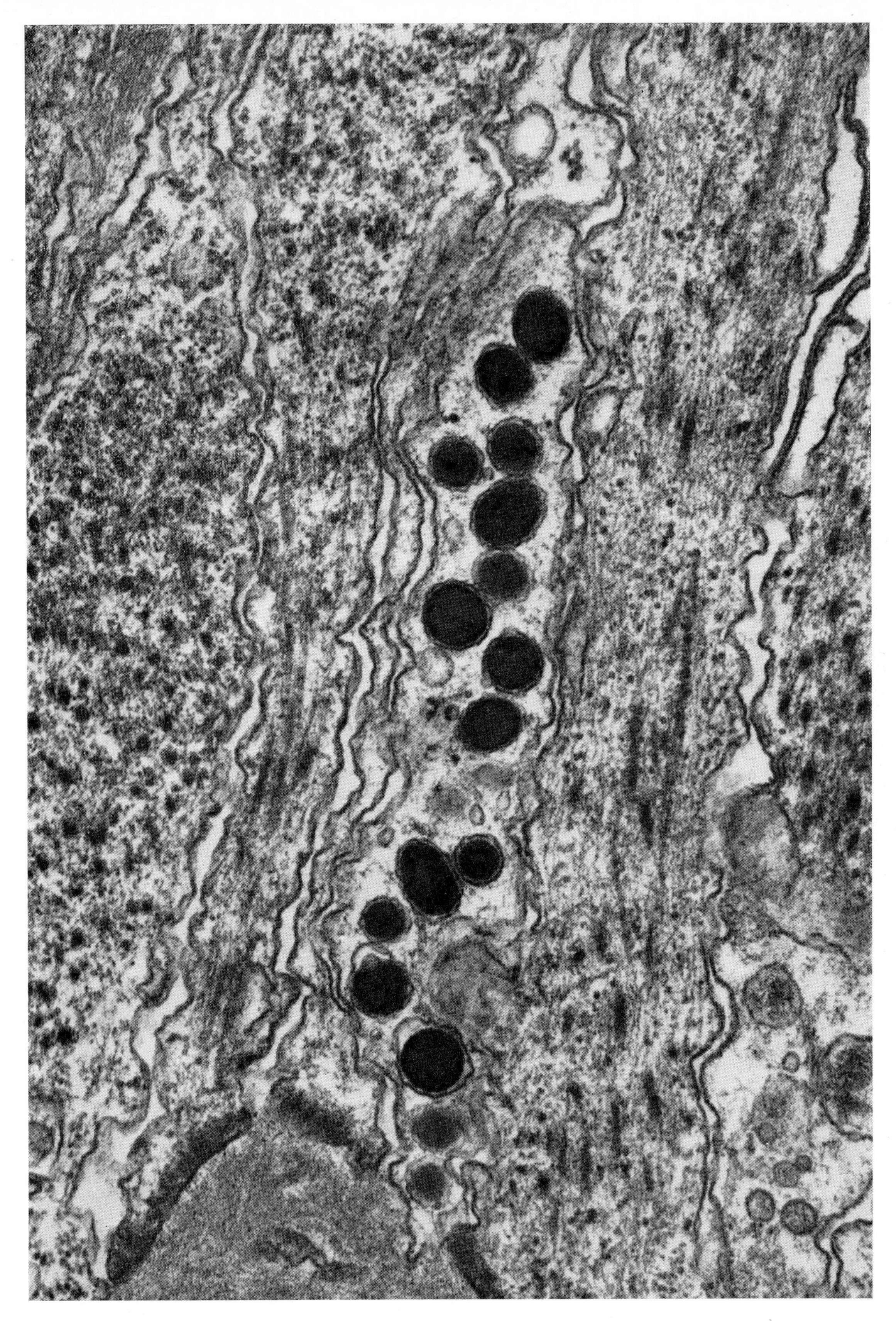

Selected reviews

Invertebrate Neuromuscular Systems. *Am. Zool.*, **13,** 237–445.

ANDERSEN, P. and J. K. S. JANSEN (eds.). 1970. *Excitatory Synaptic Mechanisms.* Universiteit Forlaget, Oslo.

BEAMENT, J. W. and J. E. TREHERNE. 1967. *Insects and Physiology.* Oliver and Boyd, Edinburgh.

BULLOCK, T. H. and G. A. HORRIDGE. 1965. *Structure and Function in the Nervous System of Invertebrates.* Freeman, San Francisco.

COTTRELL, G. A. 1967. *Symposium on Neurobiology of Invertebrates.* Akademiai Kiado, Budapest. 353–364.

COTTRELL, G. A. and M. S. L. LAVERACK. 1968. Invertebrate pharmacology. *A. Rev. Pharmacol.*, **8,** 273–298.

ENDEAN, R. 1972. Aspects of molluscan pharmacology. In *Chemical Zoology.* Vol. 7. *Mollusca.* M. Florkin and B. T. Scheer, (eds.). Academic Press, New York. 421–466.

FLOREY, E. (ed.). 1961. *Nervous inhibition.* Pergamon, Oxford.

FLOREY, E. 1965. Comparative pharmacology: neurotropic and myotropic compounds. *A. Rev. Pharmacol.*, **5,** 357–381.

FURSHPAN, E. J. 1959. Neuromuscular transmission in invertebrates. In *Handbook of Physiology*, Section 1, *Neurophysiology*, Vol. 1. H. W. Magoun (ed.). American Physiological Society, Washington. 239–254.

GERSCHENFELD, H. M. 1973. Chemical transmission in invertebrate central nervous system and neuromuscular junctions. *Physiol. Rev.*, **53,** 1–119.

GRAY, E. G. 1966. Problems of interpreting the fine structure of vertebrate and invertebrate synapses. *Rev. Gen. Exp. Zool.*, **2,** 139–170.

HOYLE, G. 1957. *Comparative Physiology of the Nervous Control of Muscular Contraction.* Cambridge University Press, London.

HOYLE, G. 1964. Muscle and neuromuscular physiology. In *Physiology of Mollusca.* Vol. 1. K. M. Wilbur and C. M. Yonge (eds.). Academic Press, New York. 313–351.

HOYLE, G. 1965. Neural control of skeletal muscle. In *The Physiology of the Insecta.* Vol. 2. M. Rockstein (ed.). Academic Press, New York. 406–449.

KATZ, B. 1949. Neuromuscular transmission in invertebrates. *Biol. Rev.*, **24,** 1–21.

KATZ, B. 1969. *The Release of Neural Transmitter Substances.* Thomas, Springfield, Illinois.

LASANSKY, A. 1971. Nervous function at the cellular level: glia. *A. Rev. Physiol.*, **33,** 241–256.

LENTZ, T. L. 1968. *Primitive Nervous Systems.* Yale University Press, New Haven.

McCANN, F. (ed.). 1969. *Comparative Physiology of the Heart: Current Trends.* Birkhauser, Basel. 220–231.

McLENNAN, H. 1970. *Synaptic Transmission.* W. B. Saunders, Philadelphia.

PAPPAS, G. D. and D. PURPURA. 1970. *Structure and Function of Synapses.* Raven, New York.

PHYLLIS, J. W. 1970. *The Pharmacology of Synapses.* Pergamon Press, Oxford.

RICHTER, D. (ed.). *Comparative Neurochemistry.* Pergamon Press, Oxford.

SAKHAROV, D. A. 1970. Cellular aspects of invertebrate pharmacology. *A. Rev. Pharmacol.*, **10,** 335–352.

TAUC, L. 1967. Transmission in vertebrate and invertebrate ganglia. *Physiol. Rev.*, **214,** 724–725.

TREHERNE, J. E. 1966. *The Neurochemistry of Arthropods.* Cambridge University Press, London.

USHERWOOD, P. N. R. 1969. Electrochemistry of insect muscle. *Adv. Insect Physiol.*, **6,** 205–271.

VON EULER, C., S. SKOGLUND and U. SÖDERBERG. 1968. *Structure and Function of Inhibitory Neuronal Mechanisms.* Pergamon Press, Oxford.

WELSH, J. H. 1968. Distribution of serotonin in the nervous system of various animal species. *Adv. Pharmacol.*, **6A,** 171–188.

WILBUR, K. M. and C. M. YONGE (eds.). 1966. *Physiology of Mollusca.* Vol. 2. Academic Press, New York.

Selected articles

ATWOOD, H. L., C. K. GOVIND and G. D. BITTNER. 1973. Ultrastructure of nerve terminals and muscle fibers in denervated crayfish muscle. *Z. Zellforsch. mikrosk. Anat.*, **146,** 155–165.

BARRANTES, F. J. 1970. The neuromuscular

junctions of a pulmonate mollusc. I. Ultrastructural study. *Z. Zellforsch. mikrosk. Anat.*, **104,** 205–212.

BENJAMIN, P. R. and A. PEAT. 1968. Myoneural junctions in the connective tissue sheath of a molluscan ganglion. *Nature, Lond.*, **219,** 1371–1372.

BERGMAN, R. A. 1967. Motor nerve endings of twitch muscle fibers in *Hippocampus hudsonius*. *J. Cell Biol.*, **32,** 751–756.

BEST, A. C. G. and Q. BONE. 1973. The terminal neuromuscular junctions of lower chordates. *Z. Zellforsch. mikrosk. Anat.*, **143,** 495–504.

BONE, Q. and K. P. RYAN. 1974. On the structure and innervation of the muscle bands of *Doliolum* (Tunicata: Cyclomyaria). *Proc. R. Soc. Ser. B*, **187,** 315–327.

BOTÁR, J. 1967. The innervation of the visceral smooth muscle and the question of nerve terminations in the *Octopus vulgaris*. *Acta Anat.*, **67,** 561–570.

BROWN, B. E. 1967. Neuromuscular transmitter substance in insect visceral muscle. *Science, N.Y.*, **155,** 595–597.

FERNÁNDEZ, J. and M. S. FERNÁNDEZ. 1972. Nervous system of the snail *Helix aspersa*. III. Electron microscopic study of neurosecretory nerves and endings in the ganglionic sheath. *Z. Zellforsch. mikrosk. Anat.*, **135,** 473–482.

GRAZIADEI, P. 1966. The ultrastructure of the motor nerve endings in the muscles of Cephalopods. *J. Ultrastruct. Res.*, **15,** 1–13.

HAMA, K. 1961. Some observations on the fine structure of the giant fibers of the crayfishes (*Cambarus virilus* and *Cambarus clarkii*) with special reference to the submicroscopic organization of the synapses. *Anat. Rec.*, **141,** 275–294.

HÁMORI, J. 1973. Electron microscope studies on neuromuscular junctions of end-plate type in insects. *Acta biol. hung.*, **14,** 231–245.

HESS, A. 1960. The fine structure of degenerating nerve fibers, their sheaths, and their terminations in the central nerve cord of the cockroach (*Periplaneta americana*). *J. biophys. biochem. Cytol.*, **7,** 339–344.

HEUSER, J. E. and C. F. DOGGENWEILER. 1966. The fine structural organization of nerve fibers, sheaths, and glial cells in the prawn, *Palaemonetes vulgaris*. *J. Cell Biol.*, **30,** 381–404.

HOLTZMAN, E., A. R. FREEMAN and L. A. KASHNER. 1971. Stimulation-dependent alteration in peroxidase uptake at lobster neuromuscular junctions. *Science N.Y.*, **173,** 733–736.

HOYLE, G. 1962. Neuro-muscular physiology. *Adv. Comp. Physiol. Biochem.*, **1,** 177–216.

JAHROMI, S. S. and H. L. ATWOOD. 1974. Three-dimensional ultrastructure of the crayfish neuromuscular apparatus. *J. Cell Biol.*, **63,** 599–613.

KERKUT, G. A., M. WOODHOUSE and G. R. NEWMAN. 1966. Nerve-muscle junction in the snail *Helix aspersa*. *Comp. Biochem. Physiol.*, **19,** 309–311.

KOMURO, T. 1970. Unusual neuromuscular junctions in the heart of the crayfish (*Procambarus clarkii*). *Z. Zellforsch. mikrosk. Anat.*, **105,** 317–324.

McKENNA, O. C. and J. ROSENBLUTH. 1973. Myoneural and intermuscular junctions in a molluscan smooth muscle. *J. Ultrastruct. Res.*, **42,** 434–450.

MILL, P. J. and M. F. KNAPP. 1970. Neuromuscular junctions in the body wall muscles of the earthworm, *Lumbricus terrestris* Linn. *J. Cell Sci.*, **7,** 263–272.

NADOL, J. B. JR and A. J. D. DE LORENZO. 1968. Observations on the abdominal stretch receptor and the fine structure of associated axo-dendritic synapses and neuromuscular junctions in *Homarus*. *J. comp. Neurol.*, **132,** 419–443.

OSBORNE, M. P., L. H. FINLAYSON and M. J. RICE. 1971. Neurosecretory endings associated with striated muscles in three insects (*Schistocerca*, *Carausius* and *Phormia*) and a frog (*Rana*). *Z. Zellforsch. mikrosk. Anat.*, **116,** 391–404.

PETERSON, R. P. and F. A. PEPE. 1961. The fine structure of inhibitory synapses in the crayfish. *J. Cell Biol.*, **11,** 157–170.

REES, D. and P. N. R. USHERWOOD. 1972. Effects of denervation on the ultrastructure of insect muscle. *J. Cell Sci.*, **10,** 667–682.

ROGERS, D. C. 1966. Fine structure of smooth muscle and neuromuscular junctions in the foot of *Helix aspersa*. *Z. Zellforsch. mikrosk. Anat.*, **99,** 315–335.

ROGERS, D. C. 1968. Fine structure of smooth muscle and neuromuscular junctions in the optic tentacles of *Helix aspersa* and *Limax flavus*. *Z. Zellforsch. mikrosk. Anat.*, **89,** 80–94.

ROGERS, D. C. 1971. The fine structure of sensory neurons and their processes in the optic tentacles of *Helix aspersa*. *Z. mikrosk.-anat. Forsch.*, **84,** 52–64.
ROSENBLUTH, J. 1962. Subsurface cisterns and their relationship to the neuronal plasma membrane. *J. Cell Biol.*, **13,** 405–422.
ROSENBLUTH, J. 1965. Ultrastructure of somatic muscle cells in *Ascaris lumbricoides*. II. Intermuscular junctions, neuromuscular junctions and glycogen stores. *J. Cell Biol.*, **26,** 579–592.
ROSENBLUTH, J. 1972. Myoneural junctions of two ultrastructurally distinct types in earthworm body wall muscle. *J. Cell Biol.*, **54,** 566–579.
ROSENBLUTH, J. 1973*a*. Postjunctional membrane specialization at cholinergic myoneural junctions in the leech. *J. comp. Neurol.*, **151,** 399–406.
ROSENBLUTH, J. 1973*b*. Membrane specialization at an insect myoneural junction. *J. Cell Biol.*, **59,** 143–150.
SMITH, D. S. 1960. Innervation of the fibrillar flight muscle of an insect: *Tenebrio molitor* (*Coleoptera*). *J. biophys. biochem. Cytol.*, **8,** 447–466.
SMITH, D. S. and J. E. TREHERNE. 1965. The electron microscopic localization of cholinesterase activity in the central nervous system of an insect (*Periplaneta americana* L.). *J. Cell Biol.*, **26,** 445–459.
TULSI, R. S. and R. E. COGGESHALL. 1971. Neuromuscular junctions on the muscle cells in the central nervous system of the leech. *Hirudo medicinalis*. *J. comp. Neurol.*, **141,** 1–15.
TWAROG, B. M. 1967. Excitation of *Mytilus* smooth muscle. *J. Physiol., Lond.*, **192,** 857–868.
UCHIZONO, K. 1966. Excitatory and inhibitory synapses in vertebrate and invertebrate animals. In *Electron Microscopy, Vol. 2. Proc. 6th Int. Cong. Electron Microscopy.* H. Ueda (ed.). Maruzen, Tokyo. 431–432.

F Muscle spindle and tendon organ

Several types of sensory receptor are found in vertebrate muscles. The simplest type is a *free nerve ending* which is distributed in fascia, intramuscular connective tissue, and in tendons. This type of ending is considered to be a pressure-pain receptor. Other types of sensory endings are more differentiated, including encapsulated sense organs known as proprioceptive mechanoreceptors. These sensory receptors in muscle are *muscle spindles*, *Golgi tendon organs* and *Pacinian corpuscles*.

Muscle spindles consist of a group of specialized thin striated muscle fibres termed intrafusal fibres and their associated motor and sensory nerve endings. The number of intrafusal fibres in each spindle varies from more than twenty in some cat muscles, to four in rats, to only one in reptiles. Two types of intrafusal fibres are present in many mammalian muscle spindles; '*nuclear-bag fibres*' which contain an accumulation of nuclei in the equatorial region, and '*nuclear-chain fibres*', which contain nuclei arranged in a row. Nuclear-bag fibres have a larger diameter and are longer than nuclear-chain fibres, extending beyond the ends of the capsule to attach to intramuscular connective tissue or tendons. Nuclear-chain fibres are confined to the spindle capsule, their ends being attached to its apices. Ultrastructural and physiological studies suggest that the nuclear-chain fibres closely resemble frog twitch-muscle fibres while nuclear-bag fibres are more like frog slow fibres. Intrafusal fibres are partly invested by a fusiform connective tissue capsule along their length (for 1–3 mm) with a central expansion of about 100 μm in diameter. They are commonly divided into three characteristic regions: the equatorial region, which is the middle segment of the encapsulated part; the myotube region, which is on both sides of the equatorial region; and the polar or end region.

Muscle spindles are supplied by large sensory nerves (afferent nerves), by small motor nerves (efferent nerves) called *gamma fibres* which emanate from gamma motor neurons in the central nervous system, by autonomic nerves and by branches of motor nerves which supply the extrafusal muscle fibres, these are called *alpha* fibres (see Fig. 24). The form of sensory ending varies considerably with the animal species. For example, the sensory endings in mammalian spindles are annular or spiral, coiling around the equatorial region of intra-

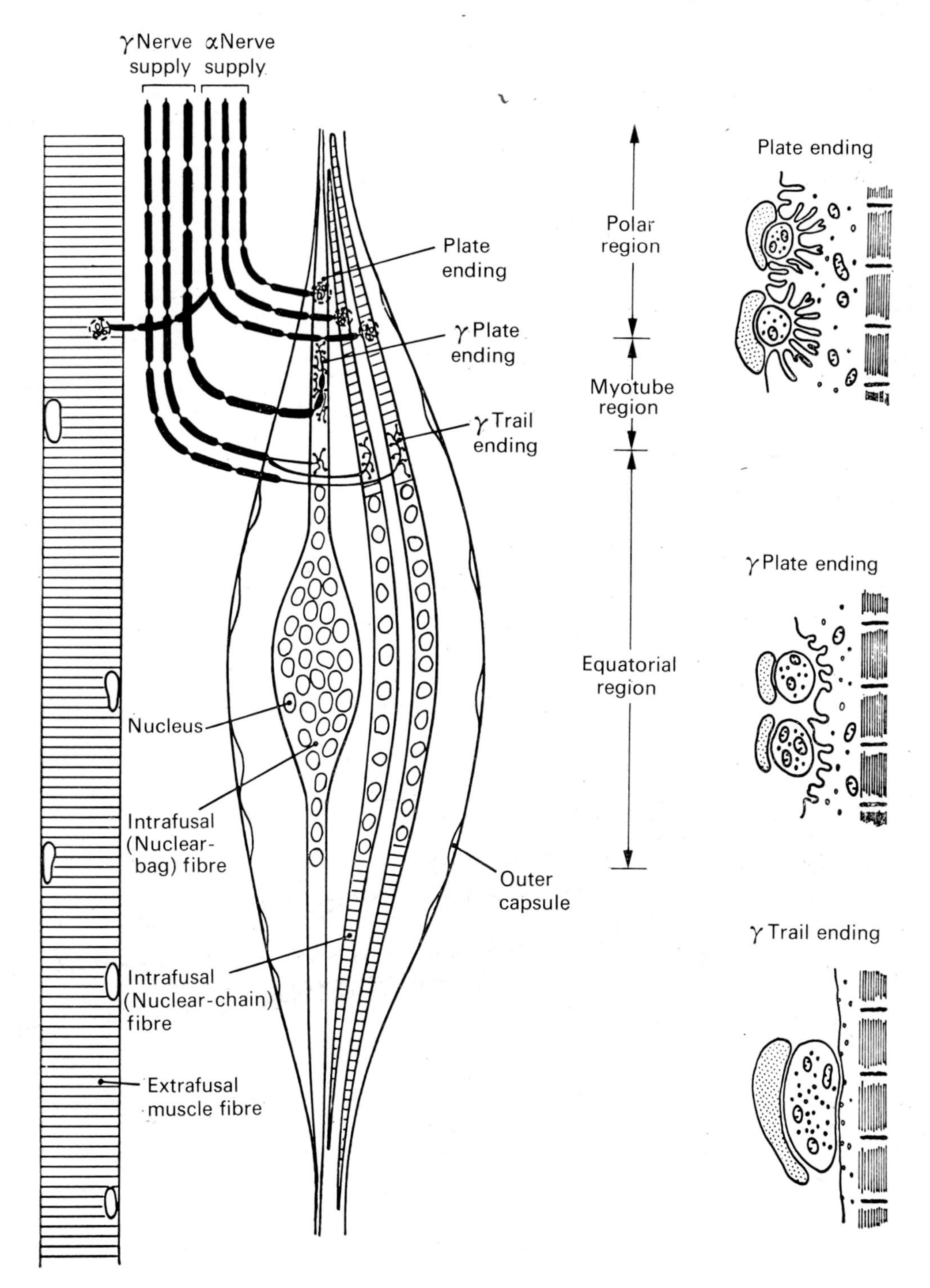

Fig. 24 Diagramatic representation of a neuromuscular spindle of a mammal (cat) showing the three types of motor endings on nuclear-bag and nuclear-chain fibres.

fusal fibres and are *annulospiral or primary endings*. Those in the frog muscle spindles consist of a number of fine varicose terminal arborizations running nearly parallel to the long axis of the muscle fibres. The motor nerves supplying the polar regions of the muscle spindle form the fusimotor system. The motor endings of fusimotor nerves are of two kinds: 'en plaque' endings mainly on nuclear-bag fibres, and 'en grappe' endings mainly on nuclear-chain fibres. The intrafusal muscle fibres are attached in parallel to the normal or extrafusal muscle fibres. The sensory endings, therefore, function as stretch receptors, when the muscle is stretched.

Golgi tendon organs are encapsulated sensory nerve endings distributed along musculo-tendinous boundaries of mammals and birds. Each receptor is supplied by one large diameter, myelinated sensory nerve and smaller accessory nerve fibres. The connective tissue capsule is about 500 μm in length and about 100 μm at its widest diameter. Densely staining tendon fasciculi in the organ are divided into several longitudinal compartments by specialized fibroblasts called septal cells.

The myelinated sensory nerve supplying the tendon organ breaks up into a number of terminal branches which have many leaf- or clasp-like granular swellings applied to the surface of the tendon fasciculi. Although muscle spindles are disposed parallel with the extrafusal fibres, Golgi tendon organs are in series with these muscle fibres. Both types of receptor respond when the muscle is stretched. When the muscle contracts, the tendon organs are stimulated, but the tension on muscle spindles is relaxed leading to cessation of afferent discharge from the spindle. Fusimotor activity of muscle spindles keeps the intrafusal fibre tonically active in advance of a contraction, so that less stretch is necessary to excite sensory endings during activity.

In invertebrates, stretch receptors are known to be present in the dorsal abdominal and thoracic muscle segments of decapod and stomatopod crustacea.

Plate 149

The *outer capsule* (Co) of the muscle spindle that surrounds the intrafusal fibres (If) consists of a number of thin attenuated cells arranged in concentric lamellae with collagen fibrils and elastic fibres interposed. These capsular cells contain numerous micropinocytotic vesicles and are invested by a basal lamina. The adjacent cellular processes are connected together by close junctions to form a continuous cellular layer. The cellular layer of the capsule is considered to be involved in the regulation of the ionic environment of the spindle. The spindle capsule is comparable in structure to the perineurium, the outer capsule of Paccinian corpuscles and the capsule of Golgi tendon organs. Intrafusal fibres are usually partly surrounded by a further cellular layer the *inner spindle capsule* (Ci) consisting of cell processes of fibroblasts which lack a basal lamina. This capsule corresponds to the muscle endomysium.

The accompanying micrograph is a transverse section through the juxta-equatorial region of a muscle spindle. Intrafusal fibres (If) are supplied by motor endings (Me) derived from thin myelinated fusimotor fibres (Nm). Note the thinness of intrafusal fibres and the small size of their mitochondria compared to those of neighbouring extrafusal fibres (Ex).

Muscle spindle in avian skeletal muscle: finch rectus femoris. Transverse section. Glutaraldehyde fixation. ×9 800.

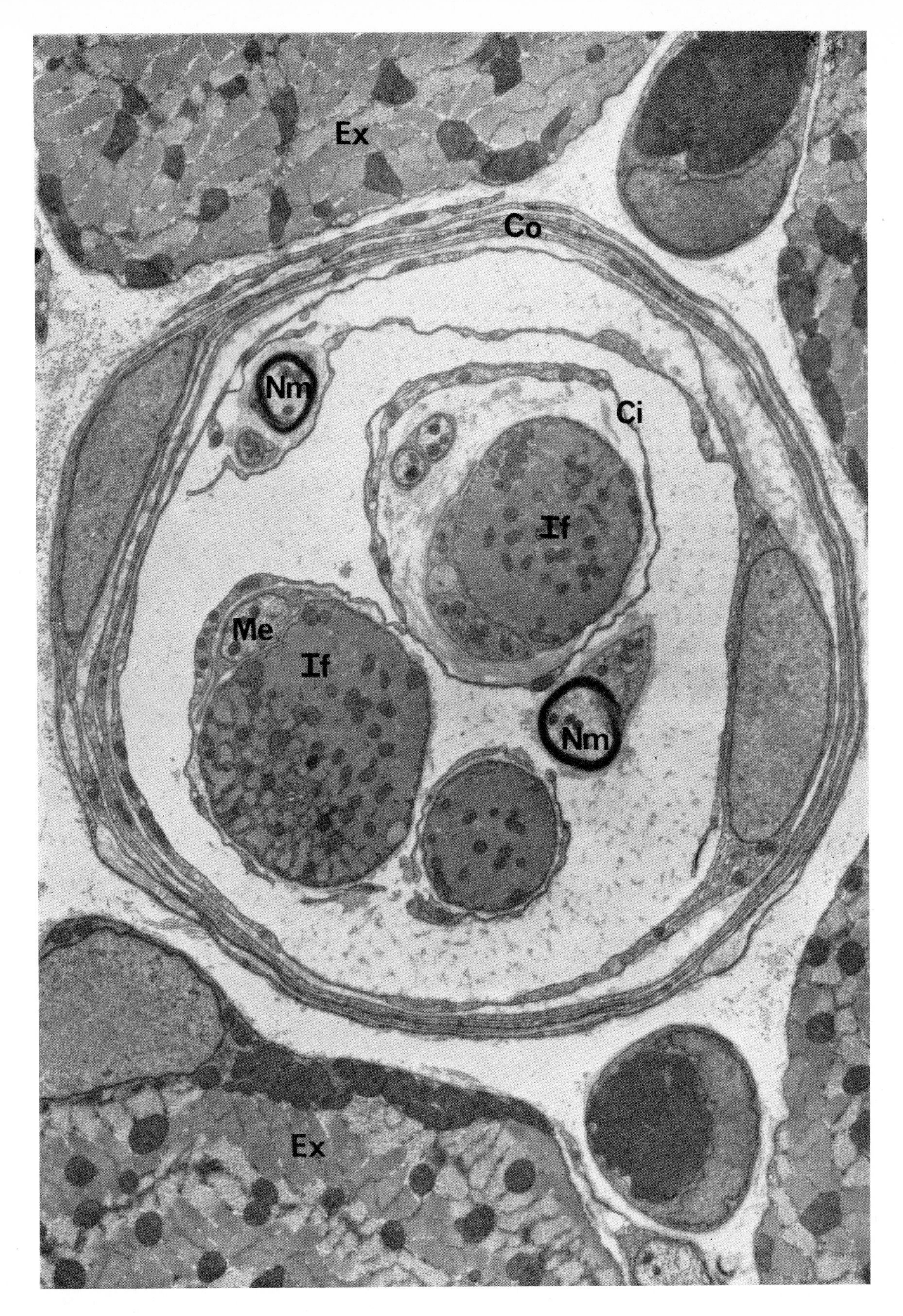
Ex
Co
Nm
Ci
If
Me
If
Nm
Ex

Plate 150

The accompanying micrograph shows the accumulation of nuclei in the equatorial region of a rat nuclear-bag intrafusal muscle fibre. The fibre is almost fully occupied by nuclei, myofilaments being confined to the peripheral portions of the cell. In some mammals such as cats, up to 100 nuclei are accumulated in this region. Since few contractile elements are present here, the intrafusal fibre is easily stretched by the extrafusal fibres, or by contraction of the myotube and polar regions of the same fibre. This leads to the mechanical deformation of sensory nerve endings (Se) which are located in the equatorial region. Ci, inner capsule.

Nuclear-bag intrafusal fibre of a mammalian muscle spindle: rat sternothyroid. Longitudinal section. Glutaraldehyde fixation. ×14 600.

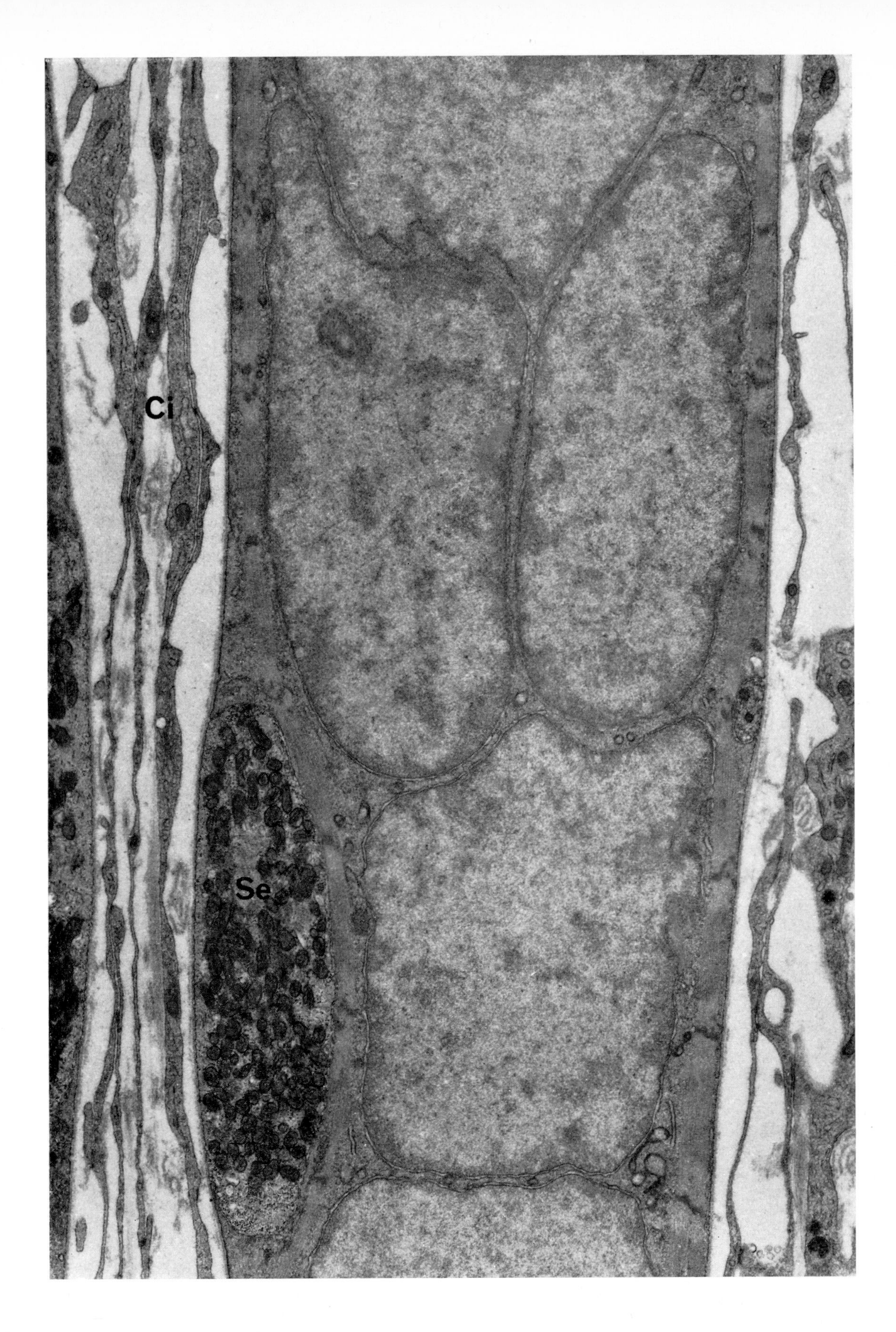
Ci
Se

Plate 151

Intrafusal fibres in some mammalian muscle spindles are innervated by two groups of sensory nerves: *group I* (primary afferent) fibres are fast conducting and *group II* (secondary afferent) fibres are slower conducting. The primary afferent nerve fibres are large (12–20 μm in diameter) and supply the equatorial regions of all the intrafusal fibres. The secondary afferent nerves are smaller (4–12 μm) and supply the adjacent areas (the myotube region). The secondary afferents mainly supply nuclear chain rather than nuclear bag fibres.

The primary sensory innervation usually has a regular annular or spiral form which coils around the intrafusal muscle fibre. In contrast, the secondary endings show less regular form. The micrograph illustrated in (*a*) depicts a typical *annulo spiral* ending. The sensory ending (Se) consists of a single naked axon containing an accumulation of mitochondria. It covers the perimeter of the intrafusal fibre (If) to form a wide sensory contact, with the pre- and post-synaptic membranes separated by about 20 nm. The muscle and ending are invested by a common basal lamina. e, electron dense material.

The tapered end of both primary and secondary endings often deeply penetrates the intrafusal fibre (*b*). The axon is separated from the surrounding muscle cells by a narrow gap less than 20 nm which is continuous with the extracellular space.

Sensory nerve endings on a nuclear-chain intrafusal fibre of a mammalian muscle spindle: rat sternothyroid. Transverse section. Glutaraldehyde fixation.

(*a*) Primary annulo spiral nerve ending in equatorial region. ×24 000.

(*b*) Sensory nerve ending embedded in a muscle cell in the myotube region. ×47 600.

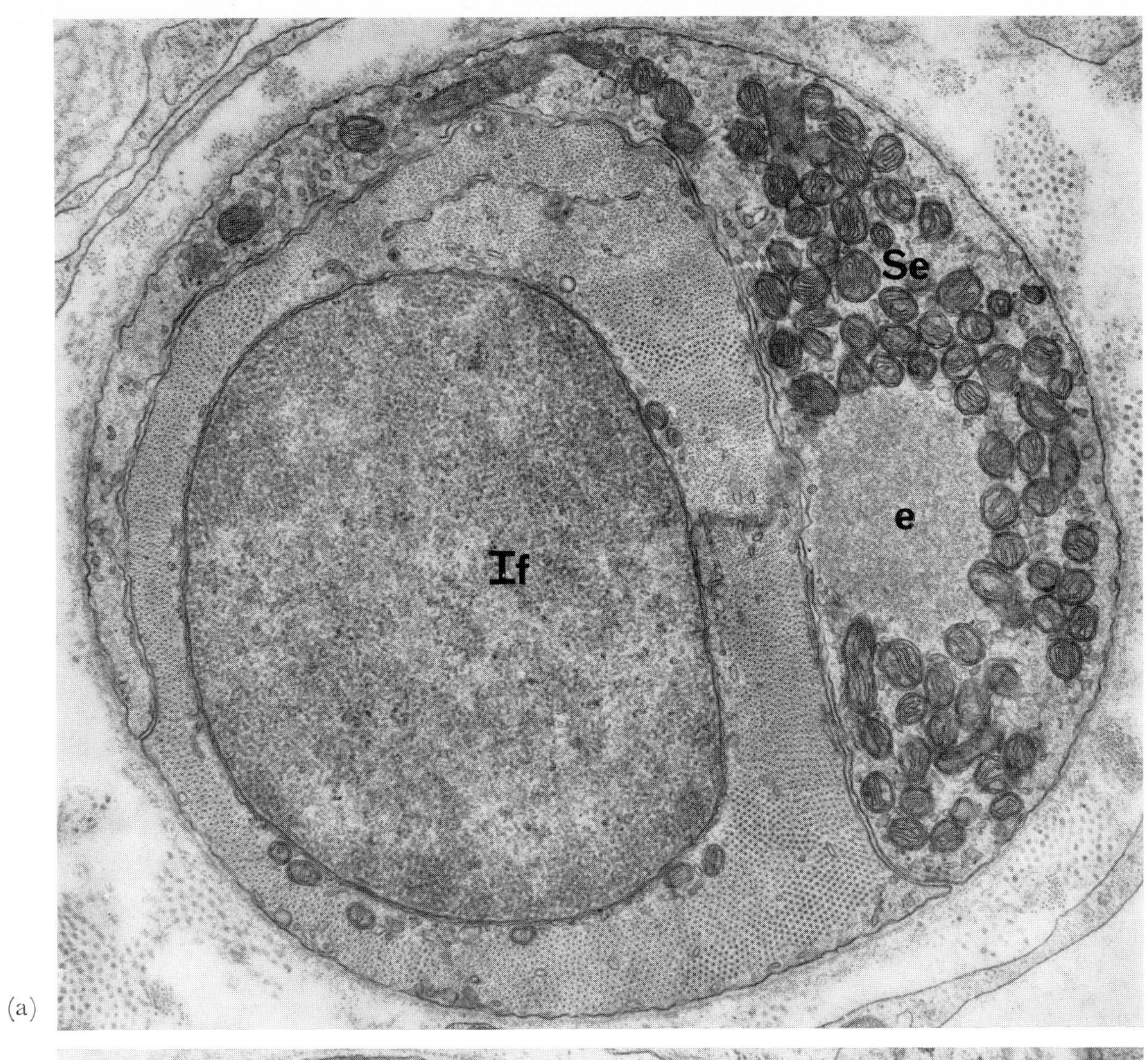

(a)

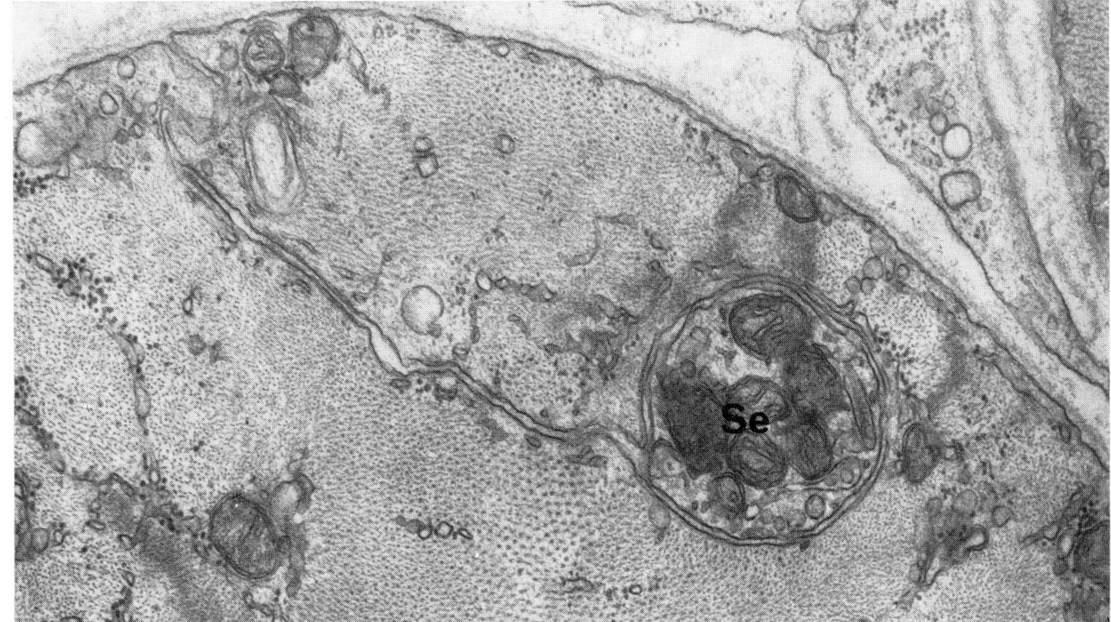

(b)

Plate 152

Muscle spindles in snakes and lizards are unique among vertebrates because they have only a single intrafusal fibre which bears the terminal ramifications of a single sensory nerve fibre; they are therefore called *monofibril spindles.* In the accompanying micrograph through the equatorial region of a lizard muscle spindle, the single intrafusal fibre (If) is surrounded by an outer capsule (Co) which is invested by a basal lamina and by an inner capsule (Ci) consisting of endomysial fibroblasts. A sensory ending (Se) covers a large percentage of the perimeter of the intrafusal fibre forming an extensive sensory contact with the surface of the muscle fibre.

Sensory nerve ending in reptilian monofibril muscle spindle: lizard ilio-femoralis. Transverse section. Glutaraldehyde fixation. ×12 400.

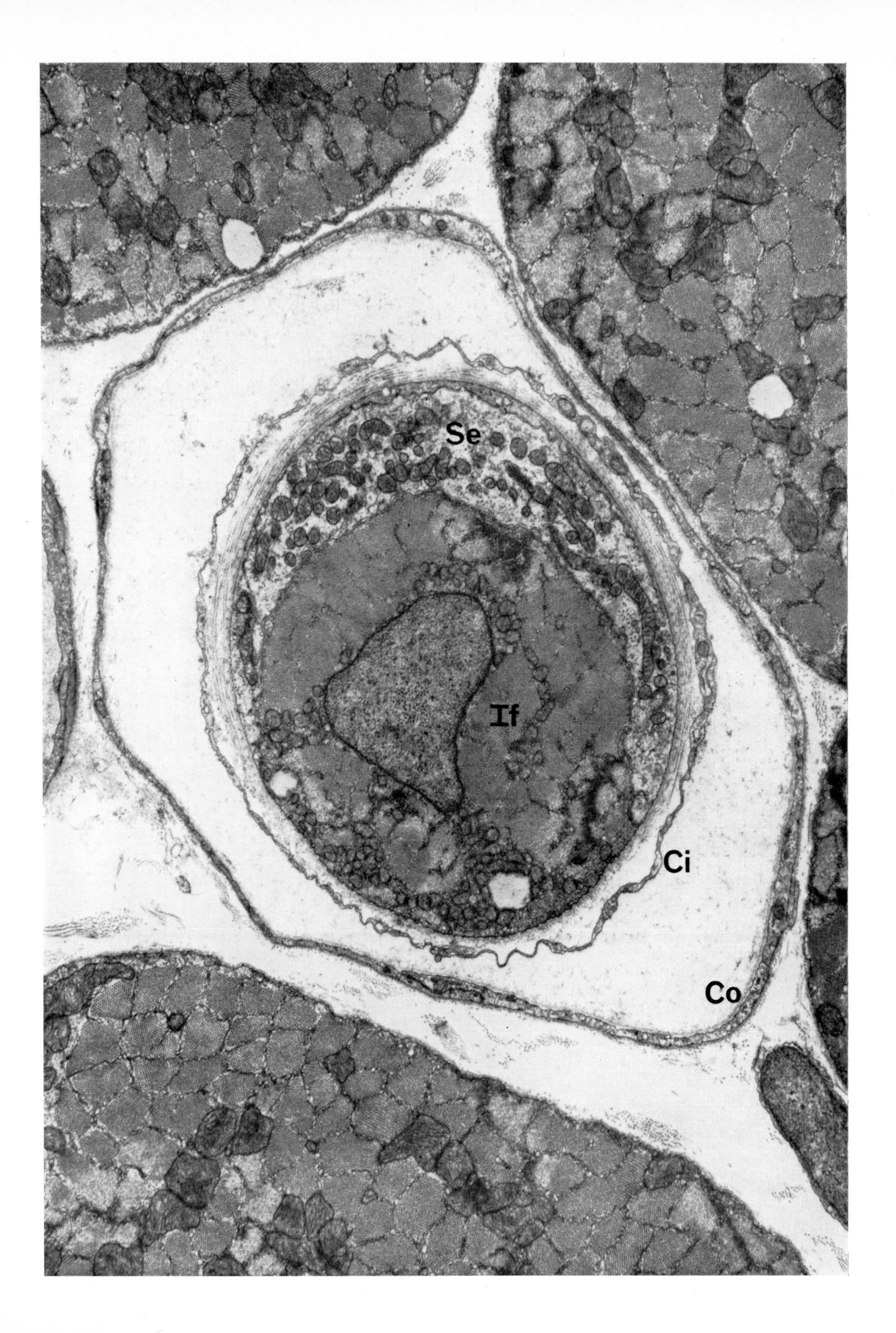
Se
If
Ci
Co

Plate 153

A characteristic feature of the sensory region of the lizard muscle spindle is the thick covering of collagen fibrils which are arranged more or less circumferentially in relation to the long axis of the intrafusal fibre. The basal lamina investing the sensory area shows a structural specialization, that is, a regular arrangement of peg-like structures at right angles to the muscle surface. These have a periodicity of about 120 nm which is approximately that shown by collagen fibrils.

Bird muscle spindles also have a similar thick collagen cap around their sensory region, but there is no comparable specialized basal lamina. The functional significance of the collagen cap is discussed in Plate 155.

Close association of sensory nerve endings (Se) and satellite cells (S) of intrafusal fibres (If) is also illustrated.

Sensory nerve ending in a reptilian monofibril muscle spindle: lizard ilio-femoralis. Transverse section. Glutaraldehyde fixation. × 36 800.

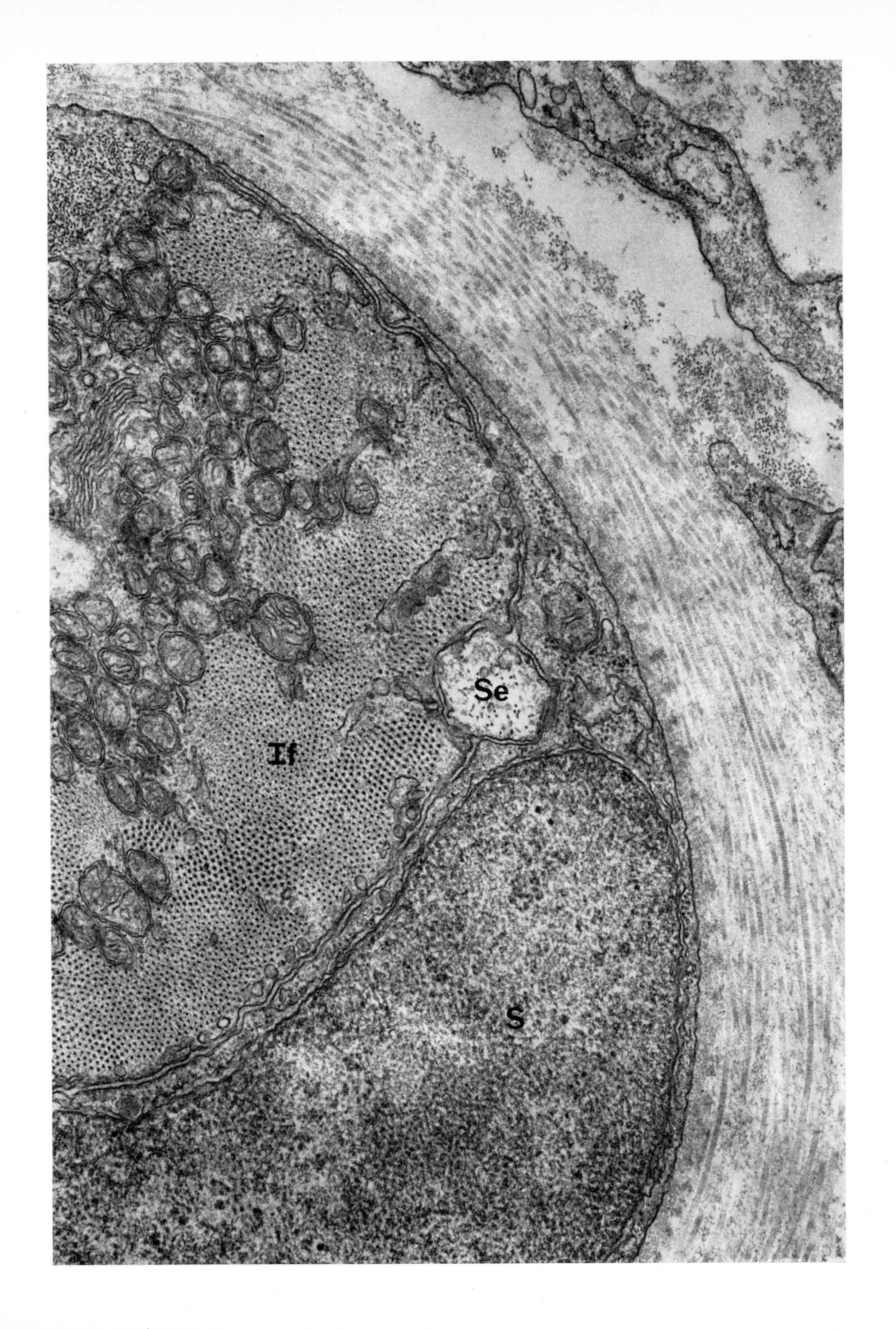
Se
If
S

Plate 154

The sensory region of the frog muscle spindle is divided into two regions: the *compact region* where the intrafusal fibres have a smooth surface and contain regularly organized closely packed myofilaments, and the *reticular region* where intrafusal fibres possess a number of irregular cytoplasmic processes containing disorientated myofibrils.

The sensory endings (Se) in the frog muscle spindle consist of a number of fine terminal varicose arborizations which are disposed longitudinally along the intrafusal fibres (If). In the transverse section through the compact region illustrated, numerous naked terminal axons with round profiles are seen in contact with the intrafusal fibres. The expanded part of the varicosities is several microns in diameter and closely applied to the muscle surface, whereas the thin intervaricose regions are less than 0.2 μm in diameter and usually separated from the muscle surface.

A number of satellite cells (S) are associated with the intrafusal fibres and some of them are intercalated between the muscle cells.

Compact region in an amphibian muscle spindle: frog extensor digitorum longi IV. Transverse section. OsO_4 fixation. ×11 800. (Reproduced from, Uehara, Y. and K. Hama, 1965, *J. Electron Microsc.*, **14,** 34.)

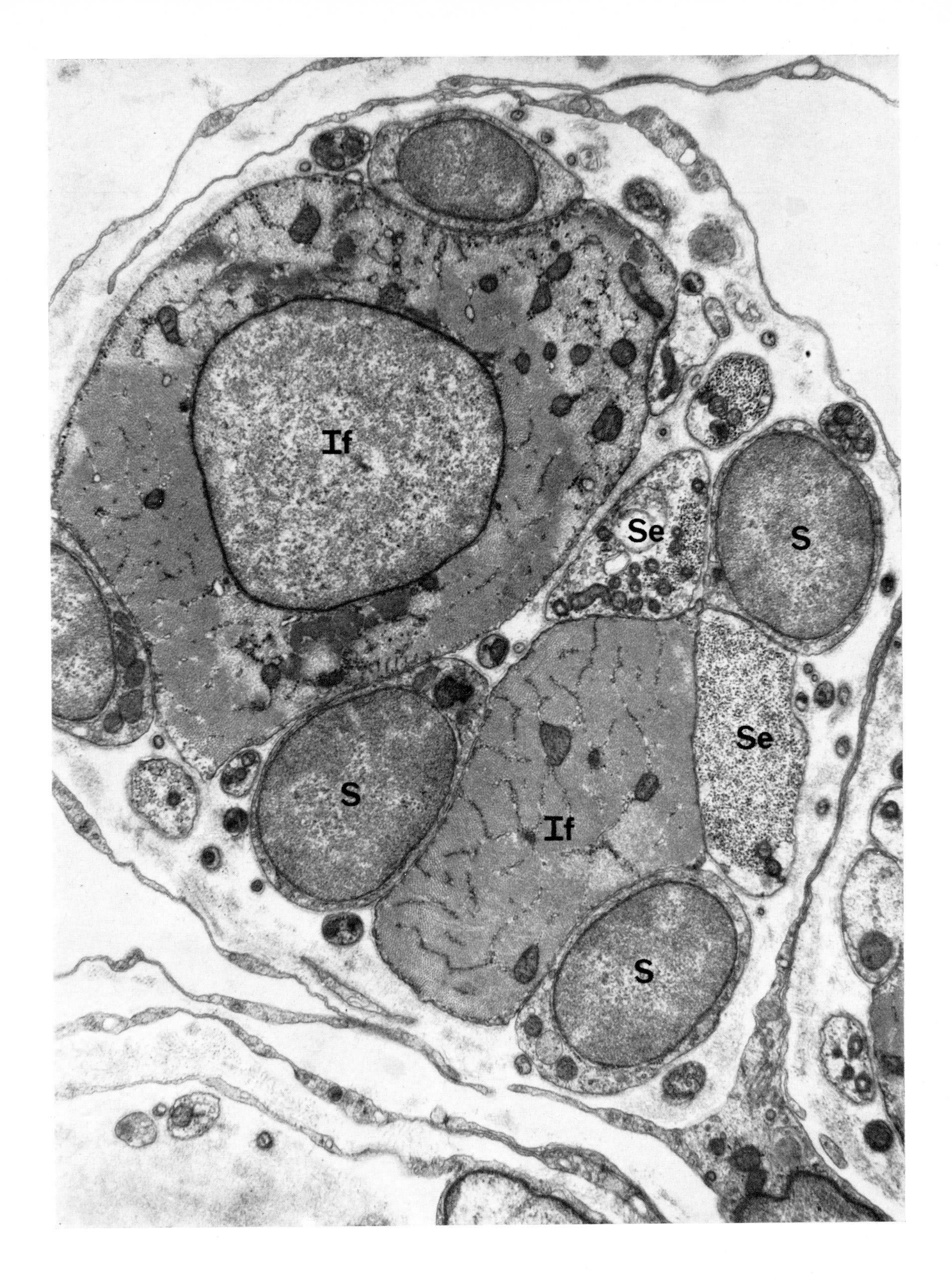
If
Se
S
S
Se
If
S

Plate 155

In the reticular region of the frog muscle spindle, the intrafusal fibres (If) are irregular in shape and varicose expansions of the sensory axons are deeply embedded in depressions on their surface. The gap between the axon and muscle membrane in these regions is less than 20 nm and no basal lamina is interposed. The varicose expanded portion of the terminal axons contain an accumulation of mitochondria and clusters of glycogen granules. However, the thin intervaricose regions of the terminal axons contain no detectable cytoplasmic compartments. In the reticular region, the sensory endings (Se) and intrafusal fibres are embedded in a compact fine filamentous material. These filamentous investments, and the collagen bundle surrounding the sensory region of the lizard muscle spindle might be involved in the protection of this region from unspecific stimuli such as pressure, or they may be involved in regulation of the ionic environment.

Reticular region in an amphibian muscle spindle: frog extensor digitorum longi IV. Transverse section. OsO_4 fixation. ×38 000. (Reproduced from Uehara, Y. and K. Hama, 1965, *J. Electron Microsc.*, **14,** 34.)

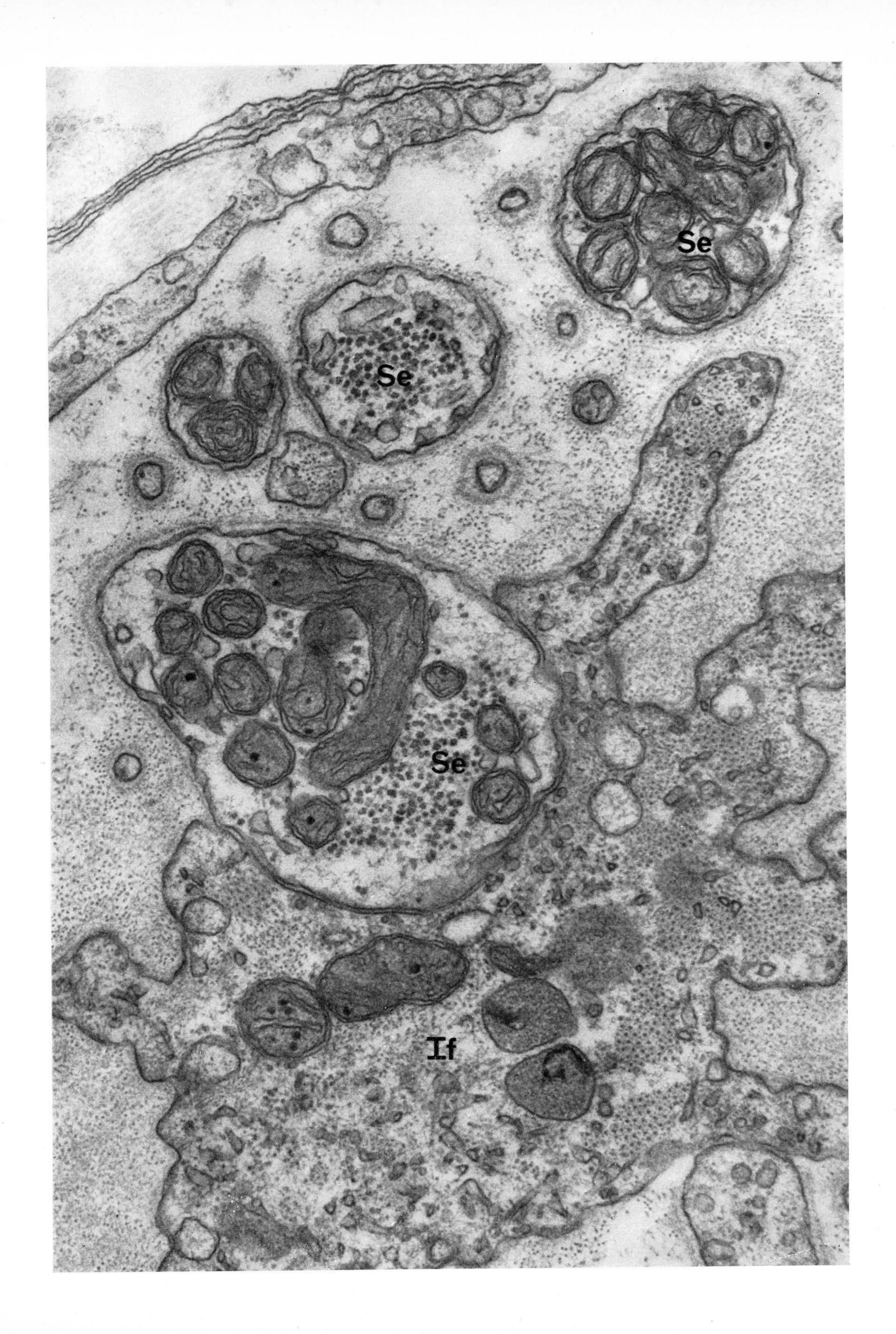
Se
Se
Se
If

Plate 156

Light microscope studies have indicated the presence of two types of gamma motor nerve endings in mammalian muscle spindles, *gamma-plates* ('en plaque' type of ending) and *gamma-trails* ('en grappe' type of ending). Gamma-plates are restricted to the polar ends of both types of intrafusal fibre. Those on nuclear chain fibres are larger with unbranched subneural folds, while those on nuclear-bag fibres are small and usually lack subneural folds. Gamma-trail endings are restricted to juxta-equatorial regions of both fibre types. No apparent morphological differences between endings on the two different fibre types have been observed, and they both lack subneural folds. This micrograph shows a typical *gamma-trail ending* (Nt) enveloped by a Schwann cell (Sw) in contact with the intrafusal fibre (If). Ac, accompanying axon.

Gamma-trail motor nerve ending in a mammalian muscle spindle: rat sternothyroid muscle. OsO_4–glutaraldehyde–OsO_4 fixation. ×27 000.

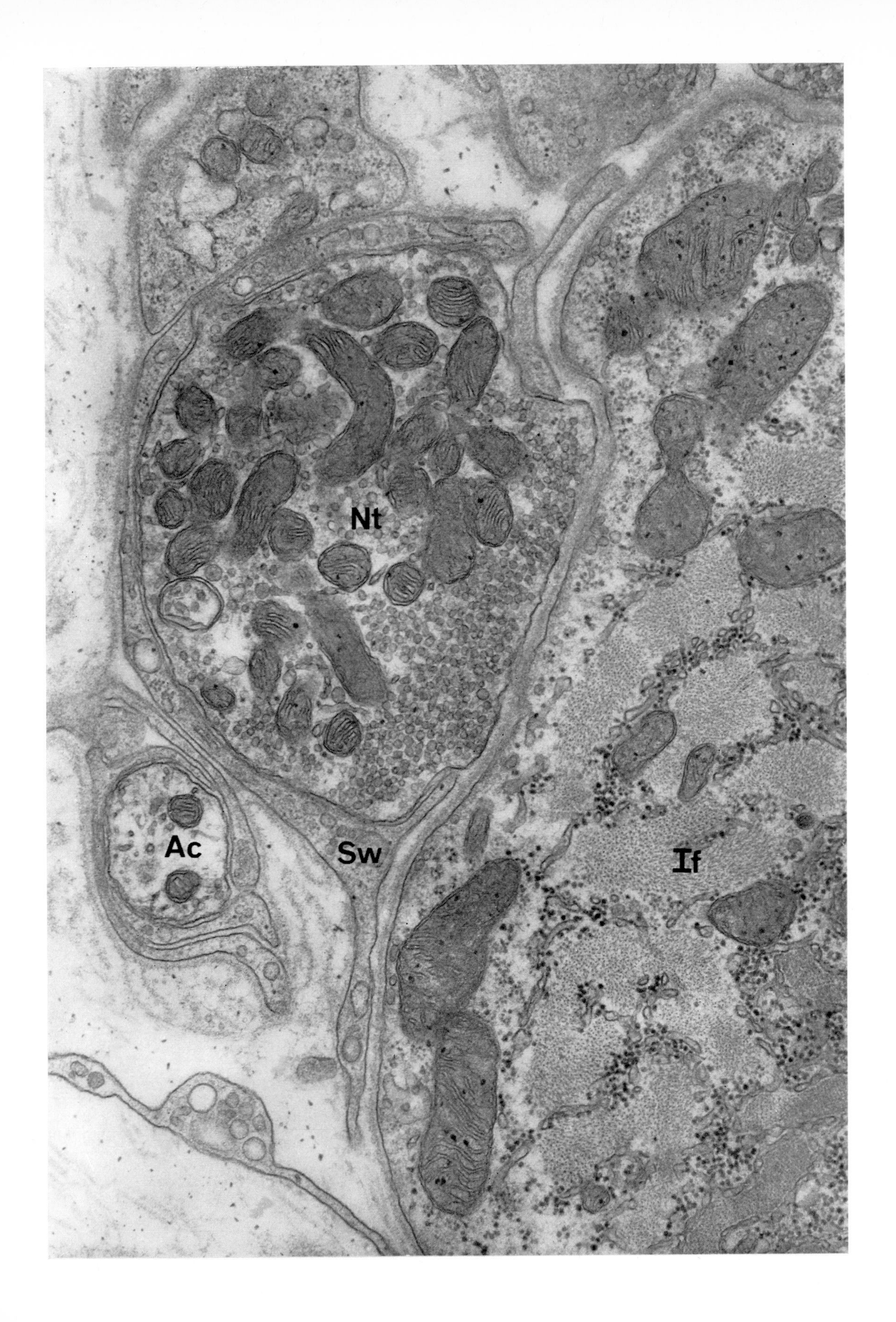
Nt
Ac
Sw
If

Plate 157

In contrast to mammalian muscle spindles, no separate fusimotor system has been shown to occur in lower vertebrates such as amphibians and reptiles. Instead, there is a common motor supply to both intrafusal and the neighbouring extrafusal fibres. In these animals, two kinds of muscle spindles have been reported to occur which contain intrafusal fibres with properties in common with the extrafusal muscle type. Thus, fast twitch muscles usually contain muscle spindles containing fast twitch type intrafusal fibres, while slow tonic muscles contain slow tonic type intrafusal fibres. As shown in the accompanying micrograph, the intrafusal muscle fibre (If) found in the slow tonic lizard iliofemoral muscle is innervated by an 'en grappe' type of ending (Ax). This has an essentially similar structure to the extrafusal 'en grappe' ending (see Plate 132). Sw, Schwann cell. 'En plaque' type of endings have been demonstrated in frog muscle spindles and these exhibit well developed subneural folds.

Motor nerve ending in a reptilian muscle spindle: lizard ilio-femoralis. OsO_4 fixation. ×75 000.

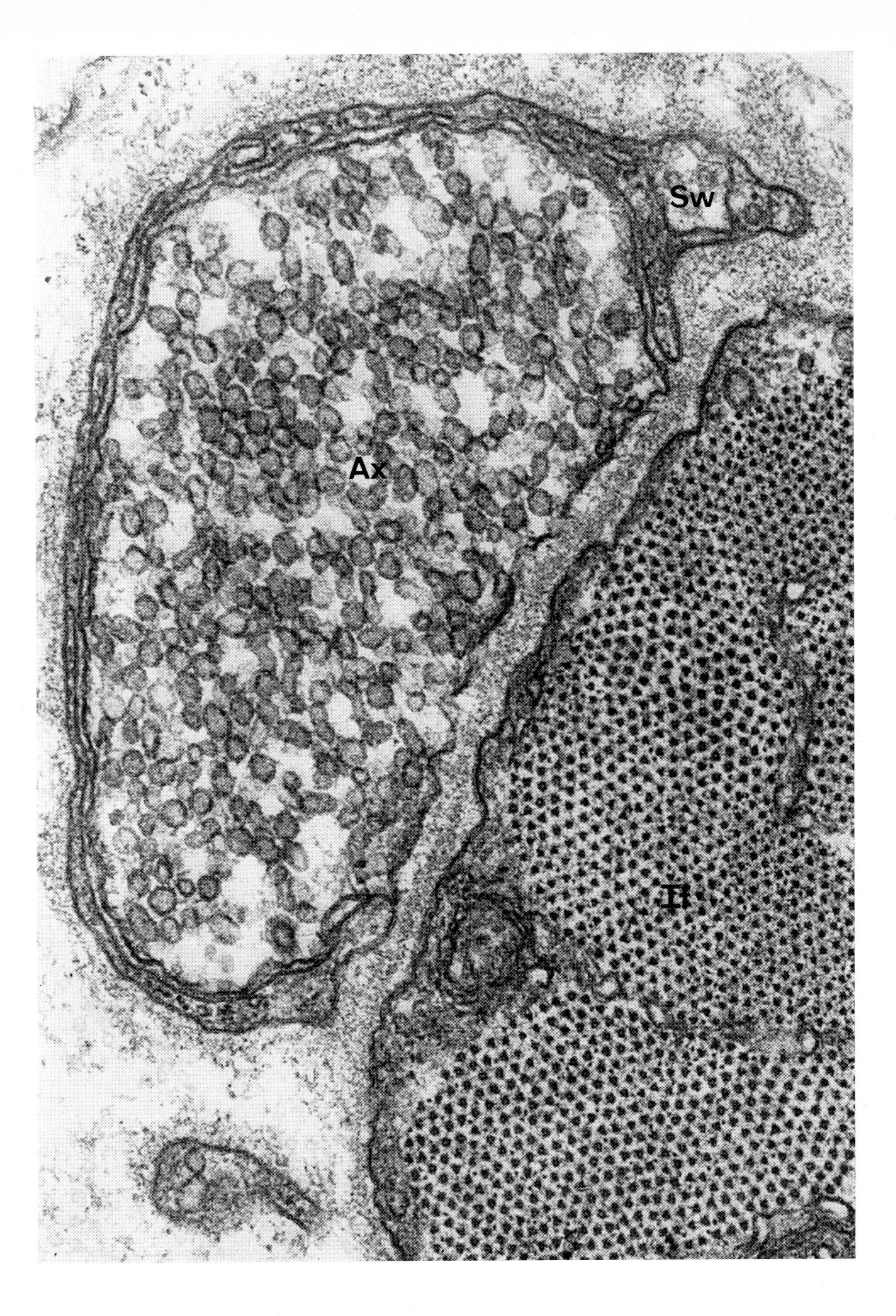
Sw
Ax
It

Plate 158

Developing rat muscle spindles are detectable as early as 16 days in utero. During prenatal development, the intrafusal fibres are closely associated to form a compact bundle. With further maturation, each intrafusal fibre gradually separates, but close association or the pairing of adjacent fibres is frequently encountered, even in adult spindles. The capsule (Co) of prenatal spindles consists of several attenuated layers of cells. However, unlike adult capsule cells, they are not invested by a basal lamina and contain a large amount of free ribosomes and rough endoplasmic reticulum. The spindle space is narrow and the capsule does not show equatorial expansion at this stage. In the developing muscle spindle illustrated, intrafusal fibres (If) can be easily distinguished from extrafusal fibres (Ex). Two types of intrafusal fibres are often recognizable: large fibres containing highly lobulated nuclei (the future nuclear-bag fibre), and small fibres containing nuclei with smooth contours (the future nuclear-chain fibres). Sensory endings (Se) are closely associated with the muscle surface, but do not exhibit regular annulospiral form. Sensory nerve fibres during prenatal life are mostly unmyelinated (Ns).

Developing muscle spindle in mammalian muscle: 20-day foetal rat sternothyroid muscle. Transverse section. OsO_4–glutaraldehyde–OsO_4 fixation. × 10 400.

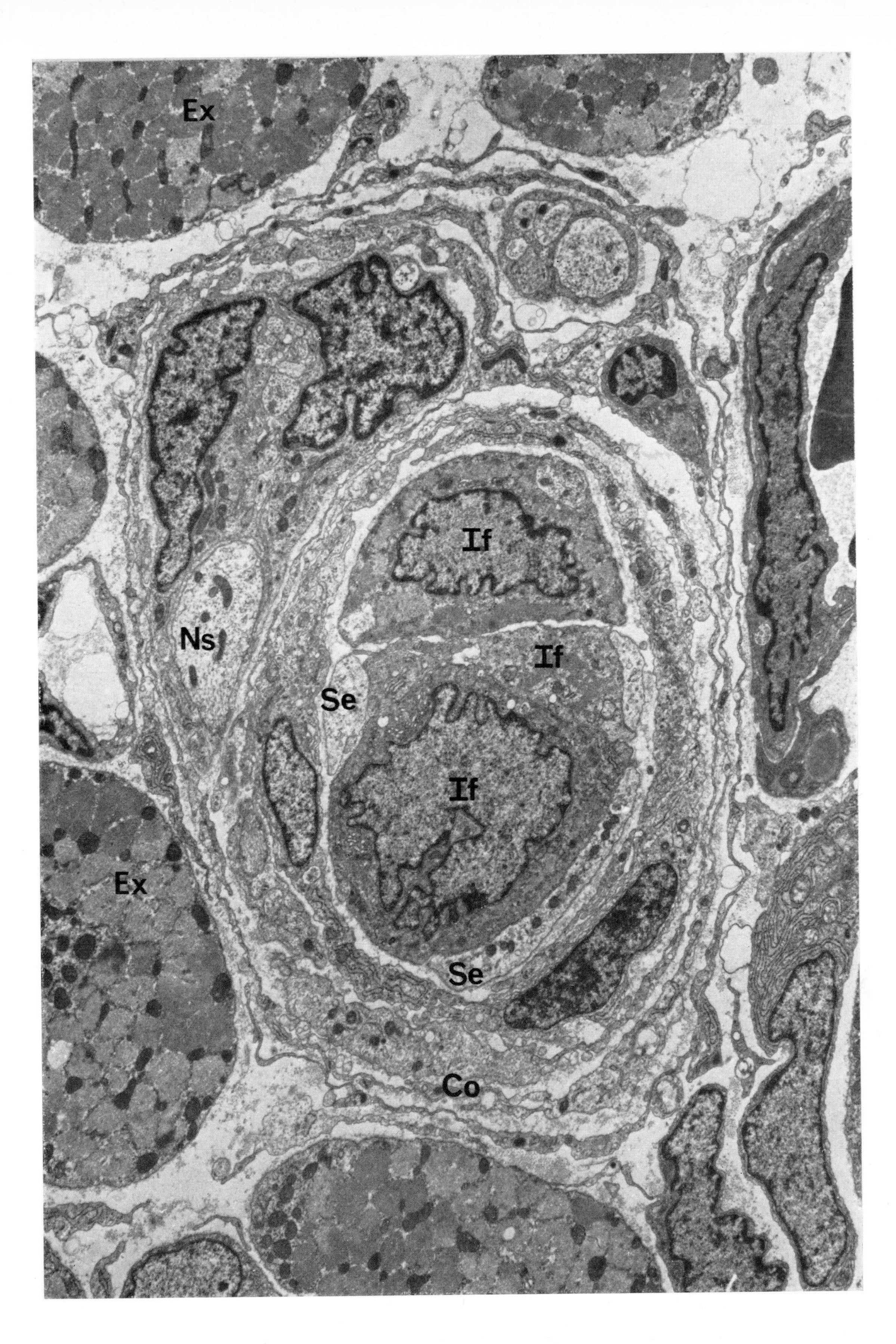
Ex
If
Ns
If
Se
If
Ex
Se
Co

Plate 159

Differentiation of the two types of intrafusal fibre has been widely studied. Light microscope studies have suggested that during prenatal life a parent fibre of each type divides by longitudinal splitting to produce daughter fibres, until the full complement of adult intrafusal fibres is attained. However, four intrafusal fibres (the complement of the adult rat muscle spindle) are already detectable in the foetal rat at 16 days. Sometimes only three fibres are seen in sections because the small nuclear-chain fibres are shorter and terminate within the capsule. The highly lobulated nuclei of the larger fibres indicate that these are the prototype of the nuclear-bag fibres. In addition to variations in the form of their nuclei as well as fibre diameter and length, the two types of intrafusal fibres also differ in their rate of maturation.

As shown in the accompanying micrograph of a 20-day-old foetal rat muscle spindle, the nuclear-chain fibre (Cf) contains only a few randomly distributed myofilaments at the periphery of the cell and has a larger amount of free ribosomes and rough endoplasmic reticulum than the nuclear-bag fibres (Bf), indicating that chain fibres are less mature in their organization than the bag fibres at this stage.

Developing muscle spindle in mammalian muscle: sternothyroid muscle from 20-day foetal rat. Glutaraldehyde fixation. ×42 000.

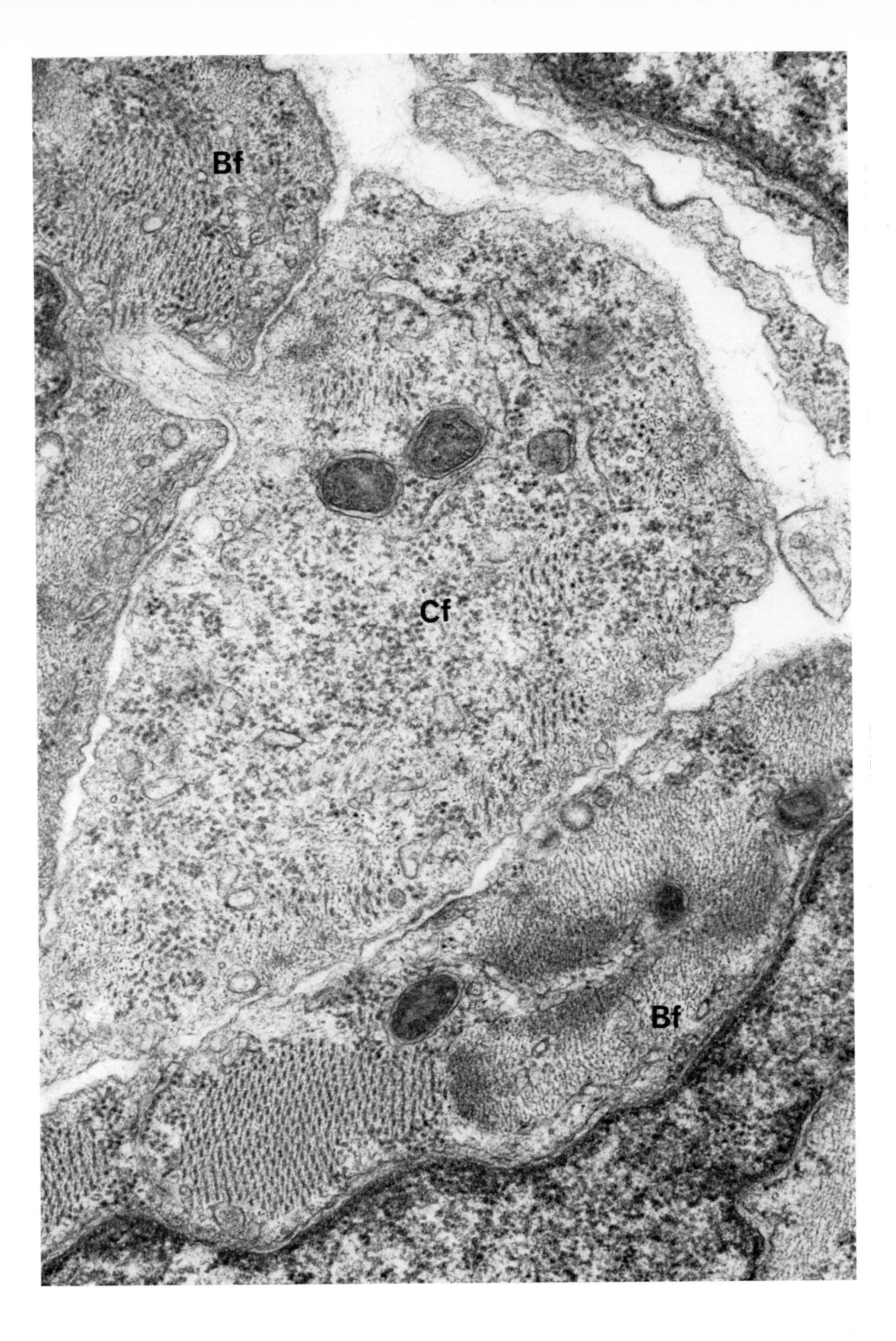
Bf
Cf
Bf

Plate 160

The first contacts of nerve and muscle in spindle development are sensory in nature and arise from the primary axons. Thus the first intrafusal fibre (nuclear-bag fibre) appears to develop when only sensory innervation is present, the second nuclear-bag fibre developing later when some motor terminals are present. The nuclear-chain fibres develop later. It has been suggested that the sensory nerves may play some role in the differentiation of different fibre types. Large granular vesicles (arrows), 100–150 nm in diameter, are present in the developing sensory nerve endings (Se). Comparable large granular vesicles have been observed in both developing and regenerating axons where they have been suggested to be storage sites for trophic substances.

Sensory endings in developing mammalian intrafusal fibres: sternothyroid muscle from 20-day foetal rat. Transverse section. Glutaraldehyde fixation. ×28 000.

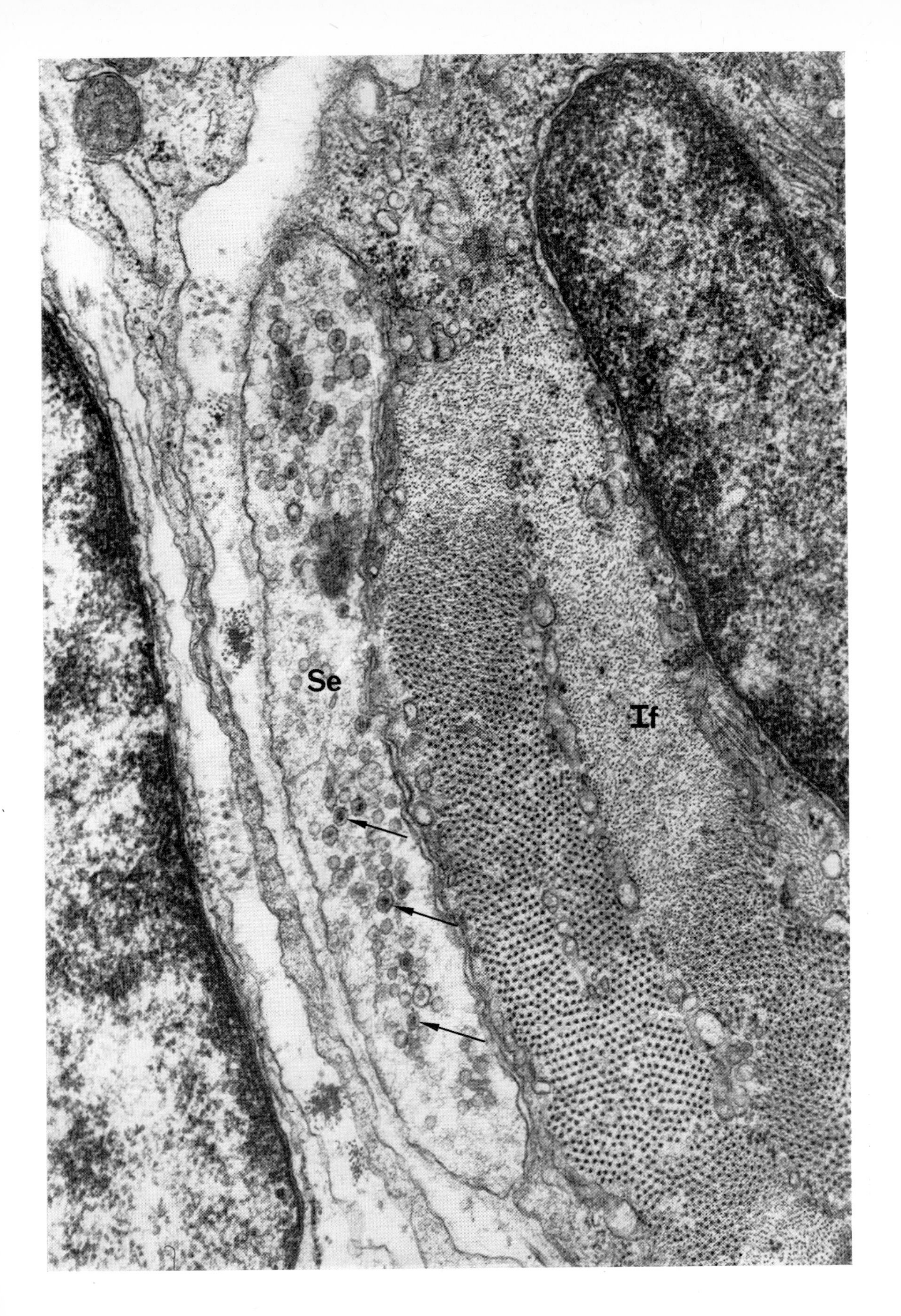
Se
If

Plate 161

Golgi tendon organs are the encapsulated sensory nerve endings found at the muscle–tendon boundary of skeletal muscle. In transverse section the capsule appears very similar to that of the muscle spindle and is composed of cytoplasmic processes in a lamella form. The lumen of the tendon organ is divided into compartments by thin cytoplasmic processes of septal cells (Sp). The septal cells resemble fibroblasts and lack a basal lamina. Within the (septal) compartments there are bundles of collagen (Cb) with characteristically variable diameter and sensory nerve terminals (Se). The nerve terminals, which are free of Schwann cell investment in regions opposing bundles of collagen, contain numerous mitochondria and a few granular and agranular vesicles.

Golgi tendon organ in avian muscle: finch biceps brachii. Transverse section. Glutaraldehyde fixation. ×33 000.

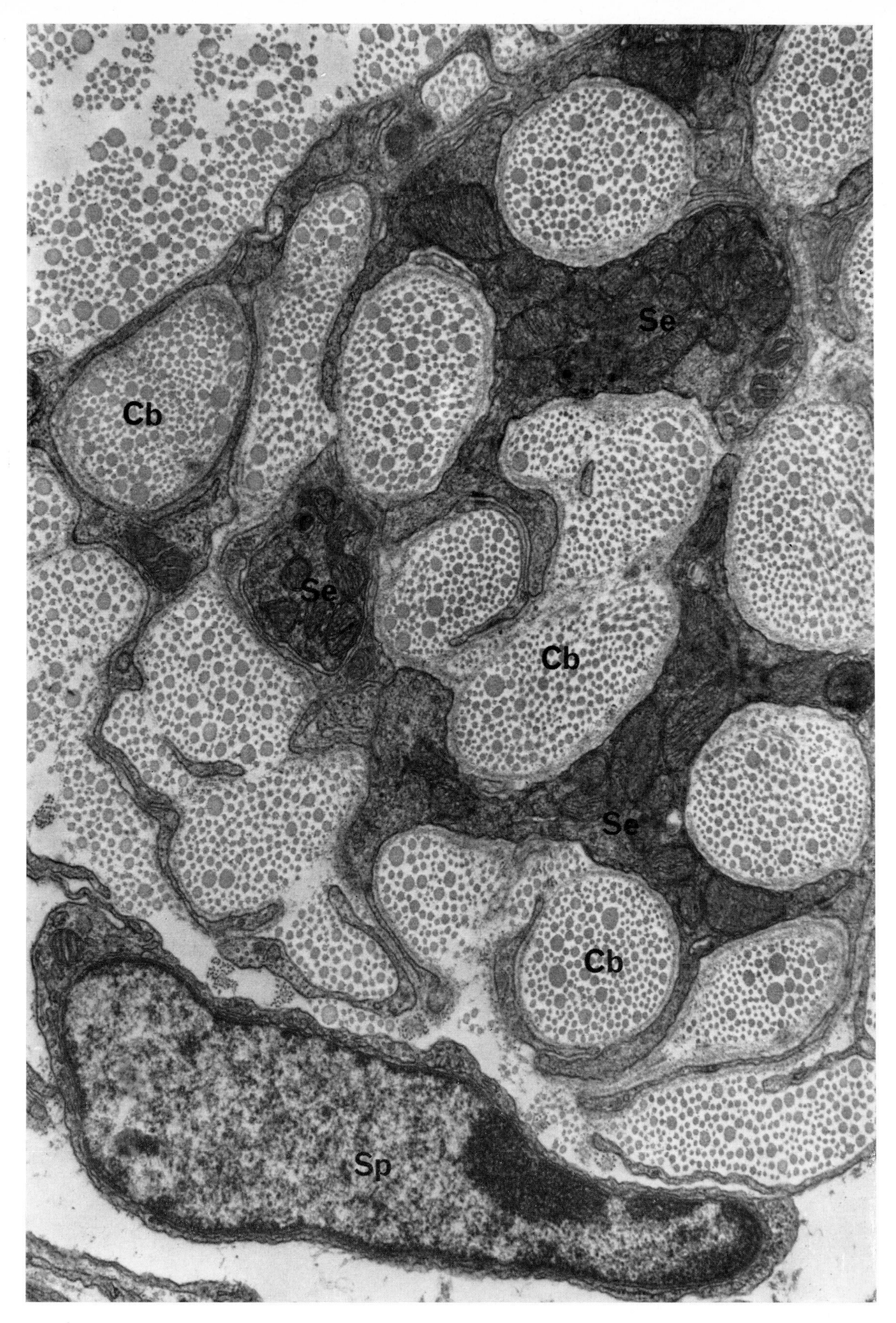
Se
Cb
Se
Cb
Se
Cb
Sp

Selected reviews

BANKER, B. Q., R. J. PRZYBYLSKI, J. P. VAN DER MEULON and M. VICTOR (eds.). 1972. *Research in Muscle Development and the Muscle Spindle.* ICS 240, Excerpta Medica, Amsterdam.

HARRISON, V. F. 1961. A review of sensory receptors in skeletal muscles with special emphasis on the muscle spindle. *Phys. Ther. Rev.*, **41,** 25–29.

LANDON, D. N. 1966. Electron microscopy of muscle spindles. In *Control and Innervation of Skeletal Muscle.* B. L. Andrew (ed.). Thomson, Dundee. 96–111.

MERRILLEES, N. C. R. 1961. Some observations of the fine structure of a Golgi tendon organ of a rat. In *Symposium on Muscle Receptors.* D. Barker (ed.). *Proc. Golden Jubilee Congr.* Hong Kong University Press, Hong Kong. 199–206.

Selected articles

ADAL, M. N. 1969. The fine structure of the sensory region of cat muscle spindles. *J. Ultrastruct. Res.*, **26,** 332–354.

ADAL, M. N. 1973. The fine structure of the intrafusal muscle fibres of muscle spindles in the domestic fowl. *J. Anat.*, **115,** 407–414.

ANDERSSON-CEDERGREN, E. and U. KARLSSON. 1966. Demyelination regions of nerve fibers in frog muscle spindle as studied by serial sections for electron microscopy. *J. Ultrastruct. Res.*, **14,** 212–239.

BANKER, B. Q. and J. P. GIRVIN. 1971. The ultrastructural features of the mammalian muscle spindle. *J. Neuropath. exp. Neurol.*, **30,** 155–195.

BANKS, R. W. and N. T. JAMES. 1973. The blood supply of rabbit muscle spindles. *J. Anat.*, **114,** 7–12.

BARNICOT, N. A. 1966. A note on the structure of spindle fibres. *J. Cell Sci.*, **1,** 217–222.

BRIDGMAN, C. F. 1968. The structure of tendon organs in the cat: A proposed mechanism for responding to muscle tension. *Anat. Rec.*, **162,** 209–220.

CORVAJA, N., V. MARINOZZI and O. POMPEIANO. 1969. Muscle spindles in the lumbrical muscle of the adult cat. Electron microscopic observations and functional considerations. *Archo ital. Biol.*, **107,** 365–543.

CORVAJA, N. and O. POMPEIANO. 1970. The differentiation of two types of intrafusal fibres in rabbit muscle spindles. An electron microscopic study. *Pflügers Arch. ges. Physiol.*, **317,** 187–197.

CROWE, A. and A. H. M. F. RAGAB. 1970. Studies on the fine structure of the capsular region of tortoise muscle spindles. *J. Anat.*, **107,** 257–270.

HESS, A. 1961. Two kinds of motor nerve endings on mammalian intrafusal muscle fibers revealed by the cholinesterase technique. *Anat. Rec.*, **139,** 173–184.

JAMES, N. T. and G. A. MEEK. 1973. An electron microscopical study of avian muscle spindles. *J. Ultrastruct. Res.*, **43,** 193–204.

JONES, E. G. 1966. The innervation of muscle spindles in the Australian opossum, *Trichosurus vulpecula,*with special reference to the motor nerve endings. *J. Anat.*, **100,** 733–760.

KARLSSON, U. and E. ANDERSSON-CEDERGREN. 1966. Motor myoneural junctions on frog intrafusal muscle fiber. *J. Ultrastruct. Res.*, **14,** 191–211.

KARLSSON, U., E. ANDERSSON-CEDERGREN and D. OTTOSON. 1966. Cellular organization of the frog muscle spindle as revealed by serial sections for electron microscopy. *J. Ultrastruct. Res.*, **14,** 1–35.

KARLSSON, U. L., W. H. HOOKER and E. G. BENDEICH. 1971. Quantitative changes in the frog muscle spindle in the passive stretch. *J. Ultrastruct. Res.*, **36,** 743–756.

KENNEDY, W. R., H. D. WEBSTER, K. S. YOON and D. H. JEAN. 1974. Human muscle spindles: Microfilaments in the group 1A sensory nerve endings. *Anat, Rec.*, **180,** 521–532.

LANDON, D. N. 1972. The fine structure of the equatorial regions of developing muscle spindles in the rat. *J. Neurocytol.*, **1,** 189–210.

MAIER, A. and E. ELDRED. 1971. Comparisons in the structure of avian muscle spindles. *J. comp. Neurol.*, **143,** 25–39.

MARCHAND, R., C. F. BRIDGMAN, E. SHUMPERT and E. ELDRED. 1971. Association of tendon organs with spindles in muscles of cat's leg. *Anat. Rec.*, **169,** 23–32.

MERRILLEES, N. C. R. 1960. The fine structure of muscle spindles in the lumbrical muscles of the rat. *J. biophys. biochem. Cytol.*, **7,** 725–742.

MILBURN, A. 1973. The early development of muscle spindles in the rat. *J. Cell Sci.*, **12,** 175–196.

OVALLE, W. K., JR. 1971. Fine structure of rat intrafusal muscle fibers. The polar region. *J. Cell Biol.*, **51,** 83–103.

OVALLE, W. K., JR. 1972*a*. Motor nerve terminals on rat intrafusal muscle fibres, a correlated light and electron microscope study. *J. Anat.*, **111,** 239–252.

OVALLE, W. K., JR. 1972*b*. Fine structure of rat intrafusal muscle fibres. The equatorial region. *J. Cell Biol.*, **52,** 382–396.

PALLOT, D. J. 1974. The structure and motor innervation of intrafusal fibres in snakes of *Natrix* sp. *J. Anat.*, **118,** 281–294.

PALLOT, D. J. and R. M. A. P. RIDGE. 1972. The fine structure of the long-capsule muscle spindles in the snake *Natrix* sp. *J. Anat.*, **113,** 61–74.

PALLOT, D. J. and R. M. A. P. RIDGE. 1973. The fine structure of the short capsule muscle spindles in snakes of *Natrix* sp. *J. Anat.*, **114,** 13–24.

RUMPELT, H.-J. and H. SCHMALBRUCH. 1969. Zum Verständris der Morphologie von Muskelspindeln bei Mensch und Ratte. *Verh. anat. Ges. Jena*, **126,** 405–410.

SCALZI, H. A. and H. M. PRICE. 1971. The arrangement and sensory innervation of the intrafusal fibers in the feline muscle spindle. *J. Ultrastruct. Res.*, **36,** 375–390.

SCHOULTZ, T. W. and J. E. SWETT. 1972. The fine structure of the Golgi tendon organ. *J. Neurocytol.*, **1,** 1–26.

STUART, D. G., C. G. MOSHER, R. L. GERLACH and R. M. REINKING. 1972. Mechanical arrangement and transducing properties of Golgi tendon organs. *Exp Brain Res.*, **14,** 274–292.

UEHARA, Y. 1969. A comparative microanatomy of the sensory terminals of the muscle spindle, as revealed by electron microscopy. *Osaka med. J.*, **21,** 21–30.

UEHARA, Y. 1973. Unique sensory endings in rat muscle spindles. *Z. Zellforsch. mikrosk. Anat.*, **136,** 511–520.

UEHARA, Y. and K. HAMA. 1965. Some observations on the fine structure of the frog muscle spindle. (1). On the sensory terminals and motor endings of the muscle spindle. *J. Electron Microsc.*, **14,** 34–42.

ZELENÁ, J. and T. SOUKUP. 1974. The differentiation of intrafusal fibre types in rat muscle spindles after motor denervation. *Cell & Tissue Res.*, **153,** 115–136.

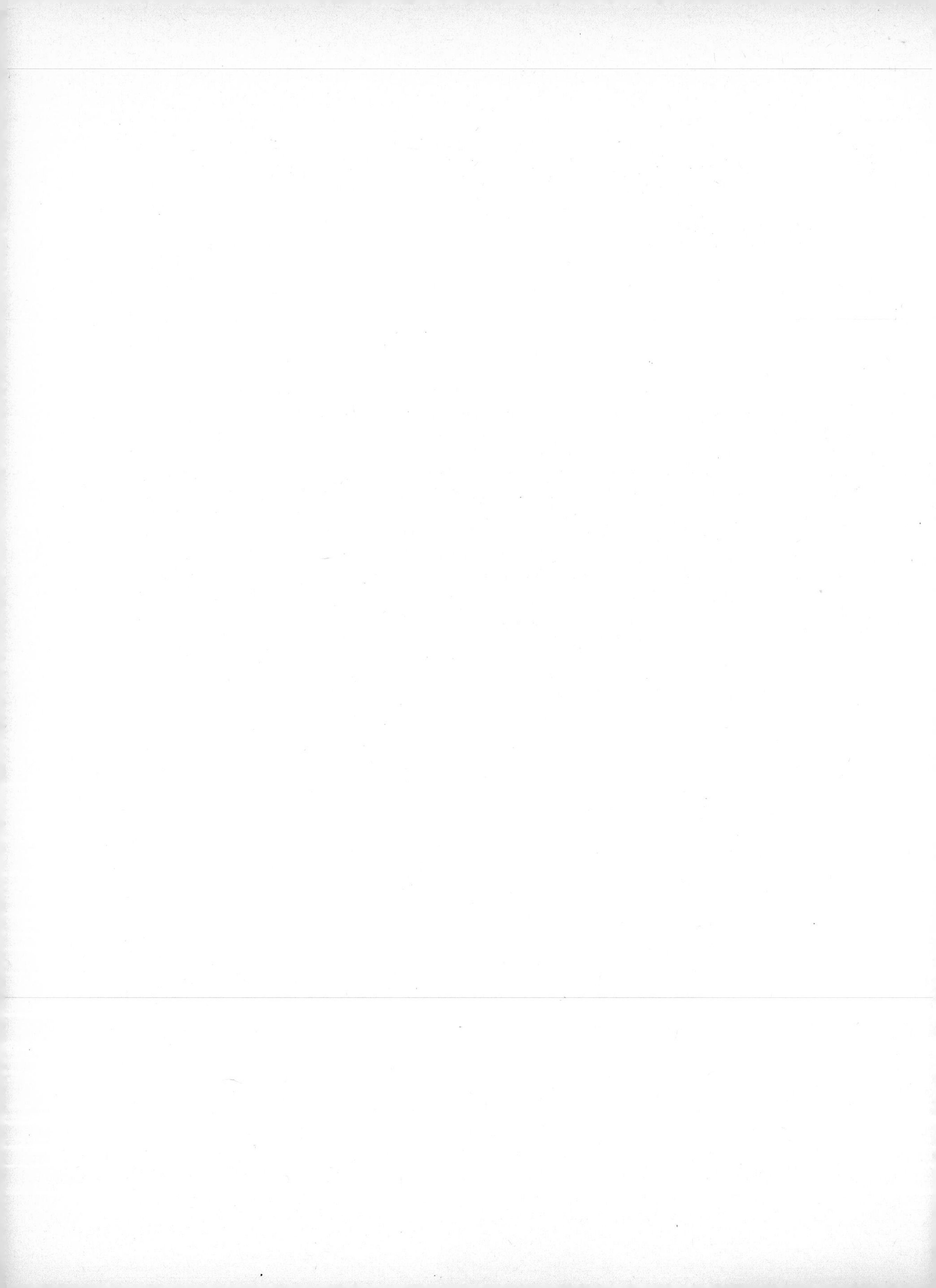

8 Vascularization of Muscle

Oxygen and nutrient substances such as glucose are vitally important for muscle contraction, so muscles usually have a rich blood supply.

Vertebrate striated muscle is particularly well vascularized. Arteries are carried in the perimysium into the muscle (see Fig. 1, p. 4). Here they branch to form the capillaries of the endomysium. Capillaries in white muscle form elongated loops parallel to the muscle fibres and have transverse branches which encircle individual fibres. Red muscles have a more extensive blood supply than white muscles, with a greater number of capillaries per muscle fibre. These capillaries run in a similar manner to those of white muscle but the branches are often dilated. Metabolites are removed from the muscle by postcapillary venules. Fewer capillaries are found in smooth muscles probably because the cells contract at a slower rate. Nutrition of smooth muscle is dependent to a considerable extent on diffusion of substances throughout the intercellular space.

Vertebrate muscle blood vessels have a sensory and a motor innervation. The motor innervation is of a dual type: a vasoconstrictor component consisting of adrenergic nerves, and a vasodilator component which includes some cholinergic nerves. All nerves to blood vessels in muscle terminate on the surface of the media and only occasionally can be found in between the vascular smooth muscle cells.

In some invertebrates, capillary beds are also present in muscles (closed circulatory system), but in others such as arthropods, a tracheal system brings oxygen directly to the muscles via a series of cuticle-lined channels continuous with the surface of the body (open circulatory system).

Plate 162

Capillaries of mammalian striated muscle consist of the endothelium (inner layer) which encloses the lumen (l), and the basal lamina (30–50 nm thick) which invests the outer part of the endothelium. One of the most characteristic features of the capillary endothelial cells (En) is the presence of plasmalemmal vesicles, which have been shown to be involved in the uptake and passage of materials across the cell. Some large particles appear to pass through the intercellular cleft between adjacent endothelial cells. Pericytes, which resemble vascular smooth muscle in many ways, are sometimes found in association with capillaries.

Capillary in vertebrate skeletal muscle: rat rectus femoris. Transverse section. Glutaraldehyde fixation. ×35 000.

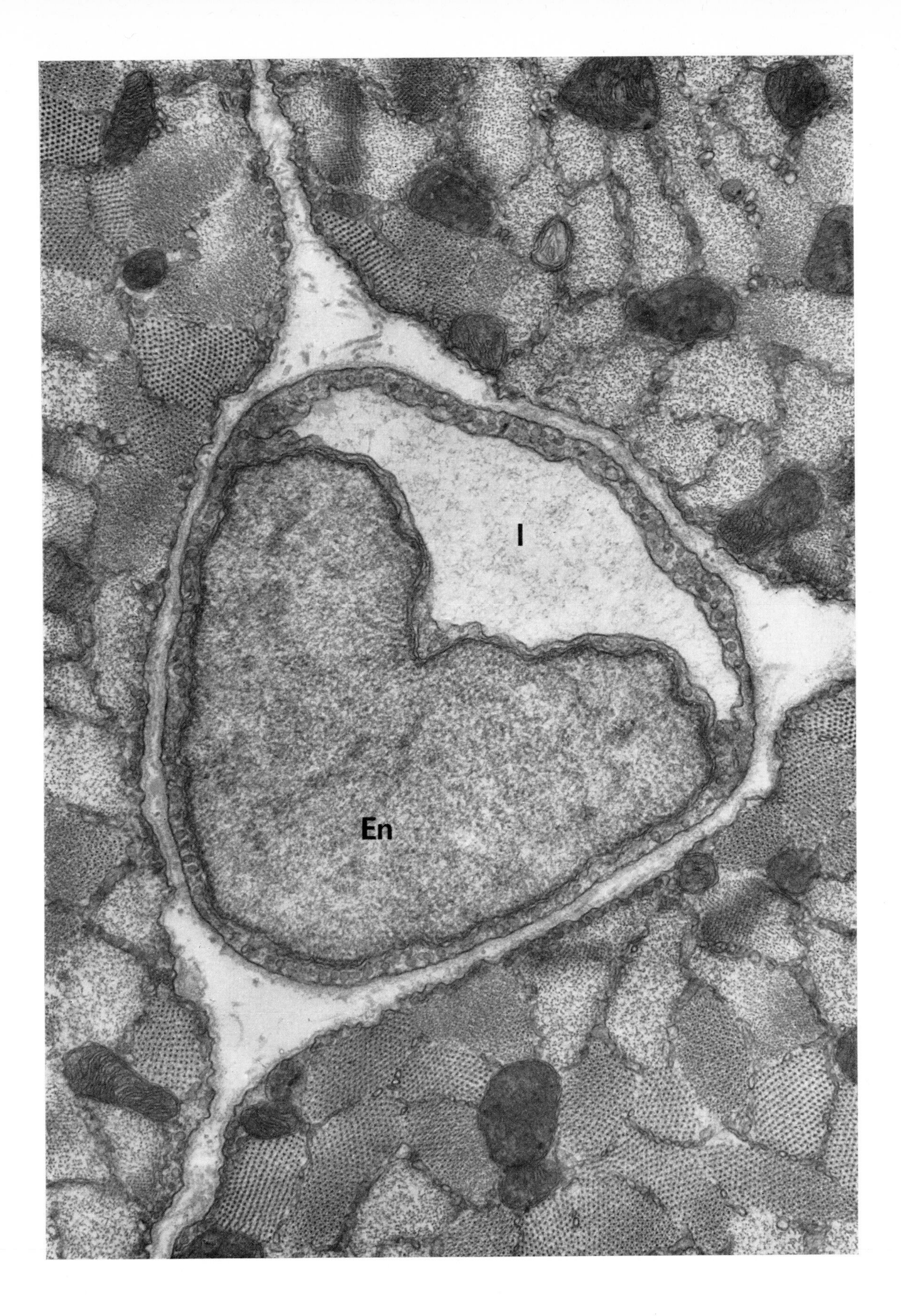
I
En

Plate 163

The earthworm circulatory system is a closed system with an extensive capillary bed. The blood pigment (B) is erythrocruorin or haemoglobin, heavy molecule iron compounds which are in solution in the plasma. Earthworm blood vessels have a basal lamina on the inside of the lumen, the presence of which has been suggested to be related to the size of the blood pigment (see also Plates 9 and 10). That is to say, it may act as a barrier to the passage of the blood pigment out of the vessels. En, endothelial cell.

Capillary in an invertebrate obliquely striated muscle: earthworm body wall. Transverse section. Glutaraldehyde fixation. ×41 500.

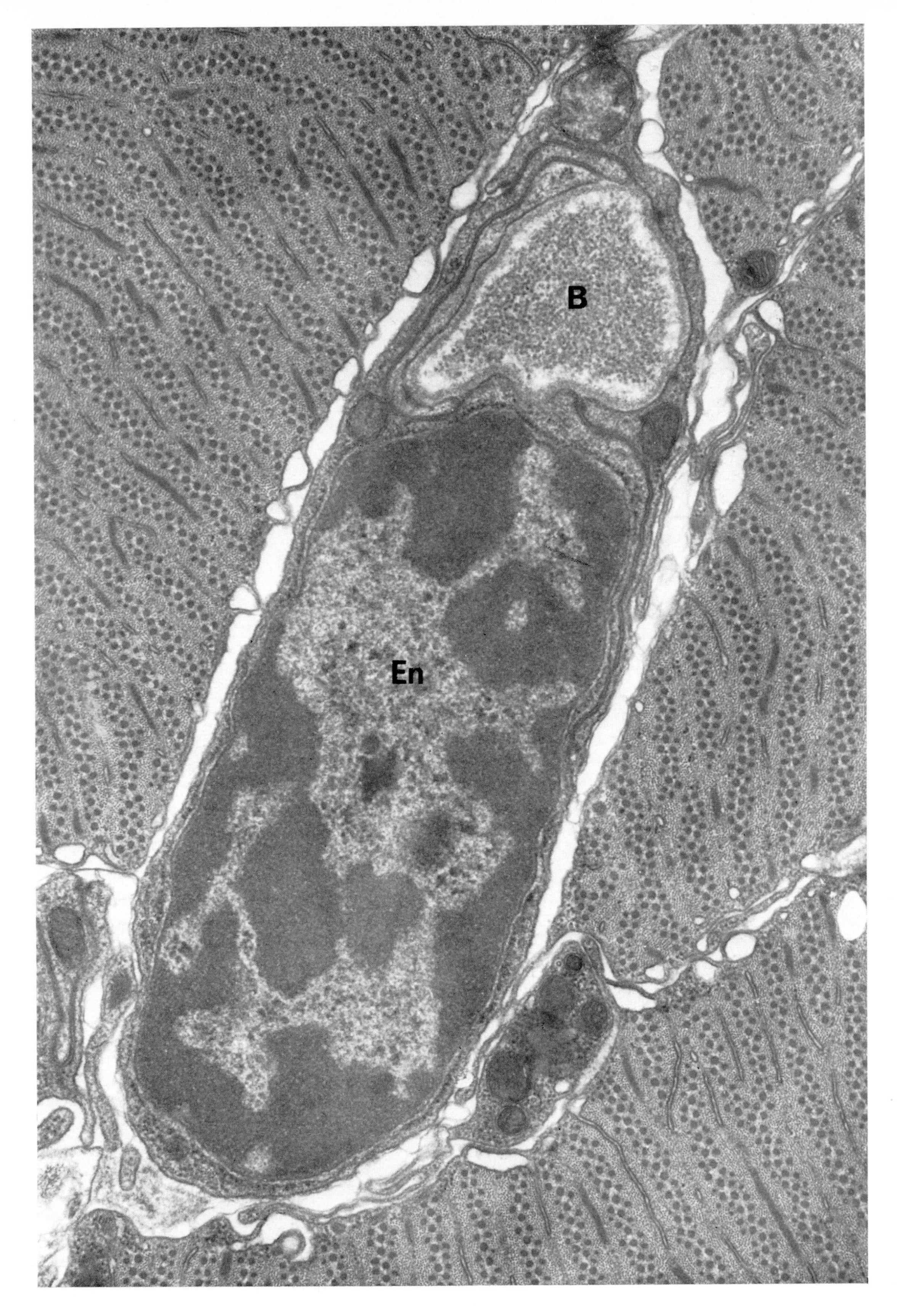
B
En

Plate 164

In the great majority of arthropods, no respiratory pigment is present and oxygen is brought directly to the tissues through a series of open channels, the *trachea* and *tracheoles*. As the tracheal system is an inward extension of the body surface, it is lined with cuticle and surrounded by an epithelium continuous with the surface epidermis. The cuticle lining the trachea is spirally orientated, giving these channels the irregular appearance seen in longitudinal section.

Tracheole in an invertebrate striated muscle: spider leg. Longitudinal section. Glutaraldehyde fixation. ×53 000.

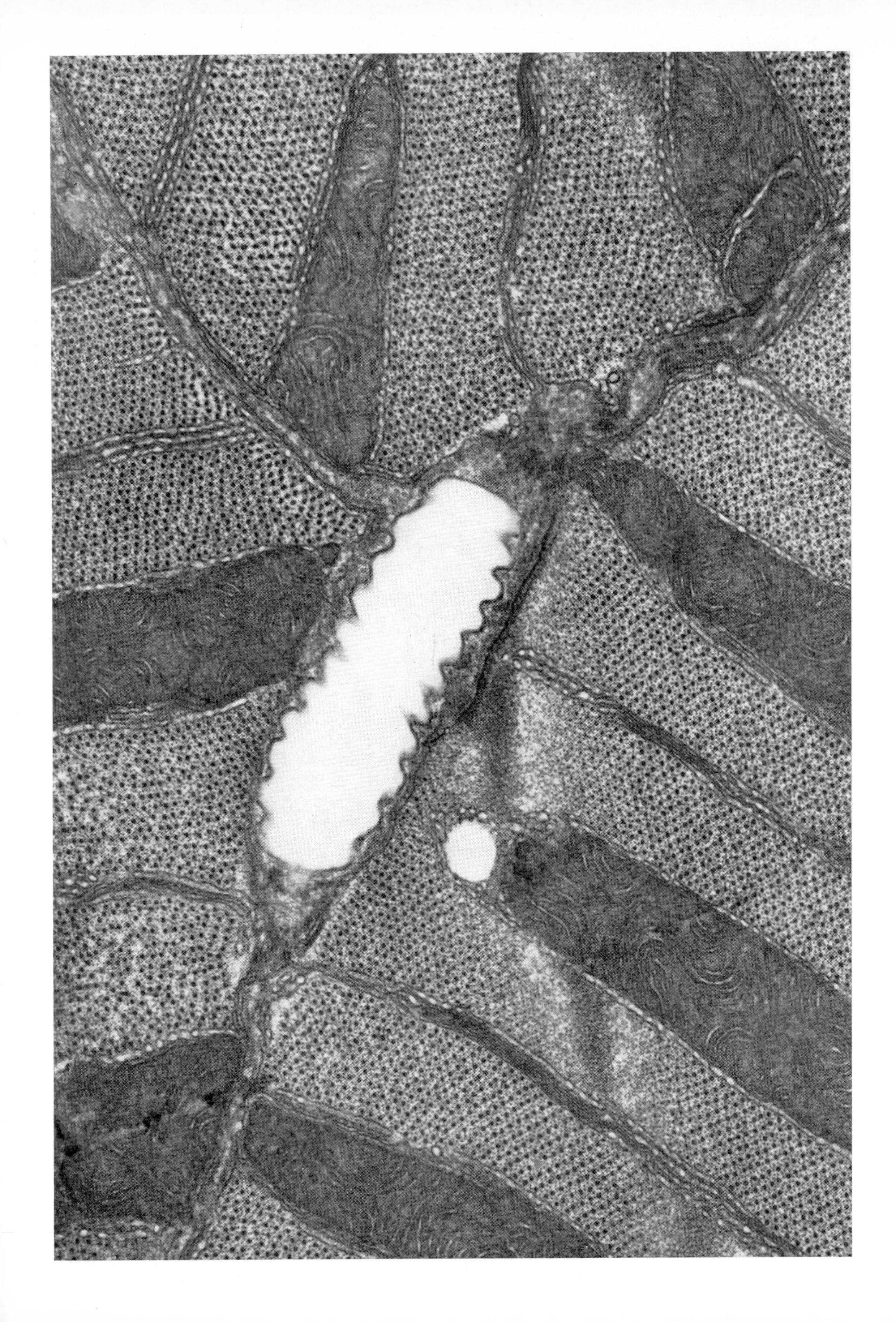

Selected articles

ANGELAKOS, E. T., P. BERNARDINI and W. C. BARRETT, JR. 1964. Myocardial fiber size and capillary-fiber ratio in the right and left ventricles of the rat. *Anat. Rec.*, **149,** 671–676.

BRUNS, R. R. and G. E. PALADE. 1968*a*. Studies on blood capillaries. I. General organization of blood capillaries in muscle. *J. Cell Biol.*, **37,** 244–276.

BRUNS, R. R. and G. E. PALADE. 1968*b*. Studies on blood capillaries. II. Transport of ferritin molecules across the wall of muscle capillaries. *J. Cell Biol.*, **37,** 277–299.

CARDON, S. Z. 1970. Effect of oxygen on cyclic red blood cell flow in unanesthetized mammalian striated muscle as determined by microscopy. *Microvasc. Res.*, **2,** 67.

CARROW, R. E., R. E. BROWN and W. D. VAN HUSS. 1967. Fiber sizes and capillary to fiber ratios in skeletal muscle of exercised rats. *Anat. Rec.*, **159,** 33–40.

GRANT, R. T. 1964. Direct observation of skeletal muscle blood vessels (rat cremaster). *J. Physiol., Lond.*, **172,** 123.

GRANT, R. T. and H. P. WRIGHT. 1968. Further observations of the blood vessels of skeletal muscle (rat cremaster). *J. Anat.*, **103,** 553–566.

HAMMERSEN, F. 1965. Zum Feinbau der Muskelkapillaren in abgeschnürten Extremitäten der Ratte. *Verh. anat. Ges., Jena.*, **60,** 367–375.

HUDLICKA, O. 1973. *Muscle blood flow. Its relation to muscle metabolism and function.* Swets and Zeitlinger B. V., Amsterdam.

LUFT, J. H. 1973. Capillary permeability. I. Structural considerations. In *The Inflammatory Process*, 2nd edn., Vol. 2. B. W. Zweifach, L. Grant, and R. T. McCluskey (eds.). Academic Press, New York. 47–93.

MAI, J., V. R. EDGERTON and R. J. BARNARD. 1970. Capillarity of red, white and intermediate fibers in trained and untrained guinea-pigs. *Experientia*, **26,** 1222–1223.

MAJNO, G., V. GILMORE and M. LEVENTHAL. 1967. A technique for the microscopic study of blood vessels in living striated muscle (cremaster). *Circulation Res.*, **21,** 823–832.

MANASEK, F. J. 1971. The ultrastructure of embryonic myocardial blood vessels. *Devl Biol.*, **26,** 42–54.

MATTER, A., L. ORCI and CH. ROUILLER. 1969 Die dreidimensionale Rekonstruktion des Kapillarperizyten im Muskel. *Verh. anat. Ges.-Jena.*, **63,** 125–130.

MELLANDER, S. 1964. Cirkulationen i skelettmuskulature. *Nord. Med.*, **72,** 1311–1316.

NICKEL, E. and E. GRIESHABER. 1969. Elektronenmikroskopische Darstellung der Muskelkapillaren im Gefrierätzbild. *Z. Zellforsch. mikrosk. Anat.*, **95,** 445–461.

RAKUSAN, K. and M. DU MESNIL DE ROCHEMONT. 1967. Capillaries in heart and skeletal muscle of dog and rabbit. *Proc. Soc. exp. Biol. Med.*, **124,** 838–840.

ROMANUL, F. C. A. 1965. Capillary supply and metabolism of muscle fibers. *Archs. Neurol.*, **12,** 497–509.

SHEA, S. M., J. B. CAULFIELD and J. F. BURKE. 1973. Microvascular ultrastructure in thermal injury: A reconsideration of the role of mediators. *Microvasc. Res.*, **5,** 87–96.

SHIRAHAMA, T. and A. S. COHEN. 1972. The role of mucopolysaccharides in vesicle architecture and endothelial transport. An electron microscope study of myocardial blood vessels. *J. Cell Biol.*, **52,** 198.

SMAJE, L., B. W. ZWEIFACH and M. INTAGLIETTA. 1970. Micropressures and capillary filtration coefficients in single vessels of the cremaster muscle of the rat. *Microvasc. Res.*, **2,** 96.

TOMANEK, R. J. 1970. Effects of age and exercise on the extent of the myocardial capillary bed. *Anat. Rec.*, **167,** 55–62.

VRACKO, R. 1970*a*. Skeletal muscle capillaries in diabetics: A quantitative analysis. *Circulation*, **41,** 271–283.

VRACKO, R. 1970*b*. Skeletal muscle capillaries in nondiabetics: A quantitative analysis. *Circulation.*, **41,** 285–297.

WELT, K., W. SCHELLER, G. SCHIPPEL and K. SCHIPPEL. 1972. Zur Ultrastruktur von Kapillaren im fetalen Skeletmuskel der

Weissen Ratte. *Z. mikrosk.-anat. Forsch.*, **86,** 531–552.

ZACKS, S. I., J. J. PEGUES and F. A. ELLIOTT. 1962. Interstitial muscle capillaries in patients with diabetes mellitus: A light and electron microscope study. *Metabolism*, **11,** 381–393.

ZWEIFACH, B. W. 1973. Microcirculation. *A. Rev. Physiol.*, **35,** 117–150.

9 Satellite Cells

The term satellite cell has been used to describe an undifferentiated mononuclear cell in skeletal muscle. It has been proposed that these cells may provide a reserve cellular pool for regeneration of damaged muscle. Support for this hypothesis is that certain muscles incapable of regeneration in the newt do not contain satellite cells. Further evidence for suggesting the role of satellite cells in regeneration is that they are metabolically active in very young animals but rapidly become inactive with age as regenerative activity is reduced. However, another possibility is that these cells may be myoblasts involved in metabolic interactions with muscle cells.

Occasional cytoplasmic continuity between satellite cells and muscle fibres has been demonstrated. It has been proposed that the satellite cells might contribute to the multinucleation of the skeletal fibres, the nucleus passing into the muscle cell via the cytoplasmic connection.

Regeneration of cardiac and smooth muscles, which do not have satellite cells, appears to be carried out by a different process, involving dedifferentiation, division and redifferentiation of existing muscle cells. Mammalian cardiac muscle has an extremely low capacity of regeneration and very few mitotic divisions of muscle cells have been observed. However, cardiac muscle cells of lower vertebrates are more capable of proliferation and subsequent regeneration. There is widespread opinion that damaged vertebrate smooth muscle is always replaced by fibrous scar tissue. This is not the case and smooth muscle, particularly in small wounds, can be reconstituted after injury. Smooth muscle cells adjacent to a small lesion dedifferentiate, then divide mitotically to produce a population of myoblasts. These invade the lesion and mature into smooth muscle cells thereby regenerating the tissue.

Plate 165

Satellite cells (S) are usually flattened against the side of a muscle fibre (Mu) in a shallow depression. They are usually separated by a gap of less than 20 nm and lie within the basal lamina of the muscle fibre. Satellite cells have little cytoplasm and, with the light microscope, their nuclei appear to belong to muscle fibres because the narrow cleft between the satellite cells and muscle fibre is beyond its resolution.

Relation between a satellite cell and vertebrate skeletal muscle fibre: rat rectus femoris. Transverse section. Glutaraldehyde fixation. ×34 300.

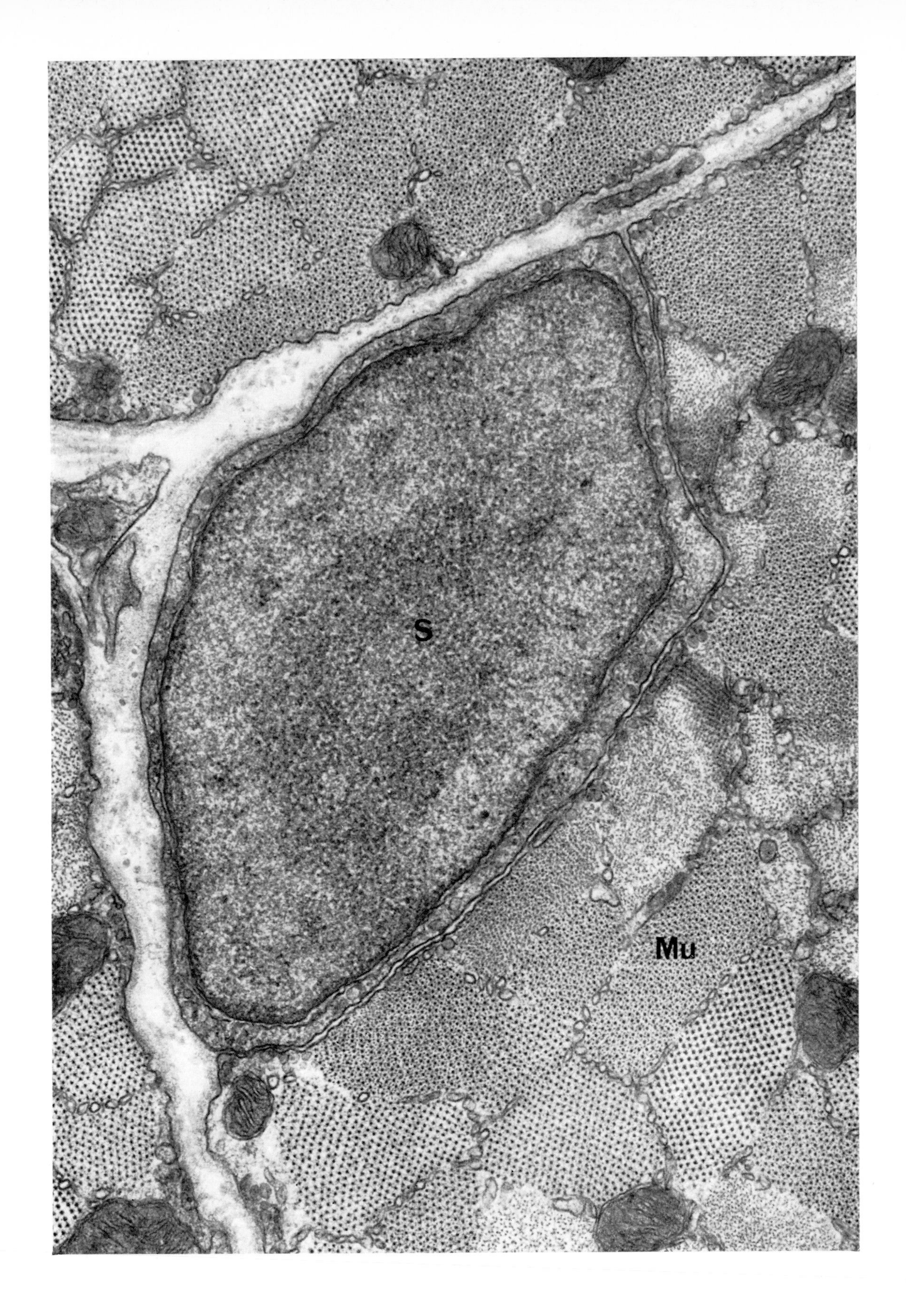
S
Mu

Plate 166

Satellite cells are more numerous in intrafusal than extrafusal muscle fibres. They are occasionally associated with sensory nerves and have been suggested to be related to Schwann cells. However, their distribution makes this seem unlikely and they may be equivalent to the satellite cells of extrafusal fibres. As shown in the accompanying micrograph satellite cells are often wedged between intrafusal fibres.

Relation between satellite cell and vertebrate muscle spindle: rat sternothyroid muscle. Transverse section. Glutaraldehyde fixation. ×30 100.

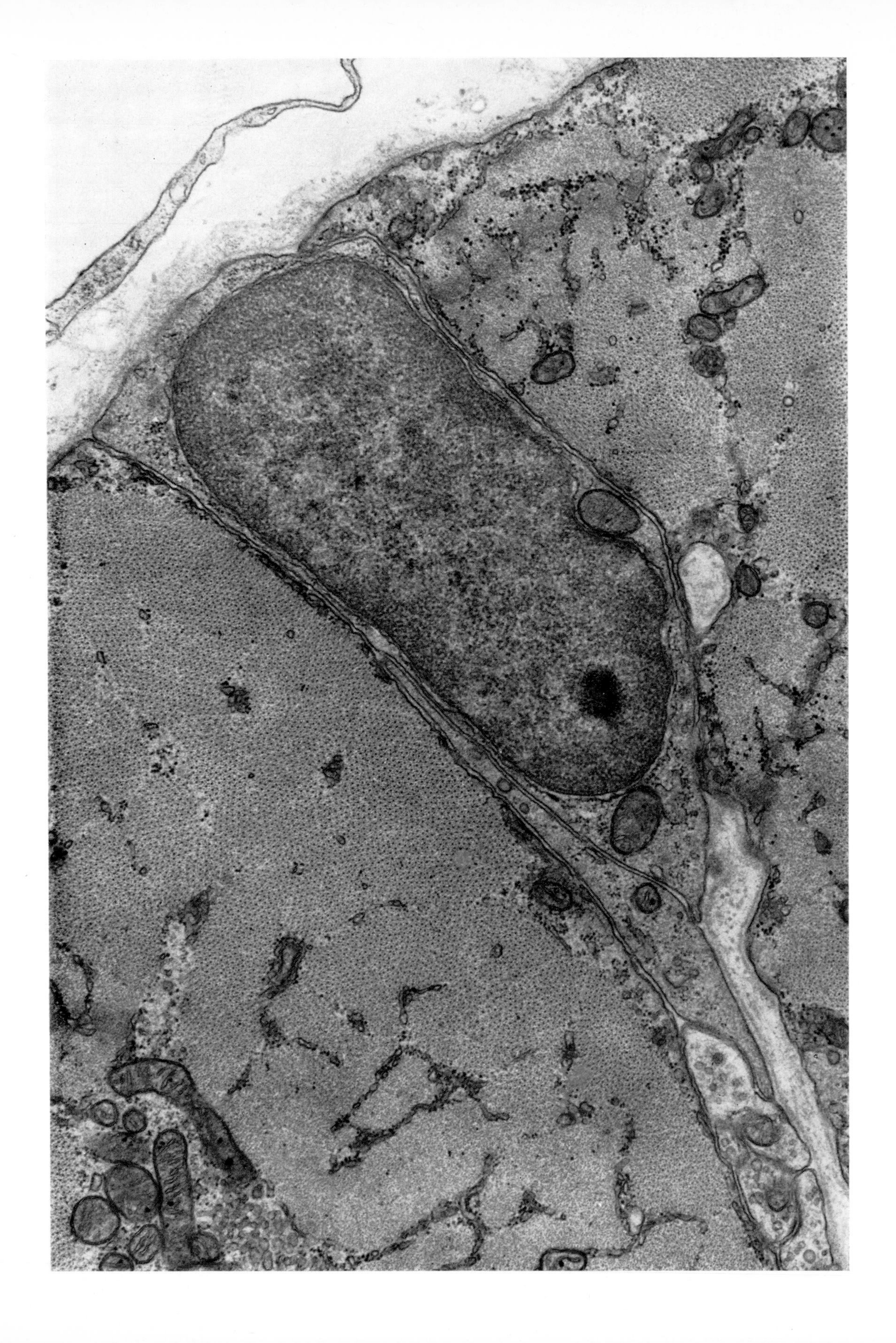

Plate 167

The function of satellite cells is not completely understood. However, at the present time there is some evidence to suggest that satellite cells provide a cellular source for myoblasts. The cell illustrated is wedged between two muscle cells; this is not usually seen in adult tissue, but is often seen in both developing and regenerating muscle.

Relation between satellite cell and developing vertebrate skeletal muscle: sternothyroid of 20-day foetal rat. Transverse section. Glutaraldehyde fixation. ×37 000.

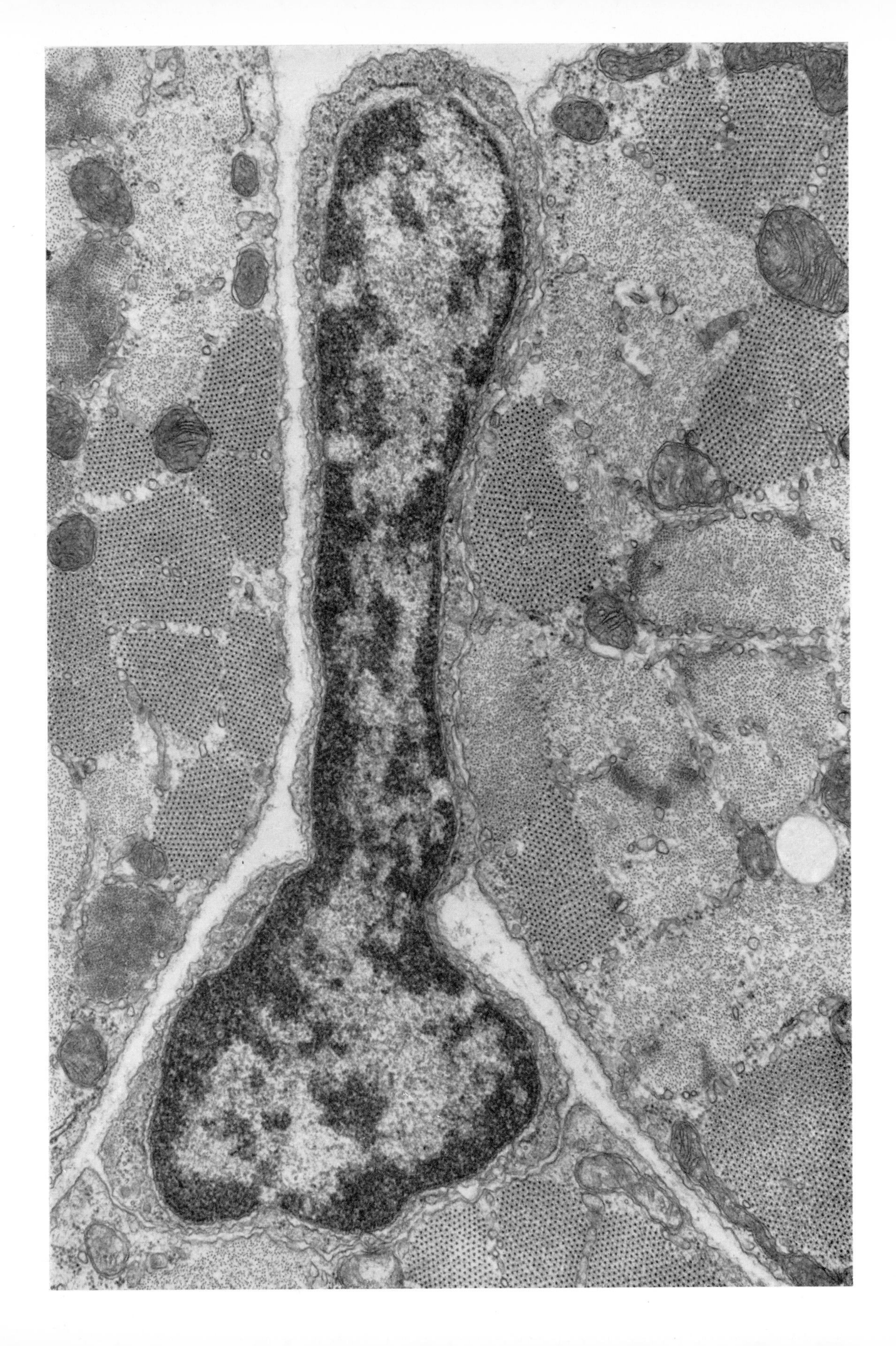

Plate 168

Many mitotic figures are seen in satellite cells in developing and regenerating tissue. However, the number of satellite cells in adult tissue is only slightly more than the number in developing tissue. This supports the suggestion that satellite cells are a source of myoblasts. Note the centrioles, Ce.

Dividing satellite cell in developing vertebrate skeletal muscle: sternothyroid of 20-day foetal rat. Transverse section. Glutaraldehyde fixation. ×34 000.

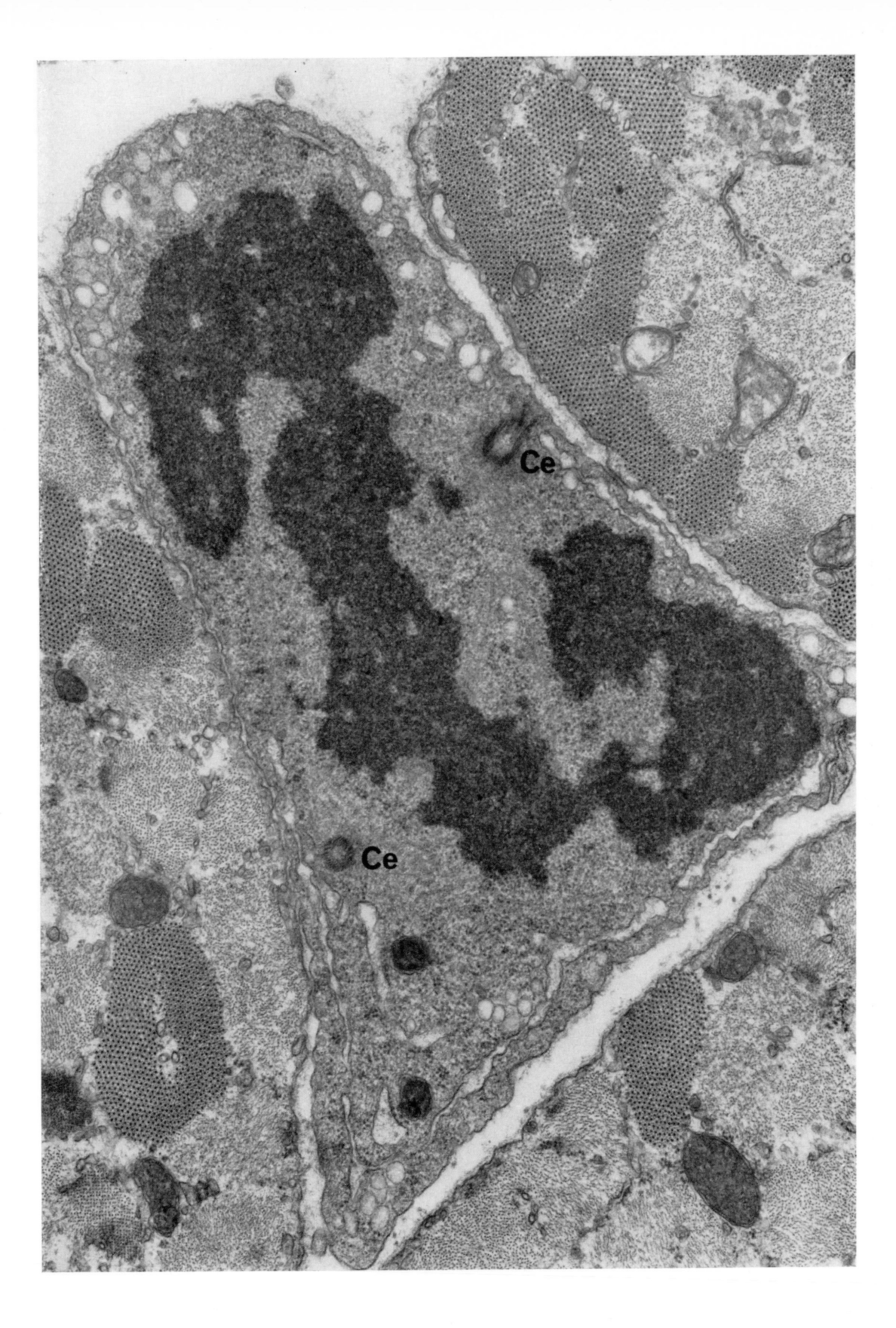
Ce
Ce

Selected articles

BECKER, R. O., S. CHAPIN and R. SHERRY, 1974. Regeneration of the ventricular myocardium in amphibians. *Nature, Lond.*, **248,** 145–147.

CAMPBELL, G. R., Y. UEHARA, T. MALMFORS and G. BURNSTOCK. 1971. Degeneration and regeneration of smooth muscle transplants in the anterior eye chamber: An ultrastructural study. *Z. Zellforsch. mikrosk. Anat.*, **117,** 155–175.

CARLSON, B. M. 1973. The regeneration of skeletal muscle—a review. *Am. J. Anat.*, **137,** 119–149.

GALANKIN, V. N. and B. V. VTYURIN. 1974. Pathways of structural compensation in the injured myocardium of newborn rats. *Bull. exp. Biol. & Med. USSR*, **77,** 573–576.

GOLDSTEIN, M. A., W. C. CLAYCOMB and A. SCHWARTZ. 1974. DNA synthesis and mitosis in well-differentiated mammalian cardiocytes. *Science, N.Y.*, **183,** 212–213.

GROSS, W. O. 1974. Ultrastructural maturation of myocytes. *Experientia*, **30,** 216.

HAY, E. D. and C. M. DOYLE. 1973. Absence of reserve cells (satellite cells) in nonregenerating muscle of mature newt limbs. *Anat. Rec.*, **175,** 339.

HESS, A. and S. ROSNER. 1970. The satellite cell bud and myoblast in denervated mammalian muscle fibers. *Am. J. Anat.*, **129,** 21–39.

ISHIKAWA, H. 1966. Electron microscopic observations of satellite cells with special reference to the development of mammalian skeletal muscles. *Z. Anat. Entw Gesch.*, **125,** 43–63.

KARLSSON, U. and E. ANDERSSON-CEDERGREN. 1971. Satellite cells of the frog muscle spindle as revealed by electron microscopy. *J. Ultrastruct. Res.*, **34,** 426–438.

MAURO, A. 1961. Satellite cell of skeletal muscle fibers. *J. biophys. biochem. Cytol.*, **9,** 493–495.

MIDSUKAMI, M. 1964. Electron microscopic studies of satellite cells in the cardiac muscle of Brachyura. *Okajimas Folia anat. jap.*, **40,** 173–185.

MOSS, F. P. and C. P. LEBLOND. 1971. Satellite cells as the source of nuclei in muscles of growing rats. *Anat. Rec.*, **170,** 421–436.

MUIR, A. R., A. H. M. KANJI and D. ALLBROOK. 1965. The structure of the satellite cells in skeletal muscle. *J. Anat.*, **99,** 435–444.

OBERPRILLER, J. O. and J. C. OBERPRILLER. 1974. Response of the adult newt ventricle to injury. *J. exp. Zool.*, **187,** 249–260.

REGER, J. F. and A. S. CRAIG. 1968. Studies on the fine structure of muscle fibers and associated satellite cells in hypertrophic human deltoid muscle. *Anat. Rec.*, **162,** 483–500.

REZNIK, M. 1969. Thymidine-H^3 uptake by satellite cells of regenerating skeletal muscle. *J. Cell Biol.*, **40,** 568–571.

RUMYANTSEV, P. P. 1973. Post-injury DNA synthesis, mitosis and ultrastructural reorganization of adult frog cardiac myocytes. An electron microscopic-autoradiographic study. *Z. Zellforsch. mikrosk. Anat.*, **139,** 431–450.

SCHULTZ, E. 1973. Changes in the morphology of the skeletal muscle satellite cell with age. *Anat. Rec.*, **175,** 438.

SCHULTZ, E. 1974. A quantative study of the satellite cell population in postnatal mouse lumbrical muscle. *Anat. Rec.*, **180,** 589–596.

SNOW, M. H. 1974. A fine structural study of the regeneration of minced skeletal muscle in the rat. *Anat. Rec.*, **178,** 468.

List of plates

D *'Intermediate'* (100 Å) *filaments*

E *Smooth endoplasmic reticulum (including sarcoplasmic reticulum) and T-tubules*

8 Vascularization of muscle

9 Satellite cells

List of figures

List of species

axolotl	*Ambystoma mexicanum*
blowfly	*Calliphora erythrocephalia*
chicken	*Gallus domesticus*
dog	*Canis familiaris*
earthworm	*Allolobophora caliginosa*
echidna	*Tachyglossus aculeatus*
frog	*Rana nigromaculata*
goldfish	*Carassius auratus*
grasshopper	*Moraba virgo*
guinea pig	*Cavia porcellus*
lizard	*Tiliqua rugosa and Takydromus tachydromoides*
love bird	*Uroloncha domestica*
millipede	Family *Iulidae*
mouse	*Mus musculus*
mussel	*Mytilus edulis*
rat	*Rattus norvegicus*
sheep	*Ovis aries*
spider	*Phonognatha wageri*
starfish	*Patiriella brevispina*
toad	*Bufo marinus*
zebra finch	*Taeniopygia castanotis*

Additional References

Muscle as a Tissue

BAJUSZ, E., and G. RONA. 1972–75. *Recent Advances in Studies on Cardiac Structure and Metabolism.* University Park Press, Baltimore (up to *Vol.* 10).

BHISEY, A. N., and J. J. FREED. 1975. Possible role of microtubules and microfilaments in cell locomotion. In *Regulation of growth and differentiated function in Eukaryote cells.* G. P. Talwar, ed. Raven Press, New York. 155–168.

BROKAN, C. J. 1975. Cross-bridge behaviour in a sliding filament model for flagella. *Soc. Gen. Physiol. Ser.*, **30,** 165–179.

BURLEIGH, I. G. 1974. On the cellular regulation of growth and development in skeletal muscle. *Biol. Rev.*, **49,** 267–320.

CAMPBELL, G. R., J. H. CHAMLEY and G. BURNSTOCK. 1974. Development of smooth muscle cells in tissue culture. *J. Anat.*, **117,** 295–312.

CHI, J. C., S. A. FELLINI and H. HOLTZER. 1975. Differences among myosins synthesized in non-myogenic cells presumptive myoblasts, and myoblasts. *Proc. natn. Acad. Sci. U.S.A.*, **72,** 4999–5003.

CROWTHER, R. A. and A. KLUG. 1975. Structural analysis of macromolecular assemblies by image reconstruction from electron micrographs. *Ann. Rev. Biochem.*, **44,** 161–182.

DURHAM, A. C. 1974. A unified theory of the control of actin and myosin in nonmuscle movements. *Cell*, **2,** 123–135.

ELLIOTT, A., G. OFFER and K. BURRIDGE. 1976. Electron microscopy of myosin molecules from muscle and non-muscle sources. *Proc. R. Soc. Ser. B*, **193,** 45–53.

FISHER, E. R. and T. S. DANOWSKI. 1974. Electronmicroscopy in the study of disorders of skeletal muscle. *Pathol. Ann.*, **9,** 345–384.

GOLDMAN, R. D. 1975. The use of heavy meromyosin binding as an ultrastructural cytochemical method for localising and determining the possible functions of actin-like microfilaments in non-muscle cells. *J. Histochem. Cytochem.*, **23,** 529–542.

HOLTZER, H. 1974. Perspectives in myogenesis. *Biochimie*, **56,** 1575–1580.

HOWALD, H. and J. R. POORTMANS, eds. 1975. Metabolic adaptation to prolonged physical exercise. *Pro. 2nd Int. Sym. on Biochem. of Exercise.*, Magglingen, Switzerland, 1973. Birkhauser Verlag, Basel, Switzerland.

HUDDART, H. and S. HUNT. 1975. *Visceral Muscle. Its Structure and Function.* Blackie Glasgow & London.

INOUE S. and R. E. STEPHENS, eds. 1975. Molecules and cell movement. *Soc. Gen. Physiol. Ser.*, **30.**

KONES, R. J. 1974. Insulin, adenyl cyclate, ions and the heart. *Trans. N.Y. Acad. Sci.*, **36,** 738–774.

KRUEGER, J. W. and G. H. PALLACK. 1975. Myocardial sarcomere dynamics during isometric contraction. *J. Physiol. Lond.*, **251,** 627–644.

LAZARIDES, E. 1975. Immunofluorescence studies on the structure of actin filaments in tissue culture cells. *J. Histochem. Cytochem.*, **23,** 507–528.

LIEBERMAN, M. and T. SANO, eds. 1976. Developmental and physiological correlates of cardiac muscle. In *Perspectives in Cardiovascular Research*, Vol. 1. Raven Press, New York.

MOSS, P. S. and R. C. STROHMAN. 1976. Myosin synthesis by fusion-arrested chick embryo myoblasts in cell culture. *Devl. Biol.* **48,** 431–437.

NELSON, P. G. 1975. Nerve and muscle in culture. *Physiol. Rev.* **55,** 1–61.

OFFERIJNS, F. G. 1975. Cryobiology of the heart. *Eur. J. Cardiol.*, **3,** 85–95.

POLLARD, T. D. 1975. Functional implications of the biochemical and structural properties of cytoplasmic contractile proteins. *Soc. Gen. Physiol. Ser.*, **30,** 259–286.

SHEPHERD, J. T. and P. M. VANHOUTTE. 1975. *Veins and their Control.* Saunders, London.

TAYLOR, D. L. 1976. Quantitative studies on the polarization optical properties of striated muscle. I. Birefringence changes of rabbit psoas muscle in the transition from rigor to relaxed state. *J. Cell Biol.*, **68,** 497–511.

TILNEY, L. G. 1975. The role of actin in nonmuscle cell motility. *Soc. Gen. Physiol. Ser.*, **30,** 339–388.

TOIDA, N., H. KURIYAMA, N. TASHIRO, and Y. ITO. 1975, Obliquely striated muscle. *Physiol. Rev.*, **55,** 700–756.

USHERWOOD, P. N. R. 1975. *Insect Muscle.* Academic Press, London and New York.

VERTEL, B. M. and D. A. FISCHMAN. 1976. Myosin accumulation in mononucleated cells of chick muscle cultures. *Devl. Biol.*, **48,** 438–446.

WOLF, S. and N. T. WERTHESSEN, Eds. 1975. The smooth muscle of the artery. *Adv. Exp. Med. Biol.* **57,** 1–373. Plenum Press, New York.

Cell Organelles

Nucleus

FRANKE, W. W. 1974. Nuclear envelopes. Structure and biochemistry of the nuclear envelope. *Phil. Trans. R. Soc. Lond. B.*, **268,** 67–93.

FRANKE, W. W. 1974. Structure, biochemistry, and functions of the nuclear envelope. *Int. Rev. Cytol. Suppl.* **4,** 71–236.

FUGE, H. 1974. Ultrastructure and function of the spindle apparatus. Microtubules and chromosomes during nuclear division. *Protoplasma*, **82,** 289–320.

Cell Organelles

Myofibrils

ELLISMAN, M. H., J. E. RASH, L. A. STAEHELIN and K. R. PORTER. 1976. Studies of excitable membranes. II. A comparison of specializations at neuromuscular junctions and nonjunctional sarcolemm as of mammalian fast and slow twitch muscle fibers. *J. Cell. Biol.* **68,** 752–774.

ETLINGER, J. D., R. ZAK, and D. A. FISCHMAN. 1976. Compositional studies of myofibrils from rabbit striated muscle. *J. Cell. Biol.*, **68,** 123–141.

HIKIDA, R. S. 1976. Regeneration of a tonic avian muscle: transformation to a twitch morphology. *Devl. Biol.* **48,** 67–79.

HOH, J. F. Y. 1975. Selective and non-selective reinnervation of fast-twitch and slow-twitch rat skeletal muscle. *J. Physiol.*, **251,** 791–802.

JEAN, D. H., R. W. ALBERS, L. GUTH and H. J. ARON. 1975. Differences between the heavy chains of fast and slow muscle myosin. *Exp. Neurol.*, **49,** 750–757.

SRÉTER, F. A., M. BÁLINT and J. GERGELY. 1975. Structural and functional changes of myosin during development. Comparison with adult fast, slow and cardiac myosin. *Devl. Biol.*, **46,** 317–325.

SRÉTER, F. A., A. R. LUFF and J. GERGELY. 1975. Effect of cross-reinnervation on physiological parameters and on properties of myosin and sarcoplasmic reticulum of fast and slow muscles of the rabbit. *J. Gen. Physiol.*, **66,** 811–822.

WROBLEWSKI, R. and E. JANSSON. 1975. Fine structure of single fibres of human skeletal muscle. *Cell Tiss. Res.* **161,** 471–476.

Cell Organelles

Myofilaments

ASHTON, F. T., A. V. SOMLYO and A. P. SOMLYO. 1975. The contractile apparatus of vascular smooth muscle: Intermediate high voltage stereoelectron microscopy. *J. Mol. Biol.*, **98,** 17–30.

BAILIN, G. 1975. Evidence for a role for cardiac myosin in regulating the contractile response. *Arch. Biochem. Biophys.* **171,** 206–326.

CAMPBELL, G. R. and J. H. CHAMLEY. 1975. Thick filaments in vertebrate smooth muscle. *Cell Tiss. Res.*, **156,** 201–216.

COHEN, C. 1975. The protein switch of muscle contraction. *Scient. Amer.* **233,** 36–45.

EBASHI, S. 1974. Regulatory mechanism of muscle contraction with special reference to the Ca-troponin-tropomyosin system. *Essays Biochem.*, **10,** 1–36.

EBASHI, S. 1976. A simple method of preparing actin-free myosin from smooth muscle. *J. Biochem.*, **79,** 229–232.

GRÖSCHEL-STEWART, U., J. H. CHAMLEY, G. R. CAMPBELL and G. BURNSTOCK. 1975. Changes in myosin distribution in dedifferentiating and redifferentiating smooth muscle cells in tissue culture. *CellTiss. Res.*, **165,** 13–22.

HILL, T. L. 1974. Theoretical formalism for the sliding filament model of contraction of striated muscle. Part I. *Prog. Biophys. Mol. Biol.*, **28,** 267–340.

HUXLEY, A. F. 1975. The origin of force in skeletal muscle. *Ciba Fdn. Symp.*, **31,** 271–290.

MEDUGORAC, I. 1975. Subunits of myosin. *Basic Res. Cardiol.*, **70,** 467–479.

MURPHY, R. A. 1976. Contractile system function in mammalian smooth muscle. *Blood Vessels.*, **13,** 1–23.

NONOMURA, Y., E. KATAYAMA and S. EBASHI. 1975. Effect of phosphates on the structure of the actin filament. *J. Biochem.*, **78,** 1101–1104.

OFFER, G. 1976. The antigenicity of myosin and C-protein. *Proc. R. Soc. Lond. B*, **192,** 439–449.

PEPE, F. A. 1975. Structure of muscle filaments from immunochemical and ultrastructural studies. *J. Histochem. Cytochem.*, **23,** 543–562.

PEPE, F. A. and B. DRUCKER. 1975. The myosin filament III C-protein. *J. Molec. Biol.*, **99,** 609–618.

POLLARD, T. D. 1975. Electron microscopy of synthetic myosin filaments. Evidence for cross-bridge flexibility and copolymer formation. *J. Cell Biol.*, **67,** 93–104.

POTTER, J. D. and J. GERGELY. 1975. The regulatory system of the actin-myosin interaction. *Recent Adv. Stud. Cardiac Struct. Metab.*, **5,** 235–244.

SHOENBERG, C. F. and D. M. NEEDHAM. 1976. A study of the mechanism of contraction in vertebrate smooth muscle. *Biol. Rev.*, **51,** 53–104.

SMALL, J. V. 1974. Contractile units in vertebrate smooth muscle. *Nature, Lond.*, **249,** 324–327.

SOBIESZEK, A. and R. D. BREMEL. 1975. Preparation and properties of vertebrate smooth muscle myofibrils and actomyosin. *Eur. J. Biochem.*, **55,** 49–60.

SQUIRE, J. M. 1975. Muscle filament structure and muscle contraction. *Ann. Rev. Biophys. Bioeng.*, **4,** 137–163.

TOIDA, N., H. KURIYAMA, N. TASHIRO and Y. ITO. 1975. Obliquely striated muscle. *Physiol. Rev.*, **55,** 700–756.

TONOMURA, Y. and A. INOUE. 1974. The substructure of myosin and the reaction mechanism of its adenosine triphosphatase. *Molec. Cell Biochem.*, **5,** 127–143.

WEISEL, J. W. 1975. Paramyosin segments. Molecular orientation and interactions in invertebrate muscle thick filaments. *J. Molec. Biol.*, **98,** 675–682.

WRAY, J. S., P. J. VIBERT and C. COHEN. 1975. Diversity of cross-bridge configurations in invertebrate muscles. *Nature, Lond.*, **257,** 561–563.

Cell Organelles

Intermediate (100 Å) filaments

COOKE, P. 1976. A filamentous cytoskeleton in vertebrate smooth muscle fibers. *J. Cell Biol.*, **68,** 539–556.

Cell Organelles

Smooth Endoplasmic Reticulum (including sarcoplasmic reticulum) and T-tubules

CARAFOLI, E. 1975. Mitochondria, Ca^{++} transport and the regulation of heart contraction and metabolism. *J. Molec. Cell Cardiol.*, **7,** 83–87.

COSTANTIN, L. L. 1975. Contractile activation in skeletal muscle. *Prog. Biophys. Molec. Biol.*, **29,** 197–224.

DULHUNTY, A. F. and C. FRANZINI-ARMSTRONG. 1975. The relative contributions of the folds and caveolae to the surface membrane of frog skeletal muscle fibers at different sarcomere lengths. *J. Physiol. Lond.*, **250,** 513–539.

FRANZINI-ARMSTONG, C. 1975. Membrane particles and transmission at the triad. *Fedn. Proc.*, **34,** 1382–1394.

FORBES, M. S. and N. SPERELAKIS. 1976. The presence of transverse and axial tubules in the ventricular myocardium of embroyonic and neonatal guinea-pigs. *Cell Tiss. Res.*, **166,** 83–90.

GERGELY, J. 1974. Some aspects of the role of the sarcoplasmic reticulum and the tropomyosin-troponin system in the control of muscle contraction by calcium ions. *Circ. Res.*, **35,** 74–82.

HASSELBACH, W., J. SUKO, M. H. STROMER and R. THE. 1975. Mechanism of calcium transport in sarcoplasmic reticulum. *Ann. N.Y. Acad. Sci.*, **264,** 335–349.

MASORO, E. J. and B. P. YU. 1974. Involvement of protein components in calcium transport. *Recent Adv. Stud. Cardiac Struct. Metab.*, **4,** 495–506.

MACLENNAN, D. H. and P. C. HOLLAND. 1975. Calcium transport in sarcoplasmic reticulum. *Ann. Rev. Biophys. Bioeng.*, **4,** 377–404.

POPESCU, L. M. and I. DICULESCU. 1975. Calcium in smooth muscle sarcoplasmic reticulum *in situ*. Conventional and X-ray analytical electron microscopy. *J. Cell. Biol.*, **67,** 911–918.

REUTER, H. 1975. Inward calcium current and activation of contraction in mammalian myocardial fibers. *Recent Adv. Stud. Cardiac Struct. Metab.*, **5,** 13–18.

RICH, T. L. and G. A. LANGER. 1975. A comparison of excitation-contraction coupling in heart and skeletal muscle: An examination of 'Calcium-induced Calcium-release'. *J. Mol. Cell Cardiol.* **7,** 747–766.

SOMMER, J. R. and R. A. WAUGH. 1976. The ultrastructure of the mammalian cardiac muscle cell—with special emphasis on the tabular membrane systems. *Am. J. Pathol.*, **82,** 191–232.

SPERELAKIS, N., M. S. FORBES, and R. RUBIO. 1974. The tubular systems of myocardial cells: ultrastructure and possible function. *Recent Adv. Stud. Cardiac Struct. Metab.*, **4,** 163–194.

WALKER, S. M., G. R. SCHRODT, and G. J. CURRIER. 1975. Evidence for a structural relationship between successive parallel tubules in the SR network and supernumerary striations of Z line material in Purkinje fibers of the chicken, sheep, dog and rhesus monkey heart. *J. Morphol.*, **147,** 459–474.

Cell Organelles

Rough Endoplasmic Reticulum and Free Ribosomes

BAG, J., R. K. ROY, A. SUTTON and S. SARKAR. 1975. Regulation of messenger RNA translation during myogenesis: Nonpolysomal cytoplasmic messenger ribonucleoprotein particles in embryonic chicken muscles. In *Regulation of growth and differentiated function in eukaryote cells*. G. P. Talwar, ed. Raven Press, New York, 111–128.

BUREŠOVÁ, M., V. HANZLIKOVÁ and E. GUTMANN. 1975. Changes of ribosomal capacity for protein synthesis, concentration and histochemical properties of muscle after implantation of fast nerve in the denervated and self reinnervated slow soleus muscle of the rat. *Pflügers Archiv.*, **360,** 95–108.

MANCHESTER, K. L. 1975. Effects of insulin and denervation on ribosome function in muscle. In *Regulation of growth and differentiated function in eukaryote cells*. G. P. Talwar, ed. Raven Press, New York, 439–452.

PALADE, G. 1975. Intracellular aspects of the process of protein synthesis. *Science, N.Y.*, **189,** 347–358.

TEPPERMAN, K., F. ESSIEN and S. M. HEYWOOD. 1975. Polysomes from cultured muscle cells: The cell-free synthesis of myosin. *J. Cell Physiol.*, **86,** 553–560.

YOUNG, R. B., D. E. GOLL and M. H. STROMER. 1975. Isolation of myosin-synthesizing polysomes from cultures of embryonic chicken myoblasts before fusion. *Devl. Biol.*, **47,** 123–135.

Cell Organelles

Mitochondria

CARAFOLI, E. 1974. Mitochondria in the contraction and relaxation of heart. *Recent Adv. Stud. Cardiac Struct. Metab.*, **4,** 393–406.

CARAFOLI, E. 1975. The interaction of Ca^{++} with mitochondria, with special reference to the structural role of Ca^{++} in mitochondrial and other membranes. *Molec. Cell Biochem.*, **8,** 133–140.

HATEFI, Y. 1975. Energy conservation and uncoupling in mitochondria. *J. Supramol. Struct.*, **3,** 201–213.
HATEFI, Y., W. G. HANSTEIN, Y. GALANTE and D. L. STIGGALL. 1975. Mitochondrial ATP-Pi exchange complex and the site of uncoupling of oxidative phosphorylation. *Fedn. Proc.*, **34,** 1699–1706.
KLINGENBERG, M. 1975. Energy transfer in mitochondrial synthesis of ATP; a survey. *Ciba Fdn. Symp.*, **31,** 23–40.
KLUG, H. 1975. Unusual mitochondria in human skeletal muscle. *Experientia*, **31,** 1207–1209.
MADDAIAH, V. T. and P. J. COLLIPP. 1975. Hormonal regulation of mitochondrial growth, structure and function. In *Regulation of Growth and Differentiated Function in Eukaryote Cells.* G. P. Talwar, ed. Raven Press, New York, 453–460.
REIJNDERS, L. 1975. The origin of mitochondria. *J. Molec. Evol.*, **5,** 167–176.
TZAGOLOFF, A. ed. 1975. *Membrane Biogenesis: Mitochondria, Chloroplasts and Bacteria.* Plenum Press, New York and London.
VALLIERE, J., A. SCARPA and A. P. SOMLYO. 1975, Subcellular fractions of smooth-mucsle —Isolation, substrate utilization and Ca^{++} transport by main pulmonary artery and mesenteric vein mitochondria. *Arch. Biochem.*, **170,** 659–669.

Cell Organelles

Golgi

WHALEY, W. G., M. DAUWALDER and T. P. LEFFINGWELL. 1975. Differentiation of Golgi apparatus in genetic control of development. In *Current Topics in Developmental Biology*, **10,** 161.

Cell Organelles

Centriole

McINTOSH, J. R., W. Z. CANDE and J. A. SNYDER. 1975. Structure and physiology of the mammalian mitotic spindle. *Soc. Gen. Physiol. Ser.*, **30,** 31–76.

Cell Organelles

Lysosomes

DINGLE, J. T. and R. T. DEAN, eds. 1975. *Lysosomes in Biology and Pathology.* Volume 4. North-Holland Research Monographs: Frontiers of Biology, Volume 43. North-Holland, Amsterdam and Oxford.
GARFIELD, R. E., S. CHACKO and S. BLOSE. 1975. Phagocytosis by muscle cells. *Lab. Invest.*, **33,** 418–427.
NEUFELD, E. F., T. W. LIM and L. J. SHAPIRO. 1975. Inherited disorders of lysosomal metabolism. *A. Rev. Biochem.*, **44,** 357–376.
SHIO, H., M. G. FARQUHAR and C. DE DUVE. 1974. Lysosomes of the arterial wall IV. Cytochemical localization of acid phosphatase and catalase in smooth muscle cells and foam cells from rabbit atheromatous aorta. *Am. J. Pathol.* **76**, 1–16.
WOLINSKY, H., S. GOLDFISHER, M. M. DALY, L. E. KASAK and B. COLTOFF-SCHILLER. 1975. Arterial lysosomes and connective tissue in primate atherosclerosis and hypertension. *Circ. Res.*, **36,** 553–561.

Cell Organelles

Leptomeric Fibrils

BOGUSCH, G. 1975. Electron microscopic investigations on leptomeric fibrils and leptomeric complexes in the hen and pigeon heart. *J. Molec. Cell Cardiol.*, **7,** 733–746.

Cell Inclusions

DE BRUIJN, W. C. and P. DENBREEJEN. 1976. Glycogen, its chemistry and morphological appearance in the electron microscope III. Identification of the tissue ligands involved in the glycogen contrast staining reaction with the osmium (vi)–iron (ii) complex. *Histochem. J.*, **8,** 143–158.
GABELLA, G. 1974. Striated muscle cells in the guinea-pig iris. *Cell Tiss. Res.*, **154,** 181–188.
HUIJING, F. 1975. Glycogen metabolism and glycogen-storage diseases. *Physiol. Rev.*, **55,** 609–658.

KONES, R. J. 1975. *Glucose, insulin, Potassium and the Heart. Selected Aspects of Cardiac Energy Metabolism.* Futura Publishing, New York.

PETTE, D. 1975. Some aspects of supramolecular organisation of glycogenolytic and glycolytic enzymes in muscle. *Acta Histochem. Suppl.* **14,** 47–68.

SRETER, F. A., K.-E. ÅSTRÖM, F. C. A. ROMANUL, R. R. YOUNG and H. ROYDEN JONES JR. 1976. Characteristics of myosin in nemaline myopathy. *J. Neurol. Sci.*, **217,** 99–116.

Muscle Cell Surface

ALMERS, W., R. H. ADRIAN and S. R. LEVINSON. 1975. Some dielectric properties of muscle membrane and their possible importance for excitation–contraction coupling. *Ann. N.Y. Acad. Sci.*, **264,** 278–292.

BORNSTEIN, P. 1974. The structure and assembly of procollagen—a review. *J. Supramol. Struct.*, **2,** 108–120.

BRETSCHER, M. S. 1976. Directed lipid flow in cell membranes. *Nature, Lond.*, **260,** 21–22.

CHAPMAN, D. 1975. Phase transitions and fluidity characteristics of lipids and cell membranes. *Q. Rev. Biophys.*, **8,** 185–235.

CHERRY, R. J. 1975. Protein mobility in membranes. *FEBS Lett.*, **55,** 1–7.

CRONAN, J. E. JR. and E. P. GELMANN. 1975. Physical properties of membrane lipids: biological relevance and regulation. *Bacterial. Rev.*, **39,** 232–256.

DOYLE, B. B., D. W. L. HUKINS, D. J. S. HULMES, A. MILLER and J. WOODHEAD-GALLOWAY. 1975. Collagen polymorphism: its origins in amino acid sequence. *J. Molec. Biol.*, **91,** 79–99.

ECKERT, R. and H. MACHEMER. 1975. Regulation of ciliary beating frequency by the surface membrane. *Soc. Gen. Physiol. Ser.*, **30** 151–164.

EDZES, H. T. and H. J. BERENDSEN. 1975. The physical state of diffusible ions in cells. *A. Rev. Biophys. Bioeng.*, **4,** 265–285.

ELBRINK, J. and I. BIHLER. 1975. Membrane transport: its relation to cellular metabolic rates. *Science, N.Y.*, **188,** 1177–1184.

GALLOP, P. M. and M. A. PAZ. 1975. Postranslational protein modifications, with special attention to collagen and elastin. *Physiol. Rev.*, **55,** 418–487.

HUANG, B. and D. MAZIA. 1975. Microtubules and filaments in ciliate contractility. *Soc. Gen. Physiol. Ser.*, **30,** 389–409.

HUIJING, F. 1975. Glycogen metabolism and glycogen-storage diseases. *Physiol. Rev.*, **55,** 609–658.

KEFALIDES, N. A. 1975. Basement membranes: current concepts of structure and synthesis. *Dermatologica*, **150,** 4–15.

LANDOWNE, D., L. T. POTTER and D. A. TERRAR. 1975. Structure–function relationships in excitable membranes. *Ann. Rev. Physiol.*, **37,** 485–508.

LEE, A. G. 1975. Functional properties of biological membranes: a physical-chemical approach. *Prog. Biophys. Mol. Biol.*, **29,** 3–56.

MARTONOSI, A. 1975. Membrane transport during development in animals. *Biochem. Biophys. Acta.*, **415,** 311–333.

MUELLER, P. 1975. Membrane excitation through voltage-induced aggregation of channel precursors. *Ann. N.Y. Acad. Sci.*, **264,** 247–264.

NIMNI, M. E. 1974. Collagen: Its structure and function in normal and pathological connective tissues. *Semin. Arthritis Rheum.*, **4,** 95–150.

READ, S. 1974. Basement membrane disease: a review. *Guys. Hosp. Rep.*, **123,** 53–65.

SATIR, P. 1975. Ciliary and flagellar movement—Introduction. In *Molecules and Cell Movement. Soc. General Physiologists Series*, **30,** 143. Raven Press, New York.

SATIR, P. and N. B. GILULA. 1975. The fine structure of membranes and intercellular communication in insects. *Ann. Rev. Entomol.*, **18,** 143–166.

SILBERT, D. F. 1975. Genetic modification of membrane lipid. *Ann. Rev. Biochem.*, **44,** 315–339.

TRUMP, B. F. and A. U. ARSTILA. 1975. *Pathobiology of Cell Membranes.* Vol. I. Academic Press, New York and London.

UITTO, J. and J. R. LICHTENSTEIN. 1976. Defects in the biochemistry of collagen in diseases of connective tissue. *J. Invest. Dermatology*, **66,** 59–79.

VAUGHAN, P. C. 1975. Muscle membrane. *Prog. Neurobiol.*, **3,** 219–250.

VEIS, A. and A. G. BROWNELL. 1975. Collagen biosynthesis. *CRC Crit. Rev. Biochem.*, **2,** 417–453.

VESSEY, D. A. and D. ZAKIM. 1974. Membrane fluidity and the regulation of membrane-bound enzymes. *Horiz. Biochem. Biophys.*, **1,** 138–174.

WHITTAM, R. and A. R. CHIPPERFIELD. 1975. The reaction mechanism of the sodium pump. *Biochem. Biophys. Acta.*, **415,** 149–171.

Muscle Attachment Sites

NAKAO, T. 1976. Some observations on the fine structure of the myotendinous junction in myotomal muscles of the tadpole tail. *Cell Tiss. Res.*, **166,** 241–254.

Cell to Cell Relationships

FORBES, M. S. and N. SPERELAKIS. 1975. The 'imaged-desmosome'. A component of intercalated discs in embryonic guinea-pig myocardium. *Anat. Rec.*, **183,** 243–258.

OVERTON, J. 1975. Experiments with junctions of Adhaerens type. In *Current topics in developmental Biology*, **10,** 1–34.

Innervation

Vertebrate Skeletal Muscle

BENOIT, P. and J.-P. CHANGEUX, 1975. Consequences of tenotomy on the evolution of multi-innervation in developing rat soleus muscle. *Brain Res.*, **99,** 354–358.

COLQUHOUN, D. 1975. Mechanisms of drug action at the voluntary muscle endplate. *A. Rev. Pharmacol.*, **15,** 307–325.

CRAWFORD, G. N. C. 1975. The growth of muscle following tenotomy. *J. Anat.*, **120,** 581–594.

DREWS, U. 1975. Cholinesterase in embryonic development. *Prog. Histochem. Cytochem.*, **7,** 1–52.

ELDEFRAWI, M. E., A. T. ELDEFRAWI and A. E. SHAMOO. 1975. Molecular and functional properties of the acetylcholine receptor. *Ann. N.Y. Acad. Sci.*, **264,** 183–202.

GAGE, P. W. 1976. Generation of end-plate potentials. *Physiol. Rev.*, **56,** 177–247.

ITO, Y., R. MILEDI, P. C. MOLENAAR, A. VINCENT, R. L. POLAK, M. VAN GELDER and J. N. DAVIS. 1976. Acetylcholine in human muscle. *Proc. R. Soc. Lond. B.*, **192,** 475–480.

LINKHART, T. A. and B. W. WILSON. 1975. Acetylcholinesterase in singly and multiply innervated muscles of normal and dystrophic chickens. II. Effects of denervation. *J. Exp. Zool.*, **193,** 191–200.

Innervation

Vertebrate Cardiac Muscle

ANDERSON, R. H., A. E. BECKER, C. BRECHENMACHER, M. J. DAVIS and L. ROSSI. 1975. The human atrioventricular junctional area: A morphological study of the AV node and bundle. *Eur. J. Cardiol.*, **3,** 11–25.

ANTONI, H. 1975. Disturbances of transmembrane ionic fluxes and their role in the pathogenesis of cardiac dysrhythmias. *Recent Adv. Stud. Cardiac Struct. Metab.*, **5,** 283–294.

JOHNSON, E. A. and M. LIEBERMAN. 1971. Heart: excitation and contraction. *Ann. Rev. Physiol.*, **33,** 479–532.

JULIAN, F. J. and R. L. MOSS. 1976. The concept of active state in striated muscle. *Circulation Res.*, **38,** 53–59.

LIEBERMAN, M., T. SAWANOBORI, J. M. KOOTSEY and E. A. JOHNSON. 1975. A synthetic strand of cardiac muscle: its passive electrical properties. *J. Gen. Physiol.*, **65,** 527–550.

LIEBERMAN, M. and T. SANO, eds. 1976. Developmental and physiological correlates of cardiac muscle. In *Perspectives in Cardiovascular Research*, Vol. I. Raven Press, New York.

MOCHET, M., J. MORAVEC, H. GUILLEMOT and P. Y. HATT. 1975. The ultrastructure of rat conductive tissue; An electron microscopic study of the atrioventricular node and the bunde of His. *J. Molec. Cell. Cardiol.*, **7,** 879–890.

POLLACK, G. H. 1976. Intercellular coupling in the atrioventricular node and other tissues of the rabbit heart. *J. Physiol.*, **255,** 275–298.

WATANABE, Y. and L. S. DREIFUS. 1975. Factors controlling impulse transmission with special reference to A-V conduction. *Am. Heart J.*, **89,** 790–803.

WELLENS, H. J. J., H. I. LIE and M. J. JANSE, eds. 1976. *The conduction system of hearts: Structure, function and clinical implications.* Lea and Febiger, Philadelphia.

Innervation

Vertebrate Smooth Muscle

AGRANOFF, B. W. 1975. Neurotransmitters and synaptic transmission. *Fedn. Proc.*, **34,** 1911–1914.

BELL, C. 1975. Vasodilator nerves in regional circulatory control. *Clin Exp. Pharmocol. Physiol. Suppl.*, **2,** 49–53.

BENNETT, A. 1975. Pharmacology of colonic muscle. *Gut*, **16,** 307–311.

BÜLBRING, E. and M. F. SHUBA, eds. 1976. Physiology of Smooth Muscle. Raven Press, New York, 1–438.

BURNSTOCK, G. 1975. Innervation of vascular smooth muscle: histochemistry and electron microscopy. *Clin. Exp. Pharmacol. Physiol. Suppl.*, **2,** 7–20.

BURNSTOCK, G. and M. COSTA. 1975. *Adrenergic Neurons—their Organisation, Function and Development in the Peripheral Nervous System.* Chapman & Hall, London.

DANIEL, E. E. and D. M. PATON, eds. 1975. *Methods in Pharmacology*. Vol. 3, *Smooth Muscle.* Plenum Press, New York and London.

DE LA LANDE, I. 1975. Adrenergic mechanisms in the rabbit ear artery. A review. *Blood vessels*, **12,** 137–160.

DUTHIE, H. L. 1974. Electrical activity of gastro-intestinal smooth muscle. *Gut*, **15,** 669–681.

JULIUS, S. and M. ESLER. 1975. Autonomic nervous cardiovascular regulation in borderline hypertension. *Am. J. Cardiol.*, **36,** 685–696.

KIRPEKAR, S. M. 1975. Factors influencing transmission at adrenergic synapses. *Progr. in Neurobiol.*, **4,** 165–210.

LANGER, S. Z. 1974. Presynaptic regulation of catecholamine release. *Biochem. Pharmacol.*, **23,** 1793–1800.

MACKLEM, P. T. and L. A. ENGEL. 1975. Physiological implications of airways smooth muscle constriction. *Postgrad. Med. J.*, **51,** Suppl., **7,** 45–52.

MOLINOFF, P. B. 1974. The regulation of the noradrenergic neuron. *J. Psychiatr. Res.*, **11,** 339–345.

NAMM, D. H. and J. P. LEADER. 1976. Occurrence and function of cyclic nucleotides in blood vessels. *Blood Vessels*, **13,** 24–47.

PATIL, P. N., D. D. MILLER and U. TRENDELENBURG. 1974. Molecular geometry and adrenergic drug activity. *Pharmacol. Rev.*, **26,** 323–392.

RAND, M. J., D. F. STORY and M. W. McCULLOCH. 1975. Inhibitory feedback modulation of adrenergic transmission. *Clin. Exp. Pharmacol. Physiol. Suppl.*, **2,** 21–26.

SMYTHIES, J. R. 1975. The mulecular structure of acetycholine and adrenergic receptors: an all-protein model. *Int. Rev. Neurobiol.*, **17,** 131–187.

SPEDEN, R. N. 1975. Muscle load and constriction of arteries. *Clin. Exp. Pharmacol. Physiol. Suppl.*, **2,** 63–65.

SU, C. 1975. Neurogenic release of purine compounds in blood vessels. *J. Pharmac. Exp. Ther.*, **195,** 159–167.

TOMITA, T. 1975. Electrophysiology of mammalian smooth muscle. *Progr. Biophys. Mol. Biol.*, **30,** 185–204.

TWEEDLE, C. D. 1976. The development and maintenance of smooth muscle in control and aneurogenic amphibians (*Amblystoma*). *Cell Tiss. Res.*, **166,** 275–283.

Innervation

Invertebrate Muscle

GARDNER, C. R. 1976. The neuronal control of locomotion in the earthworm. *Biol. Rev.*, **51,** 25–52.

MELLON, DE. F. 1974. Intergrative and organizational aspects of synaptic function in molluscs. *Prog. Neurobiol.*, **3,** 163–190.

KURIYAMA, H., N. TASHIRO and Y. ITO. 1975. On the physiological properties of the neuromuscular junction and of obliquely striated muscle in the earthworm. *Prog. Neurobiol.*, **4,** 79–161.

SHERMAN, R. G., C. R. FOURTNER and C. D. DREWES. 1976. Invertebrate nerve–muscle systems. *Comp. Biochem. Physiol. A. Comp. Physiol.*, **53,** 227–234.

Innervation

Muscle Spindle and Tendon Organ

EDWARDS, R. P. 1975. An ultrastructural study of neuromuscular spindles in normal mice: with reference to mice and man infected with Mycobacterium leprae. *J. Anat.*, **120,** 149–168.

GRANIT, R. 1975. The functional role of the muscle spindles—facts and hypotheses. *Brain*, **98,** 531–556.

PROSKE, U. and R. M. RIDGE. 1975. Extrafusal muscle and muscle spindles in reptiles. *Progr. Neurobiol.*, **3,** 3–29.

HUNT, C. C., ed. 1974. Muscle receptors. *Handbook of Sensory Physiology*. Vol. 3. Springer, Berlin and New York.

Vascularization of Muscle

ZELIS, R. 1975. *The Peripheral Circulations.* Clinical Cardiology Monographs. Grune and Stratton, New York.

Satellite Cells

BJÖRKERUD, S. 1974. Injury and repair in arterial tissue: experimental models: types and relevance to human vascular diseases —a survey. *Angiology*, **25,** 636–648.

CARLSON, B. M. and E. GUTMANN. 1975. Regeneration in free grafts of normal and denervated muscle in the rat: morphology and histochemistry. *Anat. Rec.*, **183,** 47–53.

GUTMANN, E. and B. M. CARLSON. 1976. Regeneration and transplantation of muscles in old rats and between young and old rats. *Life Sciences*, **18,** 109–114.

KELLY, A. M. and S. CHACKO. 1976. Myofibril organization and mitosis in cultured cardiac muscle cells. *Devl. Biol.*, **48,** 421–430.

LIVESON, J. A., E. R. PETERSON, S. M. CRAIN and M. B. BORNSTEIN. 1975. Regeneration in vitro of previously frozen adult mouse and human striated muscle coupled with fetal spinal cord. *Exp. Neurol.*, **48,** 624–636.

McGEACHIE, J. K. 1975. Smooth muscle regeneration. *Monogr. Devl. Biol.*, **9,** 1–90.

Index

Note: Italic page numbers refer to bibliographies